DRUGS
and
BEHAVIOR

DRUGS
and
BEHAVIOR

Edited by

Leonard Uhr
Research Psychologist

James G. Miller
*Professor of Psychiatry and Psychology
and Director*

*Mental Health Research Institute
The University of Michigan*

John Wiley & Sons, Inc.   New York • London

Foreword

Few drugs have been more widely advertised or more frequently misused than those which are classified as psychoactive. This is not difficult to understand with such widespread interest in and concern about emotional disorders as has been apparent in recent years. Moreover, most patients with physical disease have significant emotional reactions with or to their disease and would respond to the physical disease better if there could be a safe and simple way to reduce their anxiety. During the past ten or fifteen years there has been a tremendous upsurge of interest in various kinds of mental illness. Because of the high incidence of mental disorder it is obviously impossible for all to be treated by trained psychotherapists. It seems logical that a considerable percentage of them should be treated by the superficial psychotherapy or drug therapy which can be given by the family physician or the doctor who first sees the patient. Since his is the first medical contact for the person with emotional problems, what he does to a large extent may determine the patient's future course. If the situation is badly handled either by misuse of drugs or by nontherapeutic attitude, later treatment can be made remarkably more difficult.

The goal of every physician is to relieve the dis-ease of his patients and to cure their illness as often as possible. Since such a large percentage of patients present some type of emotional problem manifested by anxiety, agitation, or tension, it is obvious that any reasonable and safe means of overcoming such manifestations would have wide usage. The availability of psychoactive drugs has increased the ability of the physician without formal psychiatric training to handle many patients with emotional disturbance. Nevertheless, the use of such drugs is not all that is necessary in the treatment of mental illness—psychotherapy is still the keystone, the most important and best method.

During the past few years there has been a great volume of advertising to medical and lay public of the "tranquilizing" and now the "psychic energizer" drugs. The result has been a demand by patients for such prescription without regard to the wisdom or validity of it. In our competitive, overactive economy there is ample opportunity for tension and anxiety, some of which is decidedly unhealthy. It is for persons with such symptoms that tranquilizing drugs may be of real benefit. Unfortunately, an increasing number of people demand tranquility at the expense of effective living. With the widespread use of these drugs some individuals may lose the initiative and the responsiveness needed in our competitive culture, much of which comes from healthy anxiety.

In much of the promotional material brought to the attention of the physician, often too little emphasis is placed on the occurrence of side effects, contraindications, or potential dangers. In fact, the side effects are frequently minimized. Needless to say, the prescription of powerful drugs should never be dictated by the detail man but should be based on careful consideration of the patient's symptoms. The lay press has contributed more than its share to the dissemination of premature and incomplete accounts of the "miraculous" effects of psychoactive drugs. Some years ago when they were first described as miracle drugs, the medical editor of one of our national weekly magazines, aware that we had been doing some drug researches, asked for an interview to discuss them. In the interview, it was indicated that there was real possibility for benefit from psychoactive drugs but that they were not, in any sense of the word, miracle drugs or a panacea. He was cautioned on the side of conservatism. The article which appeared was quite sensational and unrealistic rather than conservative. Some time later, a husband criticized the treatment of his wife because he felt a certain "wonder drug" should be used in her treatment. He was surprised, indeed, to find that this drug had been used in her case over a period of two months and had not worked the miracle that he had expected it would from reading the lay article about it. Although these drugs do have a definite and important place, they are not universally successful and they vary considerably in their reactions with different patients.

Since many physical illnesses are partially or largely due to emotional factors, with the proper selection of a psychoactive drug the patient may be relieved of symptoms without a long period of psychotherapy and with a minimum of understanding of the significance of the personality reaction of the patient by the physician who is treating him.

Wide publicity has stimulated such public interest and demand for these drugs that the resultant indiscriminate use has led to a number of official protests. A serious warning has been issued by the American Psychiatric Association. The New York City Health Department has announced an amendment to the Sanitary Code requiring that tranquilizing drugs be sold only on prescription. The Food and Drug Administration has issued a careful formulation of the dangers of improper use or excessive dosage and has attempted to define limits. There are numerous reports in the literature of disappointed hopes and of dangerous or fatal consequences. All these cautions should be kept in mind. Perhaps one other warning should be stated: these drugs may make the patient sufficiently comfortable that severe physical disease may develop without the patient being aware of it or without having him report it, even if he is aware of other symptoms.

In the final analysis, it is important to bring the use of psychoactive drugs into proper focus by painstaking analysis of their pharmacology and effects on a variety of behaviors, as is done in the chapters of this book. These drugs are no final answer, but they should play a role in treatment in accordance with the needs of the patient and the specific actions of the compound in relation to those needs. Anxiety develops when there is a threat to something the individual values. Only by an awareness of the relationhip of his particular value system to his symptom can we deal properly with the patient's response to a medication—whether it be a potent drug or a placebo, whether the symptom be a manifestation of physical process, a psychological reaction, or a combination of both. It seems essential, therefore, to evaluate carefully the basic personality structure of the individuals involved and the needs they may have from the viewpoint of their own value systems before any definitive statement can be made concerning behavioral effects or therapeutic results of the drug under consideration. An awareness of this should make us sensitive to the great complexity of human behavior and lend caution to the formulation of our conclusions from any single study, whether they be positive or negative. To paraphrase Cecil Rhodes: "The little that we have done seems nothing when we look forward and see how much we have yet to do."

RAYMOND W. WAGGONER

Contributors

CORNELIS BAKKER, M.D., *Associate Research Psychiatrist, Mental Health Research Institute, and Instructor in Psychiatry, University of Michigan Medical School, Ann Arbor, Michigan*

CHESTER C. BENNETT, Ph.D., *Professor of Clinical Psychology, Boston University, Boston, Massachusetts*

FRANK M. BERGER, M.D., *President, Wallace Laboratories, New Brunswick, New Jersey*

ROBERT BERRYMAN, Ph.D., *Assistant Professor, Department of Psychology, Adelphi College, Long Island, New York*

JOSEPH V. BRADY, Ph.D., *Chief, Department of Experimental Psychology, Walter Reed Army Institute of Research, Washington, D. C., and Lecturer, Department of Psychology, University of Maryland, College Park, Maryland*

ENOCH CALLAWAY III, M.D., *Chief of Research, Langley Porter Neuropsychiatric Institute, San Francisco, California*

ARCH CARRAN, *United States Public Health Service Research Fellow, Institute for Psychological Research, University of Cincinnati, Cincinnati, Ohio*

RAYMOND B. CATTELL, Ph.D., *Research Professor and Director of the Laboratory of Personality Assessment, University of Illinois, Urbana, Illinois*

DEAN J. CLYDE, Ph.D., *Research Psychologist, Psychopharmacology Service Center, National Institute of Mental Health, Bethesda, Maryland*

JONATHAN O. COLE, M.D., *Chief, Psychopharmacology Service Center, National Institute of Mental Health, Bethesda, Maryland*

ROBERT H. CORMACK, M.A., *United States, Public Health Service Research Fellow, Institute for Psychological Research, University of Cincinnati, Cincinnati, Ohio*

ALBERTO DiMASCIO, M.A., *Principal Investigator, Psychopharmacology Research Project, Massachusetts Mental Health Center, Boston Psychopathic Hospital, Boston, Massachusetts*

ROBERT B. ELLSWORTH, Ph.D., *Research Psychologist, VA Hospital, Ft. Meade, South Dakota*

H. J. EYSENCK, Ph.D., *Professor of Psychology, Institute of Psychiatry, Postgraduate School of Medicine, University of London, London, England*

DONALD W. FISKE, Ph.D., *Associate Professor of Psychology, University of Chicago, Chicago, Illinois*

EDWIN A. FLEISHMAN, Ph.D., *Associate Professor of Industrial Administration and of Psychology, Yale University, New Haven, Connecticut*

FRITZ A. FREYHAN, M.D., *Adjunct Associate Professor of Psychiatry, University of Pennsylvania, Philadelphia, Pennsylvania, and Clinical Director and Director of Research, Delaware State Hospital, Farnhurst, Delaware*

LOUIS A. GOTTSCHALK, M.D., *Associate Professor and Coordinator of Research, Department of Psychiatry, University of Cincinnati College of Medicine, Cincinnati, Ohio*

ECKHARD H. HESS, Ph.D., *Professor of Psychology, University of Chicago, Chicago, Illinois*

HAROLD E. HIMWICH, M.D., *Director, Research Division, Galesburg State Research Hospital, Galesburg, Illinois*

AUDREY R. HOLLIDAY, Ph.D., *Research Instructor, Department of Pharmacology, School of Medicine, University of Washington, Seattle, Washington*

HOWARD F. HUNT, Ph.D., *Professor and Chairman, Department of Psychology, University of Chicago, Chicago, Illinois*

SOLOMON D. KAPLAN, Ph.D., *Chief Psychologist, Lincoln State Hospital, Lincoln, Nebraska*

MARTIN M. KATZ, Ph.D., *Research Clinical Psychologist, Psycho-pharmacology Service Center, National Institute of Mental Health, Bethesda, Maryland*

FRED S. KELLER, Ph.D., *Professor of Psychology, Columbia University, New York, New York*

G. Y. KENYON, Ph.D., *Assistant Professor of Psychology, University of Wichita, Wichita, Kansas*

GERALD L. KLERMAN, M.D., *Psychopharmacology Research Project, Massachusetts Mental Health Center, Boston Psychopathic Hospital, Boston, Massachusetts*

CONAN KORNETSKY, Ph.D., *Associate Research Professor, Department of Pharmacology and Experimental Therapeutics, Boston University School of Medicine, Boston, Massachusetts*

ALFRED B. KRISTOFFERSON, Ph.D., *Director of Research, Longview State Hospital, and Associate Professor of Psychology, University of Cincinnati, Cincinnati, Ohio*

LAWRENCE S. KUBIE, M.D., *Director, Education and Research, Sheppard and Enoch Pratt Hospital, Towson, Maryland*

ALBERT A. KURLAND, M.D., *Director of Medical Research, Spring Grove State Hospital, Baltimore, Maryland*

ROBERT LAFON, M.D., *Clinical Professor of Nervous and Mental Diseases, Faculté de Médecine, Centre Hospitalier Régional, Montpellier, France*

JULIAN J. LASKY, Ph.D., *Director, Central Neuropsychiatric Research Unit, VA Hospital, Perry Point, Maryland*

LOUIS LeGUILLANT, M.D., *Chief Physician, Centre de Traitement et de Réadaptation Sociale, Villejuif, Seine, France*

HEINZ E. LEHMANN, M.D., *Clinical Director, Verdun Protestant Hospital, and Associate Professor of Psychiatry, McGill University, Montreal, Canada*

TED A. LOOMIS, M.D., *Professor of Pharmacology, School of Medicine, University of Washington, Seattle, Washington*

MAURICE LORR, Ph.D., *Director, Neuropsychiatric Research Laboratory, Veterans Administration, and Lecturer and Research Consultant, Catholic University, Washington, D. C.*

JAMES MAAS, M.D., *Psychosomatic Fellow, University of Cincinnati College of Medicine, Cincinnati, Ohio*

JULES H. MASSERMAN, M.D., *Professor of Neurology and Psychiatry, Northwestern University Medical School, Chicago, Illinois*

JAMES G. MILLER, M.D., Ph.D., *Professor of Psychiatry and Psychology, and Director, Mental Health Research Institute, University of Michigan, Ann Arbor, Michigan*

JEAN MINVIELLE, M.D., *Assistant Physician, Centre Hospitalier Régional, Montpellier, France*

ALLAN F. MIRSKY, Ph.D., *Research Psychologist, Section on Animal Behavior, Laboratory of Psychology, National Institute of Mental Health, Bethesda, Maryland*

HARVEY NASH, Ph.D., *Associate Professor of Psychology, Northwestern University Medical School, Chicago, Illinois*

VINCENT NOWLIS, Ph.D., *Professor of Psychology, University of Rochester, Rochester, New York*

JAMES OLDS, Ph.D., *Professor of Psychology, University of Michigan, Ann Arbor, Michigan*

CHESTER M. PIERCE, M.D., *Instructor in Psychiatry, University of Cincinnati College of Medicine, Cincinnati, Ohio*

JOHN C. POLLARD, M.B., B.S. (London), *Associate Research Psychiatrist, Mental Health Research Institute, and Instructor in Psychiatry, University of Michigan Medical School, Ann Arbor, Michigan*

STANLEY D. PORTEUS, D.Sc., *Professor Emeritus, Clinical Psychology, University of Hawaii, Honolulu, Hawaii*

N. H. PRONKO, Ph.D., *Professor of Psychology, University of Wichita, Wichita, Kansas*

RALPH M. REITAN, Ph.D., *Associate Professor of Psychology, Department of Surgery, Indiana University Medical Center, Indianapolis, Indiana*

SHERMAN ROSS, Ph.D., *Executive Officer, Education and Training Board, American Psychological Association, Washington, D.C.*

H. ENGER ROSVOLD, Ph.D., *Chief, Section on Animal Behavior, Laboratory of Psychology, National Institute of Mental Health, Bethesda, Maryland*

ROGER W. RUSSELL, Ph.D., D.Sc., *Professor and Chairman, Department of Psychology, Indiana University, Bloomington, Indiana*

ROBERT A. SCHNEIDER, M.D., *Associate Professor of Medicine and of Psychiatry, Neurology and the Behavioral Sciences, University of Oklahoma Medical Center and the Oklahoma Medical Research Foundation, Oklahoma City, Oklahoma*

CHARLES SHAGASS, M.D., *Associate Professor of Psychiatry, State University of Iowa, Iowa City, Iowa*

GEORGE C. STONE, Ph.D., *Research Psychologist, Langley Porter Neuropsychiatric Institute, San Francisco, California*

ROBERT P. TRAVIS, M.A., *Assistant in Research, Department of Psychology, University of Michigan, Ann Arbor, Michigan*

LEONARD UHR, Ph.D., *Research Psychologist, Mental Health Research Institute, University of Michigan, Ann Arbor, Michigan*

STEVEN G. VANDENBERG, Ph.D., *Associate Research Psychologist and Associate Director, Schizophrenia and Psychopharmacology Joint Research Project, Ypsilanti State Hospital and University of Michigan, and Lecturer in Psychology, University of Michigan, Ann Arbor, Michigan*

RAYMOND W. WAGGONER, M.D., D.Sc., *Professor and Chairman, Department of Psychiatry, and Director, Neuropsychiatric Institute, University of Michigan Medical School, Ann Arbor, Michigan*

WILLIAM WAGMAN, M.A., *Assistant Professor, Department of Psychology, Southern Illinois University, Carbondale, Illinois*

THEODORE C. WEST, Ph.D., *Assistant Professor of Pharmacology, School of Medicine, University of Washington, Seattle, Washington*

ROY M. WHITMAN, M.D., *Associate Professor of Psychiatry, University of Cincinnati College of Medicine, Cincinnati, Ohio*

Contents

Clinical Considerations

PART II   EXPERIMENTAL   PROCEDURES   AND RESULTS

Experiments on Animals of Potential Application to Human Subjects

* *Asterisks refer to chapters reporting experimental results.*

Objective Assessment of Normal Human Behavior

Contents

Leonard Uhr and James G. Miller

Prologue

The discovery and synthesis in the past few years of a whole armamentarium of new psychoactive drugs—first psychotomimetics and tranquilizers, then, more recently, energizers—has created an entirely new problem for drug research: the objective, scientific determination of a chemical agent's effects on human behavior and experience. To delineate and explore this problem is the purpose of this book.

The experimental laboratories of the behavioral sciences have developed, for both basic and applied research, many objective techniques for measuring different types of behavior. Fuller development and greater use of such techniques should lead to important improvements in the screening procedures for new drugs and in evaluations of their usefulness for therapy. In the typical development of a drug, most of the time is spent in the study of effects on animals and of therapeutic impacts on relatively mixed groups of patients. Yet, findings about a drug's biochemical, physiological, and even behavioral effects on animals often do not predict how it will act on human beings. And far too often the clinical studies, even when they have been adequately designed and controlled, give essentially superficial and unenlightening results. For example, compounds known to act by completely different physiological mechanisms can appear to have the same therapeutic effects.

The objective behavioral study of human subjects should help in at least three ways to fill gaps in the typical development of psychoactive

Partial support for work involved in editing this book came from United States Public Health Service Grant M-1871.

1

drugs. First, the "behavioral toxicity" of this class of drug has become as important a matter as the physiological toxicity. Laboratory experiments on a drug's effects on human attention, perception, cognitive abilities, and psychomotor skills are thus necessary to provide a profile of the drug's behavioral toxicity in the same way that the medical examination, blood and urine analysis are essential to check the drug's physiological toxicity. Second, the positive therapeutic effects of the drug need far more precise and meaningful delineation than is possible today, in either clinical or behavioral study. But there are several reasons for thinking that the behavioral study is the more likely to gain in power in the next few years. For example, clinical studies rely on the judgment of one or more human observers who, no matter how brilliant, knowledgeable, well-trained, and painstaking, can inevitably take into consideration only a small amount of the information available about the full complexity of human behavior. Nor can the clinician, once he injects his own person into an interaction with the patient, continue to exercise the control over the total structuring necessary for good measurement. Possibly the greatest advances made by clinical study will be, as suggested by Freyhan and by Kubie in this book, toward the more sensitive diagnosis and more profound theoretical understanding of the patient, through careful observation by insightful clinicians. But there are many behavioral measuring techniques already waiting to be used by the psychopharmacologist, and relatively good prospects of rapid development and improvement of such methods. Third, the experimental methodology of behavioral research should lead to firmer conclusions about drug actions. Its application has, in fact, already led to striking improvements in clinical studies, through the use of such relatively elementary controls as placebos, double-blind methods, adequate sampling techniques, rating scales, and proper statistical evaluation of the significances of results.

Of prime ultimate importance will be the basic knowledge of human behavior that is bound to be gained with the addition of the psychoactive drugs to our list of experimental tools, as suggested by Russell, Eysenck, Mirsky and Rosvold, and others in this book. Drugs have fundamental advantages over surgical intervention: their time of onset, magnitude, and duration are easily controlled; and their effects are ordinarily reversible. Of course, often we do not know nearly enough about the laws or mechanism of their activities. Until now for basic behavioral research psychoactive drugs have been used primarily in animal experiments. But it has become feasible to use them with human subjects for many new sorts of experiments, especially on chemical and physiological determinants of behavior.

Various investigatory instruments enable us to isolate different fundamental variables of behavior. For several decades we have been able to extirpate numerous parts of the brain. But these have always been crude maneuvers affecting by degeneration, infection, or trauma other parts of the nervous system besides those intended. Now we have the beginnings of a reversible chemical surgery by which we can compare behavioral effects with the molecular structures of the drugs which bring them about and, by altering these structures, delve into the biochemistry of action and experience. Furthermore, since these drugs affect schizophrenia and other mental diseases, we may ultimately get clues to possible physiological and biochemical malfunctions which underlie these illnesses and thus gain insights leading to prevention or cure.

The Development of Psychoactive Drugs

In the 1950's the new drugs that affect man's behavior attracted an enormous amount of scientific and professional attention. They have become a commonplace in the everyday life of the average American, and they continue to elicit excited headlines in newspapers and magazines throughout the world. After reserpine, known for centuries in India, was given serious consideration by Western medicine, first as a hypotensive and later as a tranquilizer, there has been an accelerating use of its *Rauwolfia* congeners, of the phenothiazines, the propanediols, and miscellaneous compounds with tranquilizing properties, as well as the antidepressants, or psychic energizers, and the psychotomimetics. When we speak of psychoactive drugs, we think most immediately of the tranquilizers, although we should certainly include all these other classifications, and in addition certain sedatives, analgesics, stimulants, and perhaps even anesthetics, which in one way or another all affect behavior, and some of which have been known for decades or, like alcohol and morphia, for ages.

The increase in the use of these psychoactive compounds, particularly the tranquilizers and more recently the psychic energizers, has been fantastic. Tranquilizers are the third most common category of drugs now dispensed by general practitioners, appearing in more than 10 per cent of all prescriptions written. Many millions of patients all over the world have used them.

These drugs show real promise of important palliative or therapeutic effects. There is in them and in similar compounds yet to be synthesized much hope for patients under emotional stress, suffering from psychosomatic problems, or more deeply ill with neurosis and psychosis. Increasingly substantial evidence is coming forward that patient loads in state hospitals are decreasing and that the psychoactive drugs have been largely responsible. As reported by Jerry E. Bishop on the first page of the *Wall Street Journal* on Friday, October 23, 1959, "discharges from mental hospitals are for the first time increasing faster than still-rising admissions . . . within most mental hospitals, the whole atmosphere has been changing for the better. There's less overcrowding. . . . Thanks largely to the use of tranquilizers, special wards for disturbed patients are disappearing or taking on a look little different from that of ordinary hospital wards.

" 'Before,' says Dr. Jesse F. Casey, Director of Psychiatric and Neurological Services for Veterans Administration Mental Hospitals, 'many patients were too disturbed to take part in therapy. Now it's unusual to go into a hospital and hear patients shouting and screaming. We no longer have "disturbed wards" and it's a rare case when we have to restrain anyone.'

"More important, many patients brought back to reality with tranquilizers can maintain their mental balance merely by continuing to take the drugs. Hospitals are able to release such patients, requiring them only to make periodic visits to local psychiatric clinics. . . .

"Statisticians estimate that had the historical upward trend in patient population continued, there would now be at least 50,000 more patients in mental hospitals than there are. It would have cost the hospitals at least an additional $1500 a year to care for each of these patients." While, as the article points out, this cannot be explained exclusively by the existence of the new drugs, since new therapeutic activity and methods of ward handling are also involved, nevertheless the drugs do have central importance. Among other things they have given the psychiatrist new hope, so that once again he is becoming actively therapeutic.

The Need for Conceptual and Methodological Frameworks for Drug Studies

Many terms have been suggested in the field of psychopharmacology, but as yet there is no universally accepted terminology. Sometimes the drugs are called psychoactive, and sometimes phrenotropic. Sometimes a certain type of compound is referred to as an ata-

raxic; another time it is a tranquilizer. Sometimes we hear of antidepressants and sometimes of psychic energizers. It has been suggested
that these drugs be classified by the psychiatric or physiological symptoms which they affect, so we could speak of an antiphobic or an
antihallucinatory drug. And it has been suggested, as by Kaplan in
this book, that they be classified according to their various loci of
effect in the nervous system, e.g., autonomic drugs, which either increase or decrease its activity, and central nervous system drugs, possibly subclassified into the various subsystems which they affect.
Until we are sure that there is some relationship between symptomatology and anatomical location or between these and the variables of
behavior, it will be difficult to make any permanent classification.

In the chapters of this book it repeatedly becomes apparent that,
although a general overall conceptual system does not exist, it is
needed in order to bring biochemical, physiological, and pharmacological facts together with the behavioral and psychodynamic in
some unitary way. Berger, Freyhan, Himwich, Kubie, and others
throughout the book cope with many aspects of this problem. Such
a conceptual system is logically prior even to adequate classification
of the psychoactive drugs.

It is interesting to observe in this book that attempts at such integrative conceptual systems appear to arise more comfortably from
Europeans or those trained in Europe than from Americans, who are
still apparently bathed in America's pragmatic empiricism. In the
chapters of this book we find articles written from different theoretical points of view, including the warm humanism of Bennett; existen-
tialism as expressed in the article of Pollard and Bakker; Freudian
psychoanalysis as represented in the thinking of Kubie and various
others; derivatives of Pavlovian conditioned reflexology as found in
the work of LeGuillant and of Kaplan, who refer to such Russians
as Ivanov-Smolenski; the Hullian approach followed by Eysenck; and
Cattell's efforts to derive the dimensions of behavior, psychopathology,
and personality. An American search for fundamental dimensionali-
ties may be found in Fleishman's chapter on psychomotor behavior.

Eysenck and Cattell emphasize the importance of finding the dimensions of behavior, and certainly this is essential to a precise theory
of human behavior and of drug effects upon this behavior. It is
possible to develop "pure" tests of various variables, perhaps derived
from factor analyses, as several of the authors point out. On the
other hand, such tests frequently do not predict complex real situations well. We find it hard to get such "pure variables" out of tests

like the life-like situations discussed by Fiske, or the simulated automobile driving tests of behavior. Fleishman, in a thoughtful analysis of the future of psychomotor tests, does not deny the value of
attempting to determine pure variables or dimensions of behavior by
factor analytic or other means, but suggests that practically it may be
desirable also to develop work samples of realistic situations which
give overall scores at the same time that they include various subscores on pure factors. This may be an acceptable compromise to resolve this conceptual problem.

Fleishman emphasizes the need of apparatus for making psychomotor tests, and indeed there is continually a greater tendency to de-
part from pencil and paper tests as exclusive behavioral indices and
to employ equipment as well, partly because of the improvement in
apparatus technique with the development of electronics and information-processing systems, and partly because many of the dimensions
of behavior cannot be tested by pencil and paper alone. Another
reason has been emphasized in the development of some of the apparatuses discussed by Miller in Chapter 23. The dimensions and
measurements of mechanics and electronics have been thoroughly
analyzed by the physical sciences, and they provide great quantitative
precision. By making the human being a subsystem interacting with
other subsystems in an overall man-machine system, it may be possible to increase our understanding of the human system, employing
dimensions that the physical sciences have so successfully used for the
machine. By attempting, without committing the errors of "reduc-
tionism," to measure as many behavioral variables as possible in physical science units, we may increase our precision of measurement of
human behavior.

Katz in his discussion brings up the problem of distinguishing behavioral toxicity from positive behavioral effects. In both clinical and
experimental studies, behavioral scientists have not been satisfied
simply to refer to a change brought about by a compound. We also
want to state whether or not this change is desirable or undesirable.
Making these value judgments requires either some general understanding of the nature of health or favorable individual adjustment,
or the acceptance of certain value standards from some outside frame
of reference. In order to determine such values, a conceptual theory
which shows how values are established by systems more inclusive
than the individual or the examiner is essential.

Ellsworth makes another important point when he states in his
chapter that the measurement of behavioral adjustment in terms of

variables of behavior may be more meaningful and valid than the changes in psychopathological symptoms which are the traditional concern of clinicians and which have frequently in behavioral studies been used as a criterion—a somewhat wobbly criterion because the concepts of health and illness are not clear and because there are differences between schools and between individual clinicians in the observation of these subtle factors.

Any conceptual system analyzing drug effects on behavior must deal with several levels of behaving systems because the subject matter of psychopharmacology crosses these levels. First there are the chemical influences of molecules upon cells and organs, the problems of the biology and pharmacology of drug effects. Effects at the level of molecule, cell, and organ ultimately influence the total individual, the subject or patient around whom most attention in this field traditionally centers. Clear effects of interpersonal interactions are discussed by various writers like Bennett and Fiske, and explicit group studies of drug effects are treated by Nowlis in his chapter. And certainly there are significant social implications of the drugs, many as yet unstudied. To what extent would Western culture be altered by widespread use of tranquilizers? Would Yankee initiative disappear? Is the chemical deadening of anxiety harmful? To what extent are the Peyote cultures different because of the use of mescal, or Central American tribes unique because of their hallucinatory mushrooms? What standards of social behavior do we wish to maintain? Could psychoactive drugs provide prophylaxis for mental disease on a society-wide basis? It might be illuminating to examine the psychopharmacology of drugs and behavior within the theoretical framework of general behavior systems theory, dealing with the levels of molecule, cell, organ, individual, group, and society.

The Value of Human Subjects

The overwhelming emphasis in this book is on behavioral studies with human beings rather than with animals. The earliest psychopharmacological experiments were primarily with animals, after the tradition in pharmacology, but increasingly the emphasis has been on human research. Holliday in her chapter is modern in insisting that objective testing of behavioral effects be carried out with human beings as well as with animals before definitive statements are made, either about behavioral toxicity or about therapeutic effects. This is not to say that behavioral research with animals is not essential for studies comparing species, or investigations that cannot be carried out on man, such as those which involve extirpation of brain tissue or chronic implantation of depth electrodes. Certainly, moreover, animals can still be used for the first screening of large numbers of psychoactive drugs, even though some of the hoped-for promise in the use of operant conditioning and other animal screening techniques has not yet been fulfilled.

The chief reason for emphasizing human rather than animal research is the ancient and obvious argument that species are different —so different that generalization is unreliable. Experimentalists too often forget that they are dealing with white rats rather than human beings and make facile generalizations to other species in ways which cannot be justified. This is particularly true for the higher neural processes affected by psychoactive drugs. It is in the higher nervous system that human beings differ most from all other species of animal. Many drug effects—effects on individual differences, effects modifiable by experience, effects on language and interpersonal relationships, on emotion and temperament—essentially concern human variables which are difficult or impossible to isolate in lower species. For this reason evaluation with human beings is essential before we can say we have a thorough understanding of one of these drugs.

In many cases, animal techniques can also be applied to human beings, for example, Skinnerian operant conditioning. Sometimes research like that reported by Masserman or Hess in this book appears to deal with important variables but is difficult to adapt to human beings. In many cases we must develop specific techniques of a new sort for human beings. Wherever possible, it is certainly desirable for the sake of precision, reproducibility, and generalizability of results to emphasize the quantitative and objective tradition of experimental psychology rather than the too often uncontrolled intuitionism of the clinical fields, although there are cogent arguments (as presented, for example, by Freyhan, Kubie, and Bennett in this book) that, in doing so at the present state of scientific advancement, important variables will be neglected.

An interesting question of strategy is raised by Reitan in his chapter, when he argues that normal subjects are better for behavioral testing than patients. There seems to be a large body of opinion in this field that, after animal screening, the first behavioral research on drugs for human beings should be on normal human beings. (Let us ignore for the moment the problems surrounding the use of the word "normal.") This in a sense gives a baseline, from which psychopathological deviations can occur.   This is the philosophy which leads to the study of anatomy before pathology, of normal physiology before patho-physiology.   It is probably sound, but ultimately we are interested in possible clinical applications of these drugs and therefore, before research is completed, they, of course, must be tested with different categories of patients as well.

Some Difficulties in the Study of Human Behavior

Throughout this book the reader gets a picture of the early stages of development of a field and realizes that many of the most interesting questions are still unanswered.   We shall mention here a few examples of these questions.   One with which the editors are especially familiar is raised by the various researchers using driver-trainers to evaluate possible behavioral toxicity of tranquilizers.   Such research has been done by Marquis, Kelly, Gerard, Miller, and Uhr, by Melander, and by Kristofferson and Cormack.   Such behavioral tests seem to show that there is a measurable toxic effect on reaction time, accuracy of steering, judgment, and certain visual factors from high doses of such compounds as emylcamate, phenaglycodol, meprobamate, oxanamide, and prochlorperazine—doses more than twice the amounts used clinically.   But these studies have not shown with any consistency such toxicity in ordinary clinical doses.   On the other hand, Loomis and West have found ordinary doses of chlorpromazine, alcohol, and, to a lesser degree, meprobamate to have toxic effects on behavior.   What does this disagreement mean, assuming that the data are accurate and dependable?   Are the tests of others besides Loomis and West not sensitive enough?   That certainly is a possibility.   Were the other investigators wrong when they said they found no behavioral toxicity in ordinary doses?   Any psychoactive drug probably has some effect on behavior controlled by the nervous system, and this should show up if sufficiently delicate tests are made.   The questions then really become: How sensitive should the tests of such variables be?   And what are the alterations in behavior which make practically significant differences in performance of such everyday acts as lathe operation and auto driving?   What other factors, such as inattention, poor training, fatigue, should be studied for similar effects?   As Kristofferson and Cormack suggest in their chapter, many behavioral domains are relevant to driving or similar everyday activities.   A single test or battery of tests will not deal with all of them.   Even though a subject may do well on the driving batteries which have been devised, he may not in actual life operate an automobile well because some other aspects of driving, such as motivation, have not been properly evaluated. There are many fascinating and important issues of practical significance in this field. With millions of patients receiving psychoactive drugs continuously, it would be of serious import to the society generally if they were all kept away from machines in this world of machines, or were not allowed outside alone. We cannot be too careful about safety, but on the other hand we cannot limit the freedom of people in need of these drugs too severely. Should the Army Surgeon General ground all pilots who have taken a tranquilizer within a month? Should he ground them because of the behavioral toxicity of such drugs or because pilots who take tranquilizers must have emotional disturbances sufficiently serious to warrant the action? These are difficult questions. As yet we do not have certain answers.

There are many other interesting, controversial questions. One concerns the acceptable level of statistical significance in psychopharmacological research. Often in clinical psychological research a 5 per cent level (or $p = .05$) has been considered acceptable, while in experimental research it is usually $p = .01$, or preferably .001. The degree of precision of statements is on the whole probably going up in psychopharmacology, but, depending upon the type of behavioral variable measured and the sort of technique used, there still is a wide range in the confidence level at which an experimenter will accept his findings. There is, of course, an even wider range in the amount of control and precision he will exercise in accumulating his data.

Another statistical problem arises when many variables are tested in a single battery, say 100. Suppose that among these one finds one statistically significant difference between placebo and drug administration at the .01 level and four at the .05 level. By chance, one would have expected one at the .01 level and five at the .05 level (assuming all variables are independent, which is rarely true). Must one therefore assume that this entire study, which may have involved many patients and taken many weeks of drug administration and many hundreds or thousands of hours of testing and data analysis, is simply the result of chance? By strict statistics, that is the only view one can take, but, on the other hand, certainly the variables which developed such significant differences are worth examination. If by luck they had been studied alone, the finding would have been considered significant. These large multivariable screening studies may be throwing away important results unless a second round of tests is carried out to determine whether the significant results discovered in the original experiment hold up. The need for such costly procedures is one argument for the establishment of a number of independent centers around the country with funds from industry, private sources, and government which have the facilities necessary for animal, human-normal, and human-patient screening of drugs. If this could be done, thorough studies of the sort which are now almost infeasible financially could be carried out, with far greater objectivity and far more meaningful results than at present, when researchers are supported primarily by interested individual drug firms.

Another complex issue concerns the double-blind technique. Certainly it is necessary to control against the placebo effect and against the conscious or unconscious bias of the rater or diagnostician. But, does not the double-blind technique put a strait jacket on the clinical experimenter who frequently experiments by raising or lowering the level of the dose until he finally finds the proper one? The answer probably is "no." It is possible to raise and lower the dosages of potent drugs or of placebos equally well in a double-blind study. The clinician may not know which he is using, but, if he is free to alter these, as Lasky indicates in his chapter, he is much more likely to change dosages of potent drugs than of the placebos until he finally finds a satisfactory level, because with placebos he finds no change. Several other aspects of the complex matter of the double blind are discussed by Nash and by Kurland.

There are also many little practical problems in such research, for example, how to be sure that patients, particularly outpatients, take their medication. (Dated envelopes holding the pills and requiring signature and return by the patient may be one solution; nurses going from house to house may be another.) If the patient wishes to avoid medication, however—and psychotic patients are particularly difficult —perfect control is hard short of parenteral injection of the drug. There is also the practical problem, especially severe in studies of acute effects, of the peaking of behavioral influences of drugs with relatively rapid excretion rates which complicates the timing of behavioral testing. One wishes to maintain a constant level of the behavioral effect of the drug over a period of time, so that a lengthy battery of tests can be given. Spansules which permit continuous release of the drug may be used, although fabrication of spansules which accurately maintain a constant drug level is sometimes difficult to accomplish or impractical.

Then there is the complex issue of controls. Which is best: matched controls, own controls, or some other? Must each study have its own particular controls, or might it be more profitable to work toward the development of behavioral tests whose norms have been so thoroughly studied—equivalent to the Wasserman or the Stanford-Binet IQ—that nation-wide controls could be used by each individual experimenter for comparison purposes?

Many legal and ethical problems are involved in the practical use of drugs both in research and in clinical practice. A strict construction of the laws in most or all states would suggest that any use of drugs for an experimental purpose rather than to help or cure a patient, even with his written voluntary consent, is not legal. An individual does not have the right to consent to such an assault upon himself, and he cannot release from responsibility any professional person who experimentally administers the drug. Of course, in practice a great deal of such research in psychopharmacology and other areas has gone on for a long time, and one can argue in court that, if the research were not done, medicine simply could not advance. On the other hand, in the individual case if a patient is harmed or believes he is harmed by the drug, the experimenter is in a difficult position even if he is a properly licensed physician in an established institution. Moreover, malpractice insurance ordinarily does not cover work undertaken primarily for experimentation. One can argue that such research is widely done, one can demonstrate that it is carried out in the state prisons and federal penitentiaries under official approval, but the issue still is delicate. Particularly sensitive is the use, as subjects, of students, children, or other groups whose welfare is particularly guarded by the sympathies of the community. The strictest medical protection, with nurses and physicians available on immediate call, is a helpful safeguard in such research, practically if not legally. Furthermore, the permission in writing of the subjects or of parents or guardians if they are underage or incompetent is certainly worth obtaining, even though it does not have any definitive legal status.

There are also problems of ethics. Many thoughtful physicians deeply question the ethics of the use of placebos which are known not to help patients, particularly without their knowledge or consent. It is difficult to see how such control can be avoided, howeve if worth-while research is to be done. Although the individu patient may not gain from the research, in the long run he as part of society will profit, and later patients, perhaps including himself in a later illness, will certainly benefit from it. Perhaps, with a category of drug like the tranquilizer, of which there are a number that already have demonstrated effectiveness, it will be increasingly possible to use a standard active compound, like chlorpromazine or meprobamate, for comparison against new compounds and then attempt to compare the effectiveness of the new compound and the old compound in "chlorpromazine units" or "meprobamate units" of effectiveness, rather than always compare the new compound and an inert placebo. If we human beings were not so "self-deceptive" as to create the placebo effect, placebos might not be scientifically necessary, but, while there may be a wrong in planned silence or planned deceit, there is an even greater wrong if patients are given compounds whose effectiveness and toxicity have not been objectively evaluated.

Tomorrow and Tomorrow . . .

What will be the future of the psychoactive drugs? Prophecy is a rare gift, always difficult, particularly when based on extrapolation of a curve as short as the curve of development of psychoactive drugs. But one has a feeling that, both scientifically and in the world of human affairs, they will bulk large in the future and change things in significant, and occasionally in unpredictable, ways. For example, in their chapter Kristofferson and Cormack present evidence, supported by a number of other investigators, that meprobamate can raise the baseline of the galvanic skin response, and therefore the detection of emotional responses by this technique may be made less obvious. This was an experimental study, but it seems perhaps to confirm the judgment of some New England villagers. In Newbury, Vermont, in December, 1957, a farmer who was thoroughly disliked in the community beat his hired man. Shortly thereafter he disappeared and after a few weeks his corpse was found, trussed with a rope, floating in the Connecticut River. The assumption of many was that a "white lynching" had occurred and that his last act toward his hired man was enough to cause citizens of the community to carry out a group murder. Police and the Federal Bureau of Investigation began a lengthy investigation, administering "lie detector" tests to many members of the community. Then they discovered that some had taken a tranquilizer. So the polygraph, a relatively recent behavioral psychophysiological discovery which, in its police application as "lie detector," has become a familiar aspect of our brave new world, was possibly being cancelled out by an even more recent development, the drug that manipulates human beings, including their galvanic skin responses.

The Organization of the Book

We want to bring to the reader's attention several unusual organizational features that have been introduced into this book with the hope of increasing its usefulness.

Two general types of chapter are included in the book: (a) background, discussion, and theoretical papers, and (b) reports on specific researches conducted by the author. These papers are interspersed, according to the overall continuity given in the Contents. The first section contains what the editors considered to be the irreducible minimum in the way of background orientation for a reader who could not reasonably be expected to be conversant with more than one of the many fields—biochemistry, neurology, neurophysiology, pharmacology, psychiatry, and psychology—that converge at psychopharmacology. The second section includes chapters suggesting and describing techniques that have not yet been used in behavioral tests of drugs' effects on human subjects, along with research reports on work done or being done. The research reports are marked in the Contents by asterisks (*), and this whole group of studies is summarized in Uhr's chapter at the end of the book.

Drugs are identified in the text by their commonly accepted short chemical names. The Subject Index gives, under these names, brief references to the actions of these drugs and their behavioral effects, as determined by objective experiments mentioned in this book. This index gives the cross-referencing information necessary to untangle the confusions of nomenclature in this field. The chapter by Berger gives the short chemical or generic name, the long chemical name (if different), the structural formula, and the American trade name or names of most of the drugs discussed. (See especially pages 89 to 97.) Even though this should eliminate most of the confusion, it will not eliminate all; and we have not attempted to cope with such matters as nomenclature in Europe, occasional alternative choices in short names, and variations in spelling. Nor have we found any way of coping with the matter of the drug introduced tomorrow.

In the succeeding pages there are many challenging facts and theories, and probably a few errors and not a few fantasies. The interchange is interesting and the total impact of the behavioral studies being done today, of which these are only a selected sample, is increasingly impressive. We have tried to keep the editorial slash from completely smoothing out controversy. Incidentally, we do not always as individuals agree with the statements made here. Nor, as the reader will discover, are the contributors always pacific. But the corpus—a surprisingly large corpus—of agreement is there, an exciting picture of a burgeoning science.

PART I

*The Methodological,
Chemical, Biological,
and Clinical Context
for Psychopharmacology*

Biochemistry,

Physiology,

and Pharmacology

Chapter 1 *Roger W. Russell*

Drugs as tools in behavioral research

A basic assumption in many contemporary studies of behavior is that the behavior patterns of a living organism are related, directly or indirectly, to events taking place in various biological subsystems within the organism. Evidence of the basic validity of this assumption now covers a wide territory from the demonstration of relations between gene-controlled enzymes and behavior dysfunctions, e.g., phenylketonuria (Garrod, 1923), to present studies in psychopharmacology, with their promise of major contributions to the treatment of mental illness. This evidence has been accumulating rapidly as techniques of searching for these relations have been devised and sharpened. The general approach has been to observe the behavior of organisms in which the normal course of events in biological systems has been altered. To put this approach on an experimental basis requires systematic variation of the event which presumably is related to the behavior pattern under study.

Although behavior appears to be related most closely to events in the nervous system and particularly the central nervous system, events in other systems, e.g., the endocrine system, exert important influences. These biological systems have structural and dynamic features such that changes in one feature may be reflected by changes in the other. Basic to the dynamic features of a system are the biochemical events which characterize it in action and in its steady state. Drugs serve as the most important tools by which a research worker may produce the systematic variations in biochemical events which an experimental approach to the study of relations between biological systems and behavior requires. Drugs, as chemical agents which initiate or alter

19

responses of biological systems, serve directly as stimuli or indirectly by influencing the effects of other stimuli on a system. Changes in biological systems may, in turn, be reflected in changes of behavior.

Responses of biological systems may, of course, be altered experimentally by introducing structural changes, experimental lesions, and thus interfering with the biochemical events which normally occur in the site affected. A number of studies have demonstrated that similar effects on behavior may be produced by structural or by "biochemical lesions" (Peters, 1948) at particular localities in the body (e.g., Essig, Hampson, McCanley, and Himwich, 1950; Feldberg and Sherwood, 1955; Freedman and Himwich, 1949). Drugs have an important advantage in that the biochemical lesions they produce may be reversible. This permits research designs in which the subject's behavior is measured before creation of a biochemical lesion, when the lesion is present, and during and after recovery from the lesion. The entire course of a relation between the responses of a biological system and its behavioral correlates may be observed. Another major advantage of drugs as tools for systematically varying biochemical events is suggested by such results as those obtained by Feldberg and Sherwood (1954). By injecting various drugs directly into the lateral ventricle of the cat brain they produced a variety of sensory and motor effects which suggested

> . . . that anatomical localization alone may not be sufficient for interpreting neural mechanisms and integration, but that consideration must be given to the pharmacological sensitivity and specificity of central synapses.

Drugs may be important tools for studying the effects on behavior of different dynamic systems within the same general structural area.

In the search for relations between drug actions and behavior, drugs are used in several different ways according to the nature of the specific hypothesis being tested. The hypotheses involve three general classes of variables:

1. Drugs, as chemical agents.
2. Biological systems within the organism.
3. Behavior patterns.

Research is designed to test hypotheses which relate these three classes of variables in different ways. In some instances drugs serve as the independent variables of the research design and, in other instances, as tools for producing the behavior pattern to be studied or for varying systematically the independent variable under examination.

Our present concern is with drugs as research tools, but it will also be useful to consider the roles which drugs may play as independent variables.

Although the discussion which follows will concentrate on drugs, it will be important to remain constantly aware of the fact that overall drug-behavior interactions are dependent upon characteristics of the biochemical events affected, of the subjects employed, of the behavior patterns observed, and of the conditions under which the behavior patterns are generated (Sidman, 1956).

Drugs as Independent Variables

The use of drugs to induce sleep, to deaden the perception of pain, to produce hallucinations, and to affect behavior in numerous other ways is centuries old. Many such uses have been based on empirical observations made purely by chance. Various anesthetics are now old but very worthy examples. The tranquilizer chlorpromazine is a more modern illustration. Chlorpromazine was first suggested for its antihistaminic and sedative actions. Its effects on the regulation of body temperature and blood pressure later led to its use in surgical procedures. Incidental observations of its effects on behavior finally resulted in its present use as one of the tranquilizing drugs.

With the development of scientific method, such incidental observations led to the statement of hypotheses which could be subjected to experimental test. Since relatively little was known of the actions of drugs on biochemical events in the body, hypotheses characteristically concerned supposed relations between a drug and some aspect of behavior. In research designs to test these hypotheses, the independent variable was the presence in some degree of the drug; the dependent variables, measures of behavior. Various parameters of the independent variable, e.g., dose, route of administration, frequency and number of administrations, were varied, and then different measures of behavior were studied.

Research based upon this classical type of hypothesis has been voluminous and still remains a major focus of attention, particularly for those who are primarily interested in immediate applications of our knowledge concerning drug-behavior interactions. Specific examples have been analyzed in recent reviews (e.g., Wikler, 1957; Franks, 1958b) and in reports of special conferences and symposia (e.g., Abramson, 1956, 1957; Dews and Skinner, 1956; Himwich, 1957; Kline, 1956). Such research has provided much useful information.

Studies of chemically related drugs and comparisons of chemically dissimilar drugs have aided in the identification of psychoactive agents and in the selection of drugs best suited for use in many situations where modifications of behavior are desirable. When research of this kind establishes the existence of a relation between the administration of a drug on the one hand and behavior changes on the other, the result in terms of human welfare may be great.

As important as these applications of knowledge may be, the story will remain far from complete until much more is known about the events intervening between the administration of a drug and subsequent changes in behavior. Information about the modes of action of chemical agents on the responses of biological systems and of effects of such responses on behavior not only enhances knowledge in several scientific fields, but also provides a rational rather than a purely empirical approach to the selection and compounding of new drugs for specific practical purposes.

Drugs as Tools for
Producing "Model" Behavior Patterns

For a long time it has been known that the administration of certain drugs is followed by the appearance of what might be called "model behavior patterns" (Mayer-Gross, 1951; Rinkel, DeShon, Hyde, and Solomon, 1952). Examples are the occurrence of hallucinations and illusions after administration of such drugs as mescaline and hashish and, more recently, the production of "model psychoses" by administration of lysergic acid (e.g., DeShon, Rinkel, and Solomon, 1952; Hock, Cattell, and Pennes, 1952a). Here a drug is used as a tool to produce behavior patterns which can be studied overtly by the researcher or in terms of the subject's own introspective reports; the latter are commonly referred to as "self-experiments." Used in such a way, the drug may serve directly to stimulate a biological system, e.g., hallucinations, or indirectly by influencing the effects of other stimuli, e.g., illusions. A wide variety of physiological and psychological techniques have been applied in analyzing the characteristics of model behavior patterns (e.g., Brengelmann, Laverty, and Lewis, 1958; Elkes, 1957; Felberg and Sherwood, 1955a; Fisher 1956).

Self-experiments with mescaline were first reported about 1896. From this and many more recent reports, certain special characteristics of the behavior changes produced stand out clearly. Perception of the environment is disturbed. Time appears to be changed, to become fragmentary and discontinuous. Consciousness varies from a rather detached self-evaluation to extreme drowsiness. Certain experiences belonging to one sense become attached to another. Sensory illusions, particularly visual and tactile, appear. Frequently, but not always, these experiences are described as having been very pleasant.

The effects of other drugs are often reported as overlapping those of mescaline, though they differ in certain predominant features. For example, hashish produces special forms of dissociation of thought and excessively vigorous responses or restlessness. Auditory hallucinations, accompanied by fear and sometimes terror, characterize cocaine intoxication.

During the past few years new chemicals and chemical compounds have been discovered which produce symptoms in normal human subjects analogous to those experienced by psychotic patients. The effects are often strikingly similar despite differences in the chemical structures of the drugs. One of these new drugs, lysergic acid, has received particular attention. Like mescaline, it produces serious disorganizations of normal behavior, including disturbances of perception and thinking, changes in mood, and the appearance of hallucinations and delusions. It produces a marked aggravation of the abnormal symptoms of schizophrenic patients, and it produces mild schizophrenic-like symptoms in normal subjects.

Other drugs produce different model behavior patterns. Injection of animals with the drug bulbocapnine in suitable doses induces a condition referred to as "experimental catatonia" (e.g., Feldberg and Sherwood, 1955a). This condition frequently has a sudden onset following a latent period of 30 seconds to 3 minutes after injection of the drug. The animal develops an extremely stuporous state; it can be put in abnormal postures which are retained for many seconds or even minutes. It is extremely unresponsive to changes in its environment. Recovery is gradual, but during the effective period of the drug the animal exhibits many of the symptoms of human catatonic schizophrenics. Experimental catatonia may also be produced by the presence of various anticholinesterase drugs and of acetylcholine (ACh) in the ventricles of the brain. In certain types of mental patients injection of an anticholinesterase may aggravate the condition and cause a reappearance of the symptoms which characterized the onset of the illness.

Chemical stimulation within the central nervous system has been used to elicit behavior patterns of a more specific nature, such as "forced circling behavior" (Essig, Hampson, McCanley, and Himwich, 1950) and changes in handedness (Peterson, 1949). Well-integrated and persistent drive states have been induced by direct chemical stimulation of particular brain loci (Fisher, 1956). The techniques involved in these studies will be discussed later.

If the results from studies of model behavior patterns are to be generalized, we must be confident that the model is indeed homologous and not merely analogous to the behavior patterns copied (Russell, 1952). There is ample evidence that the two have features in common; but there are also differences which, at the present stage of our knowledge, make it risky to assume that the two are identical (Hock, Cattell, and Pennes, 1952b; Russell, 1956).

Hypotheses Involving
Changes of Intermediate Behavior

Frequently drugs are used in testing hypotheses which involve interactions between two or more forms of behavior. Depending upon the manner in which such hypotheses are stated, drugs may serve as independent variables or as tools to vary the independent variables. In either case the sequence of interactions is:

Drug ─────────────→ Behavior$_1$ ─────────────→ Behavior$_2$

Illustrative of the use of drugs as independent variables under these circumstances are reports of a research program designed to assess drug effects on emotional behavior (Brady, 1956a, b). Behavior$_2$ consisted of a bar-press response stabilized on a variable-interval reinforcement schedule prior to the final tests. Behavior$_1$ was an emotional response to a clicking noise, which also was established prior to the final tests by pairing the click with a painful electric shock to the subjects' feet. Rats and monkeys served as subjects. Superimposing the conditioned emotional response upon the bar pressing markedly depressed the rate of the latter, during the test periods. Performance during no-drug tests was then compared with test performance 1 hour after administration of relatively large doses of amphetamine and after daily doses of reserpine. Effects of the superimposed emotional response were enhanced under the influence of amphetamine; after four daily injections of reserpine, these effects were virtually eliminated. In this instance the final behavior pattern served as a means of observing the effects of the drugs on the intermediate behavior. (See Chapter 12.)

Another series of studies (Russell and Steinberg, 1955; Steinberg and Russell, 1957) also illustrates the use of drugs as tools for altering intermediate behavior. Human subjects were used. Behavior$_2$ consisted of learning a temporal maze problem; behavior$_1$ was performed on another temporal maze which, although the subjects did not know it, was insoluble. The general hypothesis was that performance on the insoluble problem would produce signs of "anxiety" and would interfere with learning the subsequent soluble problem, but that the interference could be minimized or even abolished by reducing the anxiety and the possibility of transfer from behavior$_1$ to behavior$_2$. Nitrous oxide in less than anesthetic dosage was the drug used as a tool for this purpose. The hypothesis was confirmed: whenever the drug was combined with performance on the insoluble problem, subsequent learning of the soluble maze did not differ from the learning of the same maze by control groups.

Hypotheses Requiring Functional Blocks in Biological Systems

The preceding uses of drugs as research tools have been concerned with tests of hypotheses which involve only two of the general classes of variables with which we began this discussion, i.e., drugs and behavior. It is obvious that relations between variables of these classes are dependent upon events in biological systems which intervene between them.

Wherever we turn in the world of living organisms, we find biochemical changes taking place. These changes constitute regular features of an organism's normal metabolism. The wide variety of chemical reactions involved are characterized by a velocity and completeness which is dependent upon the presence of numerous enzymes (Baldwin, 1953). These enzymes are complex organic catalysts, produced by living cells and capable of acting independently of the cells that produce them. They speed chemical reactions, which otherwise proceed slowly, to the rates necessary for the normal functioning of biological systems. For our present purposes the principal features of such biochemical reactions may be illustrated schematically as follows:

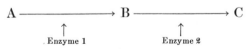

$$A \longrightarrow B \longrightarrow C$$
$$\uparrow \qquad \qquad \uparrow$$
$$\text{Enzyme 1} \qquad \text{Enzyme 2}$$

The essential function of an enzyme is to activate its substrate. In so doing, enzymes are strikingly specific, catalyzing only a small range of reactions and frequently only one. Such action is profoundly affected by a number of physical and chemical factors.

New developments in biochemistry and pharmacology clarify the nature of biochemical systems and the ways in which they are affected by drug actions. Most drugs are remarkably selective in their actions, affecting a particular step in a chain of biochemical events and often being limited to a specific tissue or group of receptor cells (Goodman and Gilman, 1956). When its mode of action is known, a drug may be used as a tool to vary a biochemical event experimentally in testing hypotheses relating the event to behavior. The drug produces a biochemical change, frequently referred to by the shorthand term "biochemical lesion" (e.g., Essig, Hampson, McCanley, and Himwich, 1950; Peters, 1948). The presence of a lesion is the independent variable; measures of behavior are the dependent variables.

Biochemical lesions may be used to create temporary "functional blocks" in a biological system whose relations to behavior are being studied. One interesting example of this use of drugs as research tools appears in a series of experiments demonstrating the equivalence of cortical and subcortical systems of the cerebrum in auditory conditioning (Girden, 1940, 1942a, b, c; Girden and Culler, 1937). Curare, the drug used, depresses the excitability of the cortex but does not affect spinal excitability (Culler, Coakley, Shurrager, and Ades, 1939). The general designs of these experiments provided for the conditioning of skeletal and autonomic responses to an auditory stimulus in normal and curarized animal subjects. The results, after check experiments which included conditioning of animals from which the auditory cortex had been removed, indicated that cortical and subcortical systems may serve as equivalents in this type of learning. That is to say, in normal animals some essential aspects of conditioning depend upon functioning of the cortex; however, when cortical functioning is depressed by curare, conditioning takes place subcortically. The divergent functions of these two systems were also made evident by the fact that conditioned responses established under the drug did not carry over to the normal state, nor did they transfer from normal to drug state. In this example the drug served as a tool to interfere with the functioning of one biological system while the relations of another to behavior were being examined.

Hypotheses Relating
Biochemical Events and Behavior

Once their modes of action are known, drugs may assist in determining quantitative relations between biochemical events and their behavioral correlates. The selective action of a drug on a specific biochemical event may be used experimentally as a means of varying the event systematically while concomitant changes in behavior are being measured. The drug, then, serves as a research tool to alter the independent variable of the hypothesis under test. Thus drugs have been used to alter biochemical events by changing the activity levels of enzymes and the concentrations of substrates upon which enzymes act.

These uses of drugs are illustrated in studies of the relations between acetylcholine (ACh) activity and a variety of behavior patterns. Normal functioning of the nervous system depends upon an entire chain of biochemical events among which is the synthesis of ACh. ACh plays its vital role as long as it is present in small quantities; beyond certain concentrations its effects are to paralyze neural transmission. This means that, during the normal functioning of nerves, ACh must not accumulate. Existing at the proper places and in adequate amounts is an enzyme, cholinesterase (ChE), which hydrolyzes ACh and inactivates it very rapidly after its release. These features of the ACh system may be diagrammed as follows:

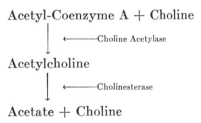

Acetyl-Coenzyme A + Choline

↑———Choline Acetylase

Acetylcholine

↑———Cholinesterase

Acetate + Choline

There have been two main experimental approaches in varying this system while searching for concomitant changes in behavior. The first has been to increase the concentration of ACh, the substrate upon which the enzyme, ChE, acts. The second has been to reduce the activity level of the enzyme by the use of certain selective inhibitors, anticholinesterases, thus preventing ACh from being inactivated at the normal rate. Since behavior depends upon neural activity, we would expect such alterations in neurochemical events to be reflected in changes of behavior.

In one series of studies (Peterson, 1949) the concentration of ACh was raised by local applications made unilaterally to motor areas of the cerebral cortex of rats. The effects were reflected in changes of handedness, a habit of long standing. In another research series (Feldberg and Sherwood, 1954; McCulloch, Ridley, and Sherwood,

1952) ACh was injected directly into the ventricles of the brain in unanesthetized animals, thus changing substrate concentrations and producing such concomitant behavior changes as depressed motor reactions and confused or reduced responsiveness to external stimulation.

Other research (Russell, 1956, 1958) reports the differential effects of chronic reductions in brain ChE on a wide variety of behavior patterns. Rats were used as subjects. The experimental groups were orally fed standardized concentrations of an organophosphorus compound[1] which maintained brain ChE activity at consistently reduced levels during the entire period of each experiment. Since there is a large margin of safety in the amount of ChE normally present in the brain, it is possible to reduce ChE activity drastically before pathological signs appear. In these experiments care was taken not to carry reductions to this level. The research design made it possible to compare performances of experimental animals with control animals whose brain ChE activity remained at its normal level.

In an extensive preliminary investigation involving a variety of test situations and different forms of motivation, it was found that the experimental animals were slower in eliminating responses which had been learned previously but were no longer adequate, less efficient in serial problem solving, and less efficient in adjusting to stresses imposed by the environment. In other behavior patterns—including locomotion, simple learning, instrumental conditioning, and visual discrimination—their performances did not differ significantly from those of control animals. These results have been substantiated in a series of more intensive experiments. The results are of interest in three main regards:

First, they show that reduction in ChE activity to the level when pathological signs appear affects some aspects of behavior significantly but not others. (This is also true of other drugs, it may be noted.)

Second, when behavior was affected, it appeared to pass through four phases as ChE activity was progressively reduced. From 60 to 100 per cent activity no significant effects were observed. There was a suggestion in the data that between 40 and 60 per cent activity there may have been a phase of heightened behavioral efficiency. Further reduction was associated with a rapid loss in efficiency, a

---

[1] O,O-Diethyl-S-ethylmercaptoethanol-thiophosphate ("systox").

phase of "behavioral toxicity." The fourth and final phase was characterized by signs of bodily toxicity, ending in convulsions and death.

Third, those aspects of behavior which were affected appeared to be important in the animal's adjustment to change in its environment. In many instances adaptive behavior requires the extinction of old behavior patterns and the formation of new ones. Under such circumstances speed of extinction may well be the pacemaker step in the series of adaptive behavior changes. The results of the experiments suggested that this pacemaker step, at least under certain circumstances, is related to brain ChE activity in such a way that high activity is associated with more rapid extinction. If this reasoning is valid, it leads to conclusions similar to those of other research workers who have related existing levels of brain ChE activity to measures of behavior rather than altering these levels experimentally. These workers have concluded that "a high ChE level is associated with an ability to maintain a probabilistic response pattern, while a low ChE level is associated with a more thorough concomitant to the dominant stimulus" (Krech, Rosenzweig, and Bennett, 1954, 1956).

The risks involved in this use of drugs as research tools make it obvious why many investigators seeking biochemical correlates of behavior have used infrahuman animals as subjects. However, there has been some research involving human subjects. An example is one study (Feldberg and Sherwood, 1955b) involving the treatment of patients suffering from chronic catatonic stupor. These patients were given intraventricular injections of several drugs, including ChE, which had the most marked effects. These effects were noticeable within a very short time after injection; and, within one to three hours, patients, who before injection had been completely unresponsive to stimulation, began to react to instructions and to reply to simple questions. Improvement continued in many cases until the patient was able to take care of his own general needs and persisted for varying periods ranging from four weeks to a number of months. Only two of the fifteen patients treated with ChE failed to show some such improvement. The most interesting finding from our present point of view was that other drugs, administered in the same manner, had different effects on behavior, suggesting that the areas of the brain reached by this technique of injection are selectively sensitive to different chemical agents.

Hypotheses Requiring
Localized Biochemical Changes

Most of the studies just considered are examples of investigations in which the biochemical lesion has been produced without experimental control over the site of the lesion in the body. However, since a particular biochemical event may occur solely or predominantly in a particular organ or tissue, the site of the lesion may in fact be limited. For example, "true" ChE is predominantly associated with nervous tissue and erythrocytes. It is also distinguished from other enzymes of the nervous system by the specificity of its action on ACh and by its sensitivity to selective inhibitors. In addition to such natural localizations or biochemical lesions, it is important for certain experimental purposes that the investigator be able to select the site of the lesion. Relations between biochemical events and behavior may well depend, not only on the events themselves, but also on the locale in which they occur. A number of different techniques have been used, and others are being developed to allow experimental control of this kind.

For example, the action of a chemical agent on a particular organ can be isolated to some extent by injecting the agent into an artery leading only to one organ. It has been demonstrated that, when this technique is used, the effects of the agent on behavior depend upon the site of the injection (Freedman and Himwich, 1949). The technique is well illustrated in a series of experiments (Aprison, Nathan, and Himwich, 1954; Essig, Hampson, McCanley, and Himwich, 1950) in which injection of an anticholinesterase drug into the right common carotid artery of several species of animals produced asymmetric biochemical lesions clearly discernible when ChE activity levels of the frontal cortex and caudate nucleus on both sides of the brain were compared. These reversible lesions induce temporary circling movements analogous to behavior patterns previously obtained by extirpation or by electrical stimulation of these specific cerebral areas.

Reference has already been made to injections of drugs directly into the lateral ventricles of the brain in unanesthetized subjects. Refinements of technique have made it possible to insert a permanent cannula which can be maintained in position for extended periods of time without apparent ill effects (Feldberg and Sherwood, 1953). Effects of injections through this route of entry into the body are undoubtedly attributable to central actions of drugs. The amounts injected are relatively small; leakage into the systemic circulation is limited by the blood-brain barrier. Use of this technique has made it possible to observe the effects of central chemical stimulation on behavior without the complications of peripheral events occurring when other routes of entry are employed.

New techniques for microinjection (Fisher, 1956; Olds, 1957; Olds and Olds, 1958) permit the production of specific biochemical lesions with at least a primary focus in very restricted sites in the nervous system. These techniques have produced results which support the view that relations between biochemical events and behavior depend, not only upon the events themselves, but also upon the site at which they occur. Maternal and sexual behavior have been elicited in male rats by injections of separate brain loci with sodium testosterone sulfate (Fisher, 1956). Microinjections of iproniazid in certain sites in the hypothalamus have been shown to have reward functions (Olds and Olds, 1958); at other points this was not so. Other chemical agents have different effects when introduced into the first sites. (See Chapter 15.)

Tests of Behavior Theory

We have seen that drugs may be used in several different ways as aids in testing hypotheses. In some instances these may be hypotheses derived from a theory of behavior or personality, and the results of testing them may be used to argue for or against the theory. Since a science is constantly moving toward systematization of its subject matter into principles, laws, postulates, or generalizations, the use of drugs as tools in testing deductions of this kind is particularly important.

Illustrative of this use of drugs to test deductions from a behavior theory are the research studies recently reported by Eysenck and his colleagues. (See Chapter 24.) In general, the results of testing Eysenck's predictions support the postulate that depressants produce extraverted behavior, stimulants introverted, although some studies (e.g., Brengelmann, 1958) have produced contradictory evidence.

There are a number of other examples of the use of drugs in testing theories incorporating the three classes of variables with which we are now concerned. Franks (1958a) has recently reviewed some of the fundamental problems illustrated in theories of conditioning. Because of its extensive contributions to the research literature we should not leave this topic without reference to research of the Pavlovian School. Its theoretical framework has been one in which behavioral events are conditional upon physiological events within the central nervous

system, upon "higher nervous activity." Many of these central events
are hypothetical constructs describable in terms of their behavioral
correlates. Observations have been made of the effects on behavior
of a large number of drugs, and these observations have, in turn,
been used in describing the characteristics of these constructs.
Ivanov-Smolensky (1954), in summarizing a number of these experiments, refers, for example, to the early work of M. K. Petrova on the
mechanism of action of bromides on "higher nervous activity." Under
the influence of bromides " . . . the reflexes, after reaching peak,
decline to a still greater degree or even completely disappear . . . ."
A bromide presumably acts in this way " . . . by intensifying the
inhibitory process . . . " and thus " . . . in conformity with the laws
of induction, strengthens the excitatory process . . . ." Such experiments, designed to study effects of drugs on the magnitude of reflexes,
have produced a diversity of results some of which diversity may be
explained by uncontrolled variables (Konorski, 1948). (For a more
recent application to tests of psychoactive drugs, see Chapter 36.)

Characteristics of Drugs
as Tools in Research

Although our present concern is with the characteristics of drugs
as tools in behavioral research, it must be remembered, as is clear from
many studies in psychopharmacology, that overall drug-biological
system-behavior interactions are also dependent upon characteristics
of the biochemical events affected, of the subjects employed, of the
behavior patterns observed, and of the conditions under which the
behavior patterns are generated.

DOSE. A logical assumption is that, when other conditions are
controlled, behavior may vary as some function of dose. That
relatively few studies of such *dose-response relations* have been reported is surprising, for there is an obvious and important need for
such information, not only for the basic understanding of biological
mechanisms underlying behavior, but also for applied purposes in the
preclinical and clinical testing of psychoactive agents. Consideration
of dose-response relations has been a fundamental aspect of certain
sciences, e.g., pharmacology and toxicology, concerned with drug
effects on biological systems. Typically, the percentage of subjects
responding is taken as a function of varying dose levels. Such
relations have been found to fit two general classes of curves, sigmoid

or ogival and hyperbolic (Drill, 1958), although there are relatively few drugs in the latter class.

The frequency of occurrence of sigmoid relations between dose and percentage of subjects responding has led to the development of certain useful indices. When dose is plotted against per cent mortality, it has long been the practice to determine a *median lethal dose* or LD_{50}, and LD_{50}'s for different drugs can be compared and the index itself can be used in defining relative doses of a single drug. When responses other than death are involved, a *median effective dose* or ED_{50} may be determined in a similar manner. It has become customary to determine both these indices in appraising the potential safety of new drugs and to compute a therapeutic ratio: LD_{50}/ED_{50}. The larger this value is, the greater is the margin of safety.

When the response involved is a behavior pattern, parameters of which can be measured quantitatively, a median effective dose could be determined. This value would represent the dose of a particular drug necessary to produce a significant change of the behavior in 50 per cent of the sample studied. Such a *median behavior dose* or "BD_{50}" could have uses similar to other indices of the same nature. It could be compared with LD_{50}'s or ED_{50}'s for somatic effects in determining margins of safety in basic and applied research on psychoactive drugs.

Dose-response relations may also be stated in terms of parameters of a response rather than in terms of percentage of subjects affected. For example, Blough (1958), in discussing a "new test for tranquilizers," used mean response time in seconds as the main measure of his dependent variable. His plots of dose-response curves showed very clearly that this measure decreased with increasing doses of pentobarbital and that increasing doses of chlorpromazine had the reverse effect. Research which is designed to provide the data necessary for describing such quantitative relations is considerably more informative than research which allows only for comparisons of responses at one dose level with responses under control conditions. Significant changes in behavior may occur at any dose between zero and the level at which toxic effects to the body appear; it is important in the study of most drug-behavior interactions to explore this range systematically.

Some of the most annoying problems in the present use of drugs as tools in behavioral research arise in the selection of doses. Comparisons of reports on effects of the same chemical agent are often difficult because of differences in doses used. Measures of behavior patterns are sometimes influenced by uncontrolled side effects of the drug, effects which are related to doses used.

DURATION OF ACTION. Another parameter of significance is the duration of action of a drug. Drugs differ in the speed with which they produce their effects after administration and in the duration of these effects. Usually drugs disappear from the blood and probably from their site of action at a rate proportional to their concentration at any given moment: the higher the concentration, the more rapid is the rate. In the case of certain drugs, effectiveness diminishes with time as the drug itself undergoes chemical change. Because of this growth and decay of drug effectiveness, standardized measures of behavior taken at different times after administration of a drug may provide quite different results.

Because of the importance of this parameter of drugs, some research workers have included studies of *time-response* as well as dose-response relations in their analyses of drug-behavior interactions. Data on these two types of relations can be obtained during a single research. Recent illustrations of the use of time-response relations may be found in an investigation on effects of reserpine on conditioned avoidance behavior reported by Smith, Wagman, and Riopelle (1956). Their research design included still a third independent variable: extirpation in various areas of the brain. Time-response curves differentiated clearly the effects of dose and area of brain damage on the behavior observed. Differential effects, which did not appear initially, reached their maximum between four and six hours after injection; recovery was almost complete after 10 hours. During some recent and as yet unpublished research[2] it was found that different forms of behavior were affected differentially after administration of reserpine and that these differential effects varied with dose level and duration of drug action. Much information would have been lost and possibly misinterpretations made had measures of behavior not been taken systematically between the time of injecting the drug and the time at which recovery from its effects occurred.

NUMBER OF ADMINISTRATIONS. Behavioral effects may appear with a series of administrations which are not produced by a single dosage. Clinical studies of psychoactive drugs often report variations in results following variations in the length of a series. Such differences may

[2] Conducted at the Primate Laboratory, University of Wisconsin, in collaboration with M. E. Levine and J. M. Lockhart.

be functions of cumulative or repair processes, dependent upon inter-actions between three parameters of a drug (dose, number of adminis-trations, and frequency of administration) or of "adaptive" processes. In the former, effects may appear after a series is underway, or effects present at the beginning of a series may be enhanced. In the latter, early effects may diminish or disappear.

FREQUENCY OF ADMINISTRATION. Repeated administration gives rise to another significant parameter of drugs as tools in research: fre-quency of administration. When intervals between doses are long, uniform effects, similar to single doses, may be achieved; shorter intervals may produce a cumulation of effects. The latter effects are due to accumulation of the drug in the body, which in turn is a function of the rate and nature of the process by which the drug is eliminated.

SPEED OF ADMINISTRATION. The speed with which a drug is admin-istered may also influence the effects it produces. For example, it is recognized in the general clinical situation that "speed shock" may result from too rapid intravenous injection. Of importance from our present point of view is the fact that a drug may accumulate locally in a section of the circulation because the rate of administration exceeds the rate at which it is removed from that local section; this may produce responses when an even distribution in the circulation would not do so.

FACTORS WHICH CONTROL OR MODIFY THE ACTION OF DRUGS. In addition to these parameters of drugs themselves, certain other factors act to control or to modify their effects on biological systems and, thereby, on behavior (Krantz and Carr, 1958). One obvious factor is the *chemical structure* of the drug itself. The development of a "biochemorphology" has helped to emphasize the importance of such qualitative differences. The characteristic actions of drugs are inti-mately related to their chemical structures. Sometimes an action is shared by dissimilar compounds. There are instances in which drugs of entirely different chemical configurations produce similar results, e.g., the central nervous system depressants nitrous oxide and ethyl ether. In other instances a particular action is lost with even the slightest change in configuration of a molecule, e.g., optical isomers. Differences in structure also change rates of absorption.

Another factor is the *vehicle* in which the chemical agent is carried.

Drug preparations frequently include solvents, such as water, alcohol, glycerin, ether, and oils, which may produce effects of their own or may influence the rate at which a drug is absorbed (Sollman, 1957).

A third factor is the *distribution* of a drug in the body after it has been absorbed. The transient process during distribution may influence the effects a drug produces. Ultimate distribution is characterized by non-homogeneity since most drugs are remarkably selective in their actions, affecting only a specific tissue or group of receptor cells. For example, a seizure focus in the central nervous system may be depressed by an antiepileptic drug without significantly altering the function of normal brain cells. The mechanism involved in such specificity may be a particular affinity of a chemical nature between the drug and components of the responding cells.

This selectivity of action of drugs for certain biological systems does not mean that relations between biological systems and behavior patterns will necessarily also be specific; at present it is difficult to find a drug whose effects are confined to a single variable of behavior (Sidman, 1956).

The *route of administration* of a drug into the body also influences its effects. There are several routes of entry: through oral administration; through injection—intravenous, subcutaneous, intraperitoneal, intramuscular, intrathecal, or intraventricular; through inhalation; through absorption—by mucous membranes, or by skin directly or by iontophoresis; and through subcutaneous pellet implantation. Variations in effectiveness of these routes are largely results of differences in rate of absorption (Beckman, 1958).

The *presence of other drugs* in the body may result in interactions which significantly modify the effects of a particular chemical agent. The combined use of drugs may give rise to one of three effects, depending upon the particular drugs involved. They may tend to summate, in which case effects produced by one alone may be achieved by lower doses of two or more in combination. One may antagonize another, thus resulting in a failure of a full dose of the latter to give its expected complete effects. One may potentiate another, whereby the full effects of the latter are produced by reduced doses.

Skillful use of drugs as tools in behavioral research requires that consideration be given to these various parameters and critical conditions. Each must be specified in a research report if the research is to meet the scientific requirement of repeatability.

Prospects

"Nervously, the U.S. is entering a new era—the era of chemical modification of the human personality" (Bello, 1957). The science writer who began his story of tranquilizing drugs in this way was referring to advances in the applied aspects of psychopharmacology which have but few rivals for human interest even in these days of phenomenal developments in scientific research and its applications. But the promise of this new era goes beyond immediate applications of psychopharmacology, important as they are. Increases in our knowledge of how drugs act are enabling us to extend our use of drugs in basic behavioral research. Such research will lead to better understanding of relations between biological systems and behavior.

The speed with which this understanding is achieved will depend upon technical advances in several allied disciplines, but there already exist techniques which could be used more fully. For example, psychologists have paid little attention to standard concepts and measures of pharmacology; other disciplines have used rough-and-ready measures of behavior when more precise psychological techniques would have added much of value. Greater standardization of terms and measures would aid greatly in comparing results of different research programs. The use by several investigators of a standard technique for studying effects of drugs and other treatments on affective behavior (Brady, 1956a, b; Hunt and Brady, 1951) is an example which needs to be followed in numerous other instances. There is a great need for more parametric studies of drug-biological system-behavior interactions.

As the number of individual studies increases, the need for systematization will become even more pressing than it is now. We have little knowledge of the processes by which biochemical events are, to use a recent phrase (Grenell, 1957), "transduced into general behavior patterns." Present theoretical models purporting to describe these processes are couched in terms of diffuse physiological mechanisms, metabolic events in specific regions of the brain, synaptic transmissions, and molecular shifts and interactions in nerve cell membranes. A decision about which, if any, of these models is adequate awaits much more information than we now possess. Equally pressing is the need for inclusion of more drug-biological system-behavior interactions in general behavior and personality theory to systematize our knowledge and to generate new hypotheses.

The use of drugs as research tools promises to aid significantly in the general development of the behavioral sciences. Recognition of their specific roles in testing different types of hypotheses and skillful use of their various characteristics will maximize their contributions.

REFERENCES

Abramson, H. A. *Neuropharmacology.* New York: Josiah Macy, Jr. Found., 1956.

Abramson, H. A. *Neuropharmacology.* New York: Josiah Macy, Jr. Found., 1957.

Aprison, M. H., Nathan, P., and Himwich, H. E. A study of the relationship between asymmetric acetylcholinesterase activities in rabbit brain and three behavioral patterns. *Science,* 1954, 119, 158.

Baldwin, E. *Dynamic aspects of biochemistry.* Cambridge: Cambridge Univer. Press, 1953.

Beckman, H. *Drugs: Their nature, action and use.* Philadelphia: Saunders, 1958.

Bello, F. The tranquilizer question. *Fortune,* 1957, May, 162–166.

Blough, D. S. New test for tranquilizers. *Science,* 1958, 127, 586–587.

Brady, J. V. A comparative approach to the evaluation of drug effects upon affective behavior. *Ann. N.Y. Acad. Sci.,* 1956, 64, 632–643. (a)

Brady, J. V. Assessment of drug effects on emotional behavior. *Science,* 1956, 123, 1033–1034. (b)

Brengelmann, J. C. D-Amphetamine and amytal: I. Effects on memory and expressive movement. *J. ment. Sci.,* 1958, 104, 153–159.

Brengelmann, J. C., Laverty, S. G., and Lewis, D. J. Differential effects of lysergic acid and sodium amytal on immediate memory and expressive movement. *J. ment. Sci.,* 1958, 104, 144–152.

Culler, E., Coakley, J. D., Shurrager, P. S., and Ades, H. W. Differential effects of curare upon higher and lower levels of the central nervous system. *Amer. J. Psychol.,* 1939, 52, 266–273.

DeShon, H. S., Rinkel, M., and Solomon, H. Mental changes experimentally produced by L.S.D. *Psychiat. Quart.,* 1952, 26, 33–53.

Dews, P. B., and Skinner, B. F. Techniques for the study of behavioral effects of drugs. *Ann. N.Y. Acad. Sci.,* 1956, 65, Art. 4, 247–356.

Drill, V. A. (Ed.) *Pharmacology in medicine.* New York: McGraw-Hill, 1958.

Elkes, J. Effects of psychosomimetic drugs in animals and man. In H. A. Abramson (Ed.), *Neuropharmacology.* New York: Josiah Macy, Jr. Found., 1957.

Essig, C. F., Hampson, J. L., McCanley, A., and Himwich, H. E. An experimental analysis of biochemically induced forced circling behavior. *J. Neurophysiol.,* 1950, 13, 269–275.

Feldberg, W., and Sherwood, S. L. A permanent cannula for intraventricular injections in cats. *J. Physiol.,* 1953, 120, 3–4P.

Feldberg, W., and Sherwood, S. L. Injections of drugs into the lateral ventricle of the cat. *J. Physiol.*, 1954, 123, 148–167.

Feldberg, W., and Sherwood, S. L. Injections of bulbocaprime into the cerebral ventricles of cats. *Brit. J. Pharmacol. Chemother.*, 1955, 10, 371–374. (a)

Feldberg, W., and Sherwood, S. L. Recent experiments with injections of drugs into the ventricular system of the brain. *Proc. roy. Soc. Med.*, 1955, 48, 853–864. (b)

Fisher, A. E. Maternal and sexual behavior induced by intracranial chemical stimulation. *Science*, 1956, 124, 228–229.

Franks, C. M. Some fundamental problems in conditioning. *Acta. Psychol.*, 1958, 14, 223–246. (a)

Franks, C. M. Alcohol, alcoholism and conditioning: A review of the literature and some theoretical considerations. *J. ment. Sci.*, 1958, 104, 14–33. (b)

Freedman, A. M., and Himwich, H. E. DFP: Site of injection and variation in response. *Amer. J. Physiol.*, 1949, 156, 125–128.

Garrod, A. E. *Inborn errors of metabolism.* Oxford: Oxford Univer. Press, 1923.

Girden, E. Cerebral mechanisms in conditioning under curare. *Amer. J. Psychol.*, 1940, 53, 397–406.

Girden, E. Generalized conditioned responses under curare and erythroidine. *J. exp. Psychol.*, 1942, 31, 105–119. (a)

Girden, E. The dissociation of blood pressure conditioned responses under erythroidine. *J. exp. Psychol.*, 1942, 31, 219–231. (b)

Girden, E. The dissociation of pupillary conditioned reflexes under erythroidine and curare. *J. exp. Psychol.*, 1942, 31, 322–332. (c)

Girden, E., and Culler, E. Conditioned responses in curarized striate muscle in dogs. *J. comp. Psychol.*, 1937, 23, 261–274.

Goodman, L. S., and Gilman, A. *The pharmacological basis of therapeutics.* New York: Macmillan, 1956.

Grenell, R. G. Considerations regarding metabolic factors in the action of chlorpromazine. In H. E. Himwich (Ed.), *Tranquilizing drugs.* Washington, D.C.: Amer. Ass. Adv. Sci., 1957.

Himwich, H. E. (Ed.) *Tranquilizing drugs.* Washington, D.C.: Amer. Ass. Adv. Sci., 1957.

Hock, P. H., Cattell, J. P., and Pennes, H. H. Effects of mescaline and lysergic acid (o-LSD-25). *Amer. J. Psychiat.*, 1952, 108. 579–584. (a)

Hock, P. H., Cattell, J. P., and Pennes, H. H. Effects of drugs: theoretical considerations from a psychological viewpoint. *Amer. J. Psychiat.*, 1952, 108, 585–589. (b)

Hunt, H. F., and Brady, J. V. Some effects of electroconvulsive shock on a conditioned emotional response ("anxiety"). *J. comp. physiol. Psychol.*, 1951, 44, 88–98.

Ivanov-Smolensky, A. G. *Essays on the pathophysiology of the higher nervous activity.* Moscow: Foreign Languages Publ. House, 1954.

Kline, N. *Psychopharmacology.* Washington, D.C.: Amer. Ass. Adv. Sci., 1956.

Konorski, J. *Conditioned reflexes and neuron organization.* Cambridge: Cambridge Univer. Press, 1948.

Krantz, J. C., and Carr, C. J. *The pharmacologic principles of medical practice.* Baltimore: Williams & Wilkins, 1958.

Krech, D., Rosenzweig, M. R., Bennett, E. L., and Krueckel, B. Enzyme concentration in the brain and adjustive behavior-patterns. *Science,* 1954, 120, 994–996.

Krech, D., Rosenzweig, M. R., and Bennett, E. L. Dimensions of discrimination and level of cholinesterase activity in the cerebral cortex of the rat. *J. comp. physiol. Psychol.,* 1956, 49, 261–268.

McCulloch, W. S., Ridley, E., and Sherwood, S. L. Effects of intraventricular aceytlcholine, cholinesterase and related compounds in normal and "catatonic" cats. *Nature,* 1952, 169, 157.

Mayer-Gross, W. Experimental psychoses and other mental abnormalities produced by drugs. *Brit. med. J.,* 1951, 2, 317–321.

Olds, J. Brain response to drugs mapped through self-stimulation. In H. A. Abramson (Ed.), *Neuropharmacology.* New York: Josiah Macy, Jr. Found., 1957.

Olds, J., and Olds, M. E. Positive reinforcement produced by stimulating hypothalamus with iproniazid and other compounds. *Science,* 1958, 127, 1175–1176.

Peters, R. A. Pharmacological and biochemical lesions. *Proc. roy. Soc. Med.,* 1948, 41, 781–792.

Peterson, G. M. Changes in handedness in the rat from the local application of aceylcholine to the cerebral cortex. *J. comp. physiol. Psychol.,* 1949, 42, 404–412.

Rinkel, M., DeShon, H. S., Hyde, R. W., and Solomon, H. C. Experimental schizophrenia-like symptoms. *Amer. J. Psychiat.,* 1952, 108, 572–578.

Russell, R. W. *The comparative study of behavior.* London: H. K. Lewis, 1952.

Russell, R. W. Brain chemistry and behavior. *Discovery,* 1956, 17, 314–318.

Russell, R. W. Effects of "biochemical lesions" on behavior. *Acta Psychol.,* 1958, 14, 281–294.

Russell, R. W., and Steinberg, H. Effects of nitrous oxide on reactions to "stress." *Quart. J. exp. Psychol.,* 1955, 7, 67–73.

Sidman, M. Drug-behavior interaction. *Ann. N.Y. Acad. Sci.,* 1956, 65, 282–302.

Smith, R. P., Wagman, W., and Riopelle, A. J. Effects of reserpine on conditioned avoidance behavior in normal and brain operated monkeys. *J. Pharmacol.,* 1956, 117, 136–141.

Sollmann, T. *A manual of pharmacology and its applications to therapeutics and toxicology.* Philadelphia: Saunders, 1957.

Steinberg, H., and Russell, R. W. Transfer effects in reactions to "stress." *Quart. J. exp. Psychol.,* 1957, 9, 215–220.

Wikler, A. *The relation of psychiatry to pharmacology.* Baltimore: Williams & Wilkins, 1957.

Biochemical and neurophysiological action of psychoactive drugs

The last few years have seen the increasing use of a new group of drugs effective for overactive psychotic patients and presenting interesting and important differences from procedures and drugs previously employed in the management of individuals with such behavioral disorders. In fact, in order to give an appropriate name to these drugs, it was necessary to invent a nomenclature. Many terms, all emphasizing one or another aspect of the actions of these drugs, have been devised. The one most frequently used is tranquilizer, indicating a sedative or calming effect without enforcement of sleep. Others are ataraxic (Fabing, 1955), denoting peace of mind, and neuroleptic and neuroplegic, indicating diminutions in the intensity of nerve function. This group of drugs, however, may be regarded as an advance guard of a long-awaited pharmacologic attack not limited only to hyperactive disturbed patients, but also to be directed against other types of behavioral disorders. To this division of drugs Gerard (1957) has applied the term psychotropic, which refers to action on the mind. Neuropharmacologic refers to the branch of pharmacology to which these drugs belong. The title psychopharmacologic drug (Himwich, 1955, 1956a) possesses certain advantages, for it indicates a medicine which influences the mind by affecting its morphologic substrate, the brain. The descriptive designation, psychopharmacologic drugs, is a broad one and embraces all medicinals which modify mental activity, including the

This chapter is reprinted, with revisions and additions, with permission, from Science, 1958, 127, 59–72.

psychotomimetic agents of comparatively early origin and the antidepressants which have recently come into renewed prominence.
This also is true of the term psychoactive drug. Himwich (1959)
gives an analysis of the comparative therapeutic effects of antidepressant as well as ataraxic drugs. This chapter, however, is
restricted largely to the discussion of some of the tranquilizing
agents.

The chief usefulness of the new drugs, which at present lies in
the field of psychiatry, is being extended into the many medical and
surgical specialties. It is true that a drug not only changes favorably
the malfunction of the organ for which it is intended but also acts,
perhaps to a lesser extent, on the entire body. Either indirectly, by
their influence on the brain, or by their influence on the peripheral
nerves, the new drugs exert potent effects on viscera of the body, including the gastrointestinal tract and the cardiorespiratory system and
the endocrine glands.

But the impact of these new drugs has extended far beyond their
immediate practical use in the management of disease. They are
also employed by the clinical investigator who seeks to unravel the
tangled skein of abnormal behavior as well as by the psychologist who
delves into intricacies of accepted normal patterns. Neurochemists
and neurophysiologists are utilizing the tranquilizers as tools in
their investigations and meanwhile are uncovering their physiological
actions in the brain and elsewhere in the body. These studies,
made on man and lower animals, permit an analysis of the structure
and function of the central nervous system, which was not possible
before. Not that the methods are new, but the tranquilization resulting from the application of these drugs had not been previously
observed. Perhaps most important, the new drugs may aid in the
production of a desirable change in our culture and remove mental
disease from the field of mysticism and superstition. They may con-
vince the public that mental disease is not a thing to be ashamed of
and that it should be placed in the same category as any other disease which can be treated by medical means.

Clinical Aspects

At this time it is hardly necessary to emphasize the magnitude of
the problem of mental disease. The title of Gorman's book, *Every
Other Bed* (1956), is suggested by the fact that half of the sickbeds in
our country are occupied by mental patients. The financial require-

ments for the maintenance of these hospitals are correspondingly great. The money comes chiefly out of the taxpayers' pockets. Only comparatively wealthy families can bear the cost of maintaining one of their members in a private institution.

The growing population of our mental hospitals indicates that advances made before the advent of new drugs were not adequate to cope with the problem of mental disease. Much was left to be desired, therefore, from the therapeutic viewpoint. Psychoanalysis is a better weapon in the management of the neuroses than of the psychoses. Electroshock is a comparatively severe procedure, for electrodes are applied to the temples of the patient and a brief, measured current is passed through his brain. The patient becomes momentarily unconscious and undergoes a convulsion. Electroshock greatly benefits patients with depression and is of value in the management of excessively hyperactive patients, helping to maintain the uneasy status quo which characterizes hospitals not using tranquilizing drugs. Insulin hypoglycemia appears to be more effective than electroshock for certain types of schizophrenia but requires highly trained physicians and is costly. In insulin hypoglycemia, the patients receive doses of insulin large enough to reduce the level of sugar in the blood. The brain is thus deprived of its chief foodstuff, and the patient sinks into coma. Another method for treating the distraught patient is to stupefy or anesthetize him with an adequate dose of one of the barbiturate drugs.

Though the immediate situation can thus be met, it is not necessarily followed by improvement in behavior. With the tranquilizing drugs, however, the patient is improved without significant modification of consciousness—a highly desirable goal in the successful therapeutic process. Even if his manic excitement is extreme and if he must be given a correspondingly large dose, which renders him sleepy, he can be easily awakened and in general can go on with his prescribed hospital activities. Through use of the new drugs, more patients have been returned to society from the state hospitals than under any previous therapeutic regime. We therefore seem to be entering a new era in the treatment of mental disease, and it remains to be seen how far this advance will take us.

Schizophrenia

What are the mental disorders to which these new drugs are applied? The field of mental disease is complex. It is not a case of a single mental disease. On the contrary, there are many categories, and each one includes several varieties. Schizophrenia is the chief disorder met with in our psychotic population. Because we do not know the cause of schizophrenia, we must limit our attack on it to empirical methods. But this is not unusual in the history of medicine, for the majority of therapeutic successes were produced on an empirical basis; witness the use of quinine long before the plasmodium of malaria was discovered.

Because the origin of schizophrenia is not known, that disease must be characterized chiefly by its symptoms. These are many and varied and, in general, may be divided into four types, which may change and merge into each other. The clinical picture is therefore not constant, and at different times the signs of one or another of these four types predominate. One of the characteristics of schizophrenia is emotional blunting, and this is a prominent change in the *simple type*. The psychiatrist is quick to observe the diagnostic paucity of facial expression and regards it as an outward lack of emotional expression or affect. Some individuals with inadequate personalities, who lose one job after another, belong to this group of patients. Sometimes the patient wears a silly and inappropriate grin. If such a patient, like Mr. M. in one of our wards, exhibits restless hyperactivity, at least that aspect of his disorder can be corrected by a tranquilizing drug.

An abnormality of the thought process is another characteristic of schizophrenia; it is developed most highly in the *hebephrenic type*. Sentences spoken may have meaning for the patient but to others are neither coherent nor logical. In the most serious distortion of the thought process, the spoken word ceases to assume sentence form and is called "word salad." Mrs. H. replies to all questions with the unintelligible statement "16–21 telephone pole." That phrase includes her usual conversational limits. After receiving a new experimental tranquilizer, she informed us, in well-constructed sentences, that she was born in a small village consisting of six homes, and that her home was situated near a telephone pole numbered 16–21.

Delusions or false ideas, and hallucinations or false sensory impressions are characteristic of the *paranoid type*. Unlike the utterances of the hebephrenic, which cannot be comprehended by the physician, those of the paranoid patient are readily understood but reveal lack of relation to reality. Mrs. G., one of the patients in our hospital, has suffered intensely for a long time from well-developed delusions of a gigantic "crime ring" which is out to get her, even penetrating into the confines of the Galesburg State Research Hospital. Recently, when she was receiving a test drug, a new serenity was observed in her demeanor. When asked about the "crime ring," she smiled, made a deprecating gesture with her hand, and said it did not bother her any more. In fact, she doubted whether it existed. This evident amelioration was maintained as long as the patient remained on this medication.

In general, hallucinations, which also occur in mental disease other than schizophrenia, yield more readily to these drugs than do delusions. Mrs. S. has placed cotton plugs in her ears for many years to shut out the voices that were so hostile and were tormenting her. During a period in which she was receiving one of the test drugs, she came for an interview without the cotton plugs in her ears. The voices no longer tormented her, or at least not to the same extent as previously.

In the *catatonic type* of schizophrenia there are marked distortions of motor activity. Stupor is one aspect, and whether with or without stupor, posturing and the assumption and maintenance of bizarre positions and mannerisms are observed. After one has raised the arm of such a patient, the patient may keep his arm up for a long time. When he walks, he may change his direction by turning at right angles only. A catatonic may also go into a furor, a period of wild overactivity, and become highly destructive.

Here we come to a very important use of tranquilizing drugs—a calming action which is being applied to various kinds of destructive patients and not only to combative schizophrenics. Taking chlorpromazine and reserpine as examples, we find two different kinds of pharmacologic actions characteristic of this group of drugs. The first, which counteracts such symptoms of schizophrenia as dissociated thought, hallucinations, and delusions, has just been described. The second drug effect is of a different type and causes a general toning down of emotional reactions and physical activity. If the ability to correct the thought processes of the hebephrenic and the paranoid patients is regarded as a specific antipsychotic power of chlorpromazine and reserpine, then the use of these drugs to combat excessive activity may be considered a nonspecific result. As has been pointed out by Barsa (1957), these two results do not necessarily occur together; either may be observed without the other. The calming action of the drug cuts across the diagnostic categories of mental disease, for it is employed in all types of overactive patients, irrespective of the diagnosis. It can even be given to an individual who has no behavioral abnormalities; in such a normal person a reduction of activity and a diminution in the response to environmental stimuli will be noted.

Use of Psychoactive Drugs with Hyperactive Patients

It must be remembered that patients with psychoses are sent to psychiatric hospitals most often because they display behavior which is not socially compatible. Psychotics who can carry on outside the hospital gates are not necessarily sent to such institutions. When a patient presents behavioral disorders that menace the life and limb of other individuals as well as his own, it is essential that he enter a hospital where he can be properly treated.

Types of hyperactive patients who secure benefits from this sedative influence include the manic, whose disorder is chiefly that of mood or affect, which is greatly elevated; the schizoaffective, in whom abnormal elation is associated with deterioration of mental abilities; and the patient with a toxic psychosis, as in delirium tremens. These patients have their hyperactivity and abnormally increased initiative reduced to more reasonable levels so that they cease to wear themselves out and are no longer a trial to the ward attendants and their fellow patients. This effect is a tremendous boon to hospitals with highly disturbed patients. Isolation rooms, in which dangerous patients were formerly incarcerated, are no longer required. Mechanical restraints, sedative wet packs, electroshock, and deep barbiturate medication are prescribed infrequently. As a result, many of these patients can now be liberated from physical restraints as well as from the psychological constraints of a locked ward. The ward doors have been opened, and privileges have been given to many patients, permitting them to traverse hospital halls and take part in various therapeutic activities—recreational, occupational, and industrial. Thus treatments have not only been made more humane, affording greater benefit to the patient, but have also effected improvement in the staff morale of the mental institutions. A hospital atmosphere is being established in state institutions to an extent that was not previously possible. One now feels that a mental hospital is not a place for the expedient management of an intolerable situation but rather a treatment center for the amelioration of disease, like hospitals devoted to other kinds of disorders.

One patient will receive most benefit from a certain tranquilizing agent, and a second from another. This is not the place to compare the therapeutic efficacy of the various tranquilizers, especially in such an early state of their development, but it is obvious that some produce a deeper sedative action than others. Each of the accepted tranquilizing drugs, when given in adequate dosage, is of aid to disturbed patients, but our experience with hyperactive patients has been widest with chlorpromazine (Kinross-Wright, 1955; Goldman, 1955; Lehmann and Hanrahan, 1954; Kline, Barsa, and Gosline, 1956) and reserpine (Browne, 1956; Ferguson, 1956; Rinaldi, Rudy, and Himwich, 1955; Proctor, 1957), drugs which have profound sedative or calming actions. But there is no way to foretell which drug will be most effective for a given patient, and therefore the psychiatrist should be prepared to employ any one in an emergency. Some drugs, like azacyclonol (Rinaldi, Rudy, and Himwich, 1956), can bring about better social adjustment, so that the atmosphere in the ward becomes friendlier, especially among patients who are only moderately disturbed. The choice of a tranquilizing drug must be decided empirically; the best one for a given patient can be found only by the process of elimination.

The most dramatic improvements are observed in the first acute attack or in the chronic patient who has developed an acute exacerbation of his disorder. At our hospital, however, tranquilizing drugs have also been found to benefit markedly patients with schizophrenia of long duration, i.e., chronic schizophrenia, as documented in the case histories presented above. But the improvements were mainly seen in patients with obvious active schizophrenic processes—those who had hallucinations and delusions or who were hyperactive, agitated, and tense. Blocked, retarded, and apathetic schizophrenics are more difficult to help. This greater intractability of the so-called "burned-out" patients, who have survived a more active phase of their disorder and who seem free of schizophrenic symptoms and excessive physical activity, is also observed with earlier methods of treating deteriorated, passive schizophrenics.

Similarly, senile patients who are irritable, quarrelsome, and apprehensive show greater improvement than patients who exhibit negativism, apathy, and withdrawal. It would appear that tranquilizing drugs are less valuable for the senile patient who does not display signs of agitation. Similarly, depressions not accompanied by anxiety and tension are less apt to be ameliorated by a psychopharmacologic agent. The treatment of the passive patient is therefore more difficult. In individuals with hypertension, apparently free from behavioral abnormalities, the use of these drugs may lead to a worsening of the mental condition if the profound sadness of a depression is induced.

Psychoneuroses

Mental diseases milder than the psychoses are the psychoneuroses or neuroses, and in some forms of these disorders tranquilizing drugs are of value. In contradistinction to the psychotic patient, the neurotic acts, by and large, as if reality has the same meaning for him as for most people. He is not subjected to persecution by a "crime ring" and does not have other bizarre experiences. He suffers, however, from great anxiety, which may not be readily identified with any particular object. Yet this anxiety is expressed in bodily symptoms: palpitation, breathlessness, weakness of limbs, tremors and pains that plague him. For that reason, in some patients, the anxiety is associated with a particular organ: the heart, the lungs, or the stomach. Neurotics who must be active in order to escape their disturbing fears are usually not helped by tranquilizers. In contrast, those with internal tensions, who cannot sleep despite use of such sedative drugs as the barbiturates, often gain relief from a psychopharmacologic agent.

For the "Normal" Population

These drugs also exhibit decided usefulness for the members of our so-called normal population who are subjected to intolerable stress. A businessman with a demanding and unreasonable supervisor or a woman with insufficient funds to run her home according to her ideal standard can gradually build up an emotional impasse so that perspective is lost, as the darker side of the situation is increasingly magnified, and a state of panic may develop. Restoration to a more objective evaluation of the situation may be secured by psychotherapeutic discussions with a physician, and an important action of tranquilizing drugs is to render the patient more receptive to other kinds of therapy. In fact, at times a psychoactive drug may be essential for a successful psychiatric interview. Ephemeral disturbances— for example, the anxiety and tension aroused by an impending surgical operation—can be pleasantly dissipated by a small dose of a tranquilizing agent.

Side Reactions

I have not mentioned the matter of occasional undesirable side reactions of the new drugs (Kline, Barsa, and Gosline, 1957; Ferguson, 1956; Tuteur and Lepson, 1957). In the first place, the drugs cause much less inconvenience than the mental disorder of the psychotic patient. Some patients can be managed by a temporary reduction of dosage—for example, a patient who exhibits an excessive fall of blood pressure. Others can be treated by a drug which counteracts the undesirable changes; a tremor of the hands resembling that of parkinsonism can be relieved by an antiparkinson drug. Patients with brain injury are more likely to exhibit a convulsion than those with an intact organ (Rudy, Himwich, and Rinaldi, 1958). The production of lactation and menstrual changes by chlorpromazine and reserpine and the power of the latter to impair libido in the male are subjects for research. Fortunately, serious complications occur rarely. A small number of patients develop jaundice, a sign of liver involvement. In some instances there may be a reduction of white blood cells. A failure in the formation of these cells is dangerous because it diminishes the resistance of the body to disease. But, on the whole, the treatment of thousands of psychotic patients with the new drugs has been relatively safe, because most suffer no side effects. Neurotic patients seem more sensitive to side reactions and even on comparatively low dosage often complain of fatigue, prostration, dizziness, and nausea.

It is apparent, then, that state hospitals have been placed on a much better basis by the use of the tranquilizing drugs, especially in the management of highly disturbed patients. The same, however, cannot be said of the private practice of psychiatrists concerned chiefly with neurotic patients. But it is also true that many patients who were formerly sent to a mental institution can now be treated outside the hospital gates. Some psychotic individuals can continue to lead productive lives and need not go to a psychiatric hospital at all. During the acute phase, they may be controlled by tranquilizing drugs in a general hospital and later may be maintained outside the hospital on appropriate doses of these medicines. On the other hand, apathetic psychotics who are not in conflict socially but who are rather withdrawn, inactive, and without signs of agitation usually cannot be raised to a higher adaptive level. They are still the despair of the psychiatrist. In evaluating the present clinical position of the psychopharmacologic drugs, it must be understood that the production of tranquilization, though a desirable end in itself, also aids other forms of therapy. A potent factor in the successful treatment of a patient with disorganized or disturbed behavior is a satisfactory relationship with a psychiatrist, and an important result of tranquilization is the facilitation of such a beneficial relationship.

Neurohormonal Changes Caused by
Reserpine and Chlorpromazine

A lead for the pharmacologic attack on schizophrenia comes from a study of indole-containing substances. Not only serotonin but also the tranquilizer reserpine and the psychotomimetic lysergic acid diethylamide (LSD) contain the indole nucleus (see Fig. 1). The idea that indoles are associated with schizophrenia is not new (Alvarez, 1924; Buscaino, 1952). In a similar vein, suggestions have been made that serotonin plays a part in brain function (Taylor, Page, and Corcoran, 1951; Gaddum, 1954). A clinical analysis of this problem became available recently with the paper of Hoffer, Osmond, and Smythies (1954). These experimenters knew that an adrenaline solution which had become pink after standing in the light for a long period of time had exerted psychotomimetic effects. They also drank a solution containing impure adrenochrome and succumbed to its influence to the extent of revealing schizophrenic-like changes in their behavior. They therefore thought that the pink solution might contain a breakdown product of adrenaline, similar to adrenochrome in being indolic in character, and pointed out that some indole-containing substances affect behavior adversely. Thus, again we have the suggestion of the pathogenic importance of indole-containing substances. However, it should be pointed out that not all such compounds evoke aberrant behavior. Moreover, drugs with entirely different chemical structures, e.g., hashish, are psychotomimetic in action. Nevertheless, it is instructive to examine the effects of serotonin.

The experiments of Welsh (1954) showed that, in the clam *Venus merceneria,* the accelerator nerve of the heart, for which serotonin is the chemical mediator, is inhibited by LSD. Gaddum and Hameed (1954) have demonstrated the antagonism of LSD to the peripheral action of serotonin in mammals and wondered whether or not this antagonism might not also apply in the brain. Woolley and Shaw (1954) made the bold hypothesis that LSD produced behavioral abnormalities by interfering with the physiological actions of serotonin in the brain. According to these investigators, LSD is enough like serotonin to be taken up by the serotonin receptors in the brain, yet is different to the extent that LSD fails to evoke serotonin effects.

These workers used the lock-and-key analogy: LSD could be introduced into the same lock as serotonin but, in contrast, could not be used to turn the lock. This suggested, of course, that mental aberrations are produced by an inadequate amount of serotonin at its site of action, the receptors with which serotonin combines.   But it is also possible that there may be an excessive concentration of serotonin in some forms of mental disease, and in a later paper these workers showed that LSD could also act like serotonin and, for example, increase the effects of that brain hormone to raise the blood pressure of anesthetized dogs (Shaw and Woolley, 1956b).   Costa (1956), in our laboratory, found that LSD can either diminish or increase the effects of serotonin, depending upon its concentration.   The serotonin-evoked contraction of a rat uterus is antagonized by LSD in a solution containing 1.0 μg. per liter but is facilitated by the psychotomimetic agent when its concentration is reduced to 0.2 μg. per liter or less. The latter result suggests that an excess of serotonin, rather than a deficiency, is a disturbing factor in mental disease.   In the present status of these investigations it is not possible to decide between these two alternatives.   In fact, both may be correct, but each may apply to different kinds of abnormalities.

Reserpine, which is so valuable in the management of combative destructive patients, reduced the concentration of serotonin in the body (Paasonen and Vogt, 1956; Pletscher, Shore, and Brodie, 1956). Furthermore, only those *Rauwolfia* alkaloids which are tranquilizers deplete the stores of serotonin (Shore, Carlsson, and Brodie, 1956). According to one explanation, the competition between the drug and serotonin displaces the latter from its receptors and, as a result, the neurohormone is eliminated from the depots in the brain and other parts of the body.   Restoration of serotonin to normal levels is protracted.   After a single dose of reserpine was injected into a rabbit, the brain serotonin was depressed to 10 per cent of normal within 4 hours and remained at this low level for 36 hours, after which it rose slowly over a period of 6 days before premedication values were attained (Pletscher, Shore, and Brodie, 1956).   After the administration of reserpine, the concentration of that drug in the brain increased rapidly to a brief maximum, but, in contrast to the long-enduring depletion of serotonin (Hess, Shore, and Brodie, 1956), reserpine diminished speedily and was practically undetectable in the brain in about 4 hours.   These results with reserpine, obtained by a fluorometric method, are in agreement with the concept that reserpine produces pharmacologic effects indirectly by its influence upon the serotonin content of the brain.   But other observations (Plummer, Sheppard, and Schulert, 1957), with a more sensitive technique, employing isotopically labeled reserpine, disclosed that the radioactive material is extractable from the brain as reserpine up to 48 hours after

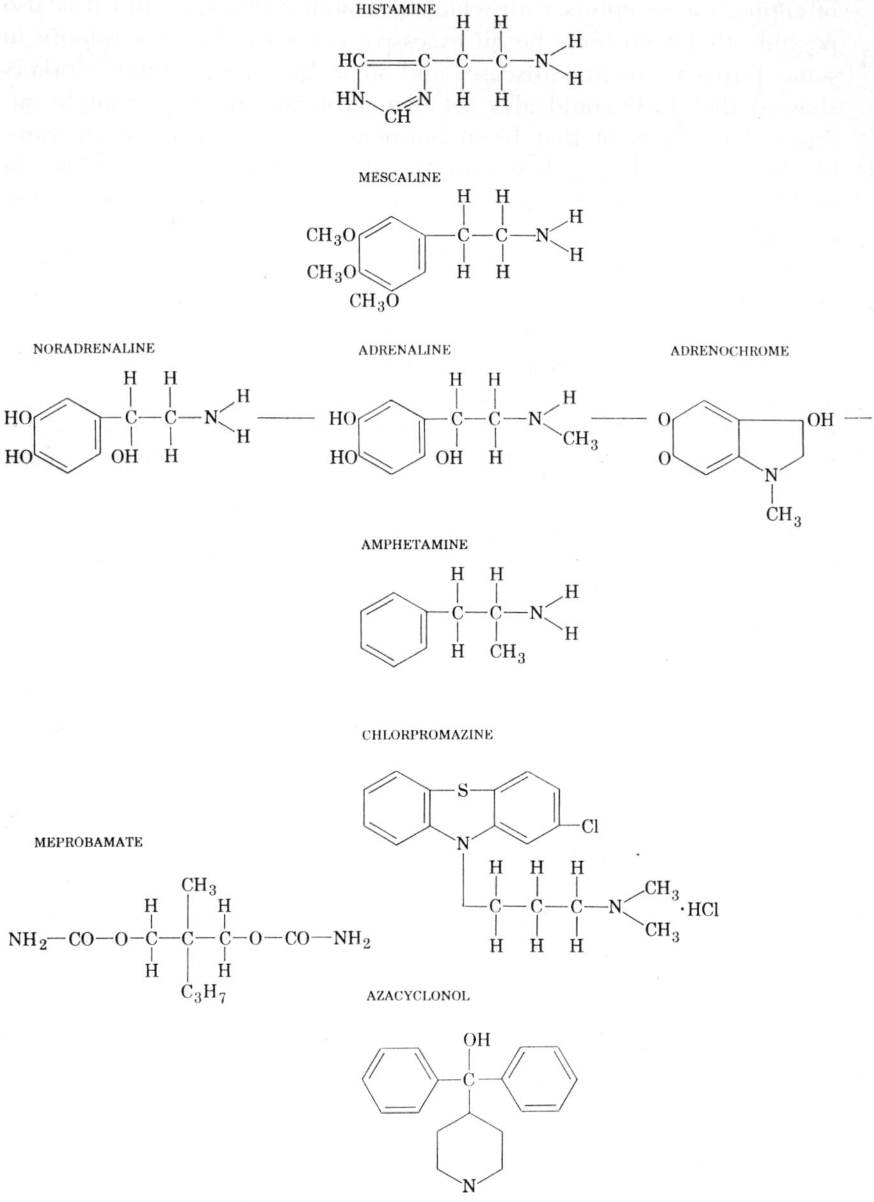

HISTAMINE

MESCALINE

NORADRENALINE   ADRENALINE   ADRENOCHROME

AMPHETAMINE

CHLORPROMAZINE

MEPROBAMATE

AZACYCLONOL

Figure 1.   Structural formulas of some neurohormones,

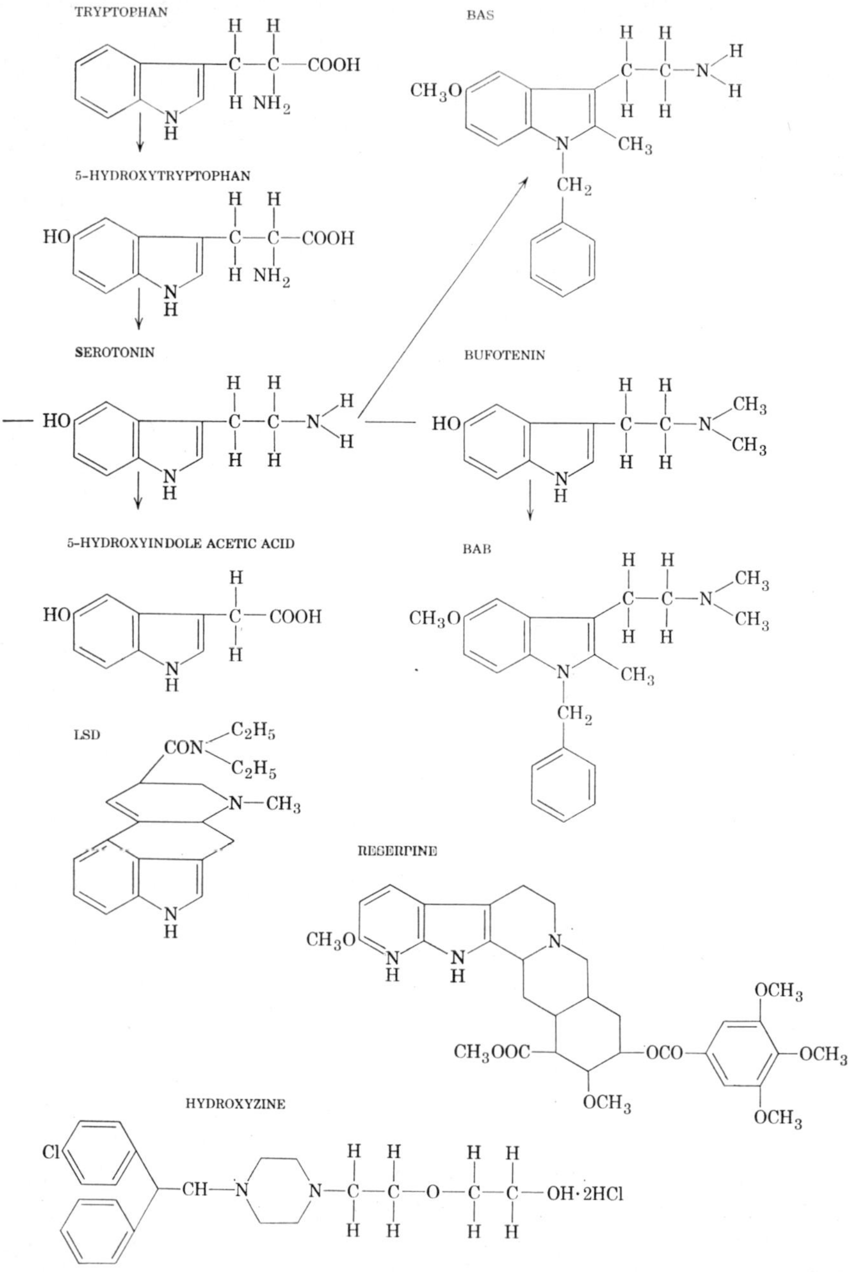

TRYPTOPHAN

5-HYDROXYTRYPTOPHAN

SEROTONIN

5-HYDROXYINDOLE ACETIC ACID

LSD

HYDROXYZINE

BAS

BUFOTENIN

BAB

RESERPINE

psychotomimetic agents, and tranquilizing drugs.

its injection. The long presence of reserpine in the brain does not necessarily exclude the theory that reserpine acts through an indirect mechanism that involves serotonin, but it is in accord with the idea that reserpine acts as such.

Additional evidence that reserpine releases serotonin has been adduced by Valcourt (1959), who observed two groups of patients, one schizophrenic and the other mentally defective, at the Galesburg State Research Hospital. A significantly increased urinary excretion of 5-hydroxyindoleacetic acid occurred during the first day of the administration of 4 mg. of reserpine. Apparently, when serotonin does not attain its binding site, it is rendered vulnerable to the amine oxidase enzyme and is metabolized to form 5-hydroxyindoleacetic acid (Fig. 1).

Even if it is proved that serotonin is important to the function of the brain, its action is not a simple one, for that hormone may serve in other ways. Because serotonin can cause smooth muscle, the type of muscle in the walls of arteries and of viscera, to contract, it is thought to be a factor in the production of high blood pressure and in the motility of the gastrointestinal tract. Only 1 per cent of the serotonin content of the body is found in the brain (Correale, 1956). Most of it occurs in the spleen and especially in the gastrointestinal tract, containing the specialized cells of the enterochromaffin system, which secrete serotonin (Erspamer, 1954). A tumor of these cells, called malignant carcinoid, is associated with abnormally high levels of blood serotonin and with an increased excretion of its metabolic product, 5-hydroxyindoleacetic acid, in the urine (Sjoerdsma, Weissbach, and Udenfriend, 1956). Behavioral changes are absent, perhaps because of the relative impermeability of the brain to serotonin (Costa and Aprison, 1957).

The similarities between serotonin, an indole amine, and the catechol amines, noradrenaline and adrenaline, are important. These similarities are not limited to their areas of distribution in the brain (Figs. 2 and 3), which in general reveal high concentrations in various subcortical areas and low ones in the cerebral cortex and cerebellum (Vogt, 1954; Costa and Aprison, 1958), nor are their resemblances confined to their chemical structures (Fig. 1), which disclose that adrenaline can be oxidized to form an indole amine, adrenochrome, and that the latter, plus the appropriate side chain, yields serotonin.

Most striking is the discovery that reserpine exerts an action on noradrenaline and adrenaline similar to that previously disclosed for serotonin; i.e., it empties their stores wherever they occur in the

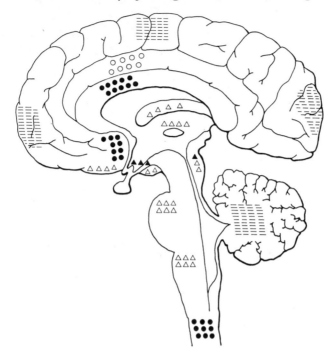

Figure 2. Serotonin content of the human brain. The areas with the highest concentration of serotonin, an indole amine, include the hypothalamus. A lower level is observed in the mammillary bodies, fornix, thalamus, and medulla oblongata. Serotonin is found in the cingulate gyrus, hippocampus, and amygdaloid nucleus in greater concentrations than in the neocortex or cerebellum, which contain the least amounts. Broken lines indicate 0.01 to 0.05 γ/g.; $\bigcirc$, 0.05 to 0.1 γ/g.; $\bullet$, 0.1 to 0.3 γ/g.; $\triangle$, 0.3 to 0.6 γ/g.; $\blacktriangle$, more than 0.6 γ/g. (Costa and Aprison, 1958.)

body. Even more significant is the observation (Brodie, Olin, Kuntzman, and Shore, 1957) that the curve for the time relationships for the release of these substances from the brain and the re-establishment to premedication values follow each other closely. Though the results are not the same when different methods for the determination of noradrenaline are used, in general there is agreement in the rapid release (Carlsson, Rosengren, Bertler, and Nilsson, 1957) from the brain and the slow return to normal values. It is obvious, then, that the releases of these amines are closely associated phenomena. Either the amines combine with the same receptor, though not necessarily

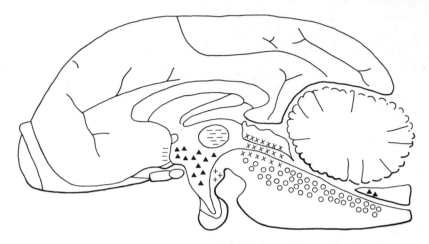

Figure 3. Medial sagittal section of a dog's brain showing the distribution of noradrenaline in micrograms per gram of fresh tissue: ▲, 1.0 μg./g.; +, >0.4 and <1.0 μg./g.; ○, >0.3 and <0.4 μg./g.; —, >0.2 and <0.3 μg./g. In the dog brain the catechol amines, noradrenaline and adrenaline, are at their highest concentration in the hypothalamus; then, in decreasing amounts, in the mammillary bodies and the reticular formation. Still lower concentrations are observed in the neocortex and cerebellum. (Vogt, 1954.)

with the same prosthetic group, or the discharge of one amine initiates the liberation of the other. Changes in the concentrations of serotonin and noradrenaline also play parts in the actions of the antidepressants iproniazid and imipramine. Iproniazid increases the amounts of serotonin (Pletscher, 1957) and catechol amines (Himwich, Costa, Pscheidt, and Van Meter, 1960). Similarly, though to a lesser extent, imipramine hydrochloride also raises serotonin (Costa, personal communication), but no changes in the catechol amines have been demonstrated as yet (Pscheidt, personal communication). These actions may be related to the ability of both antidepressants to antagonize the behavioral effects of reserpine in animals and man.

One action of reserpine, therefore, involves closely allied substances which may be included in the term "biogenic amines." Can such a conception be applied to chlorpromazine? An examination of the structure of chlorpromazine (Fig. 1) reveals two chief portions, the phenothiazine nucleus and a side chain,

$$N-CH_2-CH_2-CH_2-N$$

Suggestions arise from an examination of both portions of the chlorpromazine molecule. If the phenothiazine nucleus portion is depicted in three dimensions instead of two, it closely resembles the indole nucleus, as observed in serotonin as well as in reserpine. It does not seem, however, that chlorpromazine acts in the same manner as reserpine, for chlorpromazine does not empty the depots of serotonin and the catechol amines. Another lead comes from the examination of the side chain, which is contained in many successful phenothiazine derivatives (Himwich, Rinaldi, and Willis, 1956). As has been pointed out by Gyermek (1955) and others (Gyermek, 1955; Begany, Seifter, Pless, Huber, and Bruce, 1956), the same side chain occurs repeatedly in substances which depress the effects of amines. It must not be forgotten that the phenothiazines belong to the group of antihistaminic drugs and can usually inhibit actions evoked by histamine (Fig. 1). In fact, such a side chain will interfere with the effects of other biogenic amines, including noradrenaline, adrenaline, and serotonin (Benditt and Rowley, 1956). Chlorpromazine shares with these biogenic amines a side chain of similar construction, and perhaps chlorpromazine attaches itself to the same binding site as do these amines.

If such a generalized action may be attributed to chlorpromazine, the study of the chemical substrates of behavior becomes even broader than the indole viewpoint suggested by the pharmacologic action of reserpine, and renders every biogenic amine a fit subject for investigation in the field of behavior. But even these broad possibilities do not account for the chemical aspects of tranquilizers not included in the reserpine and chlorpromazine groups. As an example, we may cite the experiments of Costa (1956), who showed that the peripheral effects of serotonin were blocked not only by reserpine and chlorpromazine but also by azacyclonol. Moreover, meprobamate, hydroxyzine, benactyzine, and many other drugs, each with different chemical constitutions, are effective in various degrees against one mental condition or another. Until the chemical advances catch up with the clinical advances, some of the manifestations can be followed in the form of changes in nerve function.

Neurohormonal Equilibrium

Marrazzi and Hart (1957) propose a theory, depending upon an equilibrium between various hormones, that may account for results with diverse types of tranquilizers. They contrast the stimulating effects of acetylcholine, a chemical mediator of the nerve impulse across the synaptic junction between two nerves, with the inhibiting action of adrenaline, amphetamine, mescaline, and LSD. The latter group depresses and may even stop the transmission of the neural impulse from one neurone to the next. Marrazzi and Hart also report that tranquilizing drugs—reserpine, chlorpromazine, and azacyclonol —prevent the inhibitory effect of mescaline on the transmission of the nerve impulse. They regard the signs of psychosis as release phenomena, results of the removal of normal restraints. Their experimental work also discloses that the depressant influence of serotonin is more potent than that of adrenaline, amphetamine, mescaline, or LSD. They therefore suggest that mental derangement is caused by an imbalance between such inhibitory substances as serotonin and the chemical transmitter of the nervous impulse, acetylcholine. Koella, Smythies, and Bull (1959) also studied the effects of serotonin; they point out that in part these effects also depend upon a peripheral action exerted on the carotid sinus.

It is known that acetylcholine is active in the function of several cerebral areas, including the mesodiencephalic activating system, which is discussed in the next section (Rinaldi and Himwich, 1955a, b). In a way, this conception is somewhat like that of Pfeiffer and Jenney (1957): an increase of acetylcholine may exert an antischizophrenic effect, for raised concentrations of that neurohormone should antagonize the action of serotonin to block the transmission of the nerve impulse. But it is not impossible that a dearth of acetylcholine is associated with one type of abnormal behavior, perhaps psychosis, and that an excess of acetylcholine is an accompaniment of another type, neurosis. Jacobsen (1955) has suggested that the action of benactyzine in blocking acetylcholine may serve a beneficial effect in disturbances associated with supernormal concentrations of acetylcholine (Himwich and Rinaldi, 1955–56). Benactyzine exerts little influence on schizophrenic patients, but it has been termed an antiphobic drug because it is effective against abnormal fears and reduces the emotional reactivity to stress.

Anatomic Sites of Action

An important cause for the diverse effects of depressant drugs like the barbiturates and the tranquilizers is disclosed by an examination of their sites of action. It is well known that every drug may affect many parts of the body, but it must also be emphasized that some areas, usually the important ones for the therapeutic results, are more susceptible than others. Consider, for example, the barbiturates, which in general act most strongly on the parts of the brain developed later—the cortex of the cerebral hemispheres—and least strongly on the more primitive medulla oblongata, which contains vital centers for the control of heart rate, respiration, and blood pressure. Because of their pronounced effects on the cerebral cortex, barbiturates depress functions of the cortical regions concerned with the analyzing mechanisms of vision, audition, and other perceptive functions—the fine coordination of motor movements as well as thought and memory. Though the tranquilizers also affect functions ascribed chiefly to the cerebral cortex, their most potent actions are exerted on the sub-

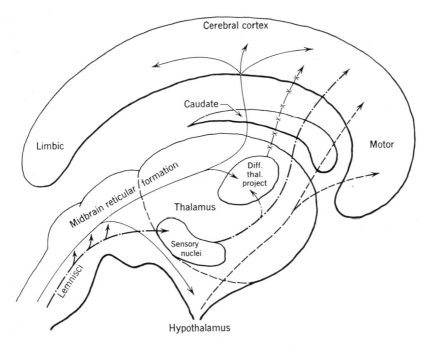

Figure 4. Mesodiencephalic activating system. Stimulation of the organism evokes impulses which travel by way of the lemnisci to the thalamic sensory nuclei and then to cortical sensory areas. The lemnisci send collateral nerve fibers to the midbrain reticular formation, and by these fibers impulses advance in the reticular formation to the diffuse thalamic projections and arouse the cerebral cortex. Collaterals bearing stimuli from the midbrain reticular formation pass to the hypothalamus, which in turn sends impulses to the cerebral cortex. (Himwich, 1955.)

cortical structures regarded as parts of the anatomic substrate of emotion: the midbrain reticular formation, the hypothalamus, and the components of the rhinencephalon (Figs. 4 and 5).

The tranquilizing drugs appear to select, for their main sites of action, these three cerebral areas, all connected with each other and with the cortex. It would seem that the visceral functions, related to the emotions, were correlated chiefly by the reticular formation in the lower vertebrates. It is also probable that, later in the evolutionary process, other centers in the hypothalamus and especially in the rhinencephalon took over much of the emotional aspect of behavior.

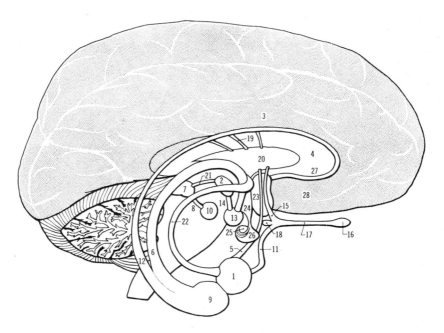

Figure 5. Semidiagrammatic section of human brain. 1, amygdala; 2, anterior nucleus of thalamus; 3, cingulate gyrus; 4, corpus callosum; 5, diagonal band of Broca; 6, fornix; 7, habenula, a nucleus of the thalamus; 8, habenulopeduncular tract; 9, hippocampus; 10, interpeduncular nucleus; 11, lateral olfactory stria; 12, longitudinal stria; 13, mammillary body; 14, mammillothalamic tract; 15, medial olfactory stria; 16, olfactory bulb; 17, olfactory tract; 18, olfactory tubercle; 19, perforating fibers; 20, septum pellucidum; 21, stria medularis; 22, stria terminalis; 23, subcallosal gyrus; 24, hypothalamus; 25, posterior pituitary gland; 26, anterior pituitary gland; 27, caudate nuclei in depth of brain; 28, septal region.

A more detailed description of the midbrain reticular formation reveals that it is an ancient cerebral area, well developed even in the Amphibia, as has been shown by the work of Herrick (1948) on the tiger salamander. In that animal the midbrain reticular formation probably serves as an important integrating mechanism, coordinating muscular and visceral activities in accordance with the sensory information evoked by changes in the environment. We owe the elucidation of the basic physiology of the reticular formation in mammals and primates to Moruzzi, Magoun, and their students (1949). These workers showed that the midbrain reticular formation acts in conjunction with the diffuse thalamic projections (Fig. 4), as ascribed by Jasper (1949). Thus the phyletically older midbrain reticular formation is united functionally with the later-developed diffuse thalamic cortical projections, and the two together form the mesodiencephalic activating system (Rinaldi and Himwich, 1955a, b). This does not mean that the mesodiencephalic activating system is independent of the rest of the brain. On the contrary, its midbrain reticular component probably receives a varying number of stimuli by way of collateral nerve fibers from the lemnisci (Fig. 4). There are therefore two parallel systems. One carries information by way of the lemnisci and the paths of the sensory thalamic nuclei to the cortex, where the messages are analyzed for specific information on the kind of stimulus, its point of application, and similar relationships to the organism. In the other system, the mesodiencephalic activating system, nerve impulses ascend in the reticular formation to the thalamic nuclei, which then send other impulses to the cortex by way of the diffuse thalamic paths. The mesodiencephalic activating system thus affords the emotional cloak which accompanies some kinds of stimulation of the body.

The parts played by the hypothalamus and the rhinencephalon will be considered below, but with this background we can proceed with the psychopharmacologic analysis of the functions of the mesodiencephalic activating system, which has been shown to be sensitive to members of the reserpine group of drugs, to chlorpromazine and other phenothiazine derivatives, and to azacyclonol. A clue to the effect of these drugs on this system is afforded by the electroencephalograph, for both stimulation and inhibition are accompanied by characteristic brain-wave patterns. Those associated with inhibition of the reticular formation are also observed, with rest or light dozing in the human being or animal, and are shown on the left side of Fig. 6A. They are characterized by high-amplitude slow waves and spindles of rapid

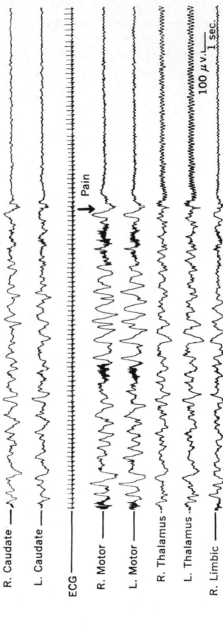

(A)

Pain Evoked Alerting Reaction

R. Caudate

L. Caudate

ECG

R. Motor

L. Motor

R. Thalamus

L. Thalamus

R. Limbic

Pain

100 μv. 1 sec.

A 4–FR–4

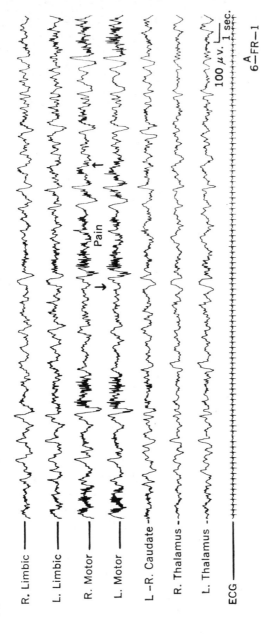

Figure 6. Alert pattern evoked by pain and prevented by chlorpromazine. (A) Bilateral leads are taken from various cerebral structures: on right side, electroencephalographic control pattern of resting rabbit; on left side, the effects of pinching rabbit's leg. (B) Change produced by chlorpromazine (5 mg./kg.) in electroencephalographic pattern in response to pain. Note the absence of the alerting reaction to pain. (Himwich, 1955.)

waves. The latter are most prominent in the motor cortex, as is seen in records obtained from a rabbit. This type of activity continues until the animal is exposed to auditory, tactile, or painful stimuli, when rapid low-amplitude waves, particularly in the cortex, appear, while a slower regular rhythm develops in the hippocampus. On the right side of Fig. 6A is seen such an alerting or arousal pattern (Bradley, 1958; Hiebel, Bonvallet, and Dell, 1954). On the other hand, when chlorpromazine is given, the reticular formation is blocked and no longer shows the alerting response (Fig. 6B). This inhibition of the reticular formation does not prevent impulses evoked by a painful stimulus from traversing the lemnisci (Fig. 4), and awareness is thus achieved by way of the cortical mechanisms. But the severity of the associated distressing emotional accompaniment of the stimulus is greatly mitigated.

A clinical example is seen in the use of chlorpromazine for the treatment of the intractable pain associated with inoperable cancer. Surely the patient is aware of the pain, but it has been largely robbed of its harrowing emotional accompaniment. It is not impossible that a patient disturbed by painful hallucinations and upsetting delusions can be similarly rendered relatively free of emotional upheavals. The ability of chlorpromazine to reduce the emotional reactions to painful stimuli is probably due to the depression of the reticular formation. Though azacyclonol is not capable of blocking the pain response, it can prevent and correct the alerting of the electroencephalogram caused by the psychotomimetic drugs, LSD and mescaline (Himwich, 1956b; Rinaldi, 1956). In contrast to chlorpromazine, reserpine, in adequate doses, activates the mesodiencephalic activating system and produces the alert pattern (Rinaldi and Himwich, 1955c). It is significant, therefore, that reserpine, despite its tranquilizing action, is not of use in the management of pain. Perhaps the greater sedative effect of chlorpromazine is due to its ability to depress the midbrain reticular formation. The Killams (1958) suggest another mechanism of action, namely that the reticular formation filters out afferent impulses, an activity which is enhanced by chlorpromazine. According to these workers, the amelioration of pain may result from a diminution of afferent impulses. It is striking that imipramine hydrochloride, which is different from chlorpromazine and is in fact an antidepressant (Kuhn, 1958), shares with the latter the ability to block the reticular formation as well as to be effective against pain (Van Meter, Owens, and Himwich, 1959). Because these two mechanisms are not mutually exclusive, it would be well to determine whether filtering of afferent impulses is also a function of imipramine hydrochloride.

But the fact that reserpine does not inhibit the mesodiencephalic activating system indicates that other centers are important for tranquilization. We therefore turn next to the consideration of the hypothalamus, which is known to contain patterns for coordinating visceral functions, increases of blood pressure, heart rate, and respiration in order to support muscular activity. This integration of visceral and muscular activities is especially essential in emergency situations, originally referred to by Cannon (1932) as the "fight or flight" reactions. This part of the brain, therefore, organizes the visceral manifestations which are overactive in disturbed patients. It would seem probable that the depression of this mechanism acts to mitigate this type of overactivity. The earliest research done on reserpine and chlorpromazine indicated that these drugs inhibited hypothalamic structures, particularly those of the posterior hypothalamic nuclei which regulate the sympathetic nerves to the viscera and blood vessels (Bein, Gross, Tripod, and Meier, 1953).

The action of reserpine can be explained in part by a depression of the sympathetic representation in the hypothalamus (Tripod, Bein, and Meier, 1954), which leaves parasympathetic activity unopposed and thus accounts for the fall in heart rate, drop in blood pressure, constriction of pupils, and the increased intestinal motility frequently observed in patients receiving that drug. These physiological changes are signs of acetylcholine activity. Acetylcholine is not only associated with the chemical transmission of the nerve impulse in parasympathetic nerves to the various organs but also with transmission within the central nervous system. With reserpine, however, the increased effects of acetylcholine may result from the failure of the opposing effects of adrenaline and noradrenaline. As we have seen, this failure may be the result of the emptying of the catechol amine depots by reserpine, in the brain and elsewhere in the body. As a consequence of this depletion, stimuli impinging on the hypothalamus fail to evoke responses from the cerebral representation of the sympathetic nervous system (Weiskrantz, 1957). It is also probable that, because of the exhaustion of the adrenaline and noradrenaline deposits in the peripheral sympathetic nerves, these nerves, too, cannot react, and thus the central effects of that drug are accentuated.

In a way, the pharmacologic actions of chlorpromazine may be compared with those of reserpine, for both exert central and peripheral effects. It is true that both drugs inhibit the hypothalamus, but chlorpromazine also depresses peripheral sympathetic nerve centers which help to regulate blood pressure; this is a second reason for the observed decreases of arterial pressure. But chlorpromazine also exerts a similar impairment of the peripheral parasympathetic nerves which usually slow heart rate, and therefore in patients receiving chlorpromazine the heart rate is characteristically rapid. Both peripheral results may be ascribed to interference with the action of acetylcholine in the transmission of the nerve impulse and therefore may be compared with the central operation of chlorpromazine to block the reticular formation (Rinaldi and Himwich, 1955d).

Pathfinding Experiments

The discussion on the parts of the brain affected by chlorpromazine and reserpine will now be extended to include those which were highlighted by the pathfinding experiments of Klüver and Bucy (1939). These workers removed the temporal lobes of monkeys, thereby changing these difficult creatures into remarkably tame animals. The primates also exhibited increased oral and sexual proclivities. Objects of all kinds were repeatedly introduced into the mouths of the animals being tested, and males, especially, attempted sexual intercourse frequently, whether or not the animal chosen for these relations was of the appropriate sex or even of the same species.

The temporal lobe includes some structures belonging to the rhinencephalon, which was first regarded as a unified system by Papez (1937), in accordance with the schema presented semidiagrammatically in Fig. 5. When the hippocampus is stimulated, it gives rise to impulses which initiate the Papez circle. These impulses are transmitted from the hippocampus (No. 9, Fig. 5), through the fornix (No. 6), to the mammillary bodies of the hypothalamus (No. 13). From that area they continue to the anterior thalamic nuclei (No. 2) and attain the cortex of the brain in the cingulate gyrus and then return to the hippocampus.

Again the phyletic point of view is enlightening. When the first air-breathing vertebrates—the amphibians and especially the reptiles —left the oceans for the land, they developed areas of the brain important for smell, the olfactory bulb (No. 16) and the olfactory tract (No. 17). The olfactory tubercle (No. 18), which receives impulses from the midbrain reticular formation, supplies an indirect connection between the latter and Papez' circle. The term rhinencephalon originates in the primarily olfactory functions of the bulb and of some of the amygdaloid nuclei (No. 1). These structures are connected, in turn, to others which have been adapted in higher animals to emotional activities. These include the remainder of the amygdaloid and septal nuclei (No. 28). Finally, the latter areas contact Papez' circle in the hippocampus, and awareness of emotional reactions is attained by way of the cingulate gyrus (Pribram and Kruger, 1954). Even today, in man, emotion and olfaction are closely associated, and this is so despite our mores, which in general require restriction of body odors.

The part of the brain concerned especially with emotional experience and the one least understood is the rhinencephalon, which is also called the limbic system or the visceral brain (MacLean, 1952). It must be noted that not only tranquilization but also the reverse reaction of rage was observed when the more forward portions of the rhinencephalon—the septal area and olfactory tubercle—were removed, and similar effects were also reported after the extirpation of the amygdaloid nuclei, the hippocampus, and the fornix (Spiegel, Miller, and Oppenheimer, 1940). Lesions of the septal region alone were also found to produce rage (Brady, 1956). Bilateral extirpation of the amygdaloid complex and the adjacent pyriform lobe rendered animals easily disturbed (Bard and Mountcastle, 1948). Many workers, however, have observed placidity and emotional unresponsiveness after the bilateral removal of the amygdala and hippocampus (Smith, 1950; Thomson and Walker, 1951; Fuller, Rosvold, and Pribram, 1957; Schreiner and Kling, 1953).

Though these results are apparently contradictory, at present the consensus is veering toward Klüver and Bucy's original conclusions (1939) because the pacifying effects of these extirpations are found more frequently. With either result, these experiments disclose relationships between the rhinencephalon and the emotional state. From this viewpoint both observations are useful, and the nature of the response may depend on other factors, for example, the immediate social environment, whether or not it is hostile, and whether the animal is being provoked or treated in a friendly fashion. The general reaction characteristic of the animal is also important, for the effects of the operation may be superimposed on an excitable animal, easily aroused, or on a calm and phlegmatic one. Analyses have been made to explain these discordant results (Schreiner and Kling, 1953; Rothfield and Harman, 1954), but for our purposes these reactions serve to point out the type of physiological activity of these parts of

Figure 7. Effect of reserpine (0.1 mg./kg.) on brain waves; records of spontaneous rhinencephalic seizures in the amygdala. (Killam and Killam, 1957.)

the brain, and they afford a basis for the appraisal of the effects of drugs upon them.

Killam and Killam (1957) report spontaneous, seizure-like waves in the rhinencephalon of a cat after the administration of reserpine. These seizures appeared first in the amygdala (AMG, Fig. 7) and then spread to the hippocampus (HIPP) and to other rhinencephalic structures, including the entorhinal cortex (ENTO) and septum (SEPT). However, the neocortex (MSS and SC) remained free of such abnormalities. Furthermore, Sigg and Schneider (1957) noted that electrically evoked, seizure-like waves in the amygdala were facilitated and prolonged by reserpine without necessarily involving neocortical areas.

Preston's observations (1956) with chlorpromazine are similar in some respects to those of the Killams with reserpine, for he reports that the amygdaloid complex is readily stimulated by chlorpromazine at a time when the activity of the neocortex, including the motor cortex which regulates voluntary muscular movements, is unchanged. The electroencephalographic alterations evoked by single daily injections of chlorpromazine into a cat (10 mg. per kg. of body weight) for a period of 5 days showed that 20 hours after the last injection there was no obvious effect in the neocortex (LG and MC, Fig. 8), while the amygdaloid nuclei (AMG) revealed spiking.

Thus, the amygdala is the part of the brain most susceptible to both drugs. Rather surprisingly, this amygdaloid hyperactivity was associated with tranquilization. With this dose of chlorpromazine, well within the human therapeutic range, a cat will not pounce upon a mouse placed in its cage but, instead, acts with apparent indifference. Though the convulsive brain waves disclosed in the amygdala were accompanied by a transformation in the behavior of the cat, overt signs of motor activity were not apparent in such animals. In general, it is known that the rhinencephalon is more easily excitable than is the neocortical mantle of the cerebral hemispheres (Liberson and Akert, 1955; Green and Shimamoto, 1953; Liberson and Cadilhac, 1953). With larger doses of chlorpromazine (Preston, 1956), which however do not exceed those administered to badly disturbed patients (Kinross-Wright, 1955b), the electrical hyperactivity spreads from the amygdala (AMG, Fig. 9) to other rhinencephalic structures, the septum (SEPT) and the hippocampus (HIPP). But only when the disturbance extends to neocortical motor areas are the characteristic violent muscular contractions of a major epileptic seizure observed. Perhaps a similar process, the initiation of seizure activity in the

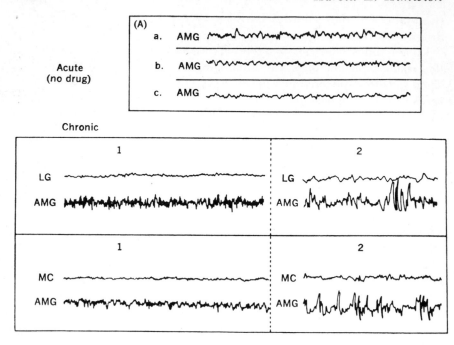

Figure 8. Comparative effects of chlorpromazine on the amygdala and cerebral cortex. (A) Spontaneous activity recorded from the amygdala in three different cats. (1) Records from two cats after a single daily injection of chlorpromazine, 10 mg./kg., for 5 days; (2) spontaneous activity recorded at a later time in the same experiment after 10 mg./kg. of chlorpromazine had been injected. Hyperactivity is present in amygdala but not in the neocortex. (Preston, 1956.)

amygdala and its spread through the rhinencephalic structures and then to the motor cortex, can explain the convulsive seizures sometimes seen in patients taking reserpine and chlorpromazine (Rudy, Himwich, and Rinaldi, 1958). Penfield (1950) has suggested that the phenomena of psychomotor epilepsy may originate in a seizure discharge in the amygdala, spreading in the centrencephalic system (Gloor, 1957). The pharmacologic effects of these two drugs may be compared with the observations of Andy and Akert (1955), who stimulated the hippocampal formation of a cat electrically and noted that, when the hippocampal discharge was propagated to include the amygdala, the cat was not affected by the presence of the mouse, an apathy which was prolonged for a short period of time after the discharge was completed and which was then replaced by an attack upon

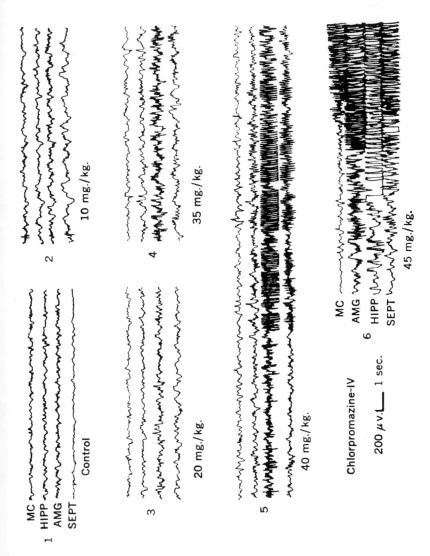

Figure 9. Effects of gradual increases of chlorpromazine upon brain. Seizure spiking is initiated in amygdala and gradually spreads to other areas. (Preston, 1956.)

the little victim. But there is more than one method by which similar
kinds of behavioral results may be obtained. Tranquilization of disturbed psychotic patients can be achieved with meprobamate (Pennington, 1957), which is neither a phenothiazine derivative nor a
reserpine-like drug (Fig. 1). Unlike these tranquilizers, meprobamate does not alter brain-wave activity of the amygdala when it is
administered in small doses which, however, depress the undulations
exhibited by the thalamus (Hendley, Lynes, and Berger, 1957).
Though the amygdala does not seem to be a site of activity for
meprobamate, yet some portion of the rhinencephalon may be involved, as suggested by experiments with animals. Rats rendered
savage by the extirpation of their septal regions are restored to their
preoperative behavior by that drug. Apparently meprobamate influences a portion of the brain which is functionally associated with
the septum. It is of more than passing interest that rats with normal
septums show little or no change in their conduct when the same
doses of meprobamate that calm the experimental animals (Hunt,
1957) are administered.

Theory for Therapeutic Effects

To bridge the gap between our information about the pharmacologic actions of reserpine and chlorpromazine and their therapeutic
results is a goal greatly to be desired. Unfortunately, we do not have
sufficient data or even the basic neurophysiologic facts to do this. It
is realized that such speculations on the mode of action of tranquilizers in man are largely based on observations of animals—a
doubtful procedure. Moreover, there is a genuine logical difficulty,
for it has not been proved that the behavioral improvements noted
with use of these drugs are due to the pharmacologic effects. The
two diverse groups of phenomena may be related to each other only
by a common causative factor—the drug.

The therapeutic effects of reserpine and chlorpromazine are of two
different kinds: one is a calming of the individual and another is
directed against schizophrenic manifestations. Can each of these two
different clinical improvements be related to specific actions of the
drugs? The decreased reactivity of tranquilized patients may be
ascribed in part to the depletion of the catechol amines, the depletion depriving the organism of part of the mechanism of reactivity.
Obviously, tension and anxiety, whether evoked by real or imaginary
emergencies, will nevertheless mobilize the autonomic nervous system.

Not only adrenaline and noradrenaline but also other hormones, including serotonin and acetylcholine, are probably released during threatening emergencies. Thus, in general, a pharmacologic action of these drugs is the removal of part of the mobilization mechanism, and the beneficial results include tranquilization and decreases of anxiety and tension. Turning to the electrophysiological portion of the analysis, we find ourselves examining the parts of the brain which help to regulate the activity of the neurohormones. A neuronal depression of the reticular formation and of the hypothalamus diminishes the actions of these portions of the brain. This depression can only render more profound the decrease in reactivity due to the emptying of the neurohormonal storehouses.

Animal experiments indicate a close relationship between rhinencephalic structure and the emotions, while drug studies have disclosed the sensitivity of the amygdala to chlorpromazine and reserpine. But here we see that a similar final effect of tranquilization is associated with an action which is quite the reverse of that seen in the hypothalamus. Inhibition of nerve function is not observed. On the contrary, the affected areas reveal abnormal hyperactivity. Does the drug-induced aberrant operation of the amygdala interfere with the functions of the rhinencephalon? If so, does such an interference afford a basis for the second action of these drugs against schizophrenic symptoms? It would seem that the normal contribution of the amygdala to the economy of the brain cannot continue when that structure is being subjected to seizures (Buscaino, 1956). Perhaps the rhinencephalic chain ceases to act physiologically because of the functional failure of the amygdaloid link—a failure which makes for a loss in a connection between the most primitive brain area (concerned with emotion), the midbrain reticular formation, and the later-developed rhinencephalon.

The diminution in reactivity of the organism probably influences the quantity or intensity of the emotional impact on the cortex. But it is difficult to see how such an amelioration can change the quality of thought so that the dissociated "word salad" of the hebephrenic patient can become less incoherent, more logical, and comprehensible. One can appreciate that a decrease in emotional intensity might mitigate the violence in the expression of hallucinatory and delusional material, but again it is more difficult to understand how such a mitigation can cause the correction of schizophrenic mentation. For that change, thinking must be altered in quality.

Though the various parts of the brain work together as a unit in a coordinated manner, we have seen that certain structures, both cortical and subcortical, are more involved than others in our emotional life. Similarly, as pointed out by Bailey (1957), some subcortical regions add a crude awareness, but for the discriminative contribution to that complex function the cortex must be included in a prominent position. The cingulate gyrus, which is a part not only of the rhinencephalon but also of the cortex, may be the area where the abnormal elements concerned with awareness and thinking enter into discriminative conscious activity. It is not said that rhinencephalic structures do not affect emotional reactions, but it is suggested, as a working hypothesis, that the cessation of rhinencephalic function is possibly a factor in the prevention of the morbid thinking of schizophrenia. This would indicate that the disease process of schizophrenia is tied up with the malfunction of certain brain areas and that the rhinencephalic circle carries impulses which are sources of the pathologic psychophysiology of schizophrenia. It is realized that a change of behavior produced by a loss of the contribution from a specific brain area, whether resulting from a physical extirpation or from functional incapacitation, does not prove that pathology in that area is the source of the disease. The removal of a part of the brain may interfere with the function of another region more directly concerned with the disease process. For example, an origin of the pathologic course may lie within the septal region, as suggested by the work of Heath and his colleagues (1958), or the warped emotional reactions may find their earlier expression in the midbrain reticular formation. But at least it can be said that the anatomic site sensitive to drug action bears a relationship to schizophrenia, because the functional diversion of that area may correct the symptomatology of the disorder.

The changes in brain waves produced by the antidepressant drug imipramine resemble qualitatively those evoked by chlorpromazine in that relatively large doses evoke rhinencephalic spikes and convulsant brain-wave patterns in rabbits (Van Meter, Owens, and Himwich, 1959). How the rhinencephalic effects of this drug will fit into the theory of interference with the Papez circle as a source of antipsychotic action still remains to be seen. It is known, however (Kuhn, personal communication), that imipramine occasionally improves psychosis. It should be pointed out, first, that in accordance with animal experiments chlorpromazine and imipramine work in different brain milieu in so far as the neurohormones are concerned (personal communications from Costa and from Pscheidt), and, second, that clinically imipramine is usually used in smaller dosage in depressed patients than is chlorpromazine for psychotic individuals, so that only especially susceptible persons exhibit either the antipsychotic or the convulsant effects of imipramine.

Frequently a depression is superimposed upon the schizophrenic process. In such a condition it has been found empirically (Kuhn, personal communication) that the combined use of chlorpromazine and imipramine produces more satisfactory results than the use of either of these drugs separately. To treat the psychosis with chlorpromazine may unmask the depression, while to use imipramine for the depression may activate the psychosis. It is perhaps an interesting correlation that both chlorpromazine and imipramine in small dosage block the reticular formation (Himwich, 1959). A similar agreement, though with opposite sign, exists between the antidepressant iproniazid and the tranquilizer reserpine. Both of these drugs activate the reticular formation (Himwich, 1959), and empirically it has been found that the use of these drugs in combination may on occasion achieve better results than either of them alone (Ferguson, Linn, Sheets, and Nickels, 1956). We are getting nearer the solution of a complex problem, but the end is not in sight.

Paths of Research

A review of the present pharmacologic data can suggest paths for future exploration. One series of observations has emphasized quantitative changes causing shifts in the neurohormonal balance, involving excesses or deficits of acetylcholine, adrenaline, noradrenaline, serotonin, or serotonin-like substances. Concentrations of serotonin in the brain can be increased by the administration of its precursor, 5-hydroxytryptophan, which provokes disturbances in the electroencephalogram and in the behavior of the rabbit (Udenfriend, Weissbach, and Bogdanski, 1957; Shore and Brodie, 1957; Costa and Rinaldi, 1958) (Fig. 1). Apparently 5-hydroxytryptophan enters the brain rapidly and, presumably, is transformed into serotonin. But that does not demonstrate that serotonin is excessive in hyperactive psychotic patients (Costa, Rinaldi, and Himwich, 1957) or that their improvement necessarily results from the decrease of serotonin in the brain. On the other hand, there is a recent suggestion that iproniazid, which increases the serotonin and catechol amine contents of the brain, benefits depressed patients (Saunders, Radinger, and Kline, 1957). Again, that does not prove that patients are depressed because of abnormally low levels of serotonin or noradrenaline in the brain. But it must be admitted that this circumstantial evidence is of such interest that it calls for further investigation of these possibilities.

An experiment to throw light on this subject would be to determine the cerebral serotonin and catechol amine contents in the brains of psychotic patients and compare them with those of nonpsychotics. A start has been made. Costa and Aprison (1958) have demonstrated that serotonin is a normal constituent of the human brain, just as it is of the brain of lower animals. It can be said conservatively that the suggestion of Woolley and Shaw (1954) on the role of serotonin is an attractive one and that it has been useful in turning up new material (Rudy, Costa, Rinaldi, and Himwich 1958). For example, Shaw and Woolley (1956a) have synthesized compounds which block serotonin, including BAB, the benzyl analog of bufotenin, and BAS, the benzyl analog of serotonin (Fig. 1). We have employed BAS in the treatment of schizophrenics on the theory that it may exert a reserpine-like action (Rudy, Costa, Rinaldi, and Himwich, 1958). The salutary results on these psychotic patients were encouraging, but the side reactions contraindicate the clinical use of BAS.

It is not justifiable, however, to separate the role of serotonin from that of the catechol amines, because the tranquilizer reserpine reduces brain serotonin and catechol amines simultaneously, and the antidepressants iproniazid and imipramine exert the reverse actions. A strong point in favor of the catechol amines is that one of them, desoxyephedrine, is able to substitute for depleted catechol amines in the brain (Everett, Toman, and Smith, 1957). Mice and monkeys, under the influence of reserpine and showing the depression, reduced mobility, and the hunched posture typically produced by that drug, are dramatically restored, apparently to normal activity, by desoxyephedrine. It is necessary to establish experimental situations in which the concentration of only one of the two neurohormones is altered in order to disentangle the effects of changing two variables at the same time. This has been accomplished by injecting either dopa or 5-hydroxytryptophan, the precursors of noradrenaline and serotonin respectively (Carlsson, Lindqvist, and Magnusson, 1957; Everett and Toman, 1959). Brodie (1958) has suggested that an excess of serotonin is tranquilizing whereas increased noradrenaline is stimulating, and this lead deserves further development. Another line of investigation is concerned more with qualitative changes in the neurohormones than with quantitative ones, and it implicates a metabolic factor in schizophrenia. This work cannot be reviewed here, but it involves the more rapid oxidation of adrenaline (Akerfeldt, 1957) or the production of abnormal oxidation products of that neurohormone (Leach, Cohen, Heath, and Martens, 1956; Hoffer and Kenyon, 1957; Rinkel, Hyde, and Solomon, 1954). As a result of an abnormal enzyme system, the metabolism of adrenaline is perverted, and an aberrant metabolic product, which may be a pathogenic factor in schizophrenia, is formed (Heath, Leach, Byers, Martens, and Feigley, 1958).

At this time, when theories of schizophrenia are actively multiplying, it would seem that the two different aspects of quantitative and qualitative changes in the hormones are not mutually exclusive. One example is afforded by Hoffer (1957), who suggests that there are two basic conditions for the production of schizophrenia: an increase in the concentration and activity of acetylcholine within the brain, and an abnormal metabolic diversion of adrenaline to some aberrant indole compound.

The inclusion of electrical changes of brain areas in our field of research diversifies the problem still more. At the present state of development of psychopharmacology it is difficult to apply Occam's razor, for each successful drug seems to differ from the others. Perhaps, when we know more, the attack will be simplified by a unitary hypothesis on the pharmacologic actions of these drugs. We are therefore left with a number of tempting speculations, and the judgment of the investigator will largely determine which one will be emphasized in his researches.

The fact that we have effective drugs will not stop the production of better ones. In that process, a guiding principle is concerned with a characteristic of the brain—the fact that it, more than any other organ, is sensitive to changes in the chemical structure of a drug (Abood and Romanchek, 1957; Grenell, 1957; Ayd, 1957; Fazekas, Shea, Sullivan, and Alman, 1957; Gallagher, Berry, Durden, and Lazenby, 1957; Rudy, Himwich, and Tasher, 1956–57). Illustrations may be drawn from the phenothiazine derivatives. Profound differences in the intensity of the therapeutic effects and the distribution of the side reactions (Himwich, Rinaldi, and Willis, 1956) may be produced either by the replacement of the chlorine atom of the nucleus with another atom or radical or by an alteration in the number of carbon atoms between the two nitrogen atoms of the side chain. Similarly, the substitution of the two methyl groups in the terminal nitrogen of the phenothiazine side ring with a piperazine ring, as seen in the first part of Fig. 10, produces greater specificity of therapeutic action, with lower dosage (Himwich, 1959). We are looking forward to the dis-

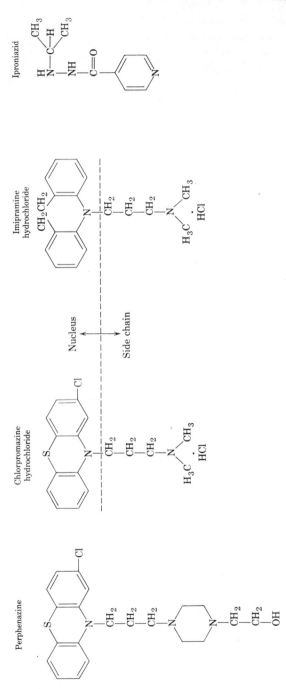

Figure 10. Structural formulas of examples of piperazine and dimethyl phenothiazine compounds and two antidepressants. Starting on the left, we see first perphenazine, offered as an example of a phenothiazine derivative with a piperazine ring in the position of the trivalent nitrogen usually terminating the side chain. In comparison, chlorpromazine with two methyl groups attached to the nitrogen is an example of a dimethyl phenothiazine. Imipramine hydrochloride differs chiefly from phenothiazines by the substitution of an ethyl linkage ($CH_2—CH_2$) in place of the sulfur in the phenothiazine nucleus. Finally, the formula of iproniazid, another antidepressant drug, is presented. (Himwich, 1959.)

covery of compounds of new chemical structures, to be used for types of patients who require not tranquilization but other kinds of therapeutic aid, for example, for the blocked and retarded individual who must be stimulated without an increase of hostility or an activation of hallucinations and delusions.

We have seen, however, that thus far in the field of psychopharmacology practice has outstripped theory. Though we recognize that tranquilizers correct certain schizophrenic symptoms, there is little agreement on the mechanism by which the improvements are achieved. Whether or not drugs effect cures is a problem for the future. But the practical value of the advance should not be underestimated. It may be compared with the advent of insulin, which counteracts symptoms of diabetes without removing their cause.

R E F E R E N C E S

Abood, L. G., and Romanchek, L. The chemical constitution and biochemical effects of psychotherapeutic and structurally related agents. *Ann. N. Y. Acad. Sci.*, 1957, 66, 812–825.

Akerfeldt, S. Oxidation of N,N-Dimethyl-*p*-phenylenediamine by serum from patients with mental disease. *Science*, 1957, 125, 117–119.

Alvarez, W. C. Intestinal autointoxication. *Physiol. Rev.*, 1924, 4, 352–393.

Andy, O. J., and Akert, K. Seizure patterns induced by electrical stimulation of hippocampal formation in the cat. *J. Neuropathol. exp. Neurol.*, 1955, 14, 198–213.

Ayd, F. J., Jr. The treatment of anxiety, agitation and excitement in the aged. *J. Amer. Geriat. Soc.*, 1957, 5, 1–4.

Bailey, P. Neurosurgical data on states of consciousness. *Congr. neurol. Sci.*, Brussels, Belgium, 1957.

Bard, P., and Mountcastle, V. B. Some forebrain mechanisms involved in expression of rage with special reference to suppression of angry behavior. *Res. Publ. Ass. nerv. ment. Dis.*, 1948, 27, 362, 404.

Barsa, J. A. The dual action of the tranquilizers. *Am. J. Psychiat.*, 1957, 114, 74–75.

Begany, A. J., Seifter, J., Pless, H. H., Huber, R. DeV., and Bruce, W. F. Tranquilizing effect of phenothiazines in cats and rabbits. *Fed. Proc.*, 1956, 15, 399–400.

Bein, H. J., Gross, F., Tripod, J., and Meier, R. Experimentelle Untersuchungen über die Kreislaufwirkung der blutdrucksenkenden Hydrazinophthalazinderivate Apresolin und Nepresol. *Schweiz. med. Wochschr.*, 1953, 83, 1007–1022.

Benditt, E. P., and Rowley, D. A. Antagonism of 5-hydroxytryptamine by chlorpromazine. *Science*, 1956, 123, 24.

Bradley, P. B. The central action of certain drugs in relation to the reticular formation of the brain. In H. H. Jasper, L. D. Proctor, R. S. Knighton, W. C.

Noshay, and R. T. Costello (Eds.), *Reticular formation of the brain.* Boston: Little, Brown, 1958, 123–149.

Brady, J. V. The paleocortex and behavioral motivation. Res. Rept. No. WRAIR-30-56. Washington, D.C.: Walter Reed Army Medical Center, 1956.

Brodie, B. B. Interaction of psychotropic drugs with physiologic and biochemical mechanisms in brain. *Modern Med.,* 1958, 68–80.

Brodie, B. B., Olin, Jacqueline S., Kuntzman, R. G., and Shore, P. A. Possible interrelationship between release of brain norepinephrine and serotonin by reserpine. *Science,* 1957, 125, 1293–1294.

Browne, N. L. M. Selection of patients for treatment with alpha-4-piperidyl benzhydrol hydrochloride. *J. nerv. ment. Dis.,* 1956, 123, 130–140.

Buscaino, V. M. Extraneural pathology of schizophrenia (liver digestive tract, reticulo-endothelial system). *Proc. first int. Congr. Neuropathol.,* Rome, 1952.

Buscaino, V. M. Épilepsie et épilepsies: 1956. *Sci. Med. ital.,* 1956, 5, 1–18.

Cannon, W. B. *The wisdom of the body.* New York: Norton, 1932.

Carlsson, A., Lindqvist, Margit, and Magnusson, T. 3,4-Dihydroxyphenylalanine and 5-hydroxytryptophan as reserpine antagonists. *Nature,* 1957, 180, 1200.

Carlsson, A., Rosengren, E., Bertler, A., and Nilsson, J. Effect of reserpine on the metabolism of catechol amines. In S. Garattini and V. Ghetti (Eds.), *Psychotropic drugs.* New York: Elsevier, 1957, 363–372.

Correale, P. The occurrence and distribution of 5-hydroxytryptamine (enteramine) in the central nervous system of vertebrates. *J. Neurochem.,* 1956, 1, 22–31.

Costa, E. Personal communication.

Costa, E. The effects of hallucinogenic and tranquilizing drugs on the serotonin evoked uterine contractions. *Psychiatric Res. Rept.,* 1956, No. 4, 11–23.

Costa, E., and Aprison, M. H. Fate of serotonin perfused through an isolated brain with intact nervous connections. *Fed. Proc.,* 1957, 16, 25.

Costa, E., and Aprison, M. H. Studies on the 5-hydroxytryptamine (serotonin) content in human brain. *J. nerv. ment. Dis.,* 1958, 126, 289–293.

Costa, E., and Rinaldi, F. Biochemical and electroencephalographic changes in the brain of rabbits injected with 5-hydroxytryptophan (influence of chlorpromazine premedication). *Amer. J. Physiol.,* 1958, 194, 214–220.

Costa, E., Rinaldi, F., and Himwich, H. E. Some relationships between tranquilization, indolalkylamines and brain structure. In S. Garattini and V. Ghetti (Eds.), *Psychotropic drugs.* New York: Elsevier, 1957, 21–25.

Erspamer, V. Pharmacology of indolealkylamines. *Pharmacol. Rev.,* 1954, 6, 425–487.

Everett, G. M., and Toman, J. E. P. Mode of action of rauwolfia alkaloids and motor activity. *Biol. Psychiat.,* 1959, 75–81.

Everett, G. M., Toman, J. E. P., and Smith, A. H., Jr. Central and peripheral effects of reserpine and 11-desmethoxyreserpine (harmonyl) on the nervous system. *Fed. Proc.,* 1957, 16, 295.

Fabing, H. D. The dimensions of neurology. *Neurol.,* 1955, 5, 603–611.

Fazekas, J. F., Shea, J. G., Sullivan, P. D., and Alman, R. W. Selective symptomatic effects of pharmacological agents in alcohol withdrawal syndromes. In H. E. Himwich (Ed.), *Alcoholism.* Washington, D.C.: Am. Ass. Adv. Sci., 1957, 125–132.

Ferguson, J. T. Improved behavior patterns in the hospitalized mentally ill with reserpine and methylphenidylacetate. *Psychiatric Res. Rept.*, 1956, No. 4, 35–43.

Ferguson, J. T., Linn, F. V. Z., Sheets, J. A., Jr., and Nickels, M. M. Methylphenidate (Ritalin) hydrochloride parenteral solution. *J. Amer. med. Ass.*, 1956, 162, 1303–1304.

Fuller, J. L., Rosvold, H., and Pribram, K. H. The effect on affective and cognitive behavior in the dog of lesions of the pyriform-amygdala-hippocampal complex. *J. comp. physiol. Psychol.*, 1957, 50, 89–96.

Gaddum, J. H. Drugs antagonistic to 5-hydroxytryptamine. In G. E. W. Wolstenholme and M. P. Cameron (Eds.), *Ciba symposia: Humoral and neurogenic factors*. Boston: Little, Brown, 1954, 75–85.

Gaddum, J. H., and Hameed, K. A. Drugs which antagonize 5-hydroxytryptamine. *Brit. J. Pharmacol. Chemotherap.*, 1954, 9, 240–248.

Gallagher, W. J., Berry, J. M., Durden, W. D., and Lazenby, W. D. Comparative study of reserpine, 11-desmethoxyreserpine, and rauwolfia alkaloids in treatment of schizophrenia. In H. E. Himwich (Ed.), *Tranquilizing drugs*. Washington, D. C.: Amer. Ass. Adv. Sci., 1957, 133–147.

Gerard, R. W. Drugs for the soul; the rise of psychopharmacology. *Science*, 1957, 125, 201–203.

Gloor, P. The pattern of conduction of amygdaloid seizure discharge. *Arch. Neurol. Psychiat.*, 1957, 77, 247–258.

Goldman, D. Treatment of psychotic states with chlorpromazine. *J. Amer. med. Ass.*, 1955, 157, 1274–1278.

Gorman, M. *Every other bed*. New York: World, 1956.

Green, J. D., and Shimamoto, T. Hippocampal seizures and their propagation. *Arch. Neurol. Psychiat.*, 1953, 70, 687–702.

Grenell, R. G. Mechanisms of action of psychotherapeutic and related drugs. *Ann. N. Y. Acad. Sci.*, 1957, 66, 826–835.

Gyermek, L. Chlorpromazine: a serotonin antagonist? *Lancet*, 1955, 269, 724.

Heath, R. G., Leach, B. E., Byers, L. W., Martens, S., and Feigley, C. A. Pharmacological and biological psychotherapy. *Amer. J. Psychiat.*, 1958, 114, 683–689.

Hendley, C. D., Lynes, T. E., and Berger, F. M. Effect of meprobamate on electrical activity of thalamus and other subcortical areas. In H. E. Himwich (Ed.), *Tranquilizing drugs*. Washington, D. C.: Amer. Ass. Adv. Sci., 1957, 35–46.

Herrick, C. J. *The brain of the tiger salamander*. Chicago, Ill.: Univer. of Chicago Press, 1948.

Hess, S. M., Shore, P. A., and Brodie, B. B. Persistence of reserpine action after the disappearance of drug from brain: effect on serotonin. *J. Pharmacol. exp. Therap.*, 1956, 118, 84–89.

Hiebel, G., Bonvallet, M., and Dell, P. Analyse neurophysiologique de l'action centrale de la *d*-amphetamine (maxiton). *Semaine hôp. Paris*, 1954, 30, 2346.

Himwich, H. E. Prospects in psychopharmacology. *J. nerv. ment. Dis.*, 1955, 122, 413–423.

Himwich, H. E. Discussion of papers on basic observations of new psychopharmacological agents. *Psychiat. Res. Rept.*, 1956, No. 4, 24–31. (a)

Himwich, H. E.   The effect of Frenquel on EEG changes produced by LSD-25 and mescaline.   In Louis Cholden (Ed.), *Lysergic acid diethylamide and mescaline in experimental psychiatry.*   New York: Grune & Stratton, 1956, 19–26.   (b)

Himwich, H. E.   Some drugs used in the treatment of mental disorders.   *Amer. J. Psychiat.,* 1959, 115, 756–759.

Himwich, H. E.   Stimulants.   *Ass. Res. nerv. ment. Dis.,* 1959, 37, 356–383.

Himwich, H. E., Costa, E., Pscheidt, G. R., and Van Meter, W. G.   Correlations between effects of iproniazid on brain activating system with brain neurohormones.   *Ann. N. Y. Acad. Sci.,* 1960, 80, 614–616.

Himwich, H. E., and Rinaldi, F.   An analysis of the activating system including its use for screening antiparkinson drugs.   *Yale J. Biol. Med.,* 1955–56, 28, 308–319.

Himwich, H. E., Rinaldi, F., and Willis, Dorothy.   An examination of phenothiazine derivatives with comparisons of their effects on the alerting reaction, chemical structure and therapeutic efficacy.   *J. nerv. ment. Dis.,* 1956, 124, 53–57.

Hoffer, A.   Epinephrine derivatives as potential schizophrenic factors.   *J. clin. exp. Psychopathol.,* 1957, 18, 27–60.

Hoffer, A., and Kenyon, M.   Conversion of adrenaline to adrenolutin in human blood serum.   *Arch. Neurol. Psychiat.,* 1957, 77, 437–438.

Hoffer, A., Osmond, H., and Smythies, J.   Schizophrenia: a new approach.   II. Result of a year's research.   *J. ment. Sci.,* 1954, 100, 29–45.

Hunt, H. F.   Some effects of meprobamate on conditioned fear and emotional behavior.   *Ann. N. Y. Acad. Sci.* 1957, 67, 712–723.

Jacobsen, E.   A new drug effective on the central nervous system.   *Danish med. Bull.,* 1955, 2, 159–160.

Jasper, H.   Diffuse projection systems: the integrative action of the thalamic reticular system.   *Electroencephalog. clin. Neurophysiol.,* 1949, 1, 405–420.

Killam, E. K., and Killam, K. F.   The influence of drugs on central afferent pathways.   In W. S. Fields (Ed.), *Brain mechanisms and drug action.* Springfield, Ill.: Charles C Thomas, 1957, 71–98.

Killam, K. F., and Killam, E. K.   Drug action on pathways involving the reticular formation.   In H. H. Jasper, L. D. Proctor, R. S. Knighton, W. C. Noshay, and R. T. Costello (Eds.), *Reticular formation of the brain.*   Boston: Little, Brown, 1958, 111–122.

Kinross-Wright, V.   Chlorpromazine treatment of mental disorders.   *Amer. J. Psychiat.,* 1955, 111, 907–912.   (a)

Kinross-Wright, V.   Formal discussion of chlorpromazine and mental health.   In *Chlorpromazine and mental health.*   Philadelphia: Lea & Febiger, 1955, 154–157.   (b)

Kline, N. S., Barsa, J., and Gosline, E.   Management of the side effects of reserpine and combined reserpine-chlorpromazine treatment.   *Dis. nerv. Sys.,* 1956, 17, 352–358.

Kline, N. S., Barsa, J., and Gosline, E.   Management of side effects of reserpine and combined reserpine-chlorpromazine treatment.   In H. E. Himwich (Ed.), *Tranquilizing drugs.*   Washington, D. C.: Amer. Ass. Adv. Sci., 1957, 149–161.

Koella, W. P., Smythies, J. K., and Bull, D. M. Factors involved in the effect of serotonin on evoked electrocortical potentials. *Science*, 1959, 129, 1231.

Klüver, H., and Bucy, P. C. Preliminary analysis of functions of the temporal lobes in monkeys. *Arch. Neurol. Psychiat.*, 1939, 42, 979–1000.

Kuhn, R. Personal communication.

Kuhn, R. The treatment of depressive states with G 22355 (imipramine hydrochloride). *Amer. J. Psychiat.*, 1958, 115, 459–464.

Leach, B. E., Cohen, M., Heath, R. G., and Martens, S. Studies of the role of ceruloplasmin and albumin in adrenaline metabolism. *Arch. Neurol. Psychiat.*, 1956, 76, 635–642.

Lehmann, H. E., and Hanrahan, G. E. Chlorpromazine. New inhibiting agent for psychomotor excitement and manic states. *Arch. Neurol. Psychiat.*, 1954, 71, 227–237.

Liberson, W. T., and Akert, K. Hippocampal seizure states in guinea pig. *Electroencephalog. clin. Neurophysiol.*, 1955, 7, 211–222.

Liberson, W. T., and Cadilhac, J. G. Electroshock and rhinencephalic seizure states. *Confin. Neurol.*, 1953, 13, 278–286.

MacLean, P. D. Some psychiatric implications of physiological studies on prontotemporal portion of limbic system (visceral brain). *Electroencephalog. clin. Neurophysiol.*, 1952, 407–418.

Marrazzi, A. S., and Hart, E. R. An electrophysiological analysis of drugs useful in psychotic states. In H. E. Himwich (Ed.), *Tranquilizing drugs.* Washington, D. C.: Amer. Ass. Adv. Sci., 1957, 9–21.

Moruzzi, G., and Magoun, H. W. Communications. Brain stem reticular formation and activation of the EEG. *Electroencephalog. clin. Neurophysiol.*, 1949, 1, 455–473.

Paasonen, M. K., and Vogt, Marthe. The effect of drugs on the amounts of substance P and 5-hydroxytryptamine in mammalian brain. *J. Physiol.*, 1956, 131, 617–626.

Papez, J. A proposed mechanism of emotion. *Arch. Neurol. Psychiat.*, 1937, 38, 725–743.

Penfield, W. Epileptic automatism and the centrencephalic integrating system. *A. Res. nerv. ment. Dis., Proc.*, 1950, 30, 513–528.

Pennington, Veronica M. Meprobamate, a tranquilizing drug with muscle relaxant properties in psychotic cases. In H. E. Himwich (Ed.), *Tranquilizing drugs.* Washington, D. C.: Amer. Ass. Adv. Sci., 1957, 125–131.

Pfeiffer, C. C., and Jenney, Elizabeth H. The inhibition of the conditioned response and the counteraction of schizophrenia by muscarinic stimulation of the brain. *Ann. N. Y. Acad. Sci.*, 1957, 66, 753–764.

Pletscher, A. Alteration of some biochemical and pharmacological effects of reserpine by iproniazid. In S. Garattini and V. Ghetti (Eds.), *Psychotropic drugs.* New York: Elsevier, 1957, 468–469.

Pletscher, A., Shore, P. A., and Brodie, B. B. Serotonin as a mediator of reserpine action in brain. *J. Pharmacol. exp. Therap.*, 1956, 116, 84–89.

Plummer, A. J., Sheppard, H., and Schulert, A. R. The metabolism of reserpine. In S. Garattini and V. Ghetti (Eds.), *Psychotropic drugs.* New York: Elsevier, 1957, 350–362.

Preston, J. B. Effects of chlorpromazine on the central nervous system of the cat: a possible neural basis for action. *J. Pharmacol. exp. Therap.*, 1956, 118, 100–115.

Pribram, K. H., and Kruger, L. Functions of the "olfactory brain." *Ann. N. Y. Acad. Sci.*, 1954, 58, 109–138.

Proctor, R. C. Azacyclonol: a new central nervous system blocking agent. In H. E. Himwich (Ed.), *Alcoholism.* Washington, D. C.: Amer. Ass. Adv. Sci., 1957, 133–139.

Pscheidt, G. R. Personal communication.

Rinaldi, F. The experimental electroencephalographic approach to psychopharmacology. *Psychiat. Res. Rept.*, 1956, No. 4, 1–10.

Rinaldi, F., and Himwich, H. E. Alerting responses and actions of atropine and cholinergic drugs. *Arch. Neurol. Psychiat.*, 1955, 73, 387–395. (a)

Rinaldi, F., and Himwich, H. E. Cholinergic mechanism involved in function of mesodiencephalic activating system. *Arch. Neurol. Psychiat.*, 1955, 73, 396–402. (b)

Rinaldi, F., and Himwich, H. E. A comparison of effects of reserpine and some barbiturates on the electrical activity of cortical and subcortical structures of the brain of rabbits. *Ann. N. Y. Acad. Sci.*, 1955, 61, 27–35. (c)

Rinaldi, F., and Himwich, H. E. Drugs affecting psychotic behavior and the function of the mesodiencephalic activating system. *Dis. nerv. Sys.*, 1955, 16, 133–141. (d)

Rinaldi, F., Rudy, L. H., and Himwich, H. E. The use of Frenquel in the treatment of disturbed patients with psychoses of long duration. *Amer. J. Psychiat.*, 1955, 112, 343–348.

Rinaldi, F., Rudy, L. H., and Himwich, H. E. Clinical evaluation of azacyclonol, chlorpromazine, and reserpine on a group of chronic psychotic patients. *Amer. J. Psychiat.*, 1956, 112, 678–683.

Rinkel, M., Hyde, R. W., and Solomon, H. C. Experimental psychiatry. III. A chemical concept of psychosis. *Dis. nerv. Sys.*, 1954, 15, 259–264.

Rothfield, L., and Harman, P. On the relation of the hippocampal-fornix system to the control of rage responses in cats. *J. comp. Neurol.*, 1954, 101, 265–282.

Rudy, L. H., Costa, E., Rinaldi, F., and Himwich, H. E. Clinical evaluation of BAS (benzyl analog of serotonin): a tranquilizing drug. *J. nerv. ment. Dis.*, 1958, 126, 284–288.

Rudy, L. H., Himwich, H. E., and Rinaldi, F. A clinical evaluation of psychopharmacological agents in the management of disturbed mentally defective patients. *Amer. J. ment. Def.*, 1958, 62, 855–860.

Rudy, L. H., Himwich, H. E., and Tasher, D. C. Clinical evaluation of two phenothiazine compounds promazine and mepazine. *Amer. J. Psychiat.*, 1956–57, 113, 979–983.

Saunders, J. C., Radinger, N., and Kline, N. S. A theoretical and clinical approach to treating depressed and regressed patients with iproniazid. Paper read at 12th annual meeting, Soc. of biol. Psychiat., 1957.

Schreiner, L., and Kling, A. Behavioral changes following rhinencephalic injury in cat. *J. Neurophysiol.*, 1953, 16, 643–659.

Shaw, E. N., and Woolley, D. W. Methylserotonins as potent antimetabolites of serotonin active both *in vitro* and *in vivo*. *J. Pharmacol. exp. Therap.*, 1956, 116, 164–176. (a)

Shaw, E., and Woolley, D. W.   Some serotonin-like activities of lysergic acid diethylamide.   *Science,* 1956, 124, 121–122.   (b)

Shore, P. A., and Brodie, B. B.   LSD-like effects elicited by reserpine in rabbits pretreated with iproniazid.   *Proc. Soc. exp. Biol. Med.,* 1957, 94, 433–435.

Shore, P. A., Carlsson, A., and Brodie, B. B.   Mechanism of serotonin-release by reserpine.   *Fed. Proc.,* 1956, 15, 483.

Sigg, E. B., and Schneider, J. A.   Mechanisms involved in the interaction of various central stimulants and reserpine.   *Electroencephalog. clin. Neurophysiol.,* 1957, 9, 419–426.

Sjoerdsma, A., Weissbach, H. S., and Udenfriend, S.   A clinical, physiologic, and biochemical study of patients with malignant carcinoid (Argentaffinoma).   *Amer. J. Med.,* 1956, 20, 520–532.

Smith, W. K.   Non-olfactory functions of the pyriform-amygdaloid-hippocampal complex.   *Fed. Proc.,* 1950, 9, 118.

Spiegel, E. A., Miller, H. R., and Oppenheimer, M. J.   Forebrain and rage reactions.   *J. Neurophysiol.,* 1940, 3, 538–548.

Taylor, R. D., Page, I. H., and Corcoran, A. C.   A hormonal neurogenic vasopressor mechanism.   *Arch. intern. Med.,* 1951, 88, 1–8.

Thomson, A. F., and Walker, A. E.   Behavioral alterations following lesions of the medial surface of the temporal lobe.   *Arch. Neurol. Psychiat.,* 1951, 65, 251–252.

Tripod, J., Bein, H. J., and Meier, R.   Characterization of central effects of serpasil (reserpin, a new alkaloid of rauwolfia serpentina B.) and of their antagonistic reactions.   *Arch. intern. pharmacodynamie,* 1954, 92, 406–425.

Tuteur, W., and Lepson, D.   Combined reserpine-chlorpromazine therapy in highly disturbed psychotics.   In H. E. Himwich (Ed.), *Tranquilizing drugs.* Washington, D. C.: Amer. Ass. Adv. Sci., 1957, 163–172.

Udenfriend, S., Weissbach, H., and Bogdanski, D. F.   Increase in tissue serotonin following administration of its precursor 5-hydroxytryptophan.   *J. biol. Chem.,* 1957, 224, 803–810.

Valcourt, A. J.   A study of the excretion of 5-hydroxyindoleacetic acid in mental patients.   *Arch. Neurol. Psychiat.,* 1959, 81, 292–298.

Van Meter, W. G., Owens, Helen, and Himwich, H. E.   The effects of Tofranil, an antidepressant drug, on electrical potentials of rabbit brain.   *Canad. Psychiat. Assoc. J.,* 1959, 4, 5113–5119.

Vogt, Marthe.   The concentration of sympathin in different parts of the central nervous system under normal conditions and after the administration of drugs.   *J. Physiol.,* 1954, 123, 451–481.

Weiskrantz, L.   Reserpine and behavioral non-reactivity.   In S. Garattini and V. Ghetti (Eds.), *Psychotropic drugs.*   New York: Elsevier, 1957, 67–72.

Welsh, J. H.   Hydroxytryptamine: a neurohormone in the invertebrates.   *Fed. Proc.,* 1954, 13, 162–163.

Woolley, D. W., and Shaw, E.   A biochemical and pharmacological suggestion about certain mental disorders.   *Proc. nat. Acad. Sci.,* 1954, 40, 228–231.

Classification of psychoactive drugs according to their chemical structures and sites of action

Tranquilizers

To define and divide one need not know the whole of existence. (Aristotle, *Analytica posteriora,* Book II, 13)

Tranquilizers are usually described as substances that reduce excitement and agitation without clouding consciousness. This definition is unsuitable for at least two reasons. It is often possible to counteract agitation without affecting consciousness with drugs not usually considered tranquilizers (such as scopolamine), drugs that had been in use long before the advent of tranquilizers. Secondly, tranquilizers at times do much more than eliminate agitation; they may facilitate social adjustment, eliminate delusions and hallucinations, or make mute patients communicative. An important characteristic of tranquilizers which is often overlooked is their ability to affect patients suffering from mental disturbances. Tranquilizers, as a rule, do not bring "peace of mind" to normal persons; they may not affect them at all or may make them feel worse. Morphine and digitalis, on the other hand, are not usually considered tranquilizers although they may bring "peace of mind" to a patient suffering from painful conditions or heart failure.

REVIEW OF PREVIOUS CLASSIFICATIONS. Numerous attempts to classify tranquilizers have been made. These have been based on the chemical structure, the pharmacological effects, the mode of action, the clinical application of these drugs, or a combination of these factors.

Berger (1957) classified the tranquilizers according to their chemical structure into four groups: the phenothiazines, the derivatives of *Rauwolfia*, the diphenylmethanes, and the substituted propanediols. According to their pharmacological properties he divided them into two distinct classes, the autonomic suppressants, and the central relaxants. The former antagonize the autonomic hormones such as epinephrine, acetylcholine, and histamine, depress conditioned reflexes, and decrease convulsive threshold. The phenothiazines, the *Rauwolfia* derivatives, and the diphenylmethanes belong to this group. The central depressants, of which meprobamate is the most important representative, affect neither the autonomic nervous system nor conditioning, but increase convulsive threshold and depress the excitability of the central nervous system.

Tripod, Studer, and Meier (1957) attempted to differentiate between tranquilizers and central nervous system depressants by the use of several pharmacological tests such as: the antagonism of these drugs to the stimulant effects of phenidylate (Ritalin) and mescaline; their effect on audiogenic seizures or metrazol convulsions; the elimination of a startle response to sound; and their effect on the ability of mice to hold on to a rotating rod. The authors concluded that it was not possible to use any of these tests as a criterion of tranquilizing properties. The drugs gave different patterns of responses and different ranking when evaluated by these methods.

Thuillier and Nakajima (1957) classified tranquilizers according to their effects on mice in which hyperkinesia and circling movements were produced by imino-α,α'-dipropionitrile. According to the responses they classified psychotropic drugs into "neuroleptics," "sedative-tranquilizers," "hypnotics," and "stimulants." Reserpine, phenothiazine, and hydroxyzine belonged to the "neuroleptics" which abolished agitation and circular movements without producing ataxia. The "sedative-tranquilizers" (benactyzine, mephenesin, meprobamate, methylpentynol carbamate) diminished agitation and circling but produced ataxia. The "hypnotics" (glutethimide, phenobarbital, and amobarbital) behaved like the preceding group and in addition showed no response to nociceptive stimuli. The "stimulants" (lysergic acid diethylamide, methamphetamine, arecoline) produced discontinuance of circling and tremors.

Hazard, Boissier, and Dumont (1958) classified the tranquilizers according to their chemical structure and discussed in a stimulating manner the difficulties involved in attempting pharmacological classifications of these agents.

Jacobsen (1958) attempted to subdivide tranquilizers according to their pharmacological properties and collected drugs with similar profiles of action into five groups which he called the "major tranquilizers" (reserpine, chlorpromazine), the "minor tranquilizers" (hydroxyzine, captodiame, promazine), the "tranquillo-sedatives" (meprobamate), "central acting anti-acetylcholines" (benactyzine), and the "transitional compounds" (azacyclonal).

Riley and Spinks (1958) reviewed the biological effects of tranquilizers according to their ability to produce sedation, affect behavior, change neurophysiological responses, antagonize psychotomimetic drugs, and affect conditioning. Their exhaustive review indicates that there is no pharmacological test unique to or distinctive of this group of agents.

The Council on Drugs of the American Medical Association (Kautz, 1958) proposed a classification of psychotherapeutic drugs according to their principal pharmacological effect. The central nervous system depressants were divided into non-selective depressants (such as analgesics, hypnotics, and sedatives) and selective depressants—subdivided into (1) anticonvulsants, (2) antihistamines, (3) antitussives, (4) non-sedative central muscle relaxants (mephenesin), (5) sedative central muscle relaxants (meprobamate, phenaglycodol), (6) central parasympathetic suppressants (benactyzine), and (7) central sympathetic suppressants (phenothiazines and rauwolfia derivatives).

Delay (1958) and Deniker (1958), utilizing both a pharmacological and a clinical approach, distinguished between neuroleptic agents and tranquilizers. According to these workers neuroleptics (so named to indicate that they are the opposite of analeptics) produce a state of psychomotor indifference, are particularly effective against excitation, and affect the autonomic and extrapyramidal systems. Chlorpromazine and reserpine are typical examples. Tranquilizers, according to Delay and Deniker, comprise a heterogenous group of agents that cannot be classified as hypnotics or neuroleptics.

Alexander (1957) from a clinical point of view distinguished between four classes: "the tranquilizers" that depress the hypothalamus and subdue excitement in psychoses (reserpine, chlorpromazine); the "relaxant drugs" (meprobamate), which do not have the inhibitory effect on drive possessed by the "tranquilizers"; the "ataractic (deconfusing) drugs" (azacyclonol), which do not depress the hypothalamus but counteract the effects of lysergic acid diethylamide and of mescaline; and the "antiphobic drugs" (benactyzine), which facilitate orienting and conditioned responses and possess a mild antidepressant action.

Vogt (1958) classified tranquilizers into two main groups according to their clinical usefulness. The first comprises drugs used mainly in psychoses (reserpine, chlorpromazine, and their congeners), and the other group consists of substances usually given to neurotics or normal people undergoing a severe emotional or physical ordeal (meprobamate, hydroxyzine, and benactyzine).

CRITERIA OF CLASSIFICATION. Tranquilization is essentially a clinical concept. Thus it is not surprising that classification of tranquilizers according to their pharmacological action has been unrewarding. Most pharmacological effects produced by these agents may be produced equally well by other drugs which are devoid of clinically useful tranquilizing properties. An example of this is the observation that various conditioned responses can be disrupted with equal facility by the tranquilizer chlorpromazine as by the analgesic morphine or the anticholinergic propantheline (Pro-Banthine). Another difficulty is the previously mentioned lack of a pharmacological test common to all tranquilizers. Classification according to the mode of action of these drugs is not practical because so little is known about this subject. Similarly, the disagreement among psychiatrists about the cause or causes of mental diseases and the difficulties with the nomenclature of mental diseases as well as the nonspecific action of tranquilizers makes their classification according to their clinical usefulness impracticable.

Before adopting a system of classification, one should give some thought to what is to be gained by constructing such a system and what is to be expected from it. The main purpose of classifying is to bring order where previously there was chaos. A desirable system of classification would divide the drugs into groups that are easily distinguished from each other and are few in number. Classification should be such that introduction of new drugs, and of new designations for old ones, would not add to the confusion in this important field. It appears that at present classification of tranquilizers according to their chemical structure is the most useful and practical method of differentiation among the drugs used in this field.

CLASSIFICATION OF TRANQUILIZERS. Classification according to chemical structure permits the inclusion, in one of five well-defined chemical classes of compounds, of all tranquilizers as well as most other drugs used in the treatment of mental disease. These are the phenothiazines, the *Rauwolfia* group, the diphenylmethanes, the propanediols, and the substituted amides.

Members within each chemical group naturally share similar pharmacological properties with other members of the group and often differ from each other only by dosage requirements. Members of any one group also tend to produce qualitatively similar psychological changes, are likely to produce their effects through similar mechanisms, and frequently affect the same structure.

Substances closely related in chemical structure are also likely to produce comparable clinical and toxic effects. For this reason classification according to chemical structure permits the prediction of the clinical usefulness and toxic properties of new compounds which may be introduced in the future.

1. THE PHENOTHIAZINE DERIVATIVES. These agents have in common the phenothiazine nucleus and differ from one another only in substituents in positions 2 and 10. Figure 1 gives the names and chemical structures of 21 compounds of this type that have been successfully used in medicine and have been commercially available. Of these 21 compounds 13 have been or are being used as tranquilizers. Phenothiazine itself, the parent compound of this whole class, has been used as a vermifuge and anthelmintic but was abandoned because of the occurrence of toxic effects such as blood dyscrasias and liver damage (Bercovitz, 1943; Hubble, 1941). The remaining compounds have been used as antihistaminics (Nos. 3, 11, and 12), antipruritics (No. 9), antispasmodics (No. 10), or in the treatment of Parkinson's disease (Nos. 2 and 4). Some of these compounds apparently possess tranquilizing action. Thus Erwin (1957) has shown that promethazine (Phenergan), which is marketed as an antihistaminic, has a tranquilizing action in psychiatric patients similar to that of chlorpromazine. In view of the close chemical similarity of these two compounds this finding is not unexpected.

Pharmacologically these compounds possess a multitude of actions. They have a blocking effect on the adrenergic nervous system, have atropine-like and antihistaminic properties, possess an antiemetic action, and produce sedation, hypnosis, and anesthesia. They also potentiate the action of analgesics, anesthetics, and other drugs. They block conditioned reflexes.

Psychologically tranquilizers of this group tend to increase introversion and decrease traits correlated with psychosis (Petrie and Le

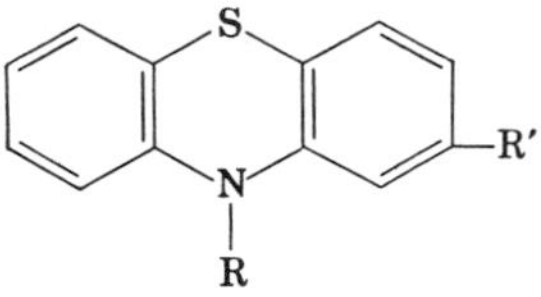

No.	R	R′	Generic Name	Trade Name
1.	H	H	Phenothiazine	
2.	$-CH_2CH_2N(C_2H_5)_2$	H	Diethazine	Diparcol
3.	$-CH_2CH(CH_3)N(CH_3)_2$	H	Promethazine	Phenergan
4.	$-CH_2CH(CH_3)N(C_2H_5)_2$	H	Ethopropazine	Parsidol
5.	$-CH_2CH_2CH_2N(CH_3)_2$	H	Promazine	Sparine
6.	$-CH_2CH_2CH_2N(CH_3)_2$	Cl	Chlorpromazine	Thorazine
7.	$-CH_2CH_2CH_2N(CH_3)_2$	$-CF_3$	Triflupromazine	Vesprin
8.	$-CH_2CH_2CH_2N(CH_3)_2$	$-\overset{O}{\overset{\|}{C}}CH_3$	Acetylpromazine	Acepromazine
9.	$-CH_2CH(CH_3)CH_2N(CH_3)_2$	H	Trimeprazine	Temaril
10.	$-CH_2CH[N(CH_3)_2]CH_2N(CH_3)_2$	H	Aminopromazine	Lispamol
11.	$-CH_2CH(CH_3)N(CH_3)_3^+CH_3SO_4^-$	H	Thiazinamium	Multergan

12. $-CH_2CH_2N$⟨ ⟩   H   Pyrathiazine   Pyrrolazote

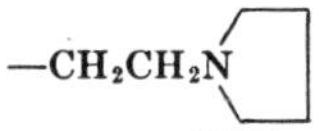

13. $-CH_2-$⟨ ⟩$-N-CH_3$ H   Mepazine   Pacatal

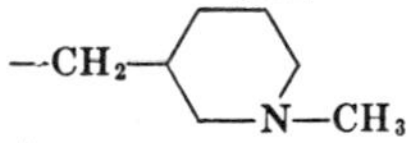

14. $-CH_2CH_2-$⟨ N-CH_3 ⟩ $-SCH_3$ Thioridazine   Mellaril

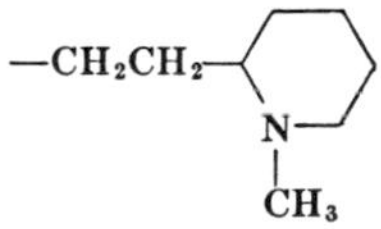

15. $-CH_2CH_2CH_2N$⟨ ⟩$N-CH_3$ Cl   Prochlorperazine   Compazine, Stemetil

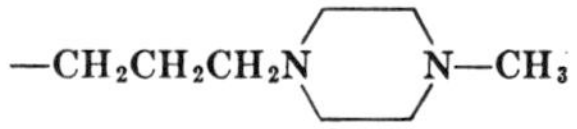

16. $-CH_2CH_2CH_2N$⟨ ⟩$N-CH_3$ $-CF_3$ Trifluoperazine   Stelazine

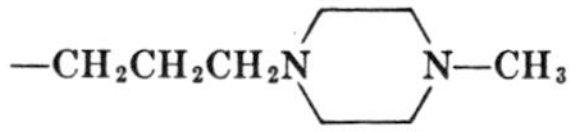

17. $-CH_2CH_2CH_2N$⟨ ⟩$N-CH_2CH_2OH$ Cl   Perphenazine   Trilafon

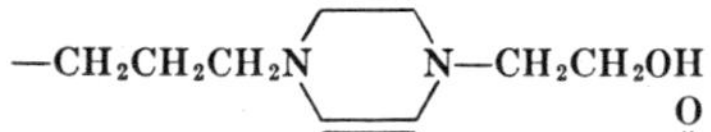

18. $-CH_2CH_2CH_2N$⟨ ⟩$N-CH_2CH_2O\overset{O}{\overset{\|}{C}}CH_3$ Cl   Thiopropazate   Dartal

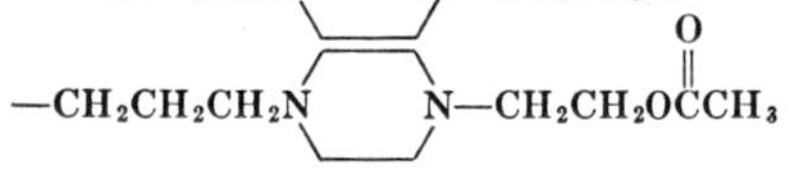

19. $-CH_2CH_2CH_2-N$⟨ ⟩$N-CH_2CH_2OH$ $-CF_3$ Fluphenazine   Permitil, Prolixin

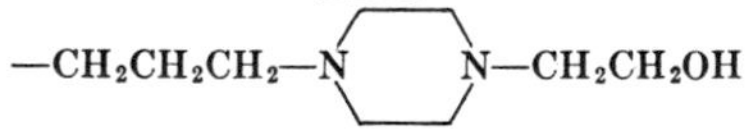

20. $-CH_2CH_2CH_2-N \overset{CH_3}{\underset{CH_3}{}}$ $-OCH_3$ Methoxypromazine   Tentone

21. $-CH_2CH_2CH_2-N$⟨ ⟩$\overset{O}{\overset{\|}{C}}-NH_2$ Cl   Pipamazine   Mornidine

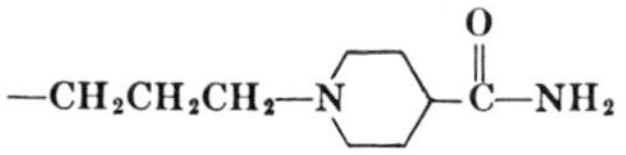

Figure 1. Chemical structure of various phenothiazines used in medicine.

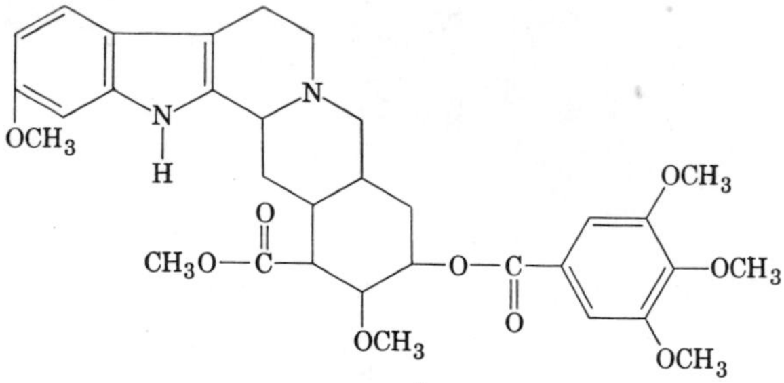

reserpine
(methylreserpate; 3,4,5–
trimethoxybenzoic acid ester)

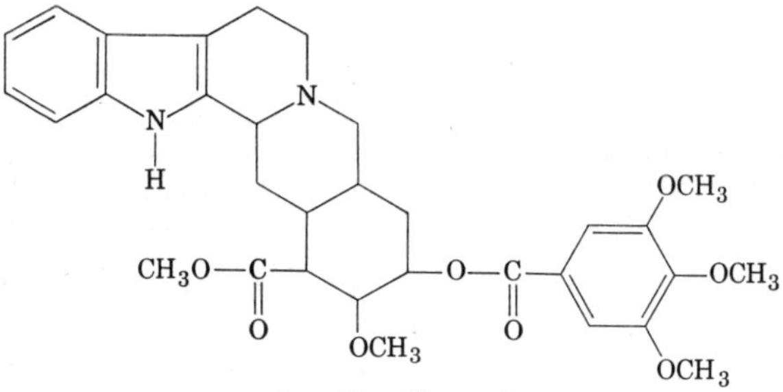

deserpidine (Harmonyl)
(11–desmethoxyreserpine)

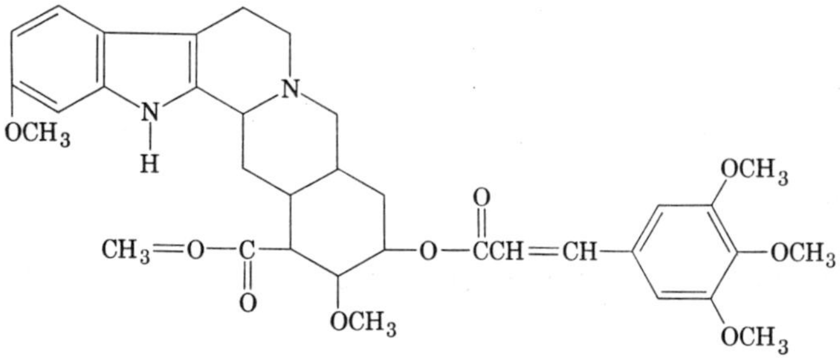

rescinnamine (Moderil)
(methylreserpate; 3,4,5–
trimethoxycinnamic acid ester)

Figure 2.   Chemical structure of the *Rauwolfia* alkaloids.

Beau, 1956). They also decrease drive and increase suggestibility (Alexander, 1957). (See Chapters 18, 29, 44, and 51.)

2. THE RAUWOLFIA ALKALOIDS. These compounds are derived from the *Rauwolfia* root which has been used medicinally for centuries in India. The following alkaloids have been isolated in the pure state and found effective as tranquilizers: reserpine (Serpasil), deserpidine (Harmonyl), and rescinnamine (Moderil). A synthetic analog of reserpine, syrosingopine (Singoserp), is recommended for the treatment of hypertension, for which the other alkaloids and the whole root also can be used. Chemically all these compounds have in common the yohimbine nucleus.

Pharmacologically these agents produce symptoms of sympathetic suppression and parasympathetic predominance (miosis, bradycardia, increased secretory and motor activity of the gastrointestinal canal, ptosis, and hypotension) by an inhibiting action on the sympathetic centers in the hypothalamus. These drugs also produce sedation but do not cause anesthesia even with an increased dosage. Reserpine and the other alkaloids that have tranquilizing properties liberate serotonin (5-hydroxytryptamine) from the intestine, blood platelets, and brain (Brodie, Pletscher, and Shore, 1955), and increase the concentration of hydroxyindoleacetic acid, the chief breakdown product of serotonin, in the urine (Berger, Campbell, Hendley, Ludwig, and Lynes, 1957).

It is not certain whether the effectiveness of *Rauwolfia* alkaloids in the treatment of mental diseases is related to release of serotonin. Certain synthetic compounds (derivatives of 1,2,3,4,6,7-hexahydro-benzo-α-quinolizines) similarly release serotonin from the brain and other body depots (Pletscher, 1957). It will be of interest to learn whether these compounds have a tranquilizing action. The *Rauwolfia* alkaloids effectively block conditioned reflexes. Psychological effects produced by them resemble those brought about by the phenothiazines.

3. THE DIPHENYLMETHANES. Compounds in this class have in common the diphenylmethane structure. It comprises many medicinals chemically close to tranquilizers that have enjoyed wide use for other purposes for many years, such as the spasmolytic adiphenine (Trasentine). The tranquilizer benactyzine (Suavitil) differs from adiphenine in possessing a hydroxyl group in place of a hydrogen. The tranquilizer hydroxyzine bears close structural resemblance to the antihistaminic chlorcyclizine (Di-Paralene) and to the motion sickness remedy, meclizine (Bonine). Other representatives of

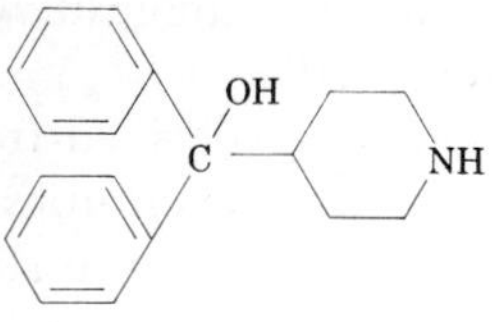

azacyclonol (Frenquel)

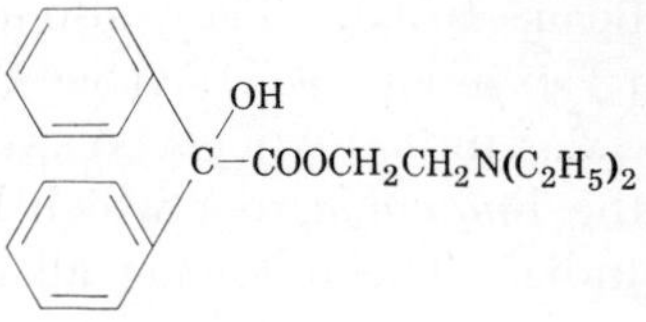

benactyzine (Suavitil)

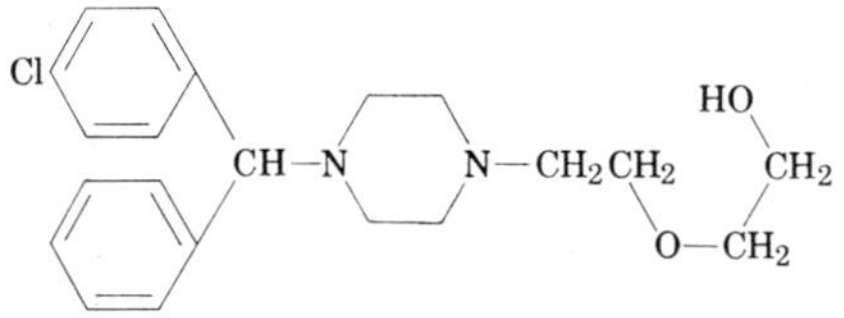

hydroxyzine (Atarax, Vistaril)

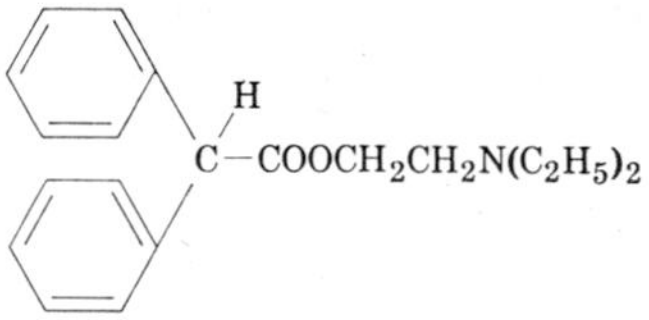

adiphenine (Trasentine)

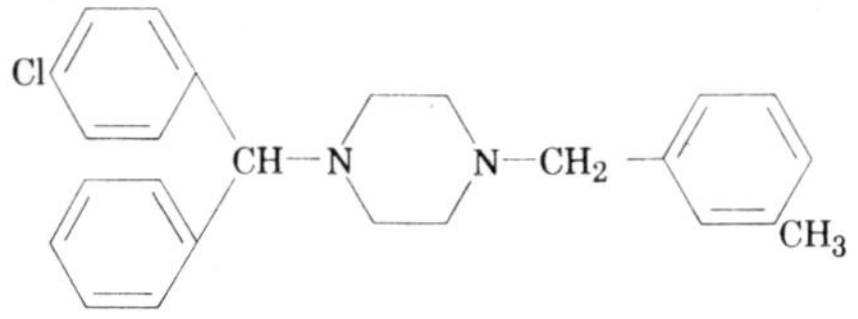

meclizine (Bonine)

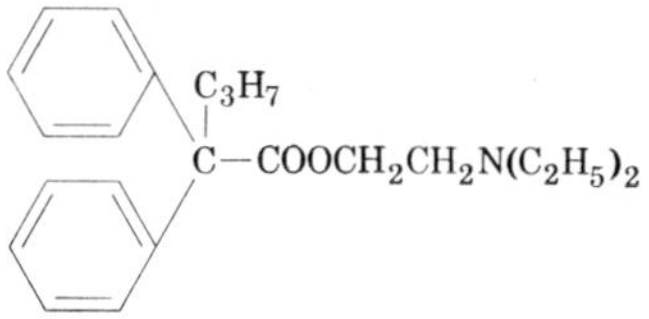

SKF No. 525-A

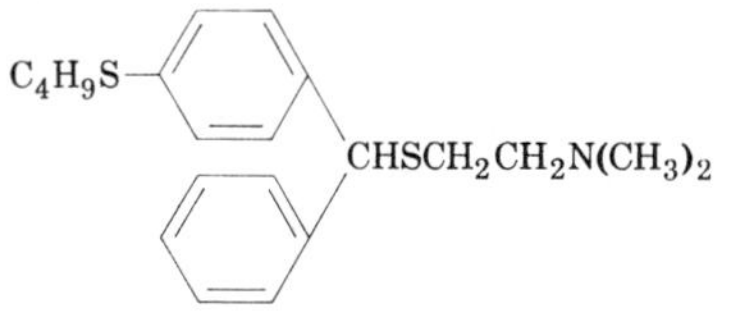

captodiame (Suvren, Covatin)

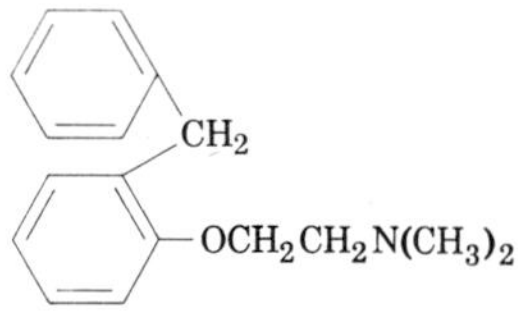

phenyltoloxamine (Phenoxadrine)

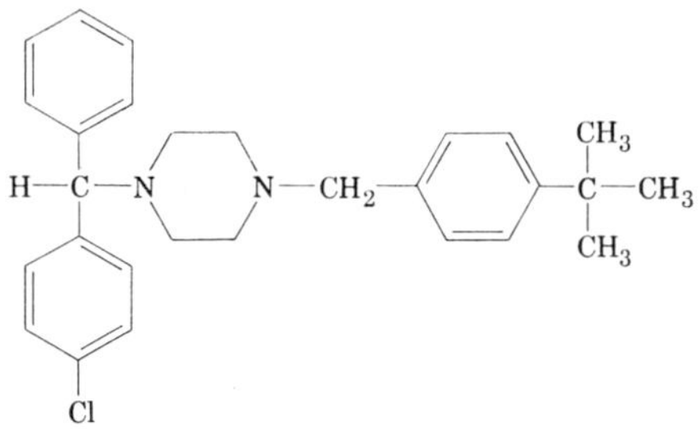

buclizine (Softran, Vibazine)
[1-(*p*-chlorobenzhydryl)-4-(*p*-*t*-butylbenzyl) piperazine]

Figure 3.   Chemical structure of tranquilizers and other chemicals derived from diphenylmethane.

this group such as captodiame bear striking structural resemblance to some of the older antihistaminics such as diphenhydramine (Benadryl). All compounds of this group are chemically related to β-diethylaminoethyl diphenylpropylacetate (SKF 525-A), which exerts a potentiating effect on many drugs by inhibiting their enzymic breakdown (Axelrod, 1954).

Pharmacologically most of these compounds have marked anti-histaminic properties. They also possess some atropine-like action and antagonize some of the effects of serotonin. They prolong the action of barbiturates and other hypnotics. In animals they do not produce sedation or hypnosis but can produce convulsions when given in sufficiently large doses. They do not block conditioning and may even facilitate it. Little is known about the psychological effects of this group of compounds. (See Chapter 51 for citations of several studies.)

4. SUBSTITUTED PROPANEDIOLS. From a strictly chemical point of view these compounds are really modified glycols, as they possess two hydroxyl groups attached to different carbon atoms. All members of this group have been evolved from the muscle relaxant, mephenesin (Berger and Bradley, 1946). It was noted that mephenesin, in addition to its relaxing properties, relieved anxiety and nervousness, and

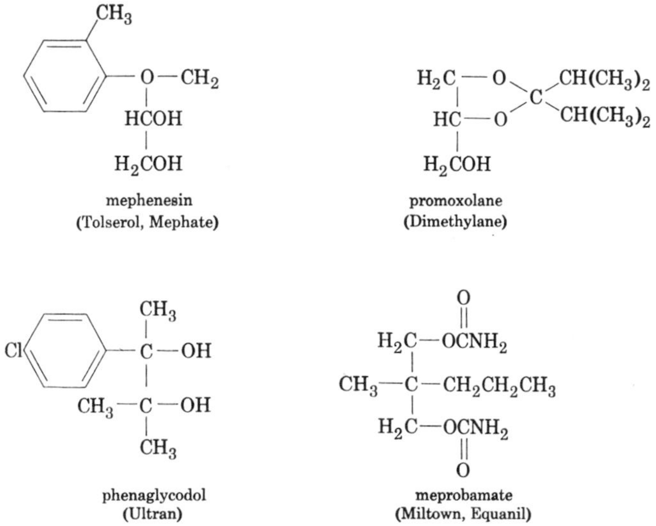

Figure 4.   The chemical structure of the substituted propanediol derivatives.

chemical modifications of the molecule were carried out to produce compounds that would be better tolerated and would have a more intense and longer duration of action (Berger, 1949, 1954).

These compounds differ pharmacologically from the phenothiazines, *Rauwolfia* alkaloids, and dephenylmethanes in not affecting the functioning of the autonomic nervous system. The propanediols relieve muscle spasm by decreasing conductivity along long interneuronal pathways. In large doses they produce reversible paralysis of voluntary muscles without disturbing vital functions such as circulation and respiration. They raise the convulsive threshold to electrical and chemical stimulation and do not affect conditioned reflexes.

Psychologically meprobamate raises the frustration threshold and permits performance of behavioral tasks under stress conditions (Holliday, Duffy, and Dille, 1958). (See Chapter 37). Compounds of this group in usual doses appear not to affect motor performance, reaction time, and other tests requiring judgment and skill. (See especially Chapters 20, 22, 26, and 51.)

5. SUBSTITUTED AMIDES. Compounds of this group have in common the structure $R—CO—NR_1—R_2$. In some cases the nature of the R, R_1, and R_2 groups is such that they form a amidic or imidic cyclic structure. Belonging to this group are many of the widely used sedatives and hypnotics such as the barbiturates and the non-barbiturate hypnotics (glutethimide, methyprylon, ectylurea, and oxanamide).

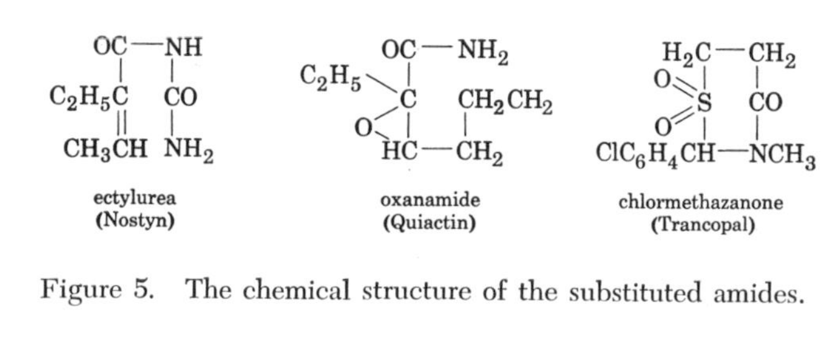

Figure 5.   The chemical structure of the substituted amides.

Pharmacologically these compounds produce sleep and, in larger doses, anesthesia. They differ from the propanediols in abolishing consciousness in doses which produce paralysis of skeletal muscles. They also possess anticonvulsant action and probably act by increasing the threshold of stimulation required for activation of neurons.

On a psychological level these compounds may increase extraversion, particularly in hyperexcitable neurotic patients, and in this manner improve their adjustment to the environment (Laverty and Franks, 1956). They impair performance in a variety of tests (Kornetsky, Humphries, and Evarts, 1957). (See Chapters 18 and 24.)

The Site of Action

. . . not every differentia precludes identity. (Aristotle, *Analytica posteriora*, Book II, 13)

Ultimately it would be desirable to define and classify tranquilizers as substances that affect certain well-defined functional units of the brain. A first step in this direction can be taken at this time. Because of the complexity of this subject it is discussed here rather than separately with each chemical group of tranquilizers.

It is possible to isolate functionally in the brain a number of structurally well-defined regions that have certain important and known functions. Four of these are of particular importance. They are the cortex, the hypothalamus, the limbic system, and the reticular formation. The cortex is the seat of thought and judgment. Neuropharmacologically the effects of drugs on the function of the cortex can be simply evaluated by observing the effects of drugs on brain-wave recordings. Of the five groups of agents only the substituted amides (the hypnotics) affect the cortex. They produce a decrease of frequency and an increase of amplitude, giving a pattern quite similar to that observed during sleep.

The hypothalamus is the location from which all autonomic functions are regulated. The phenothiazines, the *Rauwolfia* alkaloids, and the diphenylmethanes have stimulant effects on these hypothalamic centers. This can be shown by the ability of these tranquilizers to lower the convulsive threshold to electroshock seizures and chemical convulsants (Jenney, 1954; Chen, Ensor, and Bohner, 1954; Berger, Hendley, and Lynes, 1956) and to increase the effects of strychnine, which is known to heighten the excitability of the posterior sympathetic hypothalamus (Gellhorn, 1956).

The limbic system, also called the rhinencephalon or visceral brain, is a phylogenetically old area which is thought to be of vital importance in emotional processes. Anatomically it consists of the hippocampus, the amygdala, the fornix, the olfactory cortex, and related structures. The effect of drugs on these structures can be observed by analyzing spontaneous potentials or by observing the occurrence and duration of afterdischarges produced by electrical stimulation of this area. The phenothiazines and *Rauwolfia* alkaloids produce seizure discharges in the limbic system (Killam and Killam, 1956; Preston, 1956; Sigg and Schneider, 1957). These high amplitude discharges remain confined to the limbic system and do not spread readily to other areas. MacLean, Flanigan, Flynn, Kim, and Stevens (1955) produced hippocampal seizures by the local application of carbachol. Animals in which seizures were produced in this manner behaved like animals that had received reserpine or chlorpromazine; they displayed a poverty of spontaneous movements and no longer responded in an appropriate manner to a conditioned stimulus.

The propanediols and substituted amides do not alter in any way the spontaneous potentials in the limbic structures (Hendley, Lynes, and Berger, 1957) but abolish or shorten afterdischarges set up by electrical stimulation of this area (Kletzkin and Berger, 1959).

The reticular formation of the brainstem and midbrain controls wakefulness and sleep. Stimulation of this area will awaken a sleeping animal and produce an "arousal reaction" in the brain-wave pattern picked up from the cortex. Substituted amides and all hypnotics depress the reticular formation and suppress cortical arousal. The propanediols in general and meprobamate in particular do not block the reticular formation and may even slightly stimulate it (Gangloff, 1958; Kletzkin and Berger, 1959). The other three groups depress this structure slightly and perhaps indirectly by altering the quality of the sensory input.

The clinical effects obtained with tranquilizers of the five chemical groups correlate well with their characteristic neurophysiological effects.

Psychotic patients often show a lowered responsiveness to a variety of stimuli and drugs; this is due to a low reactivity of the autonomic centers in the hypothalamus. This low reactivity of the hypothalamus could be responsible for many symptoms of schizophrenia by pro-

TABLE 1. THE EFFECT OF VARIOUS CLASSES OF COMPOUNDS ON CERTAIN
FUNCTIONAL UNITS OF THE BRAIN

	Cortex	Hypothalamus	Limbic System	Reticular Formation
Phenothiazines	Not affected	Stimulated	Not affected or stimulated	Slightly depressed
Rauwolfia alkaloids	Not affected	Stimulated	Stimulated	Slightly depressed
Diphenylmethanes	Slightly depressed	Stimulated	Not affected	Slightly depressed
Propanediols	Not affected	Not affected	Depressed	Not affected or slightly stimulated
Substituted amides	Depressed	Not affected	Depressed	Depressed

ducing sensory deprivation which is known to bring about hallucinations and other symptoms of psychosis even in normal human beings. It is understandable that drugs such as the phenothiazines and *Rauwolfia* alkaloids that stimulate the hypothalamus should be of value in treating psychotic patients. It is also possible that the emotional flatness of some schizophrenics may be abolished by the stimulant action of these drugs on the limbic system.

Meprobamate and other propanediols are of value in the treatment of hyperexcitable neurotics who react to stimuli with responses of exaggerated intensity and duration. These effects can be counteracted by depressing the limbic system and by decreasing the spread and reverberations of stimuli by the blocking action of these drugs on long interneuronal circuits. Because the cortex and reticular formation are not affected, the patient is able to continue functioning in a normal manner.

The substituted amides differ from the propanediols mainly in having a depressant effect on the reticular formation.

Stimulants

Stimulants are often described as agents acting in an opposite way from the tranquilizers. They are also called psychic energizers and are frequently recommended for the treatment of depression. Why a person suffering from a depression should need a stimulant or

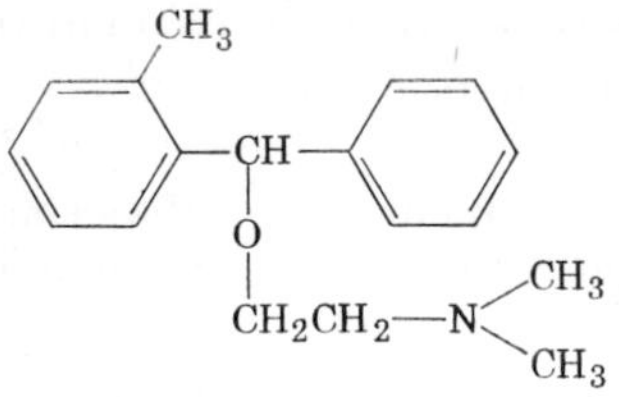

orphenadrine (Disipal)
(2-dimethylaminoethyl
2-methylbenzhydryl ether)

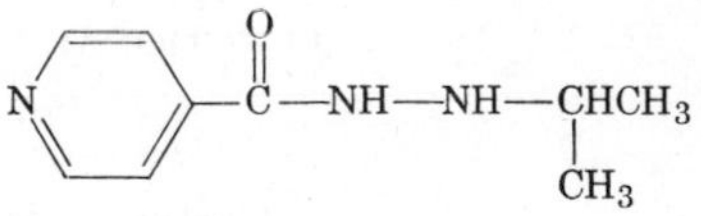

iproniazid (Marsilid)
(1-isonicotinyl-2-isopropylhydrazine)

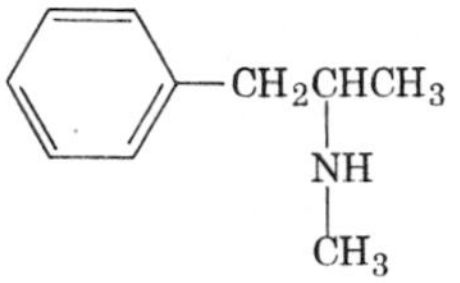

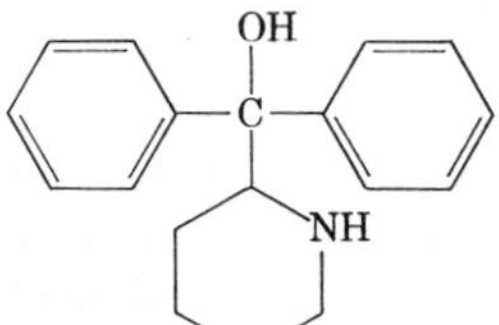

pipradrol (Meratran)
[α-(2-piperidyl)benzhydrol]

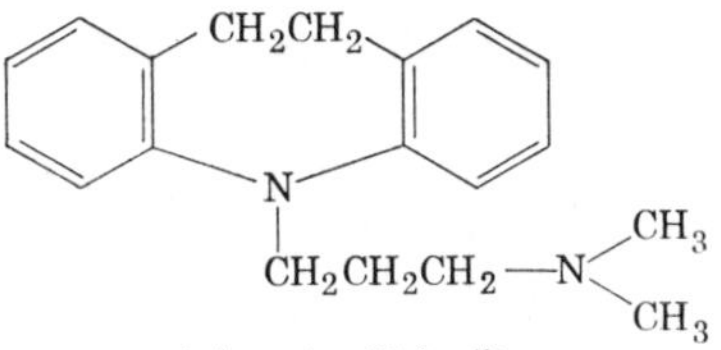

desoxyephedrine (Methamphetamine, U.S.P.)
(d-2-methylamino-1-phenylpropane)

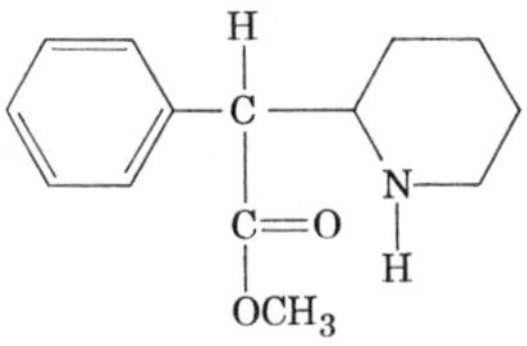

methylphenidate, phenidylate (Ritalin)
(methyl α-phenyl-2-piperidineacetate)

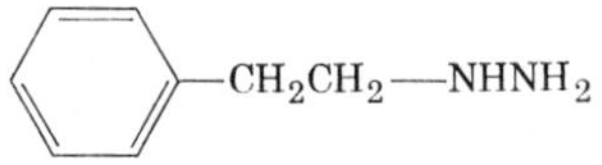

imipramine (Tofranil)
[5-(3-dimethylaminopropyl)-10,11-
dihydro-5H-dibenz-(b,f)azepine]

phenelzine (Nardil)
(β-phenylethylhydrazine)

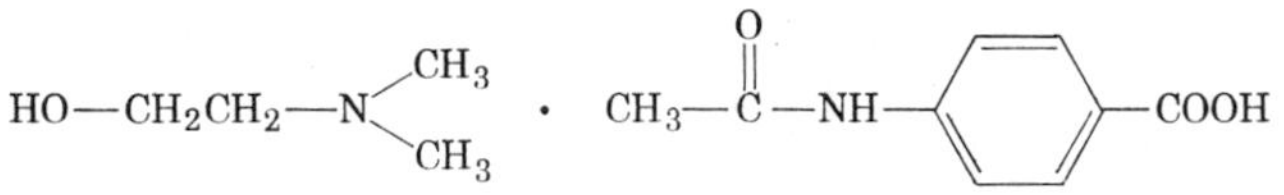

deanol (Deaner)
(4-acetylaminobenzoate salt
of 2-dimethylaminoethanol)

Figure 6.   The chemical structure of the antidepressives.

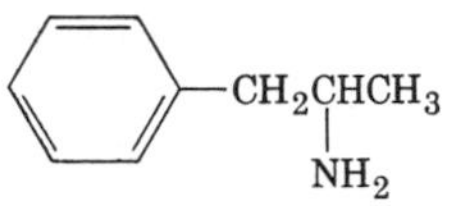

amphetamine (Benzedrine)
(*dl*-2-amino-1-phenylpropane)
[*d*-Amphetamine (Dexedrine)
is the dextro isomer.]

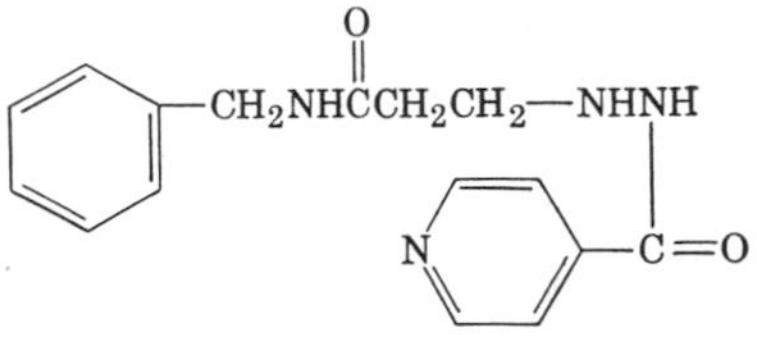

nialamide (Niamid)
[1-[2-(-benzylcarbamyl)ethyl]-
2-isonicotinyl hydrazine]

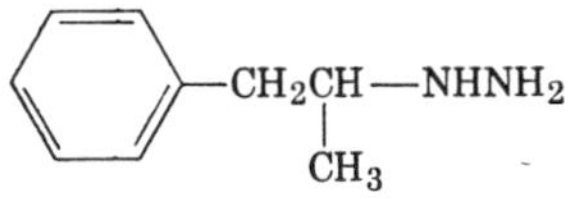

phenylisopropylhydrazine (Catron)
(β-phenylisopropylhydrazine)

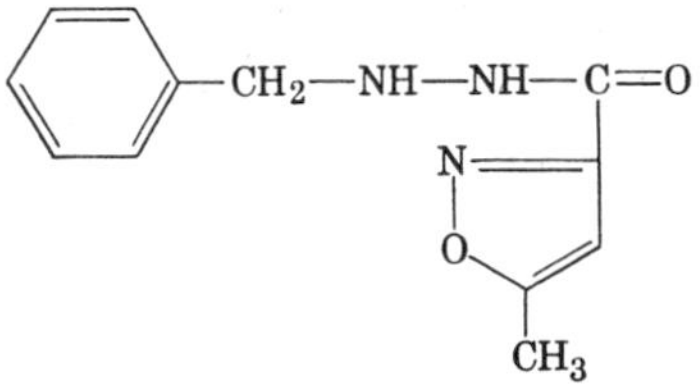

isocarboxazid (Marplan)
[1-benzyl-2-(5-methyl-3-
isoxazoylcarbonyl) hydrazine]

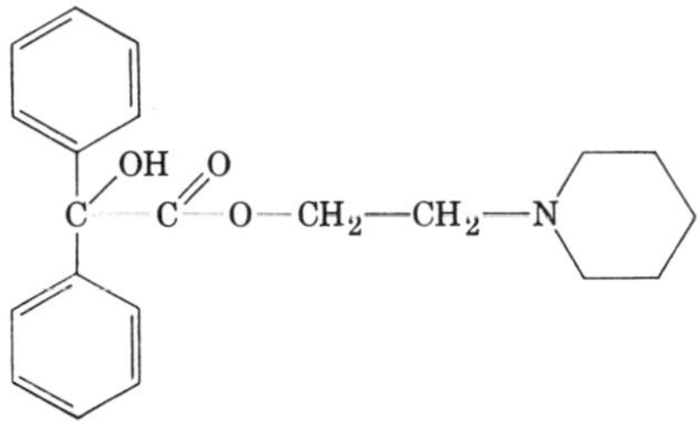

piperilate (Sycotrol)
[2-(1-piperidyl)ethyl benzilate]

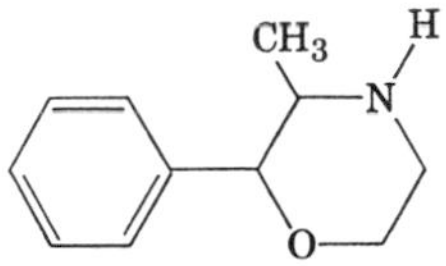

phenmetrazine (Preludin)
(2-phenyl-3-methyltetrahydro-
1,4-oxazine)

Figure 6 (Continued).

energizer is not clear. Depression has characteristics of exhaustion, so administration of stimulants to a depressed patient is like flogging a tired horse. Certain tranquilizers, such as chlorpromazine and reserpine, as suggested in this presentation, may exert their therapeutic effect by having a stimulant action on the hypothalamus. The central nervous system depressant action also possessed by these tranquilizers, although of great importance to some patients, may be merely coincidental and under some circumstances irrelevant or even harmful.

The meaning of the word "stimulant" is not made clearer by the great variety of conditions for which these agents are recommended and used. A unitary classification of them at present cannot be attempted. It is, however, possible to divide them on a utilitarian basis into a number of groups using biochemical properties as criteria for classification. On this basis, the stimulants can be divided into three groups: the analeptics, the monoaminoxidase inhibitors, and the acetylcholine precursors.

The analeptics (antidepressives) are drugs that antagonize the actions of central nervous system depressants. They produce hyperexcitability that may or may not progress to convulsions. The most important representatives of this group are amphetamine (Benzedrine) and dextro-amphetamine (Dexedrine). The stimulants pipradrol (Meratran) and phenidylate (Ritalin) differ from amphetamine in lacking adrenergic action. These stimulants have a depressant action on limbic structures, a property they share with barbiturates (Sigg and Schneider, 1957).

The enzyme monoaminoxidase is widely distributed in the body and may play an important part in the metabolism of catechol amines and serotonin. Chemically, compounds that inhibit monoaminoxidase are usually hydrazides with an R—NH—NH—R_1 group. Iproniazid (Marsalid) is the best-known agent of this type. The drug was originally tried for the treatment of depression on the assumption that it acts as a stimulant by slowing down the breakdown of epinephrine in the body. Meanwhile Axelrod (1957) has shown that epinephrine is metabolized first by transmethylation and that monoaminoxidase does not play an important part in this process.

Diethylaminoethanol (Deaner) is a possible precursor of acetylcholine. Pfeiffer (1957) presented evidence to show that cholinergic agents when given in sufficiently large doses can produce remissions in schizophrenics. Possibly lack of acetylcholine in the brain could be a cause of psychosis, and the administration of an agent that the body can readily utilize to make acetylcholine could counteract it.

In therapeutic application, tranquilizers and antidepressants (stimulants) may differ from each other much less than is generally assumed. Certain tranquilizers such as meprobamate (Miltown, Equanil) alone or in combination with benactyzine (Deprol) have been reported to be of value in the treatment of all types of depression (Hollister, Elkins, Hiler, and St. Pierre, 1957; Ruchwarger, 1956; Alexander, 1958).

Epilogue

Generally speaking, classification should involve more than the mere collection and orderly presentation of available observations. It should lead to the formulation of general principles which would assist in better comprehension of available data and enable the formulation of new concepts which, in turn, could be subjected to experimental verification. At present, insufficiency and dissipation of knowledge in these fields makes these aims unattainable.

In this presentation, whenever the pharmacological properties of tranquilizers have been enumerated, it has been stressed that these do not necessarily bear a relation to the clinical uses of the drugs. This is important to know so that we will not be misled by false assumptions. This knowledge, however, does not mean that there is any doubt about the clinical usefulness and effectiveness of the established tranquilizers. They have changed the appearance of mental hospitals and influenced clinical medicine by providing therapy in previously intractable conditions. To try to improve these agents by minor modifications of their basic chemical structure appears of limited interest at best, as it will lead only to similar drugs with perhaps higher potency or fewer side effects, but possessing the same action. What is needed are new and different drugs to prevent or cure mental diseases or alter behavior as yet unaffected by the available tranquilizers.

REFERENCES

Alexander, L. Differential effects of the new "psychotropic" drugs. *Ann. N. Y. Acad. Sci.*, 1957, 67, 758–765.

Alexander, L. Chemotherapy of depression. J. Amer. med. Ass., 1958, 166, 1019–1023.

Axelrod, J. O-Methylation of epinephrine and other catechols in vitro and in vivo. *Science*, 1957, 126 (3270), 400–401.

Axelrod, J., Reichenthal, J., and Brodie, B. B. Mechanism of the potentiating action of β-diethylaminoethyl diphenylpropylacetate. *J. Pharmacol. exp., Therap.*, 1954, 112, 49–54.

Bercovitz, Z., Page, R. C., and de Beer, E. J. Phenothiazine: experimental and clinical study of toxicity and anthelmintic value. *J. Amer. med. Ass.*, 1943, 122, 1006–1007.

Berger, F. M. The pharmacological properties of 2-methyl-2-*n*-amyl-4-hydroxy-methyl-1,3-dioxolane (Glyketal), a new blocking agent of interneurons. *J. Pharmacol. exp. Therap.*, 1949, 96, 213–223.

Berger, F. M. The pharmacological properties of 2-methyl-2-*n*-propyl-1,3-propanediol dicarbamate (Miltown), a new interneuronal blocking agent. *J. Pharmacol. exp. Therap.*, 1954, 112, 413–423.

Berger, F. M. The chemistry and mode of action of tranquilizing drugs. *Ann. N. Y. Acad. Sci.*, 1957, 67, 685–699.

Berger, F. M. and Bradley, W. The pharmacological properties of $\alpha:\beta$-dihydroxy-γ-(2-methylphenoxy)-propane (Myanesin). *Brit. J. Pharmacol.*, 1946, 1, 265–272.

Berger, F. M., Campbell, G. L., Hendley, C. D., Ludwig, B. J., and Lynes, T. E. The action of tranquilizers on brain potentials and serotonin. *Ann. N. Y. Acad. Sci.*, 1957, 66, 686–694.

Berger, F. M., Hendley, C. D., and Lynes, T. E. Effect of meprobamate (Miltown) on animal behavior. *Fed. Proc.*, 1956, 15, 400.

Brodie, B. B., Pletscher, A., and Shore, P. A. Evidence that serotonin has a role in brain function. *Science,* 1955, 122, 968.

Chen, G., Ensor, C. R., and Bohner, B. A facilitation action of reserpine on the central nervous system. *Proc. Soc. exp. Biol. Med.*, 1954, 86, 507–510.

Delay, J. Introduction a l'étude des neuroleptiques. In *Journées thérapeutiques de Paris.* Paris: G. Doin & Cie., 1958, 181–191.

Deniker, P. Tranquillisants et neuroleptiques en pratique thérapeutique. In *Journées thérapeutiques de Paris.* Paris: G. Doin & Cie., 1958, 305–326.

Erwin, H. J. Clinical observations on the use of promethazine hydrochloride in psychiatric disorders. *Amer. J. Psychiat.*, 1957, 113, 783–787.

Gangloff, H. Effect of meprobamate and phenaglycodol on spontaneous and evoked brain activity in the cat. *Fed. Proc.*, 1958, 17, 369.

Gellhorn, E. Analysis of autonomic hypothalamic functions in the intact organism. *Neurology,* 1956, 6, 335–343.

Hazard, R., Boissier, J. R., and Dumont, C. Classification pharmacologique et chimique des tranquillisants. In *Journées thérapeutiques de Paris.* Paris: G. Doin & Cie., 1958, 193–212.

Hendley, C. D., Lynes, T. E., and Berger, F. M. Effect of meprobamate on electrical activity of thalamus and other subcortical areas. In H. E. Himwich (Ed.), *Tranquilizing drugs.* Washington, D.C.: Amer. Ass. Adv. Sci., 1957, 35–46.

Holliday, A. R., Duffy, M. L., and Dille, J. M. The effect of certain tranquilizers on a stress producing behavioral task. *J. Pharmacol. exp. Therap.*, 1958, 122, 32A.

Hollister, L. E., Elkins, H., Hiler, E. G., and St. Pierre, R. Meprobamate in chronic psychiatric patients. *Ann. N. Y. Acad. Sci.*, 1957, 67, 789–800.

Hubble, D. Toxicity of phenothiazine. *Lancet,* 1941, 2, 600–601.

Jacobsen, E. The pharmacological classification of central nervous depressants. *J. Pharm. Pharmacol.*, 1958, 10, 273–294.

Jenney, E. H. Changes in convulsant thresholds after Rauwolfia serpentina, reserpine and Veriloid. *Fed. Proc.*, 1954, 13, 370–371.

Kautz, H. D. Report of the Council. Psychotherapeutic Drugs. *J. Amer. med. Ass.*, 1958, 166, 1040–1041.

Killam, E. K., and Killam, K. F. A comparison of the effects of reserpine and chlorpromazine to those of barbiturates on central afferent systems in the cat. *J. Pharm. exp. Therap.*, 1956, 116, 35. (Abstract)

Kletzkin, M., and Berger, F. M. The effect of meprobamate on the limbic system of the brain. *Proc. Soc. exp. Biol. Med.*, 1959, 100, 681–683.

Kornetsky, C., Humphries, O., and Evarts, E. V. Comparison of psychological effects of certain centrally acting drugs in man. *A. M. A. Arch. Neurol. Psychiat.*, 1957, 77, 318–324.

Laverty, S. G., and Franks, C. M. Sodium amytal and behaviour in neurotic subjects. *J. Neurol. Neurosurg. Psychiat.*, 1956, 19, 137.

MacLean, P. D., Flanigan, S., Flynn, J. P., Kim, C., Stevens, J. R. Hippocampal function: tentative correlations of conditioning, EEG, drug, and radioautographic studies. *Yale J. Biol. Med.*, 1955–56, 28, 380–395.

Petrie, A., and Le Beau, J. Psychological changes in man after chlorpromazine and certain types of brain surgery. *J. clin. exp. Psychopath.*, 1956, 17, 170–179.

Pfeiffer, C. C., Jenney, E. H., Gallagher, W., Smith, R. P., Bevan, W., Jr., Killam, K. F., Killam, E. K., and Blackmore, W. Stimulant effect of 2-dimethylaminoethanol—possible precursor of brain acetylcholine. *Science*, 1957, 126, 610–611.

Pletscher, A. Release of 5-hydroxytryptamine by benzoquinolizine derivatives with sedative action. *Science*, 1957, 126, 507.

Preston, J. B. Effects of chlorpromazine on the central nervous system of the cat: A possible neural basis for action. *J. Pharmacol. exp. Therap.*, 1956, 118, 100–115.

Riley, H., and Spinks, A. Biological assessment of tranquilizers. *J. Pharm. Pharmacol.*, 1958, 10, 657–671, 721–740.

Buchwarger, A. Meprobamate in anxiety reactions involving depression. *Med. Ann. District Columbia*, 1956, 25, 555–557.

Sigg, E. B., and Schneider, J. A. Mechanisms involved in the interaction of various central stimulants and reserpine, *Electroencephalog. clin. Neurophysiol.*, 1957, 9, 419–426.

Thuillier, J., and Nakajima, H. Action comparée des drogues psychotropes sur les "souris tournantes" provoquées par l'imino-$\beta\beta$-dipropionitrile (Souris IDPN). In S. Garattini and V. Ghetti (Eds.), *Psychotropic drugs*. Amsterdam: Elsevier, 1957, 136–158.

Tripod, J., Studer, A., and Meier, R. Essai de différenciation expérimentale d'une série d'inhibiteurs du système nerveux central. *Arch. int. Pharmacodynamie*, 1957, 112, 319–341.

Vogt, M. Pharmacology of tranquilizing drugs. *Brit. med. J.*, 1958, 2, 965–967.

Methodology

The place and purpose

of objective methods

in psychopharmacology

Scientific investigation is based on the collection of information concerning the phenomena under study. This information is usually obtained through the gathering of observational data which may be either subjective or objective in nature and may be further distinguished as being derived from either natural observation or observation under controlled experimental conditions.

The unprecedented development of successful therapeutic methods in psychiatry during the last two decades, both physiological and psychological, as well as the tremendous expansion of experimental investigation in the fields of psychopharmacology, neurophysiology, psychology, and sociology, have led to ever increasing use of objective methods in such research.

The essential factor which makes a research method scientific is the systematic approach. The systematic approach implies, in addition to the gathering of observational data, the reliable recording of these data, their rational analysis, an elimination of subjective bias, and, finally, the construction and testing of hypotheses and theories.

Orientation of Research

The methodology of behavioral research has not yet reached the stage of sophistication and clarity of the physical sciences. As in the physical sciences, however, we distinguish between the methods used in applied and those used in pure or theoretical research. The psychiatrist, for instance, frequently employs tests and experiments to assist him in the empirical manipulation of clinical problems, while at other times his principal interest is the theoretical explanation or dynamic understanding of relationships. These two orientations should be distinguished, namely, the empirical-manipulative one, in which the investigator is primarily interested in establishing the effects of certain agents on psychological processes and in the resulting quantitative data, and the theoretical-understanding orientation, in which he is mainly concerned with the clarification of action mechanisms of a physical or psychodynamic nature and with the elucidation of psychopathological phenomena as such.

Levels and Focus

Burdock, Sutton, and Zubin (1958) in a recent paper differentiated five levels of observed behavior: conceptual, psychomotor, perceptual, sensory, and physiological. We have in previous publications (Lehmann 1956) suggested a distinction of three psychophysiological levels of organization: the cortico-psychic, the sensory-psychic, and the viscero-psychic, which overlap to some extent with the five levels of Burdock and co-workers.

Whatever the purpose and the level of research may be, its specific focus should also be clearly recognized. Table 1 illustrates the different orientations that may be reflected in the investigation of a therapeutic agent. The investigator studying a psychoactive drug should clearly have in mind what he is looking for before he starts his psychopharmacological experiment.

TABLE 1.   TYPES OF THERAPEUTIC FOCUS

On unspecific "target" symptoms or signs of disorder (e.g. excitement, anxiety, confusion, weight loss) — Symptomatic

On specific—primary, basic, or fundamental—*symptoms* or signs of disorder (e.g., autistic thinking disturbance, inappropriate affect, WR of CSF) — Corrective or compensating

On process of illness (e.g., deterioration, death . . .)

On specific noxious agent (e.g., niacin deficiency, toxic substance, treponema pallidum) — Curative

Methods of Gathering Information

Information on the behavior of an individual may be obtained by three methods:

1. INTROSPECTION. A distinction must be made here between the naive and inarticulate self-observer, the naive but sensitive and articulate person, and, finally, the scientifically trained subject who is observing himself.

2. OBSERVATION BY OTHERS. This is the most commonly practiced clinical method. Again a distinction must be made between the data provided by the untrained and the sophisticated observer. Special devices such as rating scales and Q-sort techniques are frequently employed to render the data obtained by introspection or observation of others more precise.

3. TESTS. The tests may be of the type which the modern clinical psychologist employs widely, namely, projective methods which reflect complex changes in a person's psychic functioning such as the Rorschach test, or the tests may be of the psychometric type, for instance the well-known intelligence tests. Another type of psychological test procedure aims at the quantitative determination of primitive and basic psychomotor and perceptual behavior, for instance, tapping speed. Still another method of testing a person's behavior involves physiological procedures which leave the subject quite passive, as in studies of his EEG or polygraph recordings of his autonomic responses.

The above classification of exploratory methods used in psychopharmacology is rather simplified, and in practice one will frequently encounter experimental designs which combine several of the characteristics of the different basic methods.

The essential factors in determining the value of any particular method of investigation are its validity, its reliability, and its objectivity.

Validity

To validate a method is equivalent to establishing the meaning of its results beyond question. Whatever method is chosen to study a psychopharmaceutical problem, one of the basic difficulties is usually related to the question of valid criteria for the behavior under study.

The conventional definition of validity as a correlation between a test score and some outside criterion is no longer adequate. Thurstone (1952) pointed out that the test-criterion correlation is now obsolete. It is too coarse, because for many psychological functions a test's validity can only be ascertained through judges making judgments about people with regard to a factor, if this factor is not observable but an inference.

CHOICE OF CRITERIA. The problem of determining valid criteria for the functions or pathological entities to be investigated remains a central problem in psychiatry and psychopharmacology. One of the most common and most important psychiatric problems, that of anxiety, is still presenting a semantic and methodological conundrum as its meaning is differently determined according to the more or less arbitrary choice of criteria which are made the basis of a systematic investigation. In everyday life, all of us know immediately what is meant by anxiety, and nobody would question the validity of someone's statement that he is feeling anxious. On the other hand, when controlled experiments concerning anxiety are involved, the question of the exact nature of this particular condition is far from settled. The experimental psychologist, taking his cue from physical science, may choose to define anxiety operationally as the suppressing effect of anticipated pain upon a stable lever-pressing habit in trained experimental animals (Brady, 1957). The clinical psychologist, who cannot control all critical variables experimentally, may still choose an operationally defined criterion of anxiety, e.g., a person's score on the Taylor Anxiety Rating Scale. The psychiatrist working in a clinical setting, or mainly oriented along psychoanalytic lines, will determine the presence and degree of anxiety according to certain symptoms which are intuitive, behavioral, or theoretical criteria summed up by him under the general heading of clinical experience.

A disturbing methodological problem of all clinical psychiatric research lies in the fact that, in the last analysis, all diagnostic criteria are derived from clinical judgments. This basic fact is easily obscured and frequently forgotten. On the basis of original clinical judgments, secondary criteria are established by research workers who apply modern statistical devices to extract central factors, tendencies, and groupings (Eysenck, 1950). The results obtained by applying test procedures involving these secondarily derived "objective" criteria are then treated in future experiments as though they referred to primary basic and objectively established criteria. This amounts to circular reasoning as far as truly objective validation of criteria is concerned. It is frequently not realized by those who use test results as diagnostic tools to sharpen their clinical judgment that they were forged originally in the heat of clinical insight and tempered later through clinical experience—when it was found that there was a consistently high correlation between clinical judgment and the test criteria.

Constructs like schizophrenia, psychoneurosis, or anxiety are not based on direct observables but were created by clinicians. Experimental investigators later consolidated these constructs by the use of statistical procedures. While statistical procedures possess the certainty which stems from being rooted in mathematical concepts, the data analyzed by them were originally supplied by the clinician, who chose the representative groups which he estimated to be so rich in the criterion factor in question that the statistician could reliably deal with it. In the phrase "representative group" we find the crux of the problem. What is representative of a certain condition is judged subjectively by the clinician, who is not able to be any more explicit about this representative factor than to state that in his opinion it is present to a sufficiently high degree to include a subject in the criterion group. Different clinicians, however, may well choose groups which possess very different degrees of what each clinician implies to be the most important criterion factor.

There has been a strong tendency in some quarters to apply strictly operational definitions to all problems and concepts in the behavioral sciences. This tendency stems from the realization that much of the success of the physical sciences in the last half-century has been the result of such strict operationism. The problem in the behavioral sciences is, however, different in that two factors which are of little or no significance in the physical sciences play a dominant role in the behavioral sciences. These two factors are the *history* of the individual subjects and the personal *meaning* the experimental and environmental conditions have for him. As will be shown later, these two elements preclude complete control of all experimental factors and render impossible a completely operational definition of meaningful clinical entities and conditions.

TYPES OF VALIDITY. When a committee of the American Psychological Association set out to specify the desirable qualities of psychological tests (1950–1954), it was decided to distinguish four types of validity: predictive validity, concurrent validity, content validity, and construct validity (Cronbach and Meehl, 1956).

Predictive validity of a criterion makes it possible to predict the subject's future performance in the area characterized by the criterion. Certain methods used in vocational guidance to test for specific aptitudes and interests may enable the experimenter to make valid predictions of the success of a person in a given occupation.

Concurrent validity is the type of validity for which the diagnostician applies psychological tests in order to establish or confirm his clinical diagnosis. The test criterion is concurrent with the existing condition, for instance, an organic brain syndrome.

Content validity is concerned with test items which sample a particular function or factor representative of a well-defined group of criteria. Achievement tests such as school examinations are examples of tests with high content validity.

Construct validity, the last of the four categories, was also the latest to be considered by the committee. According to Cronbach and Meehl (1956), construct validation is involved whenever a test is to be interpreted as a measure of some attribute or quality which is not operationally defined. The same authors point out that much current research about tests is, in reality, construct validation, but usually without the benefit of a clear formulation of this process.

Construct validation in psychology and psychiatry at our present state of knowledge involves in most cases a considerable amount of interpretation on the part of the investigator. The difficulty of determining a valid construct of *anxiety,* or *depression,* is obvious. Some recently developed psychoactive drugs have been stated to be therapeutically effective in states of depression. At times other investigators have been unable to confirm these findings, because each researcher had a different understanding of what he meant by depression. The two parameters, *introversion* and *extraversion,* which are Eysenck's basic constructs of his personality theory (1953), or Freud's constructs of *transference* and *resistance,* which he considers fundamental requirements of all psychoanalytic theory, are other examples of important constructs which require careful validation.

Another construct of paramount importance in psychopharmacology, psychiatry, and medicine generally which is far from possessing generally accepted valid criteria is *result of therapy.* It is obviously of great value for the clinician to know whether or not a certain agent is therapeutically effective and to have at least a rough quantitative estimate of how effective it is. Present-day psychiatry, however, is deeply troubled by the absence of criteria of therapeutic results acceptable to all critical investigators. Even if the evidence as provided by observational data is identical, a number of different investigators may draw entirely different conclusions about the therapeutic effectiveness of the agent under question, depending on their scientific, clinical, administrative, or dynamic orientations.

In the physical sciences, the truth of a theory is usually said to depend on three factors: (1) predictability of results; (2) replicability of results; and (3) internal consistency of the constructs and concepts. In the behavioral sciences, the first two criteria are often hard to meet, and we then have to rely on criteria of internal consistency alone to judge the value of a theory.

Reliability

Reliability refers to the consistent recurrence of the same or closely related results on repeated testing or observation. Of the three factors, validity, reliability, and objectivity, only reliability can be regularly and accurately quantified. Its measure can be expressed in statistical terms.

The reliability of a method is not of necessity positively related to its validity. In fact, in the behavioral sciences we sometimes find a negative correlation between validity and reliability, as the validity of certain results often decreases when we try to control all experimental and environmental factors to such an extent that the test-retest reliability is raised to a maximum. Even if we are not able to control all factors but know some of them, we can make allowance for their interference, and new statistical methods of variance analysis can bring out reliable scores of the factors in which we are interested, that is, the dependent variables.

It is, of course, impossible to know or even guess at all the factors that might significantly alter a subject's performance under certain test conditions because, as was pointed out before, a subject's life history and the particular idiosyncratic meaning of the test situation for him constitute a universe of facts known to the investigator only in a most rudimentary fashion. The situation may be compared to that of an electronic computer into which a highly complex program has been fed before an experiment to be performed by an experimenter to whom the programmed instructions and the resulting behavioral action tendencies of the computer are not known. It would constitute a tremendous, probably impossible, task for the experimenter to deduce analytically from the computer's output the exact manner in which the computer had been programmed, so that he might interpret the outcome of the experiment.

INTERFERING VARIABLES. The behavior of living organisms and, above all, of the human subject is greatly influenced by the factors *meaning* and *value*, which easily give rise to emotional reactions. Such emotional reactions, to which we have referred in a previous publication (Lehmann, 1957) as interfering variables, are responsible for many individual variations and distortions of a subject's responses resulting from factors which remain unknown to the experimenter and are consequently uncontrolled. Reiser, Reeves, and Armington (1955) have demonstrated the visible effects of subtle variations in laboratory procedures and in the experimenter upon circulatory responses in healthy young subjects. Sloane, Saffran, and Cleghorn (1958) studied the responsivity of the adrenal cortex to corticotropin by measuring the increase of 17-hydroxycorticosteroid excretion in the urine of psychoneurotics, schizophrenics, and a normal control group. The resting levels of hydroxycorticosteroid excretion in the normal control group were found to be higher than in the psychoneurotic group consisting of patients with phobic, obsessional, hysterical, anxiety, and depressive symptoms. The authors concluded that the control subjects who had to make a special journey to the hospital for testing showed variable degrees of anxiety resulting from this procedure—a difficult factor to control. Beecher (1957) seriously questions the reliability of such well-established objective methods as the Hardy-Wolff-Goodell method of determining the pain threshold in human subjects because of what he calls the processing and reaction components of pain, which are dependent on idiosyncrasies of personal life histories, values, cognitive meanings, and emotional reactions.

Inert substances or placebos, when received with the understanding that they will produce certain effects, do indeed cause such effects to appear in 20 to 60 per cent of the subjects tested (Wolf and Pinsky 1954; Lasagna, Mosteller, von Felsinger, and Beecher, 1954). The double-blind method represents certainly a step ahead in methodology for controlling such factors, but it is by no means foolproof. We have recently found that giving a placebo capsule in a well-controlled double-blind experimental procedure produced test-retest differences which were larger and of greater significance than the administration of effective doses of psychoactive drugs (Lehmann and Knight, 1960). There are three factor groups which have to be considered in the evaluation of any test repetition:

1. The practice or learning effect of the test or method upon the individual.

2. A variety of rather poorly understood and largely uncontrollable variables such as metabolic, endocrinological, and neurophysiological changes which we usually call spontaneous but which are often the result of certain rhythms established within the organism. Changes due to meteorological and other environmental factors also are often not under the experimenter's control. Finally, the subject's trend of thoughts, his train of emotions and fantasies, also have to be seriously considered under this heading since they might bring about substantial alterations in any behavioral performance.

3. The so-called placebo-responses which are based on explicit or implicit suggestions inherent in the experimental situation and which are only partly under the control of the experimenter. However, placebo-responses occur also when neither the experimenter nor the experimental subject has any conscious information about effects which the placebo or drug under question might produce.

Even the most sophisticated experimental designs can only provide statistical evidence, which may have considerable reliability when applied to a population of subjects but which furnishes a questionable basis for predictions concerning an individual subject. Somehow one is reminded of the methodological impasse of the physical sciences. Experimental and theoretical physicists alike recognized long ago that statements about individual atoms or molecules cannot be made meaningful, as we have no way of measuring their behavior reliably. On the other hand, physicists can measure, with extremely high precision, the macroscopic behavior of systems, since this involves statistical laws of quantum mechanics which have become a familiar tool of the modern physicist. To what extent is it permissible to develop an analogy between an individual molecule and an individual subject?

Objectivity

Whereas good validity and high reliability are essential requirements for an acceptable method of investigation in psychopharmacology, a high degree of objectivity of such methods is of lesser importance. There are four main reasons which may determine the choice of an objective method in preference to others:

1. Results obtained by objective methods lend themselves more easily to intersubjective verification.

2. Objective methods sometimes enable the investigator to reveal basic mechanisms underlying the behavioral criteria. An example

is furnished by the study of varying degrees of arousal through the electroencephalogram, which not only provides a convenient operational measure of arousal but also illuminates some of the underlying neurophysiological mechanisms of this state.

3. By employing objective methods of investigation, psychopharmacologists join hands with other investigators in the basic sciences who rely principally on objective procedures. In doing so, they can foster a rapprochement between the behavioral and the physical sciences. The motive for the choice of objective methods in this case would be to improve communication. The tying together, for instance, of psychiatric, psychological, pharmacological, and chemical investigations into one scientific framework by adjusting the experimental design accordingly has rendered interdisciplinary teamwork more practical and more fruitful.

4. Built-in checks and balances of objective methods tend to neutralize the comparative shortcomings of less experienced or less competent experimenters.

INTROSPECTIVE DATA. In principle, however, data obtained through introspection are perfectly acceptable in psychological, psychiatric, and psychopharmacological research. Carnap (1956) states, "Psychological concepts are properties, relations, or quantitative magnitudes ascribed to certain space-time regions (usually human organisms or classes of such). Therefore, they belong to the same logical types as concepts of physics. . . . " and later, "Although many of the alleged results of introspection were indeed questionable, a person's awareness of his own state of imagining, feeling, etc., must be recognized as a kind of observation, in principle not different from external observation, and therefore as a legitimate source of knowledge. . . . " That the effects of drugs on a person's psychic functioning can be studied with scientific validity and reliability through introspection and self-observation of specially trained research workers has been demonstrated by an interdisciplinary group in Cincinnati (Gottschalk, Kapp, Ross, Kaplan, Silver, MacLeod, Kahn, Van Maanen, and Acheson, 1956). They concluded that this method can be employed only with trained subjects and that it involves the study of the man as well as of the drug.

SPURIOUS OBJECTIVATION. We must be on guard against substituting objective criteria which are frequently associated with the basic criterion construct for the basic construct itself. For instance, the autonomic manifestations of emotions which so consistently accompany emotional states are sometimes treated as though they were the emotional state *per se*. This is certainly not so. Basowitz, Korchin, Oken, Goldstein, and Gussack (1956) described an experiment in which a number of subjects received small doses of adrenalin intravenously. Two subjects showed remarkable reactions: one, because the investigator became alarmed at the excessive changes in blood pressure and pulse rate, although the subject himself did not feel particularly anxious; the other, because the subject complained of great anxiety and seemed to approach a state of panic, although his circulatory responses showed no significant changes.

A certain and sometimes considerable measure of objectivity is lent to any method merely by its use in a systematic and rational manner. Systematic rationality possesses one of the principal values of objectivity, namely, to render the data intersubjectively verifiable. Logical reasoning, unlike feelings, opinions, and intuitions, takes place under identical conditions and results in identical conclusions in the most different individuals.

BEHAVIOR RATING SCALES. Over and beyond the rational approach to the observation of behavioral phenomena, objectivity may be introduced into non-experimental methods by employing precisely defined observational criteria to be recorded on check lists. Behavioral rating scales are often employed in systematic clinical studies. The most widely used are those developed by Malamud and Sands (1947), Wittenborn (1950), and Lorr (1953). Because the trained observer can make unique contributions to the study of human behavior, such rating scales are most valuable in principle, but they frequently present practical shortcomings because of their length and the demands they make on the rater's experience with the scale. Since one of the main advantages of the best rating scales is their comprehensiveness, considerable time is often required to complete such a scale. Shorter scales which are often constructed *ad hoc* for the assessment of particular behavior sectors are useful, but their value is often restricted because of their lack of validation on a sufficiently large sample. It is usually assumed that a high interjudge reliability is an indication of an equally high objectivity, but here again one must be on guard against rash conclusions since, after all, rating scales depend on the subjective judgments of the raters which are always subject to the influence of extraneous factors such as values, customs, and cultures prevalent at the place where the rating is done. Such extraneous factors may produce a spurious and distorting uniformity of results.

QUESTIONNAIRES. Self-observation can be given a comparatively high degree of objectivity by structuring it through questionnaires which have been validated statistically against clinically established "criterion groups." The Minnesota Multiphasic Personality Inventory based on the sorting of answers to a number of standardized questions is probably the best-known of such clinical and research devices.

It has now become possible to apply modern statistical analysis to self-observational and self-appraisal data of an individual through the recently developed Q-sort technique (Stephenson, 1953). This technique relies on the differential sorting of a variety of questions by an individual. The questions are written on cards, and the person is asked to sort them in several different ways according to different criteria which he is asked to apply; for instance, the way he himself would answer a certain question, the way others would answer it, and the way he thinks it should be answered ideally. This method has been put to service in a carefully cross-validated study by Rogers and Dymond (1954), who have used the Q-technique as one of their main attacks on the intensely challenging problem of the effects of psychotherapy on personality structure.

Relative Emphasis of Validity-Reliability-Objectivity

The relative importance and usefulness of validity, reliability, and objectivity vary according to the purpose of the research. Investigations in psychiatric theory and practice which are mainly concerned with interpersonal relationships or intrapersonal dynamics at present usually place more emphasis on validity than on reliability and sometimes dispense almost entirely with objectivity. On the other hand, research that is concerned with treatment results in large groups of patients, and particularly research into the effects of physical agents on psychiatric patients, such as shock therapy or drugs, must rely mainly on the reliability of the results obtained. Anyone working at the empirical-manipulative level in behavioral science will have to be content, at least for the time being, with less complex but more precise results than the investigator working at the theoretical-understanding level. Figure 1 represents an attempt to display graphically on a 1–7 scale the magnitude of validity, reliability, and objectivity factors in the various investigational methods available to the psychopharmacologist, all of which have been used in drug studies. It will be noted that, although the interview yields the highest rating with regard to validity, it is only halfway up the scale of objectivity.

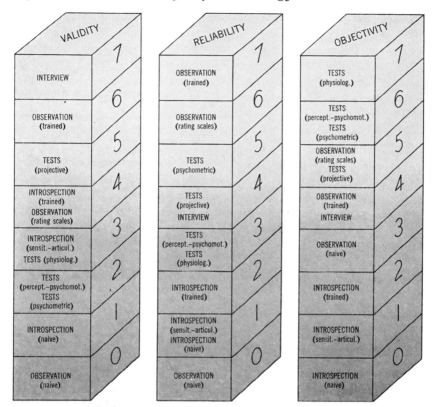

Figure 1. The relative weights of validity, reliability, and objectivity in a number of psychiatric and psychological exploratory methods of investigation.

Physiological tests are at the top of the objectivity scale but in the lower half of both reliability and validity gradients. Others would probably give a different distribution of these weightings, but the graph will serve as a general illustration of the varying proportion of each of the three factors involved in the different methods.

Quantity, Quality, and Value

Modern psychology and psychiatry have developed a number of methods which allow for quantification, that touchstone of physical science, to a much greater degree than was possible 10 or 20 years ago. What is quantified by these new methods is either the statistical incidence of certain behavior items to which Ryle (1949) refers as "public performances," or the magnitude of some physiological or biochemical measures. The intensity of direct personal experiences of a perceptual, emotional or cognitive nature—Ryle's "private episodes"—cannot be quantified by existing methods. Frequently, in dealing with psychopharmacological problems, the researcher is compelled either to accept or to postulate certain value judgments which transport his whole area of research well out of the domain of the laws and methods governing physical science. This is particularly true of many research problems involving the effectiveness of therapy, since the very concept of therapy involves value judgments.

It has recently been shown that a number of psychological processes are not linear but curvilinear in distribution, usually in the form of a "U" or paraboloid, if they are plotted against value-weighted standards such as goodness of performance or presence of pathology. An example can be found in the graph of arousal of consciousness plotted against excellence of performance (Stennet, 1957). We have found in our experimental study of the effects of a variety of psychoactive drugs on basic perceptual and psychomotor functions that perceptual functions tend to have their optimum of performance somewhere between the minimum and the maximum of the range recorded, whereas for psychomotor functions maximum performance usually is also optimum performance (Lehmann, 1957). In other words, perceptual functions like the level of arousal may have a paraboloid distribution in relation to the performance level.

The Realm of Psychopharmacological Research

In present-day psychopharmacology we find ourselves on the proving ground for true interdisciplinary research efforts—true in the sense that not only a cooperative relationship is established and maintained between research workers of different disciplines but principally because the investigator must have full command of a variety of conceptual and methodological frames of reference. In order to work creatively in his field, he must be able to act as a skillful participant-observer in interpersonal relationships. He must be able to design his experiments with conscientious regard for controls and statistical validation. He must be able to conceive biochemical, neurophysiological, and behavioral action mechanisms, and he must have a critical knowledge of, and a sound respect for, the dynamic theories of intrapersonal processes. Only then will he be really free to choose among these approaches. Only then will he be able, to best advantage, to decide when and to what extent in the experimental design projective techniques should be used to throw light on intrapersonal dynamics; when interviews to reveal interpersonal processes; when behavioral rating scales to measure observable behavior; and when various psychometric, physiological, or biochemical tests would be indicated. Let us consider a few illustrations of the imaginative and eclectic, yet critical, combination of a number of different methods in the designing of experimental psychiatric research which seems to hold promise.

RESEARCH ON ANGER. Funkenstein, King, and Drolette (1957), for example, in a many-pronged attack on the problem of the way different personalities handle stress and failure, used attitude questionnaires, introspection, observation of behavior, interviews, projective tests, and physiological tests. Their aim was to demonstrate cross-correlations between early life history, personality type, and endocrinological responses in their subjects as an extension of Funkenstein's previous work, in which he showed that subjects with elevated epinephrine excretion under stress tend to manifest anger directed inward, and subjects excreting more norepinephrine, anger directed outward. Such endocrinological differentiation of what has usually been treated as an unitary affect, namely anger, into two objectively separated components opens intriguing possibilities for future research into the physiological substrate of psychodynamics.

EXPERIMENTS ON ANXIETY. Other emotional states have recently come under the critical crossfire of experimental investigation. Notable examples are anxiety and tension. When Spence and Taylor (1951) reported that anxious subjects as identified by their scores on the Taylor Manifest Anxiety Scale could be conditioned more easily than non-anxious subjects, this problem was taken up in many other laboratories.

Spence and Taylor assumed that increased anxiety represented an increase in total drive, and they interpreted the facilitation of conditioning responses as an effect of this increased drive. Hilgard, Jones, and Kaplan (1951) pointed out that the eyelid response to an air puff stimulus is defensive in nature, and they ascribed the higher conditioning rate of anxious subjects to an increase of a specific defensive drive in such subjects rather than to an increase of total drive. Bindra, Paterson, and Strzelecki (1955) found no facilitation of the classic conditioning in anxious human subjects when they used an autonomic function, namely salivary conditioning, instead of a defensive function as in the eyelid conditioning experiments. This finding supports the view that a specific factor, rather than total drive, is increased in anxious persons. Kamin, Bindra, Clarke, and Waksberg (1955) used a discrimination task and pain tolerance as tests to be correlated with the subject's scores on the Taylor Manifest Anxiety Scale (1953). These workers thought that they could distinguish two independent factors in clinical anxiety, one a general upset or arousal factor and the other a specific avoidance tendency.

Spence (1953) pointed out that in some experiments his anxious subjects were found to be superior in the conditioning situation, while the opposite was found in certain cognitive learning situations. In another experiment, he demonstrated that anxious subjects perform better than the non-anxious when dealing with comparatively simple learning tasks but are inferior to non-anxious subjects when the task is more complicated.

Other recent work (Davidson, Andrews, and Ross, 1956; Malmo, 1957) has demonstrated the different effects of chronic manifest anxiety such as is clinically seen in anxiety neurotics and in experimentally induced acute stress. While chronic anxiety seems to have a priming function on a person's response to stress, it does not always allow for an experimental distinction between anxious and non-anxious groups. On the other hand, the experimental difference between acutely stressed and non-stressed subjects is usually quite striking. These results make it clear that a great deal is to be hoped for from further advances in our understanding of anxiety through experimental work with human subjects; also, that we can look forward to a more objective analysis of the nature of anxiety which will lay the ground for more valid studies of drug effects upon it.

Cattell has recently published the I.P.A.T. Anxiety Scale (1957). It is a self-administering questionnaire which takes only a few minutes of a subject's or patient's time and can be scored rapidly to yield diagnostic standard scores. The author states that the construct validity of the 40 test items has been established by the fact that they correlate significantly with "depressive anxiety," "guilt proneness" and "ego weakness." These very constructs, as well as the author's claim that the test is intended to give a measure of the degree to which the patient "is or is not conscious of his anxiety" raise again many of the methodological problems discussed before. For practical experimental work, however, such standardization of clinical inferences is an acceptable and often indispensable tool.

CONDITIONING. Conditioning of human subjects is now being used increasingly as an exploratory tool in psychiatric research and can be useful to psychopharmacology. A distinction must be made between the so-called classical conditioning which Pavlov introduced and the operant conditioning which has been developed by Skinner (1953) and his school. In the classical conditioning situation, the unconditioned stimulus, which may be pleasant or unpleasant in its effects, is presented to the subject. He is then conditioned by frequent association of the unconditioned with an originally indifferent conditioned stimulus to react to the conditioned stimulus in the same manner as to the unconditioned. The subject, in classical conditioning, plays a passive role. In operant conditioning, on the other hand, the subject is quite active as he himself must produce through some operation, for instance the pressing of a lever, the unconditioned stimulus, which is usually a rewarding one. Classical conditioning can be designed to evoke autonomic, neuromuscular, perceptual, electroencephalographic, verbal responses, etc. Operant conditioning usually relies on psychomotor responses. A number of investigators employing the classical conditioning method found that schizophrenic patients were more easily conditioned than normals (Welch and Kubis, 1947; Schiff, Dougan, and Welch, 1949; Spence and Taylor, 1953). One group of workers reported no difference between normals and schizophrenics but reported facilitation of conditioning in manic-depressive patients (Pfaffman and Schlosberg, 1936). A linear relationship between severity of schizophrenic illness and conditionability (highest in normals, lower in treated, and lowest in untreated patients) was found by Peters and Murphree (1954). Impaired conditionability in patients with organic brain disease was reported by Reese, Doss, and Gantt (1953). Operant conditioning in schizophrenics with such rewards as candy, cigarettes, or the projection of interesting pictures for the lever-pressing responses has been demonstrated to have a curvilinear relationship with the severity of schizophrenic illness; that is, the operant motor behavior is highest in moderately ill patients and lower in the less severely ill and the more severely ill patients (King, Merrell, Lovinger, and Denny, 1957). Lindsley (1956) found peculiar phenomena in some of the chronic schizophrenics he studied with operant conditioning methods. One patient's responses, for instance, could not be extinguished even after very long periods without reinforcement. The same author reported a significantly high correlation between operant conditioning responses of the patients and the scores on a ward behavior rating scale, although no correlation of the conditioning with the Rorschach test and IQ measurement could be detected. Conditioning methods have also been used in the study of effects of psychoactive drugs on human subjects (Winsor, 1958). One may expect to witness an expansion of the use of conditioning procedures, both classical and operant, in psychiatric research, as these methods permit us to combine a fair degree of complexity with a high measure of objectivity and reliability and with excellent quantifiability. Such techniques open wide vistas for assessing drug effects.

Objectivity in Psychopharmacological and Psychiatric Research

In drug studies the methods used to evaluate the behavioral base-line and the developing changes under the influence of the drug should be characterized by a high degree of objectivity and reliability. Furthermore, any test procedures used must be repeatable and should lend themselves to easy quantification. In order to minimize the influence of emotional reactions and the personality factor, we have concentrated in our own psychopharmacological research on rather primitive and comparatively meaningless and culture-free test procedures which allow for the greatest reduction of what we have called the interfering variables (Lehmann and Csank, 1957).

Conclusion

I should like to conclude my discussion with a plea that the development of *objective evaluation standards for a clinical psychiatrist's performance* be seriously considered, not necessarily with regard to his success as a therapist but with respect to his competence as a diagnostician, a prognostician, and a research worker. One could conceive of methods that would permit "calibration" of the performance of a clinical research-psychiatrist in a manner similar to the calibration of a complex research instrument. To do good research on brain waves, it is not sufficient to have an electroencephalograph. It must also be a reliable and well-calibrated apparatus. The research psychiatrist should be used to better advantage as a research instrument than is now being done. His sensitivity, bias, recording ability, and stability of performance could be objectively determined and compared against standards. In a time when we employ ever more complex new instrumentation in research on the psychiatric drugs, it is appropriate also to make better use of the oldest and most complex of all psychiatric research instruments, the methodologically sophisticated and clinically experienced psychiatrist.

REFERENCES

Basowitz, H., Korchin, S. J., Oken, D., Goldstein, M. S., and Gussack, H. Anxiety and performance changes with a minimal dose of epinephrine, *Arch. Neurol. Psychiat.*, 1956, 76, 98–105.

Beecher, H. K. Measurement of subjective responses. *Neuropharmacology* (*Trans. third Conf.*), 1957, 177–204.

Bindra, D., Paterson, A. L., and Strzelecki, J. On the relations between anxiety and conditioning, *Canad. J. Psychol.*, 1955, 9, 1–6.

Brady, J. V. A comparative approach to the experimental analysis of emotional behavior, in P. H. Hoch and J. Zubin. *Experimental psychopathology*. New York: Grune & Stratton, 1957, pp. 20–33.

Burdock, E. I., Sutton, S., and Zubin, J. Personality and psychopathology, *J. abnorm. soc. Psychol.*, 1958, 56, 18–30.

Carnap, R. The methodological character of theoretical concepts. In H. Feigl and M. Scriven (Eds.), *Minnesota studies in the philosophy of science.* Vol. II. Minneapolis: Univer. of Minnesota Press, 1956, 38–76.

Cattell, R. B. Ipat Anxiety Scale (Self Analysis Form). Illinois Inst. Person. and Abil. Testing, 1957.

Cronbach, L. J., and Meehl, P. E. Construct validity in psychological tests. In H. Feigl and M. Scriven (Eds.), *Minnesota studies in the philosophy of science.* Vol. II. Minneapolis: Univer. of Minnesota Press, 1956, 174–204.

Davidson, W. Z., Andrews, T. G., and Ross, S. Effects of stress and anxiety on continuous high-speed color naming, *J. exp. Psychol.*, 1956, 51, 13–17.

Eysenck, H. J. Criterion analysis—an application of the hypothetico-deductive method in factor analysis, *Psychol. Rev.*, 1950, 57, 38–53.

Eysenck, H. J. *The structure of human personality.* New York: Wiley, 1953. (Out of print.)

Funkenstein, D. H., King, S. H., and Drolette, M. E. *Mastery of stress.* Cambridge: Harvard Univer. Press, 1957.

Gottschalk, L. A., Kapp, F. T., Ross, W. D., Kaplan, S. M., Silver, H., MacLeod, J. A., Kahn, J. B., Jr., Van Maanen, E. F., and Acheson, G. H. Explorations in testing drugs affecting physical and mental activity, *J. Amer. med. Ass.*, 1956, 161, 1054–1058.

Hilgard, E. R., Jones, L. V., and Kaplan, S. J. Conditioned discrimination as related to anxiety, *J. exp. Psychol.*, 1951, 42, 94–99.

Hull, C. L. *Principles of behavior.* New York: Appleton-Century, 1943.

Kahn, R. L., and Fink, M. Changes in language during electroshock therapy. In P. Hoch and J. Zubin (Eds.), *Psychopathology of communication.* New York: Grune & Stratton, 1958, 126–139.

Kamin, L. J., Bindra, D., Clark, J. W., and Waksberg, H. The interrelations among some behavioural measures of anxiety. *Canad. J. Psychol.*, 1955, 9, 79–83.

King, G. F., Merrell, D. W., Lovinger, E., and Denny, R. M.   Operant motor behaviour in acute schizophrenics.   *J. Pers.*, 1957, 25, 317–326.
Lasagna, L., Mosteller, F., von Felsinger, J. M., and Beecher, H. K.   A study of the placebo response.   *Amer. J. Med.*, 1954, 16, 770–779.
Lehmann, H. E.   Neurophysiologic activity of chlorpromazine in clinical use.   *J. clin. exp. Psychopath.*, 1956, 17, 129–141.
Lehmann, H. E.   Methods of evaluation of drug effects on the human central nervous system.   Paper read at Ass. Res. in nerv. ment. Dis., New York, 1957.
Lehmann, H. E., and Csank, J.   Differential screening of phrenotropic agents in man: psychophysiological test data.   *J. clin. exp. Psychopath.*, 1957, 18, 222–235.
Lehmann, H. E., and Knight, D. A.   Placebo-proneness and placebo-resistance of different psychological functions.   In press, 1960.
Lindsley, O. R.   Operant conditioning in schizophrenia.   *Psych. Res. Rep.*, No. 5, 1956.
Lorr, M.   Multidimensional scale for rating psychiatric patients.   *U.S. Vet. Adm. Tech. Bull.*, TB 10-507, 1953.
Malamud, W., and Sands, S. L.   A revision of the psychiatric rating scale.   *Am. J. Psychiat.*, 1947, 104, 231.
Malmo, R. B.   Anxiety and behavioural arousal.   *J. Psychol. Rev.*, 1957, 64, 276–287.
Peters, H. N., and Murphree, O. O.   The conditioned reflex in the chronic schizophrenic.   *J. clin. Psychol.*, 1954, 10, 126–130.
Pfaffman, C., and Schlosberg, H.   The conditioned knee jerk in psychiatric and normal individuals.   *J. Psychol.*, 1936, 1, 201–206.
Reese, W. G., Doss, R., and Gantt, W. H.   Autonomic responses in differential diagnosis of organic and psychogenic psychoses.   *Arch. Neurol. Psychiat.*, 1953, 70, 778–793.
Reiser, M. F., Reeves, R. B., and Armington, J.   Effect of variations in laboratory procedures and experimenter upon the ballistocardiogram, blood pressure, and heart rate in healthy young men.   *Psychosom. Med.*, 1955, 17, 185–199.
Rogers, C. R., and Dymond, R. F.   *Psychotherapy and personality change.*   Chicago: Univer. of Chicago Press, 1954.
Ryle, G.   *The concept of mind.*   London: Hutchinson's Univer. Lib., 1949.
Saslow, G., Matarazzo, D. J., and Guze, S. B.   The stability of interaction chronograph patterns in psychiatric interviews.   *J. consult. Psychol.*, 1955, 19, 417–430.
Schiff, E., Dougan, C., and Welch, L.   The conditioned PGR and the EEG as indicators of anxiety.   *J. abnorm. soc. Psychol.*, 1949, 44, 549–552.
Schwarz, B. E., Sem-Jacobsen, C. W., and Petersen, M. C.   Effects of mescaline, LSD-25, and adrenochrome on depth electrograms in man.   *Arch. Neurol. Psychiat.*, 1956, 75, 579–587.
Skinner, B. F.   *Science and human behavior.*   New York: Macmillan, 1953.
Sloane, R. B., Saffran, M., and Cleghorn, R. A.   Autonomic and adrenal responsivity in psychiatric patients.   *Arch. Neurol. Psychiat.*, 1958, 79, 549–553.
Spence, K. W.   Current interpretations of learning data and some recent developments in stimulus-response theory.   In *Learning theory, personality theory, and clinical research.*   New York: Wiley, 1953, 1–21.
Spence, K. W., and Taylor, J. A.   Anxiety and strength of the UCS as deter-

miners of the amount of eyelid conditioning. *J. exp. Psychol.*, 1951, 42, 183–188.

Spence, K. W., and Taylor, J. A. The relation of conditioned response strength to anxiety in normal, neurotic and psychotic subjects. *J. exp. Psychol.*, 1953, 45, 265–272.

Stennett, R. G. The relationship of performance level to level of arousal. *J. exp. Psychol.*, 1957, 54, 54–61.

Stephenson, W. The study of behavior: Q-technique and its methodology. Chicago: Univer. of Chicago Press, 1953.

Taylor, J. A. A personality scale of manifest anxiety. *J. abnorm. soc. psychol.*, 1953, 48, 285–290.

Thurstone, L. L. The criterion problem in personality research. Psychometric Laboratory Report, No. 78. Chicago: Univer. of Chicago Press, 1952.

Welch, L., and Kubis, J. The effect of anxiety on the conditioning rate, and stability of the P.G.R. *J. Psychol.*, 1947, 23, 83–91.

Winsor, T. Conditioned vasoconstrictive responses of digital vessels. *Arch. Surg.*, 1958, 76, 193–199.

Wittenborn, J. R. A new procedure for evaluating mental hospital patients. *J. consult. Psychol.*, 1950, 14, 500.

Wolf, S., and Pinsky, R. H. Effects of placebo administration and occurrence of toxic reactions. *J. Amer. med. Ass.*, 1954, 155, 339–341.

The design and conduct of experiments
on the psychological effects of drugs

Because experiments on the psychological effects of drugs are generally complex, it is desirable to be clear about basic principles of design.

Basic Principles of Design

ELIMINATION OF BIAS. An experiment may begin with such a question as, "Does Compound X relieve pain?" Seeking an answer, the investigator may compare the pain reported by subjects before and after the administration of Compound X. This comparison may of course be biased, for factors other than the drug, like perhaps spontaneous recovery from illness, may have lessened the pain. To reduce the likelihood of bias, results obtained from subjects treated with Compound X are compared with results obtained from "control" subjects not treated with the drug.

However, in clinical studies serving therapeutic as well as scientific functions, the use of control subjects raises obvious problems. As a way of minimizing these problems, Lasagna (1955b) has suggested that a drug of uncertain potency can be evaluated, in a controlled clinical study, by comparing it with a "standard" drug whose therapeutic value has been adequately determined. (Morphine has been used as a standard of analgesic potency, for example by Keats, Beecher, and Mosteller [1950].) By this means bias can be avoided without recourse to an untreated control group, and therapeutic bene-

Republished by permission from J. nerv. ment. Dis., 1959, 128, 129–147.

fits can meanwhile be conferred by the standard drug, should the new drug prove to be valueless.

In any event, once the investigator has decided to compare a given set of dosage forms, he must assign subjects to the various dosage forms on a *strictly random* basis, if a valid test of significance is to be applied to the experimental findings.[1]

REDUCTION OF EXPERIMENTAL ERROR. A program of research is effective when it yields rich results per unit expenditure of time, effort, or money. To remain effective a research program must continue to uncover fruitful leads without dissipating excessive energy in pursuit of stray leads. To insure himself against too many unproductive side excursions, the investigator rejects results which fail to reach statistical significance at a specified level; the 5 per cent level is selected quite frequently.

Research efforts are also dissipated when drug effects that actually exist are masked by excessive "experimental error." By "experimental error" is meant the random variations in response which are found to occur naturally after medication. Experimental error may be attributed to variations among subjects before the onset of the experiment; to variations—either environmental or internal to the subject—during the course of the experiment; or to measurement error. Thus variations in reported feelings after drinking a couple of martinis may be due to individual differences in regard to body size or customary alcohol intake, to variations in the emptying time of the stomach, to changes in the social environment, to fluctuations in room temperature or barometric pressure, to changes in composition from one batch of martinis to the next, to spontaneous fluctuations in fatigue or body temperature, or to the unreliability of self-ratings.

It is desirable that the investigator anticipate major sources of error and attempt to control them. He may, for example, establish a controlled laboratory environment for his subjects, regulating room temperature, humidity, illumination, and acoustic noise. Or he may attempt to reduce error by the judicious selection of subjects, by the choice of an appropriate experimental design, or by auxiliary statistical

---

[1] In evaluating the results of a study in which a drug is compared with a placebo or with a standard drug, the *t*-test is applied; when *each* of several drugs is compared with a placebo or with a standard drug, it is most appropriate to apply Dunnett's test (1955). When the distribution assumptions for the *t*-test and for Dunnett's test do not apply (Cochran, 1947; Eisenhart, 1947), the data may be transformed (Bartlett, 1947), or evaluated by means of "non-parametric" methods (Moses, 1952; Siegel, 1956).

analysis of the experimental findings. Naturally, the effort to control a given source of error should be proportional to the degree of disturbance expected from the source of error. Considered throughout this paper are various ways of minimizing the kinds of error which are likely to disturb investigations of the psychological effects of drugs.

SELECTION OF SUBJECTS. Before subjects can be assigned to treatment conditions, they must first be recruited. This task is less simple than might appear at first glance. If, for example, the results obtained from the experimental sample are to be generalized to a specific population, it is necessary to select subjects in such a way that they truly represent this population. In non-clinical studies the population of interest is usually "adult human beings in western society," or even "the entire human race." Although it is hardly possible to obtain thoroughly representative samples of substrata of these, larger populations have been studied occasionally, as in the evaluation of vaccines.

In studying the psychological effects of drugs on human subjects, representative samples are ordinarily obtainable only for "captive" populations, such as those of a hospital or prison. While a so-called captive population may be readily available, and while representative and even complete sampling of this restricted population may be possible, the value of findings obtained from a population of this kind may be quite limited. Thus results obtained after administration of meprobamate to the entire population of X State Mental Hospital have only limited generality, if the investigator is trying to learn about the anti-anxiety effects of the drug, not so much because the particular hospital may be unrepresentative, but because the anxiety prevalent in institutionalized mental patients may differ markedly, both in kind and in degree, from that typical of patients seen in office practice. The value of findings relating to the psychological effects of drugs may, moreover, be impaired, should the captive subjects prove to be uncooperative, poorly motivated, or irresponsible.

Unfortunately, the main interest of the investigator too often lies in some group other than the one which happens to be available.

In order to avoid the risks associated with captive subjects, many investigators deliberately choose to work with selected volunteer subjects. The data obtained by Lasagna (1955b) and by Lasagna and von Felsinger (1954) suggest, however, that an unusually large number of those who volunteered for certain drug experiments suffered from severe psychological maladjustment and were therefore quite unrepresentative of the population-at-large. Clearly, there are disadvantages in the use of either volunteer or captive subjects. The choice between these two kinds of subjects must depend on subject availability, on the kinds of psychological tasks employed to measure the drug effects, as well as on the incentives which can be employed to improve the motivation of subjects reluctant to participate.

The responses of the atypical subjects of Lasagna and von Felsinger (1954) to the drug treatments appear to have been determined, in part, by the pre-experimental pathology of these subjects. The dependence of drug effects on psychopathology and on pre-experimental differences in personality has been noted by other investigators (Bellak, 1948; Hollister, Traub, and Beckman, 1956; Lindemann and Malamud, 1934; von Felsinger, Lasagna, and Beecher, 1955). The effects of drugs are, indeed, modified by a number of characteristics of the individual.

Since differences among individuals affect response to drugs, these differences would also be expected to affect experimental error. Lasagna and von Felsinger (1954) did, in fact, note that the responses of their atypical subjects increased experimental error (although not to the point of obscuring the typical effects of the drugs under study). The reduction of experimental error, by correcting for personality predispositions or other characteristics of the individual, or by care in the selection of subjects, is discussed later in this paper.

SOME EXPERIMENTAL DESIGNS.[2] The simplest kind of drug study is one in which two or more dosage forms are compared (nitrous oxide plus oxygen versus air, for example (Steinberg, 1954)), under standard conditions. Since drug effects may vary with the circumstances surrounding the experiment, it is often desirable to study the effects of a drug over a range of conditions. A "factorial design" (Fisher, 1947), which is an experimental arrangement for studying drug effects over a range of conditions, permits broader generalizations to be drawn with greater efficiency than does a series of separate studies, each limited to a single set of conditions. By furnishing estimates of the interactions between dosage forms and conditions of experimentation, a factorial study also provides information on the conditions which govern the appearance of a given drug effect.

[2] The investigator with little statistical background could profit from a fuller introduction to the subject of experimental designs, such as can be found in Fisher (1947), Finney (1955), and Cochran and Cox (1957). He would find it useful, moreover, to consult a statistician, not only after his data are obtained, but also during the planning of the experiment, before its design is fixed.

Factorial designs have been used extensively in a series of studies conducted at the School of Aviation Medicine (e.g., Hauty, 1954; Hauty, Payne, and Bauer, 1957b; Pearson and Bauer, 1956). In one of these investigations Payne (1955) studied the joint effects of cerebral depressants, motivation, and overlearning on verbal retention. Although the main effects of these three factors were not well established in this study, the interactions among the factors did indicate that both overlearning and motivational feedback are able to forestall an impairment of function by the depressants.

The efficiency of experimentation can be further increased by segregating from experimental error the effects of known sources of error which may not be readily eliminated. Dividing the experiment into relatively homogeneous time units, each of which is a miniature version of the experiment as a whole, is one way of minimizing unwanted variations which occur as the experiment progresses. This design (termed "randomized blocks") is quite suitable for controlled clinical studies (with either ambulatory or hospitalized psychiatric patients) to which subjects are admitted in chronological sequence.

Psychopharmacologists have long recognized that observations on the psychological effects of drugs might be affected by the temporal order or sequence of presentation of drugs or of tests. One of the earliest arrangements for eliminating bias due to order of presentation involved the alternation of drug days and non-drug days. Another scheme for balancing order of presentation is the "crossover" (or "switchback") design, in which dosage form A is presented before dosage form B to one half of the subjects, while dosage form B is presented before dosage form A to the other half of the subjects (see Barmack, 1940); for modified crossover designs see Goodnow, Beecher, Brazier, Mosteller, and Tagiuri (1951) and von Felsinger, Lasagna, and Beecher (1953).

The crossover design is a special case of the "Latin square" design. The Latin square *resembles* randomized blocks in that it segregates some unwanted variation from experimental error. It *differs from* randomized blocks both in its greater complexity (it segregates the effects not of one source of unwanted variation, but of two independent sources of unwanted variation) and in its greater efficiency. The efficiency of the Latin square is usually gained at the expense of the requirement that all interactions be zero, a requirement which, according to McNemar (1951), seriously restricts the use of the Latin square in psychological research. Although there are situations in which interactions are permitted (Gourlay, 1955), and although small interactions are tolerated, in practice, for the remaining situations, the investigator of the psychological effects of drugs is well advised to avoid the use of the Latin square unless he has expert statistical guidance. Some of the difficulties attending the use of the Latin square in studying the psychological effects of drugs are treated in a later section on learning.

In the Latin square all interactions are omitted from the analysis. The efficiency of experimentation can be increased considerably by the deliberate neglect of one or another interaction between dosage forms and conditions of experimentation. Where such interactions are neglected, the effects of these interactions become indistinguishable from the natural variations in the responses being studied, and the neglected interactions are said to be "confounded" with experimental error. For instances of such confounding, the reader is referred to the "split-plot" designs used in several of the studies conducted at the School of Aviation Medicine (e.g., Hauty, 1954; Hauty, Payne, and Bauer, 1957a; Payne and Hauty, 1955). (The split-plot design, it should be noted, may prove useful for studying temporal variations in drug effects; the interaction of drugs with trials can provide a precise estimate of the effects of drugs on learning, for example.)

The investigator may be interested in comparing different quantities or concentrations of the same drug to determine the "regression" (or dependence) of drug effects on dosage. Test performance may, for example, be related to drug concentration in the body fluids (Goldberg, 1943). Drug effects may be related to the quantity of drug administered; thus Keats, Beecher, and Mosteller (1950) indicated that the analgesic potency of a drug can be assayed by relating the dose-response curve to the percentage of pain relief afforded by a standard dose of morphine. Regression studies are by no means incompatible with the designs discussed above; when different quantities of the same drug are included in a factorial design, for example, it is possible to examine the data for regression of drug effects on quantity of drug (cf. Payne, Hauty, and Moore, 1957).

Another technique for increasing the efficiency of experimentation is the analysis of covariance. This procedure corrects experimental observations for the effects of known, but uncontrolled, sources of error (Edwards, 1950; Fisher, 1947; Gourlay, 1953). The correction is applicable when the response to medication is shown to be dependent on an available accessory measure (such as IQ) which is not usually utilized in designing the experiment proper. Although the analysis of covariance is not performed until after the completion of the experiment proper, the selection of accessory measures requires the same thoughtful planning as is required in the design of the experiment proper. A poor choice of accessory measures absorbs effort better spent obtaining additional responses to medication. Good judgment in the choice of accessory measures is especially important, for the opportunity to collect the desired accessory data may be lost once the experiment proper has begun.

The analysis of covariance is by no means the only procedure for utilizing accessory measures. Accessory measures can also be employed to arrange a matched or balanced design (see Steinberg, 1954, for an example), or they can be incorporated into an "index of response," such as the difference between the post-drug and pre-drug values of a given variable (Jellinek and McFarland, 1940). The "difference-score" method, though somewhat less precise than the analysis of covariance, is in common use in psychological research. (But note that it is only appropriate to subtract measures which are on the same scale.) The use of the difference-score method is usually justified, both because of its computational simplicity and because the underlying assumptions do not usually lead to serious error. See Cox (1957) for a thorough discussion of accessory measurements. For instances of the use of the difference-score method in psychopharmacological research, see Goodnow, Beecher, Brazier, Mosteller, and Tagiuri (1951), Steinberg (1954), and von Felsinger, Lasagna, and Beecher (1953); for instances of the use of covariance analysis to adjust post-drug values for pre-drug values of the same variable, see the studies conducted at the School of Aviation Medicine.

The full potentialities of accessory measurements have yet to be realized in psychopharmacological research, despite the frequent adjustment of post-drug values for pre-drug values of the same variable. Covariance analysis could be used profitably to explore the dependence of drug effects on suggestibility and on other personality traits (Haggard and Jellinek, 1942; Lindemann and Malamud, 1934; von Felsinger, Lasagna, and Beecher, 1955), as well as to correct for any such personal characteristics which are found to modify drug effects.

ESSENTIAL DESIGN CONSIDERATIONS VERSUS ECONOMIC DESIGN CONSIDERATIONS. Although some of the basic principles of experimental design have been disseminated widely, one or another of these principles is frequently neglected in studies on the psychological effects of drugs. To be sure, some basic principles are not widely known, while others are difficult to grasp. But even principles which appear to be understood when separately considered may, when interwoven into a design of some complexity, turn out to be a source of difficulty for the investigator.

Consider, for instance, a study by Lehmann and Csank (1957), who wished to determine the effects of each of six drugs on various psychological and physiological measures. Responses were studied before and after medication, and the difference in response was attributed to the medication. A control group was not included in the original study, since the investigators believed the responses to be uninfluenced by learning or by other confounding factors.

After the original study, the investigators, apparently feeling that their conclusions were open to question, decided to check their assumption that the change in response following medication was due to the medication alone. They therefore repeated the study, using in place of the previous six drug groups a single control group, subjects for which were presumably selected after completion of the experiment proper.

Although a control group was introduced to avoid confounding drug effects with the effects of factors like learning, drug effects nevertheless managed to remain confounded, since bias had not been ruled out in assigning subjects to the control group. The structure of this experiment was impaired once the opportunity was lost to assign subjects to drug and control groups at random from a common pool of applicants. Subsequent efforts to bolster the experiment, no matter how vigorous, could not undo the effects of the investigators' original decision regarding the design of the experiment.

This design shortcoming is by no means atypical. It reflects a common difficulty in distinguishing clearly between design features (such as randomization) which *must* be incorporated into a scientific experiment, and design features (such as the use of baseline measures obtained before medication) which only increase the efficiency of experimentation. Psychopharmacologists have too often discarded *essential* design features in their experiments while retaining *economic* design features. In view of the serious consequences of failure to discriminate economic from essential considerations, it seems worthwhile to distinguish the two kinds of considerations more precisely.

The following considerations are *essential* to sound experimentation:

1. It is essential to eliminate or to segregate the effects of any factor which introduces bias into the experiment.

2. To avoid confounding drug effects with the effects of factors such

as learning, it is essential that observations obtained under the influence of a given drug form be compared with observations obtained under control or standard conditions.

3. If results are to be generalized to a given population, it is essential that subjects be representative of that population. (Representativeness implies the use of a randomizing procedure in the selection of subjects; a strict, rather than haphazard, randomizing procedure must be employed.) Because of practical difficulties in sampling those populations which are of greatest interest to the investigator, the representative sampling requirement is usually more relevant to the interpretation of findings than to the design and conduct of the experiment. (Since the subjects of any two studies are rarely representative of the same population, the results of different studies are, strictly speaking, rarely directly comparable to each other.)

4. It is essential to include a randomizing operation in the assignment of subjects to treatment conditions; a strict, rather than haphazard, randomizing procedure must be employed.

5. In order to obtain an estimate of experimental error, it is essential to include a minimum of two observations for each dosage form. The minimum number of observations *for the experiment as a whole* depends on the kinds of confounding which are to be permitted or excluded from the experiment. Decisions about the kinds of confounding to be permitted or excluded rest in part on economic considerations. A decision to obtain more than the required minimum number of observations depends entirely on economic considerations.

6. The analysis of variance is based on several assumptions which must, theoretically, be satisfied (Eisenhart, 1947). Considerable departures from the assumptions can occur in practice, however, without appreciable error (Cochran, 1947). Remedial measures are, moreover, often applicable, where departures from the assumptions are excessive (Bartlett, 1947). The fulfillment of the assumptions underlying the analysis of variance may therefore be regarded as a quasi-essential feature of studies in which the analysis of variance is employed. Similar considerations apply to special designs, such as the Latin square (which assumes zero interactions; see preceding section) or the usual form of covariance analysis (which assumes linearity of regression).

The following considerations relate to *efficiency* of experimentation:

1. Some designs are more efficient than others. The relative efficiency of two designs depends on the designs themselves (the Latin

square is more efficient than randomized blocks, for example) as well as on the circumstances surrounding a given study.

2. Experimental error can be reduced by physical manipulation of various sources of error. Regulation of error by laboratory controls may be expensive or difficult to achieve in certain instances.

3. The fewer the subjects selected from a given population, the smaller is the likelihood of a given drug effect being detected, and the less precise is the estimate of that effect. The number of subjects selected is usually limited, however, by considerations of time, energy, and money. There is, furthermore, a "law of diminishing returns" relating to subjects: a given increase in the number of subjects is more effective when the original number of subjects is small than when the original number of subjects is large.

4. For the detection and estimation of drug effects, the investigator's energies are more richly rewarded by an increase in the number of subjects selected than by a corresponding increase in the number of observations obtained per subject.

5. Experimental error can be reduced by the use of accessory information, such as baseline measures obtained prior to medication. This accessory information can be utilized in various ways (see above) the relative merits of which are discussed by Cox (1957). The collection of accessory information is recommended only when this information is distinctly related to the drug effects being studied, and when the effort and expense of collecting the accessory information are less than the effort and expense of examining additional subjects, or of manipulating various sources of error by physical means. When, on the other hand, subjects are available in adequate numbers, but for limited periods of time, methods of reducing experimental error which do not involve accessory information are indicated.

Before leaving this topic, it is worth noting one more important distinction between essential and economic design considerations. Whereas the investigator can permit himself little leeway in the application of the essential considerations, *each* of which must be satisfied without regard to the others, he may employ one or another economic measure to achieve a given reduction in experimental error. The economic measures operate in concert, competing with one another for inclusion in a given design. Application of the essential considerations depends largely on the investigator's knowledge of these considerations, and on his willingness to apply them rigorously. Application of the economic considerations depends, on the other hand, on the investigator's capacity to appreciate the many psychological, pharmacological, and other facets of the experimental situation, each in proper perspective, and on his capacity to muster his resources to handle, simultaneously and in as judicious a manner as possible, the various practical problems facing him.

Application of the economic considerations is further complicated by another "law of diminishing returns," distinct from the "law" mentioned above, which relates only to number of subjects. The present "law" derives from the fact that economic measures may not only complement one another, but may also provide alternative means to the same end. As economic measures accumulate in a given experiment, there is an increasing likelihood that any newly introduced measure will duplicate the functions of one or more pre-existing economic measures and will therefore make no new contribution to the experiment. The investigator should therefore be aware of the precise functions which each economic measure is expected to serve, so that he may best judge the degree to which a newly introduced measure is likely to improve the experiment as a whole.

Psychological Considerations
Affecting Experimental Outcomes

SUGGESTION. Suggestion is a process that may readily alter the effects of physical treatments administered to human subjects. No one is more aware of this problem than the physician, who has traditionally assigned sugar pills to patients who need to be reassured by some material token of the physician's continuing concern for their welfare. It is not surprising, then, that the placebo—an inert "dummy" substance bearing a superficial resemblance to the active drug studied— has become closely identified with attempts to control suggestion, in studies on the psychological effects of drugs or of other physical treatments (Lasagna, 1955a).

The attitude of the subject toward the experimenter may introduce bias into the results and increase experimental error. In most experimental situations the subjects desire to forward rather than to impede the aims of the investigation (Rosenthal and Frank, 1956). Their wish to comply with rather than to resist the supposed effects of the treatment is likely to favor spurious positive results.

Experiments designed to manipulate the effects of drugs on sensory thresholds, by means of suggestion, indicate the kinds of distortion that can be introduced by suggestion. When a hand lotion was applied to subjects by Gault and Goodfellow (1940), for the ostensible purpose of decreasing chafing, tactile sensitivity was found to be unaffected. The tactile sensitivity of other subjects (to whom the lotion was introduced as a recently developed sensitizing agent) was found to increase. When alcohol was used to remove the lotion from the latter group of subjects, ostensibly for the purpose of returning tactile sensitivity to normal, the threshold was found to rise.

In an experiment by Goodfellow (1946) on coffee drinking, in which subjects were not aware that decaffeinated and regular coffee were being administered on different occasions, auditory thresholds were altered in a similar way by both drinks. After subjects were informed that decaffeinated coffee was being used "just to prove that it was the caffeine that depressed the threshold," all thresholds returned to normal.

Precautions are ordinarily taken, in experiments on drug effects, to reduce the effects of suggestion. Systematic errors due to suggestion can be reduced if the conditions affecting suggestion are kept approximately the same for control and treated subjects. It is customary to administer a placebo to control subjects. While untreated as well as placebo control groups may be employed in a single study, as a further check on the effects of suggestion, this appears to be an uneconomical procedure, since negligible differences have been observed, to date, between untreated and placebo groups (e.g., Hauty and Payne, 1955; Mackworth, 1950; Payne and Hauty, 1954).

The administration of a placebo to control subjects is one aspect of the "double-blind" procedure. This now classical feature of drug studies, in which information regarding the drug treatment assigned to a given subject is withheld from both examiner and subject, is designed further to reduce the effects of suggestion. Knowledge of the treatment assigned to a particular subject may influence the examiner as well as the subject. While some examiners might "bend over backward" to avoid inducing the subject to produce the desired results, there would undoubtedly be many instances in which spurious positive results would be favored by the examiner's knowledge of the treatments assigned to particular subjects. "Blindness" on the part of the examiner reduces the temptation (conscious or otherwise) to alter the atmosphere of the examination, the manner of presentation of test procedures, or the quantification of subjective impressions.

The effectiveness of the double-blind procedure may be vitiated somewhat by drug effects which provide clues, to the subject or to the examiner, regarding the treatment assigned to the subject (Baker and Thorpe, 1957). Placebos employed for research purposes are generally made up to resemble the active substance in appearance, taste, and smell. If the subject has had experience with the active substance, however, and knows or suspects that placebos are being employed in the investigation, he may be led to suspect (in the absence of expected subjective drug effects) that he is the recipient of a placebo. Consideration should therefore be given to the use of placebos which duplicate or mask at least some of the subjective effects of the drug, provided that these effects are incidental to the drug effects being investigated. Thus Mead (1939), studying the effects of ethyl alcohol on performance, succeeded in masking at least the gustatory and gastric sensations following administration of the alcohol by adding peppermint oil to both the control and alcohol doses (also see Hartocollis and Johnson, 1956; Nash, 1959). The investigator would also do well to avoid announcing or acknowledging the use of a placebo, and to employ subjects who are unfamiliar with the use of placebos (Lasagna, 1955b).

Observations pertaining to the validity of the double-blind procedure were made in a study comparing the effects of placebo, caffeine (approximately equivalent to that in two cups of coffee), and two strengths of ethyl alcohol (approximately equivalent to that in two martinis and in four martinis) (Nash, 1959). Although the examiner, working "blind," was unable to distinguish between placebo, caffeine, and "two-martini" subjects, on the basis of their gross behavior, he was able to distinguish subjects in these three groups from the "four martini" subjects. The double-blind procedure thus appears to be of uneven value, being more useful with some dosage forms than with others. It becomes all the more important, then, that the examiner institute measures to increase his "blindness"; that he pay attention to his desires regarding the outcome of the experiment, so that he can prevent these desires from interfering seriously with the experiment; and that he strive for the utmost objectivity in the conduct of the examination. The investigator would also do well, in reporting the results of a study, to indicate the extent to which the double-blind procedure is likely to have achieved its objective in that study.

Additional means are desired for reducing the effects of suggestion on experimental error (the above procedures are primarily designed to reduce bias). Jellinek (1946) and Beecher, Keats, Mosteller, and Lasagna, 1953) have indicated that the inclusion in the experiment of individuals who react to placebo can increase experimental error appreciably, and, conversely, that discrimination among drugs can be sharpened by screening out "placebo reactors." The findings of Lasagna, Mosteller, von Felsinger, and Beecher (1954) suggest that, in comparing the analgesic effects of drugs on postoperative pain, the investigator might well avoid the use of subjects who behave in an immature, dependent, and outwardly responsive fashion. It may also be possible to correct experimental findings for individual differences in suggestibility, by means of the analysis of covariance, provided that appropriate measures of suggestibility can be obtained, and provided that the effects of suggestion are independent of the experimental treatments.[3]

CONFOUNDING OF THE PSYCHOLOGICAL EFFECTS OF DRUGS. A *given* psychological effect of a drug may be masked by psychological phenomena other than suggestion. This section is devoted to problems of confounding that arise in studies of the effects of a drug on *specified* psychological functions.

THE TEST SITUATION. It is important for the investigator to be clear about the kinds of drug effects that he wishes to study. Having a clear idea of the psychological functions which are of primary interest to him, the investigator is able to distinguish the dependent variables of the investigation from those psychological effects which are of secondary interest to him, but which may interfere with the conduct of the investigation. Once the dependent variables are specified, it remains for the investigator to select indices representing these variables. A response is said to be an index of a given psychological function when variations in that response are correlated with variations in the function in question.

Responses which are determined largely by a single function are said to be related *univocally* to that function (Guilford, 1954).

[3] A special form of suggestion may give rise to error when subjects are examined in groups. A subject's need for achievement may be stimulated or depressed when he can compare his performance with those of others (when, for example, he can see that others work more rapidly than he). Communication among subjects should therefore be minimized, unless the investigator is specifically interested in the influence of group processes on drug effects. Recent findings (Nowlis and Nowlis, 1956) suggest that certain drug effects may be altered radically by the atmosphere of the group in which the subject finds himself. Group conditions also appear to modify response to medication in animals (Chance, 1946; Gunn and Gurd, 1940). If it should be established that drug effects can be modified by group conditions, it would be of interest to learn how this modification is brought about.

A univocal relation between response and function is established and maintained by means of appropriate constraints, both external and internal to the subject. The most obvious of these constraints is provided by the experimental task with which the subject is confronted. Appropriate instructions are provided, in addition, to guard against misunderstanding of the task. The constraints provided by the task and by the instructions are not sufficient to guarantee that the subject will actually be engaged by the task. Some subjects approach the experimental task motivated by strong inner needs to perform to the best of their ability. Other subjects are strongly motivated to be helpful to the examiner; when the inner need to excel is insufficient to engage such subjects in the task, they may yet be engaged by means of persuasion, approval, monetary reward, or feedback of results from the examiner.

A test score represents a given psychological function only if minimal "boundary conditions" are met. The response ceases to be a measure of the given function when a minimum of cooperativeness and motivation on the part of the subject is lacking. These are not the only boundary conditions that must be satisfied to preserve the univocal relation between a response and the function it purportedly represents. It is also presupposed that the subject is able to understand the instructions, to perceive the task, and to communicate his responses. Thus, when a pencil-and-paper test of abstract reasoning is administered to a person, it is assumed that he can see and write. But, if the subject's ability to receive or transmit information is impaired, his test score cannot be taken to represent his capacity to reason abstractly.

CONFOUNDED EFFECTS. The experimenter's attempts to establish the boundary conditions for a given test may be undermined by the very experimental treatment that is being applied. A drug may so alter boundary conditions within the subject that responses to the test may not represent the psychological function in question. Thus a test may be invalidated by a drug-induced reduction in the subject's cooperativeness or motivation, or by a blocking of the subject's channels of communication.

Several steps can be taken to deal with the problems associated with the confounding of the psychological effects of a drug.

1. Dosage strengths which are likely to produce undesirable confounding effects in a substantial number of subjects should be avoided whenever possible.

2. A drug may block channels of communication which, while utilized in a given test of a function, are not essential for the exercise of the function itself. When the relation between a test and the function it represents is disrupted by such a blocking of communication, the test should be redesigned, if possible, to utilize channels of communication which remain open. Thus a test involving visual presentation of stimuli and graphic response might possibly be converted to auditory presentation and vocal response, should a given dose of a drug impair vision and handwriting but leave speech and hearing unimpaired.

3. When the measurement of drug-induced changes in capacity is affected by drug-induced changes in attitude, the examiner might wish to conduct the examination of each subject in a manner designed to elicit the best performance of that particular subject. Treating each subject in such an individual manner involves subjective judgments on the part of the examiner, who should therefore be wary lest his personal attitudes toward the subject obscure the actual drug effects. Such individualized treatment of subjects is even more risky in the study of drug-induced changes in attitude than it is in the study of drug-induced changes in capacity.

4. The confounding of drug-induced changes in capacity by drug-induced changes in attitude can be reduced by careful selection of subjects. Given a drug which reduces the subject's desire to please the examiner, for example, there is less likelihood of such confounding with subjects having a strong inner need for achievement than with subjects whose strivings are prompted by the desire to gain approval from others.

5. When the confounding of drug effects cannot be avoided, one of two procedures may be followed:

The first procedure is simply to eliminate those subjects in whom the confounding effects occur. This is practical only when the confounding is readily detected, and when it does not occur in too large a fraction of the experimental sample. In studying the acute effects of one of the phenothiazine derivatives on abstract reasoning, for example, one might wish to eliminate those subjects who find it difficult to take a paper and pencil test because their vision has been blurred by the drug.

A second approach centers on attempts to reveal the confounding of drug effects by an analysis of the data. The regression of test performance on the confounding variable may be studied, if a measure of the confounding variable is available. The analysis of covariance cannot, however, be employed to correct for the confounding of two or more effects of the same experimental treatments (Gourlay, 1953). Factor analysis might be employed to separate the confounded effects; a properly selected test battery must be administered, however, if the variance associated with the secondary, disturbing factors is to be segregated from the variance associated with the direct action of the drug on the dependent variable.

LEARNING. Learning is another psychological factor which can distort the measurement of the psychological effects of drugs. Learning may be a source of difficulty when response sets are progressively altered as the subject becomes more familiar with the tasks, or when specific stimulus elements of a pretreatment test are recalled during post-treatment testing.

Progressive alteration of response sets may give rise to several problems:

1. Various investigators (e.g., Fleishman, 1953; Fleishman and Hempel, 1954, 1955) have shown that the psychological functions underlying test performance may shift as response sets are altered during the course of a test. Such a shift in psychological functions reduces the likelihood that a test score will be related univocally to a given psychological function.

2. There is an increase in experimental error when practice effects during a test differ from subject to subject.

3. Drug effects under study become confounded with some of the practice effects, if response sets are altered during the post-treatment testing as well as during the pretreatment testing, and if learning is affected by the experimental treatments.

4. When crossover or Latin square designs are used, drug-induced changes in learning capacity may readily be confounded with the drug effects which are of primary interest to the investigator. In the crossover design, for example, half of the subjects are first tested in the drug-free state, and the remainder is first tested in the drugged state. The results of such a crossover study may be biased (Jellinek and McFarland, 1940); for example, the drug may impair the capacity of subjects who are first tested in the drugged state to understand the task which is set before them.

These problems relating to the response sets of the subject can be minimized when the investigator limits himself to bright subjects or to easy tests. It is desirable, in any event, to make sure that subjects receive adequate test instructions, that subjects work sample problems to test their understanding of the instructions, that subjects learn about their performance on the sample problems, and that sufficient experience be gained before the test proper so that subjects are operating near the flat portion of the practice curve during the test proper. These suggestions are particularly important when crossover or Latin square designs are used.

Learning may adversely affect the experimental results in yet another way. Post-treatment performance on verbal tests (such as tests of memory for meaningful material) and on projective tests may be distorted because the subject remembers the specific stimulus elements of the task, or the responses to the task, from the pretreatment period. Subjects may remember the earlier material in different degrees, and memory of the earlier material may be affected by the experimental treatments. Alternate test forms which are equivalent or parallel should be provided if the post-treatment testing takes place within hours, weeks, or possibly even months of the pretreatment testing (Guilford, 1954).

The reports of von Felsinger, Lasagna, and Beecher (1953) and of Mackworth (1950) illustrate how some of the problems relating to learning can be handled.

Pharmacological Considerations
Affecting Experimental Outcomes

The psychological effects of a drug are influenced by the subject's pharmacological history as well as by a host of physiological factors intervening between the experimental administration of the drug and the response of the subject to the experimental task. Some of these influences are discussed below.

SECONDARY DRUG EFFECTS. There are many ways of classifying the effects of a drug. The drug effects which are of primary interest to the investigator are distinguishable from those of secondary interest, once the investigator specifies the dependent variables of the study. Physiological as well as psychological effects may be considered secondary in a given investigation. A most important class of secondary drug effects, in almost any investigation of the psychological effects of drugs in human beings, are those (toxic) effects producing serious physical illness or death (Goodman and Gilman, 1955).

The non-toxic secondary effects may be classified on the basis of their interference or non-interference with the investigation. Aside from the production of serious illness or death, secondary effects may interfere with the investigation in several ways.

1. They may alter the expected course of drug effects by interfering with the absorption or metabolism of the drug. Thus pylorospasm induced by an oral dose of a drug may hamper or prevent further absorption of the drug (Haggard, Greenberg and Lolli, 1941).

2. They may prevent the realization of the boundary conditions required for given interpretations of psychological test scores. This has been discussed in an earlier section.

3. They may interfere with investigations of the mechanisms of drug action. One may wish to correlate the psychological and physiological effects of a drug which acts directly on the central nervous system, in order to form inferences relating behavior to central nervous action. Such inferences may be invalid, however, should the drug affect the central nervous system indirectly, as well as directly. Thus mild distress resulting from direct irritation of the gastric mucosa by the drug may distract the subject from a psychological task, confounding drug effects mediated directly by the central nervous system with effects mediated by the gastric mucosa. This confounding is not the problem in investigations of the *overall* effects of a drug, but it is troublesome when the investigator focuses his attention on a *given kind* of drug action.

SHORT-TERM VERSUS LONG-TERM EFFECTS. The acute effects of a single dose of a drug may differ qualitatively as well as quantitatively from the chronic effects of repeated doses.

Investigations of the psychological effects of drugs on normal human subjects are typically concerned with the acute effects of a single, isolated dose. In these investigations, subjects are generally examined after the drug has been absorbed, but before it has been metabolized. For drugs such as reserpine, which produce their psychological actions after the drug has been metabolized, the investigator will usually wish to study the delayed effects of the drug.

The short-term effects of a single dose may be affected by a history of repeated use of the drug prior to the start of the experiment (Goodman and Gilman, 1955; Jellinek and McFarland, 1940). Goldberg (1943) found, for example, that a given drug effect could be produced in abstainers by a lower blood alcohol concentration than that required for chronic drinkers. In studying a drug whose effects are modified by habituation, the investigator may wish to limit himself to subjects having a specified amount of experience with the drug. He can, alternatively, control degree of experience by means of a factorial design. Adjustment for degree of experience, by means of covariance analysis, is a third possibility—but note that placebo groups, or other treatment groups whose performance is unaffected by habituation to the drug in question, cannot be included in the covariance analysis. Since information relating to habituation must usually be based on the subject's testimony, this is one more reason for having reliable subjects, particularly when a stigma is attached to accurate reporting of the subject's experience with, say, a narcotic drug.

A series of doses may be administered by the investigator, in place of a single dose, as when a graduated increase in dosage is required to bring the internal concentration of, for example, a bromide up to a desired level; or, in clinical studies, when little therapeutic effect is expected from a single dose; or in order to minimize undesired effects which may be most prominent after the first few doses (as with some tranquilizers). Experimental error may be introduced from many sources when doses are repeated over a long time, unless the subject is institutionalized, or unless some other form of rigorous control over his daily activities is instituted.

CONTROL OF EFFECTIVE DRUG CONCENTRATIONS. While the experimental treatment consists of the administration of a given dose of the drug, the action of the drug depends on its concentration at the sites at which the given action is effected. There is no one-to-one correspondence between the dosage level and the effects of the drug at its sites of action, since the intensity of the drug effects depends on the route by which the drug is administered, the pathways in the body along which it travels, the stages in which it is processed in the body, and the rate of processing at each stage (Goodman and Gilman, 1955). Where the experimenter is interested in studying the mechanisms of drug action, he would do well to develop techniques for controlling the concentration of the drug at its sites of action. Such controls are desirable even when there is only a secondary interest in mechanisms of action, since these controls are frequently of value in reducing bias and experimental error. This is especially true in investigations of the acute effects of drugs. Several procedures for controlling the concentration of the drug at its sites of action are considered.

1. Typically, the investigator wishes to study the *action of a given dose* of a drug. After being absorbed, this dose is distributed among the various body fluids. When a given quantity of drug is administered to different individuals, the drug concentration at a given site of action tends to vary inversely with the overall volume of body fluid. In order to correct for individual differences in the volume of the body fluids, doses are administered in proportion to the weight or surface area of the body (Goodman and Gilman, 1955; Lasagna, 1956), either of which is an index of the volume of the body fluids. The administration of drugs on the basis of body weight or surface area results in a substantial reduction in experimental error. (Jellinek and McFarland [1940] provide an example of how experimental efforts can be vitiated by a failure to consider body weight or surface area.) When doses are administered without regard to body fluid volume, covariance analysis can be employed, at times, to adjust drug effects for body weight or surface area.

When doses are administered according to body weight or surface area, the experimental treatment can no longer be stated in terms of the absolute quantity of drug administered, since the quantity of drug varies from individual to individual for a given experimental treatment. The experimental treatments are defined in terms referring to the interior of the body: the independent variable is the anticipated concentration of the drug in the body fluids, after absorption is completed. Adjustments for body weight or surface area take into account only the volume of the body fluids; errors due to other "internal" factors, such as variation in the emptying time of the stomach, are unaffected.[4]

2. In studying the *acute effects* of a drug, the investigator may wish to compare the subject's performance on various tests administered

[4] In clinical studies dosage is frequently varied according to the examiner's *personal* evaluation of the subject's situation, rather than on the basis of some *objective* criterion such as body weight. Thus an investigator of the chronic effects of repeated chlorpromazine administration, suspecting that the optimal therapeutic dose differs markedly from situation to situation, may vary the dose from subject to subject, and from time to time for a given subject. This procedure is commendable as a therapeutic technique for use with a drug of established potency. It is, furthermore, clearly appropriate in experiments designed to determine whether individual adjustment of dosage is an effective procedure. Individual adjustment of dosage is of questionable value, however, in experiments designed to evaluate the effects of a drug of unknown potency, for it presupposes that the examiner can detect the very drug effects whose existence is being questioned by the investigator, and whose confirmation awaits the completion of the experiment.

during a single session. Since temporal variations in the drug effects, during the period of test administration, may introduce bias or increase experimental error, it is desirable to maintain the drug effects at a uniform level throughout the testing period. Several methods are available for maintaining drug effects at a uniform level.

Drugs administered orally tend to be absorbed in the small intestine; the temporal course of the drug effects depends, therefore, on the condition of the gastrointestinal tract. Taken on an empty stomach, a drug tends to be absorbed more readily (Haggard, Greenberg, and Lolli, 1941); consequently, the rate of rise and decline of the drug effects is more rapid, and the plateau at the peak of the drug concentration curve is of briefer duration.[5] When a drug is ingested after a meal (particularly when the contents of the meal prolong the emptying time of the stomach), the effects of the drug are somewhat reduced in intensity, but more prolonged and more uniform in time. Quantities of drug which have been metabolized or excreted can be replenished by maintenance doses. Drug levels in the body can be maintained more smoothly, in theory, by the use of sustained release preparations (adequate information regarding the efficacy of these preparations is not yet available, however). For any of these techniques of oral administration, it is important to avoid the use of highly irritating doses, since pylorospasm may prevent the full absorption of the dose and may produce effects which mask the drug effects under study.

When there is a series of drugs, such as the barbiturates, which produce similar effects but vary in respect to the duration of their actions, the investigator can select a long-acting drug to maintain the drug effects at a uniform level over a prolonged period. The long-acting barbiturates, however, have unpleasant after-effects.

A uniform drug concentration can also be maintained in the blood, over a long interval, by the use of continuous intravenous injection. This method has several distinct advantages (some of which are also enjoyed in the continuous administration of gaseous drugs [Steinberg, 1954]) as follows:

> That component of experimental error resulting from variation in the rate of absorption from the gastrointestinal tract is eliminated.
> An almost instantaneous control of the rate of change of drug

[5] There are exceptions to this generalization. Drugs such as reserpine have long-delayed effects. The decline of the effects of drugs which are not too readily metabolized, such as methyl alcohol, depends very little on the rate of absorption.

concentration in the blood is possible; this is in marked contrast to the situation existing after the oral ingestion of a long-acting drug or of a sustained release preparation.

Undesirable after-effects of a drug are minimized, since the introduction of the drug into the blood stream is readily halted as soon as the experiment is completed.

Sensory cues to the nature of the drug administered are reduced.

Continuous intravenous administration is not without disadvantage, however. The following observations seem relevant here:

Subjects with inaccessible veins suffer some physical trauma— which can be minimized by care in applying the needle.

Subjects may grow anxious over insertion of the needle, or at the sight of their own blood; care is required to avoid provoking undue anxiety.

Movement of the injected limb is hampered.

Injections lasting much longer than an hour tend to be uncomfortable.

Several investigators (e.g., Brown, 1940; Newman, 1935, 1941) have been enthusiastic in recommending continuous intravenous injection, despite its limitations. The method is frequently employed in the clinic, and it appears to be worthy of greater attention by investigators planning experimental studies.

Maintaining the concentration of a drug at a uniform level in the blood, or even at the sites of drug action, does not in itself insure that the *effects* of the drug will be maintained at a uniform level (Newman, 1941). Mirsky, Piker, Rosenbaum, and Lederer (1941), observing that the effects of ethyl alcohol declined even when the blood levels were maintained over a period of hours, postulated a central nervous adaptation (habituation effects occurring within a few hours). The possibility of a short-term adaptation of the central nervous system should be kept in mind when subjects are examined for lengthy periods under the influence of drugs (Beecher, 1952).

3. There is likely to be some *temporal variation in the concentration* of the drug at the sites of its action, whatever the mode of drug administration; this variation is, moreover, likely to be correlated from subject to subject. If, furthermore, drug effects vary in time because of a short-term central nervous system adaptation to the drug, this variation is also likely to be correlated from subject to subject. Given such systematic variations in time, a comparison of test scores obtained at widely spaced intervals during a single test session is likely to be biased.

These sources of bias, which are absent in the control group and are therefore unaffected by the use of a control group, may be minimized by randomizing the order in which the psychological tests are administered. Randomization of test order has two disadvantages.

The first such disadvantage is that subjects must be examined singly. The efficiency of experimentation which may be achieved when subjects are examined in groups cannot then be realized.

A second problem is that the internal concentration of the drug, at the time any given test is administered, becomes more variable from subject to subject. If the drug actually affects the functions being studied, there will be an increase in experimental error for the treated subjects; if there is a control group of untreated or placebo subjects, however, there will be no corresponding increase in experimental error for this group. Since procedures for handling heterogeneity of variance may be cumbersome, it is advisable to minimize variations in drug concentration by one of the methods suggested above, even if the order in which tests are administered is randomized. When variations in drug concentration are well regulated, the increase in experimental error for all treatments combined is likely to be small.

Bias due to temporal variations in drug concentration (or to adaptation) may be greatly reduced, even when subjects are examined in groups, provided that the tests are presented in two opposite orders, each order being employed for one half of the subjects. The reversal of test order removes these sources of bias only when the rate of change of drug concentration (or adaptation) is symmetrical about the midpoint of the testing period. Such symmetry is more likely to exist when sustained release preparations or long-acting drugs are employed, or when drugs are administered after a meal.

The symmetrical placement of equivalent subtests about the midpoint of the testing period also provides a means of minimizing bias due to temporal variations in drug concentration. Such a procedure was followed by Hartocollis and Johnson (1956), who compared the effects of alcohol on several tests of verbal fluency. Bias due to temporal variations can be eliminated almost completely by combining the symmetrical placement of equivalent subtests with the presentation of tests in opposite orders to different groups of subjects.

4. The *adequacy of the investigator's efforts to control the concentration* of the drug in the body fluids can be evaluated, at times, by analyzing the drug content of samples of body fluid. (For many drugs, such as the barbiturates [cf. Goodnow et al., 1951] and most of the psychopharmacological agents that have excited interest in recent years, satisfactory methods for determining drug levels in small

quantities of body fluid have yet to be developed.) The estimate of drug concentration based on a particular sample of fluid may differ appreciably from the concentration at the sites of drug action, especially when the drug is first being absorbed (Goodman and Gilman, 1955; Haggard and Jellinek, 1942). This suggests that the analysis of samples obtained from sites such as the finger-tip which may be remote from the sites of drug action is most meaningful when the drug concentrations of the various body fluids have reached equilibrium. It should be noted that, for a given drug level of finger-tip blood, the effects observed during the early absorption phase are unlikely to have the same intensity as the effects observed after equilibrium has been reached.

When the internal concentration of the drug varies excessively, from subject to subject, or from test to test, there is a corresponding increase in experimental error. Some of the lost information might be recovered by analyzing the regression of drug effects on drug concentration in the body fluids. (Goldberg's investigations [1943] indicate that striking relationships may be observed by studying the regression of performance on blood alcohol level.)

Conclusion

A large number of factors is seen to have a bearing on the design of studies relating to the psychological effects of drugs. In designing a particular study, the investigator takes as his starting point the objectives which he wishes to realize. Which drug effects are to be studied? Which drug comparisons are desired? Is interest focussed on acute drug effects or on chronic drug effects. Is a laboratory study or a clinical study desired? Which kinds of confounding are especially to be avoided; which kinds of confounding can be tolerated?

In order to realize his objectives, the investigator needs an adequate understanding of the many psychological and pharmacological factors which affect the outcomes of studies on the psychological effects of drugs. He should, moreover, appreciate those design features (such as randomization) on which the validity of his conclusions depend, as well as those design features (such as analysis of covariance) which affect the efficiency with which he utilizes the resources available to him. With such understanding, the investigator is ready to formulate procedures capable of eliciting answers to the questions he poses, economically and without bias or undesired confounding.

REFERENCES

Baker, A. A., and Thorpe, J. G. Placebo response. *Arch. Neurol. Psychiat.*, 1957, 78, 57–60.

Barmack, J. E. The effect of 10 mg. of benzedrine sulfate on the Otis test scores of college students. *Amer. J. Psychiat.*, 1940, 97, 163–166.

Bartlett, M. S. The use of transformations. *Biometrics*, 1947, 3, 39–52.

Beecher, H. K. Experimental pharmacology and measurement of the subjective response. *Science*, 1952, 116, 157–162.

Beecher, H. K., Keats, A. S., Mosteller, F., and Lasagna, L. The effectiveness of oral analgesics (morphine, codeine, acetylsalicylic acid) and the problem of placebo "reactors" and "non-reactors." *J. Pharmacol. exp. Therap.*, 1953, 109, 393–400.

Bellak, L. *Dementia praecox.* New York: Grune & Stratton, 1948.

Brown, R. R. The order of certain psychophysiological events following intravenous injections of morphine. *J. gen. Psychol.*, 1940, 22, 321–340.

Chance, M. R. A. Aggregation as a factor influencing the toxicity of sympathomimetic amines in mice. *J. Pharmacol. exp. Therap.*, 1946, 87, 214–219.

Cochran, W. G. Some consequences when the assumptions for the analysis of variance are not satisfied. *Biometrics*, 1947, 3, 22–38.

Cochran, W. G., and Cox, G. M. *Experimental designs.* (2nd ed.) New York: Wiley, 1957.

Cox, D. R. The use of a concomitant variable in selecting an experimental design. *Biometrika*, 1957, 44, 150–158.

Dunnett, C. W. A multiple comparison procedure for comparing several treatments with a control. *J. Amer. statis. Ass.*, 1955, 50, 1096–1121.

Edwards, A. L. *Experimental design in psychological research.* New York: Rinehart, 1950.

Eisenhart, C. The assumptions underlying the analysis of variance. *Biometrics*, 1947, 3, 1–21.

Finney, D. J. *Experimental design and its statistical basis.* Chicago: Univer. of Chicago Press, 1955.

Fisher, R. A. *The design of experiments.* (4th ed.) Edinburgh: Oliver and Boyd, 1947.

Fleishman, E. A. A factor analysis of intra-task performance on two psychomotor tasks. *Psychometrika*, 1953, 18, 45–55.

Fleishman, E. A., and Hempel, W. E., Jr. Changes in factor structure of a complex psychomotor test as a function of practice. *Psychometrika*, 1954, 19, 239–252.

Fleishman, E. A., and Hempel, W. E., Jr. The relation between abilities and improvement with practice in a visual discrimination reaction task. *J. exp. Psychol.*, 1955, 49, 301–312.

Gault, R. H., and Goodfellow, L. D. Sources of error in psycho-physical measurements. *J. gen. Psychol.*, 1940, 23, 197–200.

Goldberg, L. Quantitative studies on alcohol tolerance in man. *Acta Physiol. Scand.* (Suppl. XVI), 1943, 5.

Goodfellow, L. D. Significant incidental factors in the measurement of auditory sensitivity. *J. gen. Psychol.*, 1946, 35, 33–41.

Goodman, L. S., and Gilman, A. *The pharmacological basis of therapeutics; a textbook of pharmacology, toxicology, and therapeutics for physicians and medical students.* (2nd ed.) New York: Macmillan, 1955.

Goodnow, R. E., Beecher, H. K., Brazier, M. A. B., Mosteller, F., and Tagiuri, R. Physiological performance following a hypnotic dose of a barbiturate. *J. Pharmacol. exp. Therap.*, 1951, 102, 55–61.

Gourlay, N. Covariance and its applications in psychological research. *Brit. J. statist. Psychol.*, 1953, 6, 25–34.

Gourlay, N. F-test bias for experimental designs of the Latin square type. *Psychometrika*, 1955, 20, 273–287.

Guilford, J. P. *Psychometric methods.* (2nd ed.) New York: McGraw-Hill, 1954.

Gunn, J. A., and Gurd, M. R. The action of some amines related to adrenaline. Cyclohexylalkylamines. *J. Physiol.*, 1940, 97, 453–470.

Haggard, H. W., Greenberg, L. A., and Lolli, G. The absorption of alcohol with special reference to its influence on the concentration of alcohol appearing in the blood. *Quart. J. Stud. Alcohol*, 1941, 1, 684–726.

Haggard, H. W., and Jellinek, E. M. *Alcohol explored.* Garden City, N. Y.: Doubleday, 1942.

Hartocollis, P., and Johnson, D. M. Differential effects of alcohol on verbal fluency. *Quart. J. stud. Alcohol*, 1956, 17, 183–189.

Hauty, G. T. The effects of drugs upon the components of hand steadiness. *USAF Sch. Aviat. Med. Proj. Rep.*, Proj. 21-1601-0004, Rep. No. 5, 1954.

Hauty, G. T., and Payne, R. B. Mitigation of work decrement. *J. exp. Psychol.*, 1955, 49, 60–67.

Hauty, G. T., Payne, R. B., and Bauer, R. O. Effects of normal air and *dextro-amphetamine* upon work decrement induced by oxygen impoverishment and fatigue. *J. Pharmacol. exp. Therap.*, 1957, 119, 385–389. (a)

Hauty, G. T., Payne, R. B., and Bauer, R. O. Effects of oxygen and *dextro-amphetamine* upon work decrement. *USAF Sch. Aviat. Med. Proj. Rep.*, Rep. No. 56–127, 1957. (b)

Hollister, L. E., Traub, L., and Beckman, W. G. Psychiatric uses of reserpine or chlorpromazine: Results of double-blind studies. In N. S. Kline (ed.), *Psychopharmacology.* Washington, D. C.: Amer. Ass. Adv. Sci., 1956, 65–74.

Jellinek, E. M. Clinical tests on comparative effectiveness of analgesic drugs. *Biometrics Bull.*, 1946, 2, 87–91.

Jellinek, E. M. and McFarland, R. A. Analysis of psychological experiments on the effects of alcohol. *Quart. J. Stud. Alcohol*, 1940, 1, 272–371.

Keats, A. S., Beecher, H. K., and Mosteller, F. Measurement of pathological pain in distinction to experimental pain. *J. appl. Physiol.*, 1950, 3, 35–44.

Lasagna, L. Placebos. *Sci. Amer.*, 1955, 193, 68–71.

Lasagna, L. The controlled clinical trial: Theory and practice. *J. chron. Dis.*, 1955, 1, 353–367. (b)

Lasagna, L. Drug effects as modified by aging. *J. chron. Dis.*, 1956, 3, 567–574.

Lasagna, L., Mosteller, F., von Felsinger, J. M., and Beecher, H. K. A study of the placebo response. *Amer. J. Med.*, 1954, 16, 770–779.

Lasagna, L., and von Felsinger, J. M. The volunteer subject in research. *Science*, 1954, 120, 359–361.

Lehmann, H. E., and Csank, J. Differential screening of phrenotropic agents in man: Psychophysiologic test data. *J. clin. exp. Psychopath.*, 1957, 18, 222–235.

Lindemann, E., and Malamud, W. Experimental analysis of the psychopathological effects of the intoxicating drugs. *Amer. J. Psychiat.*, 1934, 90, 853–879.

Mackworth, N. H. Researches on the measurement of human performance. Med. Res. Counc. Spec. Rep. Ser., Rep. No. 268, 1950.

McNemar, Q. On the use of latin squares in psychology. *Psychol. Bull.*, 1951, 48, 398–401.

Mead, L. C. The effects of alcohol on performances of different intellectual complexity. *J. gen. Psychol.*, 1939, 21, 3–23.

Mirsky, I. A., Piker, P., Rosenbaum, M., and Lederer, H. "Adaptation" of the central nervous system to varying concentrations of alcohol in the blood. *Quart. J. Stud. Alcohol*, 1941, 2, 35–45.

Moses, L. E. Non-parametric statistics for psychological research. *Psychol. Bull.*, 1952, 49, 122–143.

Nash, H. Psychological effects of ethyl alcohol and caffeine. *Amer. Psychol.*, 1959, 14, 373. (Abstract)

Newman, H. W. Alcohol injected intravenously. Some psychological and psychopathological effects in man. *Amer. J. Psychiat.*, 1935, 91, 1343–1352.

Newman, H. W. *Acute alcoholic intoxication.* Palo Alto, Calif.: Stanford Univer. Press, 1941.

Nowlis, V., and Nowlis, H. The description and analysis of mood. *Ann. N. Y. Acad. Sci.*, 1956, 65, 345–355.

Payne, R. B. Some psychological factors governing the impairment of verbal retention by cerebral depressants. *USAF Sch. Aviat. Med. Proj. Rep.*, Rep. No. 55-52, 1955.

Payne, R. B., and Hauty, G. T. The effects of experimentally induced attitudes upon task proficiency. *J. exp. Psychol.*, 1954, 47, 267–273.

Payne, R. B., and Hauty, G. T. Effect of psychological feedback upon work decrement. *J. exp. Psychol.*, 1955, 50, 343–351.

Payne, R. B., Hauty, G. T., and Moore, E. W. Restoration of tracking proficiency as a function of amount and delay of analeptic medication. *J. comp. Physiol. Psychol.*, 1957, 50, 146–149.

Pearson, R. G., and Bauer, R. O. The effects of morphine-nalorphine mixtures on psychomotor performance. *USAF Sch. Aviat. Med. Proj. Rep.*, Rep. No. 55–137, 1956.

Rosenthal, D., and Frank, J. D. Psychotherapy and the placebo effect. *Psychol. Bull.*, 1956, 53, 294–302.

Siegel, S. *Nonparametric statistics for the behavioral sciences.* New York: McGraw-Hill, 1956.

Steinberg, H. Selective effects of an anaesthetic drug on cognitive behavior. *Quart. J. exp. Psychol.*, 1954, 6, 170–180.

von Felsinger, J. M., Lasagna, L., and Beecher, H. K. The persistence of mental impairment following a hypnotic dose of a barbiturate. *J. Pharmacol. and exp. Therap.*, 1953, 109, 284–291.

von Felsinger, J. M., Lasagna, L., and Beecher, H. K. Drug-induced mood changes in man. 2. Personality and reactions to drugs. *J. Amer. med. Ass.*, 1955, 157, 1113–1119.

Placebo effect

Perhaps the best introduction to this presentation is to indicate immediately the relative status of the placebo in the schema of research methodology dealing with drugs and the capacity of the placebo to bring about therapeutic changes in behavior. Drug evaluators, in the behavioral sciences particularly, are confronted with two phenomena which must be distinguished if they are to make conclusive statements regarding drug reactivity: (a) the specific, pharmacologically induced effects of the drugs themselves, and (b) the reactions of the subjects to non-specific stimulation. The relative influence of either of these phenomena determines to what extent investigators can generalize their results. If phenomenon (a) is immediately convincing in terms of objective criteria, then phenomenon (b) requires little or no attention. On the other hand, to the extent that phenomenon (a) is less obvious, the analysis of phenomenon (b) becomes more important.

In psychiatric research, where subjective evaluation plays so important a role, the exact, pharmacologically induced effects of our drugs are not always immediately discernible. It has, therefore, become necessary to use placebos in drug research. Thus we can control to some measure those factors other than the pharmacological one which can alleviate psychopathology in patients, i.e. which result in "placebo reactivity." Little is known about the "why" of placebo reactivity. The evidence so far tells us only that it is the resultant of many variables. Also, our experience tells us that its experimental control is essential if we are to say anything definitive about the effects of unknown drugs.

In two reviews Kurland (1957, 1958) has outlined some of the complexities of the placebo effect. The primary aspects of this material will be presented below, complemented by data from other reports relating to placebo reactivity which have since appeared in the literature.

A review of the literature indicates that there are four categories into which most studies on placebo and placebo reactivity can be grouped. These are: (1) definition of placebos; (2) determination of the range of placebo reactivity; (3) factors influencing such reactivity; and (4) personality variables relating to placebo reactivity.

Definitions of Placebo

The extent to which the placebo has been utilized, knowingly or unknowingly, in the past century is perhaps best indicated by a statement made by DuBois (1946): "In the light of our present knowledge, about one-third of a list of 160 drugs in the New York Hospital pharmacopoeia of 1810 would be considered inert. One-sixth to one-third of the drugs in the same pharmacopoeia of 20 years ago would also be considered inert."

A trend at present might well be indicated by the appearance of a report by Fellner (1958) in an article to which he gave the intriguing title, "Tranquilizing drugs in general practice, or the triumph of the impure placebo." He pointed out that among psychiatrists the impression is constantly gaining ground that the average physician in general practice uses tranquilizers far too often and at far too low a dosage. There is good evidence that the pharmacologic effect of the tranquilizing drugs given in such "conservative" dosages is negligible.

Because of the widespread and apparently successful use of inert, or nearly inert, substances, there have been more and more attempts to define this phenomenon. Fischer and Dlin (1956) define the placebo as "the agent employed with or without some ritual, but always with the suggestion or implication of its power or helpful properties," and placebo reaction as "the physiologic and psychologic reaction to the administration and acceptance of the placebo . . . ." This reaction can be positive or beneficial, or it can be negative and detrimental.

Out of Beecher's studies (1955) an operational definition of the term "placebo" as applied to experimental studies of drug action has evolved. He views it as an aid in distinguishing drug actions from the effects of suggestion and as a controlling factor in the unbiased assessment of experimental results. Also, an essential element of this definition is that placebo must be used in double-blind fashion; that is, undetectable as a placebo by observer as well as by subject. Implicit in the last stipulation is the occasional need for disguising the placebo by adding another drug which will mimic the side effects of the compound under study. It may thus be seen that a placebo need not always be a pharmaceutically inert agent. The terms "positive" and "negative" placebo identify the presence or absence of a mimetic action.

Whatever one's definition of the placebo, the doctor-patient relationship is essential to its use. This relationship provides the emotional overtones without which no changes, positive or negative, will take place in the patient. As Wolf and Hagans (1957) have stated, the placebo must be recognized as "a symbol of the availability of doctors to help." This must be qualified in specific situations. Obviously the postoperative patient in pain would interpret a placebo quite differently from the schizophrenic patient in an acute panic state.

Determination of the Range of Placebo Reactivity

One of the earliest and most extensive surveys of placebo reactivity, totaling 15 studies and involving 1082 patients with physical and psychiatric illnesses, was conducted by Beecher (1955). He found that placebos were reported as having an average effectiveness of 32.2 per cent ± 2.2 per cent. He also studied the "toxic" and other subjective side effects of placebos. Kurland (1957) evaluated the range of placebo reactivity reported in a small sampling of psychiatric studies. A range of 4 to 52 per cent was found, and the observation was made that there was no study utilizing placebos in which some degree of activity was not reported.

In a subsequent study by Hanlon, Sheets, and Kurland (in preparation), on chronically psychotic patients who were given placebos for several months, an initial amelioration of symptoms was eventually followed by an exacerbation at the end of three months. In a study of shorter duration, Hampson, Rosenthal, and Frank (1954) found that the greatest decrease in distress following placebo administration is experienced during the first two-weeks period. After that, a slight but statistically insignificant rise in distress occurs, but at the end of eight weeks the placebo effect is again as great as after two weeks. In view of the contradictory findings of these two studies, the question of the time course of placebo reactivity is still unanswered.

Wolf, Doering, Clark, and Hagans (1957) recently shed some interesting light on the consistency of placebo reactivity. Initially they felt that experimental subjects could be categorized according to their proclivities for reacting to placebo medication. They had observed, from a study of agents tested for their ability to prevent ipecac-induced nausea and vomiting in volunteers, that none was more effective or more consistent in its total effect than the placebo. They then attempted to answer the question whether or not the occurrence of a placebo reaction in one situation could be used to predict the response of a patient to placebo at a subsequent testing. They found that their data did not enable them to differentiate the placebo reactors from the non-reactors. The intraindividual variation in response to placebo was found to be as great as the interindividual variation. The validity of predictions about placebo responses was not enhanced by increasing the number of placebo tests performed on any individual.

In contrast to the above is the report of Hankoff, Freedman, and Engelhardt (1958). They attempted to use the response of recently discharged schizophrenic patients to a three-week course of placebo as a prognostic indicator of subsequent clinical course, assessed in terms of incidence of rehospitalization and how soon this occurred after discharge. They found that among their group of 33 patients, who had had short-term hospitalization and who had currently been under drug treatment at a clinic, 18 could be classified as reactors and 15 as non-reactors according to psychiatric progress notes. When the reactors and non-reactors were grouped according to clinical course, a striking finding was seen. In the group which was rehospitalized immediately not a single patient had shown a favorable placebo response, whereas 9 of the 11 patients who remained well enough not to return to a hospital had favorable placebo reactions. In an intermediate "delayed hospitalization" group, 9 out of 16 had favorable placebo reactions.

The use of placebo reactivity as a prognostic indicator is intriguing. However, the complexities of such an approach are emphasized by such studies as that of Good, Sterling, and Holtzman (1958) on the termination of chlorpromazine treatment with schizophrenic patients. These authors found that withdrawing chlorpromazine after it had been established as a treatment routine led to no noticeable regression in behavior or intellectual functioning for at least 10 to 12 weeks. Other investigators such as Kinross-Wright (1955) have reported that some paranoid schizophrenics relapse within 48 hours, and others not for 2 or 3 months, upon termination of chlorpromazine treatment. Therefore it is hard to tell how long a tranquilizer should be withdrawn before a prognostic trial of placebo is begun. In a study by

Tuteur, Stiller, and Glotzer (1958) a group of 33 outpatients, who had initially displayed extremely regressed schizophrenic behavior and who had recovered on chlorpromazine therapy, were placed on placebos for an average of 10 months after discharge. Eleven of these patients relapsed within a few weeks while on placebo but recovered when placed on active medication again; the others did not relapse. Can we call any of these incidents placebo reactivity, or is there the possibility that other, more basic phenomena are being neglected because of our use of the term "placebo reactivity"? Only systematic research will answer this question.

Lasagna, Laties, and Dohan (1958) have presented data to indicate that subjective response to a placebo can mimic certain actions of active drugs such as "peak effects," "cumulative effects," and "carry-over effects." In recording the verbal expressions of pain relief of postoperative patients to morphine and placebo, these authors noted a remarkable similarity in the contours of frequency response curves at different times after the administration of both medications. Of particular interest in this study is the long-term or "carry-over effect" of placebo. In explanation of this carry-over there are only speculations. One possibility is that patients who are improved on placebo may feel (at least temporarily) that the placebo has achieved a "cure" and that further medication is not needed. In view of their findings, the authors offer an interpretation of the long-term effects of placebo in terms of simple learning theory, with abrupt withdrawal of a cue followed not by an immediate cessation of a response but by a gradual and irregular decline. A number of as yet unrecognized factors must operate to create varying intensities of placebo reactivity. Let us attempt to examine some of these factors.

Factors Influencing
Placebo Reactivity

The importance of expectations in placebo reactivity is dramatically emphasized by Wolf and Hagans (1957) in the case of one patient suffering from a gastric fistula. For some period of time Wolf had been evaluating the actions of many drugs on the patient's stomach, observing the gastric secretion, gastric motility, and the state of the vessels in the mucosa. One agent was prostigmine, a drug which the patient had learned to despise because it caused an intense engorgement of his mucosa with a marked increase in the production of acid which spilled out on his abdominal wall and burned the mucocutaneous junction. Prostigmine also caused intestinal cramps, frequently followed by diarrhea. Soon Wolf noticed that no matter what he administered, even tap water, he would get the typical prostigmine-like effect. Then he made up a large red capsule filled with inert material and gave it to the patient, saying: "Tom, I know you don't enjoy this, but your participation in these studies is important because of your unique situation, and I am afraid I will have to go ahead with it." The patient immediately had a most violent prostigmine-like response; gastric juice poured forth from his stomach, his abdominal cramps became intense, and he had a sudden bowel movement.

This case emphasizes the importance of considering the placebo effect from a standpoint of prior learned experiences. Along this same line, Gliedman, Gantt, and Teitelbaum (1957) presented three separate groups of conditioned reflex studies, which, they thought, shed further light on this matter. In these studies they demonstrated: (1) how a person's affect can be conditioned, making it possible for him to realize his expectations from a therapeutic situation; and (2) the importance of "pre-excitatory states" for conditioning, which suggests that the ability of doctors to produce such states is related to the type of response subsequently observed. Feldman (1956) demonstrated the positive nature of this relationship nicely in a study comparing the doctor's attitude toward a drug being administered and the patient's response.

That there seems to be logarithmic relationship between the intensity of a conditioned stimulus and the elicited conditioned reflex (Sutherland, 1953) may also be connected with the placebo phenomenon if the doctor is looked upon as a complex signal for a conditioned response. Since the conditioned response varies logarithmically with the strength of the stimulus, the greater the stimulus (i.e., distress), the greater is the response and the more susceptible is the individual to modification by a variety of means, including placebos. Any therapeutic intervention, including placebo, used by a doctor activates mechanisms of adjustment, since human beings react to their own deviations from equilibrium, these deviations triggering restorative processes (Gliedman, Gantt, and Teitelbaum, 1957). Lack of reaction may be taken to indicate the relative absence of restorative processes.

The placebo acquires properties as a signal in addition to its physical characteristics, and the same signal may produce at different times (according to the inner state of inhibition) a positive reaction, a negative one, or no reaction. It cannot be said that the patient is not responding to a placebo when no specific external response is observed, because, as Sutherland (1953) has pointed out, with present techniques the evaluation of the inner state of the patient is most imperfect.

We have already referred to another issue that must be considered. Are we dealing with the same placebo effect phenomenon in a patient who gains temporary relief from a "one-shot" administration of a placebo while suffering from a brief somatic ailment, such as postoperative discomfort, as we are in a chronically ill psychotic patient to whom placebos are administered for several weeks as a part of a control study, and as a result of which the patient shows a gradual improvement in hospital behavior? In the former the disturbance is brief and the patient is extremely apprehensive concerning his discomfort; in the latter the patient may have long ceased to have insight into or be reactive to his illness.

Personality Variables
Relating to Placebo Reactivity

Lasagna, von Felsinger, and Beecher (1955) attempted to screen out some of the more important psychological variables associated with the euphoria-dysphoria and stimulated-sedated reactions by studying subjects who deviated markedly from the expected responses to placebo and drug therapies. They found atypical responses most frequently in those whose personality structures were inadequate in dealing with everyday stresses and were fraught with impulsivity, hostility, anxiety, and fear of loss of control. These workers postulated that such persons are predisposed to be alarmed by what they perceive as physiological concomitants of therapy. This alarm adds to their already heightened tension and further threatens their precarious control. On the other hand, a well-balanced personality conceivably integrates whatever such sensations he receives into on-going activity without disturbance and with pleasant affect.

Trouton (1957), in an examination of the psychological mechanisms of placebo reactions, felt that there were well-defined groups of placebo reactors and non-reactors. The consistent reactors were found to be older, conscientious, church-goers with a greater acceptance of pain and suffering than the consistent non-reactors. Rorschach tests also indicated that reactors were less mature and more dependent on outside stimuli than non-reactors. Trouton attempted to explain some of these findings on the basis of their relation to learning theory, with the inference that secondary suggestibility is a trait related to the placebo reaction. Introverts, he thought, tend to acquire placebo reactions more easily and lose them less readily than extraverts. Fischer and Dlin (1956), in a study of 75 patients with psychosomatic complaints who were classified as psychotic, severe neurotic, and mild neurotic, found that the negative pill reactors exceeded the positive pill reactors in the psychotic group (41 per cent negative; 35 per cent positive). The negative and positive pill reactors were approximately equal in the severe neurotic group (32 and 34 per cent respectively); and the positive reactors exceeded the negative reactors in the mild neurotic group (75 and 12 per cent respectively).

The placebo reaction is generally accepted to be a manifestation of suggestion. As such, it might be presumed to be most marked in conversion hysteria. However, Eysenck (1947), on the basis of a review of the literature on suggestibility and tests which supposedly measure this trait, stated that there is little evidence of a significant correlation between suggestibility and hysteria. This finding is at variance with the popular belief.

Even with the well adjusted, efforts are being made to define the effects of unknown and uncontrollable factors in the placebo situation. In an interesting study discussed elsewhere in this book (see Chapters 4 and 48) Gottschalk and co-workers, using a group of sophisticated observers, noted individual differences in the dosage levels at which drug effects could be detected. Also, the psychological effects of the drug differed among individuals and in the same individual at various times.

R E F E R E N C E S

Abramson, H. A., Jarvik, M. E., Levine, A., Kaufman, M. R., and Hirsch, M. W. Lysergic acid diethylamide (LSD-25): XV. The effects produced by substitution of a tap water placebo. *J. Psychol.*, 1955, 40, 367–383.

American Journal of Psychiatry. Comment. Psychiatric implications of the "placebo effect." *Amer. J. of Psychiat.*, 1958, 114, 662–664.

Baker, A. A., and Thorpe, J. G. Placebo response. *Arch. Neurol. Psychiat.*, 1957, 78, 57–60.

Beecher, H. K. The powerful placebo. *J. Amer. med. Ass.*, 1955, 159, 1602–1606.

DuBois, E. F. The use of placebos in therapy. *N. Y. S. Med. J.*, 1946, 46, 1.

Eysenck, H. J. *Dimensions of personality.* London: Routledge & Kegan, 1947.

Feldman, T. E. The personal element in psychiatric research. *Am. J. Psychiat.*, 1956, 113, 52–54.

Fellner, C. H. Tranquilizing drugs in general practice, or the triumph of the impure placebo. *Amer. Practit. Dig. Treat.*, 1958, 9, 1265–1268.

Fischer, H. Keith. Psychiatric progress and problems of drug therapies. *G. P.*, 1957, 16, 92–96.

Fischer, H. K., and Dlin, B. M. The dynamics of placebo therapy: a clinical study. *Amer. J. med. Sci.*, 1956, 232, 504–512.

Foley, E. F., Rosenwald, A. K., and Smith, C. M. Placebos—a panel on the theoretical and practical implications of their use in experimental and clinical medicine. *Ill. med. J.*, 1957, 112, 215–218.

Gliedman, L. H., Gantt, W. H., and Teitelbaum, H. A. Some implications of conditioned reflex studies for placebo research. *Amer. J. Psychiat.*, 1957, 113, 1103–1107.

Gliedman, L. H., Nash, E. H., Jr., Imber, S. D., Stone, A. R., and Frank, J. D. Reduction of symptoms by pharmacologically inert substances and by short-term psychotherapy. *Arch. Neurol. Psychiat.*, 1958, 79, 345–351.

Good, W. W., Sterling, M., and Holtzman, W. H. Termination of chlorpromazine with schizophrenic patients. *Amer. J. Psychiat.*, 1958, 115, 443–448.

Graves, C. C. Drug therapy for the emotionally and mentally disturbed; the psychiatrist's point of view. *J. Iowa State med. Soc.*, 1957, 47, 15–16.

Hampson, J. L., Rosenthal, D., and Frank, J. E. A comparative study of the effects of mephenesin and placebo on the symptomatology of a mixed group of psychiatric patients. *Bull. Johns Hopkins Hosp.*, 1954, 93, 170–177.

Hankoff, L. D., Freedman, N., and Engelhardt, D. M. The prognostic value of placebo response. *Amer. J. Psychiat.*, 1958, 115, 549–550.

Hanlon, T. E., Sheets, C. S., and Kurland, A. A. Placebo and drug reactivity of hospitalized lobotomized patients. In preparation.

Kinross-Wright, V. *Chlorpromazine and mental health.* Philadelphia: Lee & Febiger, 1955.

Kline, N. S. Psychopharmacology symposium. The major controversies and needs in present day psychopharmacology (circa 1957). Paper read at Int. Cong. Psychiat., Zurich, September, 1957.

Kurland, A. A. The drug placebo—its psychodynamic and conditional reflex action. *Behav. Sci.* 1957, 2, 101–110.

Kurland, A. A. The placebo. In J. H. Masserman and J. L. Moreno (eds.), *Progress in psychotherapy.* Vol. 3. New York: Grune & Stratton, 1958, 204–211.

Lasagna, L., Laties, V. A., and Dohan, L. J. Further studies on the "pharmacology" of placebo administration. *J. clin. Invest.*, 1958, 37, 533–537.

Lasagna, L., von Felsinger, J. N., and Beecher, H. K. Drug-induced mood changes in man. *J. Amer. med. Ass.*, 1955, 157, 1113–1119.

Meath, J. A., Feldberg, T. M., Rosenthal, D., and Frank, J. D. Comparison of reserpine and placebo in treatment of psychiatric outpatients. *Arch. Neurol. Psychiat.*, 1956, 76, 207–214.

Rashkis, H. A., and Smarr, E. R. Psychopharmacotherapeutic research. A triadistic approach. *Arch. Neurol. Psychiat.*, 1957, 77, 202–209.

Rosenthal, D., and Frank, J. D. Psychotherapy and the placebo effect. *Psychol. Bull.*, 1956, 53, 294–302.

Sutherland, G. F. Comparative conditional neuroses. *Ann. N. Y. Acad. Sci.,* 1953, 56, 377–379.

Trouton, D. S. Placebos and their psychological effects. *J. ment. Sci.,* 1957, 103, 344–354.

Tuteur, W., Stiller, R., and Glotzer, J. Results with chlorpromazine on chronically nude, incontinent, combative and noisy patients. *Dis. nerv. Sys.,* 1958, 339–342.

Weinberg, H. B. Drug therapy for the emotionally and mentally disturbed; the internists's point of view. *Iowa State Med. Soc.,* 1957, 47, 17–19.

Wolf, S., Doering, C. R., Clark, M. L., and Hagans, J. A. Chance distribution and the placebo reactor. *J. lab. clin. Med.,* 1957, 49, 837–841.

Wolf, S. G., and Hagans, J. A. The placebo. *J. Okla. State med. Ass.,* 1957, 50, 387–393.

Wolf, S., and Pinsky, Ruth H. Effects of placebo administration and occurrence of toxic reactions. *J. Amer. med. Ass.,* 1954, 155, 339–341.

Behavioral toxicity

The concept of a pharmacology of behavior must make the pharmacologist think about the possible adverse behavioral effects of psychiatric drugs, even as the cardiovascular pharmacologist is aware of both the therapeutic and toxic pharmacologic properties of digitalis. The psychologist, in investigating the effects of such new and potent drugs on various psychological functions, must wonder whether any effects he may find are good or bad. The psychiatrist, provided with a drug which can both quiet the hyperactivity of a disturbed schizophrenic and can also make him rigid with parkinsonian-like side effects, must also be concerned lest such a drug be primarily therapeutic in some instances but primarily antitherapeutic in others.

The term "behavioral toxicity" was first used at the conference on the evaluation of pharmacotherapy in mental illness in the fall of 1956 by Brady (1959) to describe the adverse effects of drugs on behavior or psychological functioning in animals. Brady's study (1959; see also Chapter 12) of the effects of reserpine on lever pressing in rats and monkeys illustrates the concept quite well. In this experiment hungry rats and monkeys had been trained to press a lever for an orange juice reward. They also learned that a continuous clicking noise would be followed after three minutes by a painful shock. In the untreated animal the clicking noise produced a complete suppression of all lever pressing for the orange juice reward. In the reserpine-treated animal there was a general overall decrease in the rate of lever pressing, but the clicking noise no longer caused suppression of this activity and, in fact, did not even alter the rate of lever pressing. In this study the effect of reserpine in making the animals able

166

to work for a reward in a "threatening" situation could be considered a desirable pharmacological effect, while the overall decrease in lever pressing of the reserpine-treated animals could be considered a form of behavioral toxicity. Obviously, value judgment is involved in interpreting any drug effect as being either "therapeutic" or "toxic."

Although the phrase "behavioral toxicity" is relatively new, the underlying concept is by no means new or unfamiliar. Concern about the possible adverse effects of caffeine on psychological functioning in normal persons led to the classical study carried out by Hollingworth (1912). The effects he obtained from small doses in normal subjects were primarily in the direction of improved psychological and psychomotor functioning, and popular fears about the behavioral toxicity of the drug were shown to be exaggerated. The potentially undesirable effects of ethyl alcohol upon behavior are well known to every policeman and most of the general public.

The recent history of other non-drug therapies in psychiatry, particularly the twenty years' experience with lobotomy (Greenblatt, Arnot, and Solomon, 1950), have made psychiatrists aware that major alterations in brain function may produce a variety of end results. Therapeutic successes have been reported, but in other cases greatly decreased anxiety and symptom relief have been coupled with insensitivity, egocentricity, and major defects in social behavior. Sometimes the operation has led only to incontinence and further deterioration. The transient confusion and memory defects produced by electroconvulsive therapy are other striking examples of undesirable results of an effective therapy well known to the clinical psychiatrist.

World War II and the Korean War focused attention on the effects of a variety of drugs on human performance. Complex motor skill was required of pilots during both wars, and the need for drugs which could effectively prevent motion sickness in pilots without interfering with skilled behavior of this sort led to the studies by Payne, Hauty, and Moore (1954, 1955) which clearly demonstrated the adverse effects of a combination of dimenhydrinate (Dramamine) and hyoscine on sustained performance at a complex psychomotor task. Because the emphasis in these studies was on specific types of performance, the term generally used to describe this adverse drug effect was "performance decrement" rather than behavioral toxicity, but the similarity of the two concepts is obvious. World War II also stimulated a great deal of interest in the effects of amphetamine and methamphetamine as agents potentially able either to improve performance or to prevent the decrement in performance which usually results from fatigue or sleep deprivation. In general, the results indicate that both drugs are effective in delaying or mitigating the fatigue-induced performance decrement, without causing adverse behavioral effects in most subjects (Cuthbertson and Knox, 1947; Newman, 1947; Tyler, 1947).

The work of Nowlis and Nowlis (1956) at the University of Rochester and of Beecher, von Felsinger, and Lasagna (Lasagna et al., 1955; von Felsinger et al., 1955, 1956) at the Massachusetts General Hospital have extended the investigation of drug effects on behavioral responses to include the study of drug effects on mood and other subjective feeling states. Although the concept of behavioral toxicity arose from Brady's study of objective, measurable behavioral responses in the operant situation, any broad consideration of behavioral toxicity in man must take into account both the subjective mood changes and the objective performance changes induced by drugs.

The Phenomena of Somatic Toxicity

Before proceeding to a more detailed consideration of behavioral toxicity, it is desirable to consider the way in which general pharmacology approaches the various phenomena which can be loosely grouped under the general heading of somatic or "organ" toxicity. Almost any drug, if given in great quantity, will produce adverse effects of some type and, usually, even death. Such abnormally large doses are commonly called "toxicological," and the effects so produced may have no relevance to problems encountered in the general clinical use of a drug except when large amounts are taken with suicidal intent. On the other hand, many unpleasant effects of a drug may appear when the drug is given in usual therapeutic dosages or at levels a physician might reasonably prescribe in attempting to produce a desired therapeutic effect. Such unpleasant drug actions are considered side effects, are often closely related to the desirable pharmacological properties of the drug, and can be produced in almost any patient if moderately large doses of the drug are used, although there may be considerable individual difference in this regard. Almost everyone can get palpitations and unpleasant jittery feelings from amphetamine if he takes a large enough single dose; but some individuals may feel pleasantly stimulated and slightly euphoric at a dose which produces no unpleasant side effects, while others, even at low doses, develop side effects which, presumably, interfere with or prevent the more pleasurable psychopharmacological effect.

With many drugs one will occasionally encounter individuals who react in a most atypical manner. Such special sensitivity reactions can include both allergic responses such as skin rash and rarer and more serious hypersensitivity reactions like agranulocytosis. The work of Lasagna, von Felsinger, and Beecher (1955) describes a typical subjective response to amphetamine and morphine observed in a small percentage of a group of normal subjects which may constitute a psychological equivalent of the atypical somatic drug responses described above.

Two other pharmacological phenomena are involved in the discussion of behavioral toxicity. These are the problems of tolerance and physiologic dependence. Some drug effects, both toxic and therapeutic, appear only when the drug is first administered, and under chronic drug administration cease to occur after a few days or can only be reproduced by increasing the dosage given. The disappearance of the initial sedative effect of chlorpromazine after a few days is an obvious example. The problem of physiological dependence, i.e., the appearance of withdrawal symptoms when a drug is stopped after prolonged administration, is not strictly a matter of behavioral toxicity except in so far as a person suffering severe withdrawal symptoms may be behaviorally incapacitated or a person fearing such withdrawal symptoms may be driven to behave in an abnormal manner to obtain the drug on which he is dependent.

Up to this point I have discussed primarily acute or short-range drug effects. There is also the possibility that a drug may cause long-range adverse effects on behavior either by producing some type of neurological lesion or by disturbing the individual's ability to learn by experience, hampering his emotional development, or altering his methods for coping with his environment.

Do the present psychiatric drugs have important adverse effects upon human behavior? There are two sources of information about such undesirable effects. First, the clinical observations made by psychiatrists, physicians generally, and occasionally others, on patients receiving drugs for therapeutic reasons should provide some evidence concerning undesirable drug effects. Second, experimental studies designed to measure the effects of drugs on psychomotor performance, cognitive functions, subjective emotional states, or social behavior in patients or in normal subjects should also provide such evidence. At present both types of data suffer from serious shortcomings.

Clinical observations by psychiatrists or anecdotal reports by others are frequently difficult to interpret because of the lack of experimental controls. For example, one article reports that a man injured himself while operating a heavy machine in a factory after taking an antihistamine (Slater and Francis, 1946). It is possible that drug-induced sedation made him function ineptly and injure himself. On the other hand, it is possible that his allergy made him so uncomfortable that he was unable to attend properly to the task at hand. The problem is equally complex when one considers the tranquilizing drugs. The Army has made a ruling that none of its pilots should operate a plane for at least four weeks after taking a tranquilizing drug. From the report of this ruling which appeared in a local newspaper (Haugland, 1957) it was difficult to be sure what reasoning lay behind the decision, but the newspaper account of the decision stressed the principle that no man anxious or upset enough to have to take a tranquilizing drug should be flying an airplane. There was probably also some concern lest the drugs interfere with flying skills. In all such accounts there inevitably is a confounding of the effects of the drug and the effects of the emotional condition for which the drug is administered.

The problem in experimental studies of drug effects on psychological functioning is quite different. Here experimental controls may often be excellent but, however statistically significant the results may be, the practical significance of the findings may remain in doubt. If a drug interferes with simple reaction time or with paired associate learning or with critical flicker frequency in normal subjects, what are the implications of these findings for the clinical use of the drug? If a drug does not interfere with performance on an artificial machine which simulates automobile driving, how sure can one be that real automobile driving is not impaired? The problems in generalizing from the psychological or psychopharmacological laboratory to real life situations are impressive, particularly when one takes into account the possibility that disturbed psychiatric patients may respond to drugs differently than do normal college students.

This chapter will examine separately the evidence from the clinic and from the psychological laboratory and will then attempt to assess the current state of our knowledge and the implications of this for future research in this area.

Clinical Behavioral Toxicity

The most impressive characteristic of the psychiatric drug literature is the absence of serious concern about adverse effects these drugs may be having upon behavior. The majority of the uncontrolled studies emphasize the desirable therapeutic effects of these agents and, when discussing side effects, concern themselves primarily with non-behavioral forms of toxicity such as hypotension, jaundice, or skin rashes. Two possibilities, of course, exist. One is that behavioral toxicity occurs but is not noted. Clinicians who deal with seriously ill hospitalized psychotics may not be aware of minor undesirable alterations in behavior or may attribute them to the illness rather than the drug; and clinicians seeing outpatients may see them only in the interview situation and may not be able to detect adverse behavioral phenomena which occur only when the patient is at home or at work. The other possibility, of course, is that behavioral toxicity may simply not be a serious clinical problem.

One obvious form of behavioral toxicity is excessive sedation. This is mentioned as a side effect of almost every tranquilizing drug, though the newer phenothiazines, particularly prochlorperazine, perphenazine, and trifluoperazine, may show less sedation and may even have stimulant effects in some cases (Goldman, 1958). Part of the problem here may be a matter of dosage. Excessive sedation may be a passing phase which occurs while the clinician is attempting to arrive at the optimal dosage for a particular patient. Also, some clinicians feel that tolerance for the initial sedative effects of the tranquilizers develops rapidly, leaving the patient calm but not sleepy after a few days. In any event, this form of behavioral toxicity is most prevalent early in treatment and should be taken into account by practicing physicians who must judge whether a patient should drive a car or operate dangerous machinery when first taking drugs of this class. I am not aware of any published reports of serious injury occurring in a patient because of this drug effect, but events of this sort may be relatively infrequent or the relative contributions of psychiatric condition and drug may be so unclear as to make formal publication unlikely.

As in the case with sedation, the parkinsonian syndrome is also a relatively clear-cut pharmacological action of most of the phenothiazines and the *Rauwolfia* alkaloids. Severe parkinsonism with marked stiffness and tremor can obviously interfere strikingly with many types of behavior. These agents can produce a "pharmacological strait jacket" in which the patient is so stiff and sedated as to make any type of behavior, disturbed or otherwise, impossible. This gross state may occasionally be preferable to violent assaultive behavior, but most clinicians would agree that, when it occurs in the course of drug therapy, it constitutes a clear case of behavioral toxicity. In its milder forms the parkinsonian syndrome may be an important form of behavioral toxicity which is not always readily apparent. In 1955, I saw a female patient with a severe anxiety neurosis who had received reserpine from a general practitioner for several months. Her anxiety was considerably relieved by reserpine, but she was bothered by stiffness in the arms and legs which made her unable to do her housework or care for herself or her family. Her physician contemplated treating her for arthritis. Since the stiffness disappeared when the reserpine was stopped, it is probable that it was a manifestation of mild parkinsonism and, in this case, seemed clearly to constitute a toxic behavioral effect of the drug. Similar episodic data are involved in the case described by Gross (1958) of a released state hospital patient on maintenance drug therapy who lost a job as a draftsman because his inking was too heavily done. Brooks (1958) has observed similar difficulties in the fine manual work (like sewing and knitting) of hospitalized patients on drug therapy. The extent to which minimal drug-induced parkinsonism seriously interferes with fine psychomotor skills is unclear, as is also the extent to which such symptoms are controlled by antiparkinsonian medication.

More bizarre extrapyramidal symptoms involving acute spasms of the muscles of the face and neck (Freyhan, 1958a, b) sometimes occur early in the course of treatment with the newer phenothiazines. These acute symptoms also interfere with behavior, but their effects are so dramatic and apparently respond so well to antiparkinsonian medication as to warrant only passing mention here.

Another form of behavioral toxicity associated with the clinical use of the phenothiazine derivatives is "akathisia" (Freyhan, 1958b; see also Chapter 8), a syndrome characterized in its milder forms by inner feelings of unrest and jumpy sensations in the legs. In more severe cases it can develop into overt agitated hyperactivity accompanied by great anxiety and discomfort. Delay, Deniker, Green, and Mordret (1957) feel that this condition resembles some postcephalitic states observed after the influenza epidemic in 1918. The reported rapid response of this syndrome to antiparkinsonian medication (Freyhan, 1958b) supports the thesis that it is neurological or, better, neuropharmacological in origin. It must be differentiated from the increased anxiety observed by Sarwer-Foner (1957) and Schlesinger (1959) in patients for whom drug-induced fatigue and hypoactivity are anxiety-provoking for dynamic reasons.

This second type of atypical response to tranquilizing drugs is said to occur in patients whose security rests heavily upon their ability to be active, athletic, strong, and masculine. These defenses may become exaggerated in the course of their psychiatric illness and may make therapy with one of the phenothiazines appear to be indicated. In many hyperactive disturbed patients, drug-induced hypoactivity, fatigue, and lethargy are received with relief and they decrease anxiety, but in some the drug interferes with a major defense mechanism and produces greater anxiety, sometimes accompanied by psychotic disorganization and panic.

Many physicians (Stevenson, 1957; Felix, 1957; Allman, 1957; Rose, 1958) have worried about a more subtle adverse effect of the tranquilizing drugs, the excessive relief of necessary anxiety. It is difficult to tell to what extent these fears are justified. Savage and Day (1958) report that reserpine, in a few schizophrenic patients, seemed to relieve the anxiety previously produced by the psychotherapy situation and allowed the patients to feel more comfortable with the therapist and to talk more easily about inconsequential matters. They felt that this effect was superficial and did not permit the patients really to gain from the therapy sessions and may have actually enabled the patients to avoid coming to grips with their real problems. It is possible that the administration of drugs to patients in psychotherapy may either relieve anxiety to such an extent that they no longer feel any need to work on real personal and interpersonal difficulties, or the drugs may, without relieving anxiety, be used by the patient as a reason for denying the need to face his problems. An example of the latter phenomenon has been described by Cole (1959). On the other hand, Winkelman reports (1959) that chlorpromazine and prochlorperazine enable some patients to control acting-out behavior which disrupts both their personal lives and their psychotherapy and enable them, instead, to talk about their problems in the therapeutic hour and to make more progress in therapy. There are also some controlled studies (Meszaros and Gallagher, 1958; Cowden, Zax, Hague, Finney, and Sproles, 1955, 1956) which show drugs and various types of psychotherapy and milieu therapy to work synergistically in hospitalized chronic psychotics. The absence of adequate controlled studies of the effects of drugs on the psychotherapeutic process makes it difficult to tell whether or not drug-induced oversuppression of anxiety is a serious problem. Most discussions of this problem have been primarily theoretical in nature and have stressed the usefulness of healthy amounts of anxiety in driving people to try to do well in their school work or business careers and in motivating them to try to modify their own behavior, work out their emotional problems, and be sensitive to the needs of others. The importance of anxiety in the learning process has also been stressed. Unfortunately, there is no evidence either to confirm or deny the possibility that psychiatric drugs cause adverse effects by suppressing "good" anxiety.

An example drawn from the popular press (Kelly, 1957) illustrates both the phenomena described above and the value judgments which come to the fore when one attempts to decide whether or not too much anxiety has been alleviated. Two businessmen, brothers, are described. Both had been successful, but one was overanxious and fearful, the other was irascible and obnoxious. Both were allegedly given tranquilizing drugs and both became more relaxed, cheerful, and agreeable. However, both their businesses also began to make less money. Is this behavioral toxicity, or is this, all in all, a desirable pharmacotherapeutic end result?

A slightly different kind of drug effect was noted by a minister (Baker, 1957) who took meprobamate for several days. He described himself as feeling much more relaxed and carefree, but his colleagues and his wife observed that he was much less sensitive to the needs of others and they felt that his work performance had deteriorated. It is difficult to tell how much weight, if any, to give anecdotes of this sort, but studies which take into account both the patient's subjective response to therapy and information from other informants concerning alterations in his behavior are obviously needed.

Some concern has been expressed about the possibility that drugs may interfere with learning in children. The only controlled study relevant to this point (Freed, 1958) showed that chlorpromazine improved reading skill in children with reading disability more than did an inert placebo. Several child psychiatrists who deal primarily with institutionalized, disturbed children feel that drugs often are helpful in enabling such children to benefit considerably from classwork, particularly when they had been so anxious, hyperactive, and distractable prior to drug therapy that they were essentially unable to learn at all.

A similar problem arises concerning the effects of drugs on driving. I know of no data which indicate that patients receiving drugs are more liable to have accidents than are the general population, nor do I know of any data indicating that they are *not* more liable. I suspect that drugs may enable some anxious patients to be safer drivers and may make others sleepy enough or careless enough to be less safe drivers. It is impossible yet to tell which possible effect is more common.

The above examples all illustrate a central problem, that of individual differences both in psychic state before drug therapy and in response to any given drug. Until much more is known about the effects of various specific drugs in a variety of specific types of patients, it will not be possible to make definite statements about the presence or absence of behavioral toxicity resulting from excessive suppression of anxiety. Even after more scientific knowledge is available, the practical management of this problem will continue to be determined primarily by the clinical judgment of the individual physician treating the individual patient. He will continue to be the final judge of whether a given drug in a given patient is alleviating anxiety in a desirable manner or is producing too much apathy and unconcern.

A slightly different problem exists with respect to affective depression. The *Rauwolfia* alkaloids have been described as causing, or being associated with, the occurrence of pathological states of affective depression (Achor, Hanson, and Gifford, 1955; Faucett, Litin, and Archer, 1957; Freis, 1954). This phenomenon is seen most clearly in patients who are receiving these drugs for hypertension. It is unclear whether these depressions are related to a special interaction between the drug and the personality structures of some hypertensive patients or whether this is a general problem in the use of these agents.

At least two drugs, iproniazid and imipramine, employed in the treatment of depressions involve the opposite danger. Depressed patients may sometimes develop manic excitements while on drug therapy, and patients with schizophrenic features sometimes develop schizophrenic excitements (Ayd, 1958; Dally, 1958; Lehmann, Cahn, and de Verteuil, 1958). These reactions may be linked to the dosage used or they may be unpredictable, atypical drug responses, but in either event they represent serious forms of behavioral toxicity.

Another problem which might be associated with the clinical use of psychiatric drugs is the possible occurrence of irreversible brain changes. The only positive evidence on this point is derived from work with animals and is of questionable clinical significance. Both chlorpromazine (Roizin, True, and Knight, 1957) and reserpine (Windle and Cammermeyer, 1958) have been reported to produce fine neuropathological changes at the cellular level in monkeys. In both studies only a few monkeys were observed and essential controls were lacking. At the clinical level there is a complete lack of evidence that irreversible neurological changes occur in patients after prolonged drug administration. The absence of reported cases does not prove that such phenomena do not occur; on the other hand, if such phenomena were appearing frequently and were constituting a major problem, one would think that at least preliminary reports would have reached the literature by this time.

A second effect of prolonged drug administration can be the occurrence of physiological and/or psychological dependence of the type encountered with the barbiturates. Meprobamate has been definitely shown to be capable of producing physiological withdrawal reactions in both animals (Essig, 1958) and man (Ewing and Haizlip, 1958; Mohr and Mead, 1958). In man, however, these reactions seem to occur only when dosages of 3200 to 6400 mg. per day are maintained for some time and then abruptly stopped. Since, in general clinical practice, dosages as high as these are not usual and since the drug is rarely stopped abruptly, the phenomenon seems not to constitute a major public health problem, but it should be kept in mind by clinicians using this drug. It may be unfair to single out meprobamate for criticism, since no studies of this sort have been carried out on the other minor tranquilizers and non-barbiturate sedatives. It is entirely possible that all agents with significant central nervous system depressant properties may produce withdrawal effects if given for long periods in large amounts.

The problem of psychological dependence is more elusive. Neither reserpine nor the phenothiazines seem to be perceived as pleasure-producing agents by normal subjects, and there have been almost no reports of addiction to any of the tranquilizing drugs. On the other hand, it is possible that many people with neurotic symptoms which are relieved by these agents may feel dependent on this effect and may wish to continue taking them for long periods. Such patients may experience anxiety when the drug is stopped. In such instances it must be difficult to tell whether the patient is experiencing real psychic withdrawal symptoms or whether the pre-existing psychic symptoms are reappearing after being masked by the drug. It is even possible that such an increase in symptoms might result from the patient's feeling that his therapist is purposefully frustrating him by depriving him of the drug.

This last, entirely non-pharmacological, type of undesirable reaction deserves mention here, even though it cannot be considered to be pharmacologically induced behavioral toxicity. The reactions of patients to getting a pill or, as in the possibility noted above, being refused a pill, can be intense and serious. These are usually considered placebo reactions, though it is probable that the patient is reacting not only to the pill itself but also to the physician pre- scribing the pill and to the setting in which the pill is administered. Sedation is frequently noted by patients receiving inert placebos, and even parkinsonian syndromes have been noted to occur in patients receiving placebos. The administration of every pill or capsule, no matter how pharmacologically active the drug may be, carries with it the possibility of "placebo" response, either positive or negative. Most of the recent work has focused on the positive, symptom-reliev- ing properties of placebos, but future research on clinical behavioral toxicity will certainly have to take into account negative, adverse "placebo" responses both to placebos and to potent drugs.

Experimental Behavioral Toxicity

It is interesting to note that most of the work on the effects of drugs on animal behavior involves phenomena which may reasonably be classed as behavioral toxicity. Even Brady's study (1959) on the effects of reserpine on lever pressing while a warning signal is being presented can be considered behavioral toxicity as readily as it can be called a beneficial pharmacological effect. The same reasoning applies to all the work on the classical conditioned avoidance response where drugs are shown to abolish the response to the warning signal but not the response to the painful shock. A similar effect in man would make a patient not associate, say, an approaching automobile with impending danger and would postpone his avoidance reaction until he was actually hit by the car's bumper. Drug-induced dis- turbances in timing behavior or drug-induced changes in activity level may also be called behavioral toxicity. I know of only three studies in which a drug actually improved an animal's ability to function. Blough (1958) has shown that chlorpromazine enables a pigeon to stand still longer to achieve a food reward than it can without the drug. Boren (1958) has shown that amphetamine en- ables a rat to work more steadily at strained fixed-ratio schedules (i.e., 100 bar presses for each food pellet), while untreated rats show long pauses after each reward. Gonzalez and Ross (1959) have shown that chronic low chlorpromazine dosages enable rats to change set on the Lashley jumping stand more rapidly than can placebo- treated controls. In this situation the rat has learned to jump through one of two doors to get a food reward. This door is then "locked" and the jumping rat bumps his nose and falls into a net. He must then

learn to shift and use the other, now open, door. This door is then
"locked" and the first door reopened, and so on. The chlorpromazine-
treated rats can change from one door to the other more efficiently
than untreated rats.

As in the clinical examples of behavioral toxicity, one is faced with
a value judgment. In each of the three instances above, the drug-
induced alteration in response appears favorable. However, the same
change which Blough observed, an increased ability or tendency to
stand still, might serve a pigeon badly if it were hunted by a hawk, or
a rat made hyperactive by amphetamine might work itself to exhaustion, etc. It becomes impossible to judge the therapeutic or toxic
nature of a drug effect without reference to the setting in which it
has been observed. Even when the setting is taken into consideration,
a value judgment is still demanded of the observer. In clinical
situations, value judgments may be easier to make or may be more
readily agreed upon by observers with diverse viewpoints; for example, parkinsonism would probably be judged undesirable by almost
anyone, but the problem still exists.

In controlled clinical trials in patients one encounters situations
in which an increase in social aggressiveness and verbal coherence in
a chronic schizophrenic are judged by the psychiatrist to represent
improvement, and by the nurse to be an intolerable interference with
ward routine. Behavioral toxicity, like beauty, may be chiefly in the
observer's eye.

Research reports on behavioral toxicity in human subjects readily
fall into two groups of "basic" and "applied" studies. In basic studies
a drug effect on a relatively discrete function or series of functions
is measured, and the relevance to behavioral toxicity is either unstated
or hypothetical. In "applied" studies the functions measured or the
task chosen has obvious and explicit relevance to possible toxic effects
of a drug on such "real life" activities as flying or automobile driving.

The "basic" studies are often productive of clear findings; for example, 400 mg. of chlorpromazine in a single dose significantly impairs
performance on a continuous performance task which requires the
subject to discriminate rapidly either all X's or all X's preceded by
A's, from a series of briefly and rapidly presented letters (Primac,
Mirsky and Rosvold, 1957; see also Chapter 29).

The significance mentioned above is only statistical. It is much
more difficult to tell whether this effect has practical significance,
that is, whether it would interfere with driving or typing to an extent
which would be noticed by others. Lehmann and Csank (1957),

using a more extensive battery of tests, have been able to show significant differences among six known drugs, caffeine, dextroamphetamine, reserpine, secobarbital, chlorpromazine, and prochlorperazine; they used acute administration of single doses. (See also Chapter 4.) Their battery of simple, quantifiable measures certainly appears useful in discriminating among drugs (e.g., prochlorperazine resembles a stimulant in some respects and chlorpromazine in other respects) and may well be useful in predicting the clinical activity of new compounds. It is somewhat more difficult to go from their battery to conclusions concerning a drug's potential for behavioral toxicity. What type of behavioral toxicity would one, for example, expect from a drug which reduces flicker fusion frequency and afterimage sensitivity without affecting reaction time, tapping speed, or recall of digits forward?

In addition, almost all published studies on normal subjects deal with single doses of the drug in question and may have only limited relevance to the clinical situation where chronic drug administration is the rule. Furthermore, a drug may impair a given type of performance in normal subjects and may improve it in patients, or—and this would be more confusing and seems more probable a drug may improve performance only in some patients.

One also encounters the problem posed by Clark (1959) in which the practical significance of a real drug effect—for example, on depth perception—may depend on the patient's realization, or lack of realization, that his performance is altered. A driver aware of such a defect may drive more carefully or rely on other cues, while a driver unaware of this defect may crumple fenders. The difference in driving performance of a man who has just lost the use of one eye and a man who has had time to adjust to and compensate for this loss may be considerable. Insight, judgment, and the use of compensatory mechanisms can all contribute to the true significance of a real drug-induced alteration in psychological functioning.

There have been several attempts to reproduce in the laboratory tasks which resemble automobile driving or airplane flying and to study the effects of drugs on these tasks. These have an appealing face validity. One is tempted to assume that, since meprobamate does not impair performance of the AAA driver-trainer (Marquis, Kelly, Gerard, and Rapoport, 1957; Kelly, Miller, Marquis, Gerard, and Uhr, 1958; see also Chapter 20), it also does not interfere with driving on the road. Performance of a small group of subjects on the simulated driving apparatus used by Loomis and West (1958) did appear to be impaired by secobarbital, meprobamate, and chlorpromazine, and this might lead one to the opposite conclusion. (See also Chapter 22.) Similarly one tends to assume that performance on the Cambridge Cockpit (Davis, 1948) of the USAF SAM Multidimensional Pursuit Test (Payne and Hauty, 1954) is the same as flying a real plane.

In point of fact, none of the above situations is actually equivalent to real flying or driving, though the Defense Department and the aircraft industry have put more work into developing a machine which simulates flying than the automobile industry has put into driving machines. The fact that the West and Loomis apparatus gives a measure of the time the "car" is *off* the "road" illustrates the unreality of the device. Furthermore, performance in a laboratory setting may introduce, in some individuals, either boredom or hostility toward an unreasonably demanding task and thus show performance decrement that might or might not occur in real life. Or the task may be free of the emotional stresses and sudden emergencies that are encountered in city driving or during actual flight.

Conclusion

The clinician faced with the problem of judging a drug's potential for inducing behavioral toxicity must utilize his own experience and must judge the practical significance of both "basic" and "applied" studies of the drug's effect on various types of behavior. The psychologist interested in attacking the problem of behavioral toxicity will have to study the effects of drugs on a variety of discrete psychological functions and also on complex psychomotor and cognitive functions which resemble real-life situations more closely. It may be possible in the future to develop a practical battery of such tests which can give some information both about a drug's mechanism of action and its potential for behavioral toxicity, but such a battery will have to be validated against the presence or absence of adverse effects from the drugs under consideration in real-life situations. In the long run this will involve studies of automobile accidents and reports by other observers, family, friends, and employers concerning the drug-treated patient's performance at work or at home. As has been noted in the section on clinical behavioral toxicity, it will be difficult to disentangle the effects of the drug from the effects of the psychiatric condition for which it was given. There lies ahead a great deal of research at both laboratory and clinical levels. Its interpretation will continue to require great care and sound value judgments. The person who must make the final decision about a drug's use for a single patient will continue to be the individual clinician, though research findings will enable him to make better decisions based on more adequate knowledge.

REFERENCES

Achor, R. W. P., Hanson, N. O., and Gifford, R. W., Jr. Hypertension treated with rauwolfia serpentina (whole root) and with reserpine. Controlled study disclosing occasional severe depression. *J. Amer. med. Ass.*, 1955, 159, 841–845.

Allman, D. B. Do tranquilizing pills change your personality? *Amer. Wkly*, Oct. 27, 1957, 13.

Ayd, F. J., Jr. The treatment of depression and debilitation with Marsilid. *Bull. Sch. Med. Univer. Maryland*, 1958, 43, 9–12.

Baker, J. (Rev.) A personal report on tranquilizers. *Washington Sunday Star*, June 9, 1957, A-28.

Blough, D. S. New test for tranquilizers. *Science*, 1958, 127, 586–587.

Boren, J. Behavior profiling and drug evaluation. Paper read at Amer. Ass. Adv. Sci., Washington, D. C., Dec. 26–31, 1958.

Brady, J. V. Procedures, problems and perspectives in animal behavioral studies of drug activity. In J. O. Cole and R. W. Gerard (Eds.), *Psychopharmacology: problems in evaluation.* Washington, D. C.: N.A.S.-N.R.C., 1959.

Brooks, G. Personal communication. 1958.

Clark, L. Discussion of paper "General pharmacological and toxicological considerations in the screening of drugs for use in psychiatry." In J. O. Cole, and R. W. Gerard (Eds.), *Psychopharmacology: problems in evaluation.* Washington, D. C.; N.A.S.-N.R.C., 1959.

Cole, K. G. Discussion of paper "Populations, behaviors and situations; some ecological considerations in child drug research," by Borstelman, L. J. In S. Fisher (Ed.), *Child research in psychopharmacology.* Springfield, Ill.: Thomas, 1959.

Cowden, R. C., Zax, M., Hague, J. R., and Finney, R. C. Chlorpromazine: alone and as an adjunct to group psychotherapy in the treatment of psychiatric patients. *Amer. J. Psychiat.*, 1956, 112, 898–902.

Cowden, R. C., Zax, M., and Sproles, J. A. Reserpine alone and as an adjunct to psychotherapy in the treatment of schizophrenia. *Arch. Neurol. Psychiat.*, 1955, 74, 518–522.

Cuthbertson, D. P., and Knox, J. A. C. The effects of analeptics on the fatigued subject. *J. Physiol.*, 1947, 106, 42–58.

Dally, P. J. Indications for use of iproniazid in psychiatric practice. *Brit. med. J.*, 1958, 1, 1338–1339.

Davis, D. R. Pilot error, Air Ministry, A.P. 3139 A. London: His Majesty's Stationery Office, 1948.

Delay, Jean, Deniker, P., Green, A., and Mordret, M. Le syndrome excitomoteur provoqué par les médicaments neuroleptiques. *Presse medicale,* 1957, 65, 1771–1774.

Essig, C. F. Withdrawal convulsions in dogs following chronic meprobamate intoxication. *Arch. Neurol. Psychiat.,* 1958, 80, 414–417.

Ewing, J. A., and Haizlip, T. M. A controlled study of the habit forming propensities of meprobamate. *Amer. J. Psychiat.,* 1958, 114, 835–6.

Faucett, R. L., Litin, E. M., and Archer, R. W. P. Neuropharmacologic action of rauwolfia compounds and its psychodynamic implications. *Arch. Neurol. Psychiat.,* 1957, 77, 513–518.

Felix, R. H. What you ought to know about tranquilizers. *U. S. News and World Rep.,* 1957, June, 62–72.

Freed, H. The use of tranquilizers in a child psychiatry clinic. Paper read at Amer. Orthopsychiatric Ass., New York, March, 1958.

Freis, E. M. Mental depression in hypertensive patients treated for long periods with large doses of reserpine. *New Engl. J. Med.,* 1954, 251, 1006–1008.

Freyhan, F. A. The neuroleptic action and effectiveness of prochlorperazine in psychiatric disorders. *Psychiat. Res. Rep. No. 9,* 1958, 32–45. (a)

Freyhan, F. A. Occurrence and management of extrapyramidal syndromes in psychiatric treatment with trifluoperazine. In *Trifluoperazine: clinical and pharmacological aspects.* Philadelphia: *Lea & Febiger,* 1958, 195–205. (b)

Goldman, D. The results of treatment of psychotic states with newer phenothiazine compounds effective in small doses. *Amer. J. med. Sci.,* 1958, 235, 67–77.

Gonzalez, R. C., and Ross, S. The effects of chlorpromazine on the course of discrimination-reversals in the rat. Paper read at Eastern Psychol. Ass., Atlantic City, N.J., April 3, 1959.

Greenblatt, M., Arnot, R., and Solomon, H. C. (Eds.). *Studies in lobotomy.* New York: Grune & Stratton, 1950.

Gross, M. Personal communication. 1958.

Haugland, V. Army grounds "tranquilized" flyers for four weeks after taking new drugs. *Washington Star,* April 21, 1957, A-1.

Hollingworth, H. L. The influence of caffeine on mental and motor efficiency. *Arch. Psychol.,* 1912, 3, 22.

Kelly, E. L., Miller, J. G., Marquis, D. G., Gerard, R. W., and Uhr, L. Effects of continued meprobamate and prochlorperazine administration on the behavior of normal subjects. *Arch. Neurol. Psychiat.,* 1958, 80, 247–252.

Kelly, T. Should tranquilizers worry us? *Washington News,* Jan. 8, 1957, 2.

Lasagna, L., von Felsinger, J. M., and Beecher, H. K. Drug-induced mood changes in man. 1. Observations on healthy subjects, chronically ill patients, and "postaddicts." *J. Amer. med. Ass.,* 1955, 157, 1006–1020.

Lehmann, H. E., Cahn, C. H., and de Verteuil, R. L. The treatment of depressive conditions with Imipramine (G 22355). *Canad. psychiat. Ass.,* 1958, 3, 155–164.

Lehmann, H. E., and Csank, J. Differential screening of phrenotropic agents in man: Psychophysiologic test data. *J. clin. exp. Psychopath. quart. Rev. Psychiat. Neurol.,* 1957, 18, No. 3, 222–234.

Loomis, T. A., and West, T. C. Comparative sedative effects of a barbiturate and some tranquilizer drugs on normal subjects. *J. Pharmacol. exp. Therap.,* 1958, 122, *4,* 525–531.

Marquis, D. G., Kelly, E. L., Miller, J. G., Gerard, R. W., and Rapoport, A. Experimental studies of behavioral effects of meprobamate on normal subjects. *Ann. N. Y. Acad. Sci.*, 1957, 67, 701–710.

Meszaros, A. F., and Gallagher, D. L. Measuring indirect effects of treatment on chronic wards. *Dis. nerv. Sys.*, 1958, 19, 167–172.

Mohr, R. C. and Mead, Beverley T. Meprobamate addiction. *New Engl. J. Med.*, 1958, 259, 865–868.

Newman, H. W. The effect of amphetamine sulfate on performance of normal and fatigued subjects. *J. Pharmacol. exp. Therap.*, 1947, 89, 106–108.

Nowlis, V., and Nowlis, Helen H. The description and analysis of mood. *Ann. N. Y. Acad. Sci.*, 1956, 65, 345–355.

Payne, R. B., and Hauty, G. T. The effects of experimentally induced attitudes upon task performance. *J. exp. Psychol.*, 1954, 47, 267–273.

Payne, R. B., and Moore, E. W. The effects of some analeptic and depressant drugs upon tracking behavior. *J. Pharmacol. exp. Therap.*, 1955, 115, 480–484.

Primac, D. W., Mirsky, A. F., and Rosvold, H. E. Effects of centrally acting drugs on two tests of brain damage. *Arch. Neurol. Psychiat.*, 1957, 77, 328–332.

Roizin, L., True, C., and Knight, M. Structural effects of tranquilizers. Paper presented at meeting of the Ass. Res. nerv. ment. Dis., December, 1957.

Rose, T. F. The use and abuse of tranquilizers. *Canad. med. Ass. J.*, 1958, 78, 144–148.

Sarwer-Foner, G. J. Psychoanalytic theories of activity-passivity conflicts and of the continuum of ego defenses; experimental verification, using reserpine and chlorpromazine. *Arch. Neurol. Psychiat.*, 1957, 78, 413–418.

Savage, C., and Day, Juliana. The effects of a tranquilizing drug (reserpine) on psychodynamic and social processes. *Arch. Neurol. Psychiat.*, 1958, 79, 590–596.

Schlesinger, H. J. "Hypothesis-oriented" research in psychopharmacology. In J. O. Cole, and R. W. Gerard (Eds.), *Psychopharmacology: problems in evaluation.* Washington, D. C.: N.A.S.-N.R.C., 1959.

Slater, B. J., and Francis, F. N. Benadryl, a contributing cause of an accident. *J. Amer. med. Ass.*, 1946, 132, 212.

Stevenson, Ian. Tranquilizers and the mind. *Harper's Magazine*, 1957, 215 (July), 21–27.

Tyler, D. B. The effect of amphetamine sulfate and some barbiturates on the fatigue produced by prolonged wakefulness. *Amer. J. Physiol.*, 1947, 150, 253–262.

von Felsinger, J. M., Lasagna, L., and Beecher, H. K. Drug-induced mood changes in man. 2. Personality and reactions to drugs. *J. Amer. med. Ass.*, 1955, 157, 1113–1119.

von Felsinger, J. M., Lasagna, L., and Beecher, H. K. The response of normal men to lysergic acid derivatives (di- and mono-ethyl amides) *J. clin. exp. Psychopath.*, 1956, 17, 414–428.

Windle, W. F., and Cammermeyer, Jan. Functional and structural observations on chronically reserpinized monkeys. *Science*, 1958, 127, 1503–1504.

Winkelman, N. W. A psychoanalytic study of phenothiazine action. In N. S. Kline (Ed.), *Psychopharmacology frontiers,* Boston: Little, Brown, 1959.

Psychopharmacology and
the controversial clinician

The introduction of chlorpromazine by Delay and Deniker (1952) triggered an unprecedented interest in psychoactive drugs. Psychopharmacology has since emerged as a science *sui generis,* exuding immense vitality and stimulating rigorous investigative productivity. It would be erroneous, however, to assume that recent clinical discoveries of new prototype compounds in pharmacotherapy have universally enhanced the clinicians' prestige as psychopharmacological investigators. Differences in psychiatric orientation in the United States and Europe must be kept in mind when we compare the fairly dispassionate reception of the new psychoactive drugs in Europe with the often strongly protagonistic or antagonistic attitude which has prevailed in America. Controversies on matters of psychopharmacological research, and on the clinician's role in particular, have, therefore, been more pronounced and positions more separated in the United States.

The rapid discovery of varieties of psychoactive drugs has caught the medical profession in a dilemma of unpreparedness. But this holds equally true for scientists concerned with behavior. An expansion of conceptual fields and investigative techniques has been forced upon each specialty and discipline. As a result, we seem to pass through some temporary confusion of scientific identities. The pharmacologists, confronted with the complexities of assessing drug behavioral effects, have turned into experimental psychologists and psychopathologists. Psychiatrists, overwhelmed by the sudden intrusion of drugs, have turned into self-styled clinical pharmacologists or have dedicated themselves to the task of fitting psychoanalytical concepts into drug behavioral models. And experimental psychologists, sociologists, and biometricians have embarked on evaluating psychoactive compounds without the benefit of the historical knowledge of psychiatric treatment and its manifold theoretical implications. It is already quite apparent that no one can be productive in the field of psychopharmacology while holding on to traditional methods or frames of reference. The need for multidisciplinary cooperation is, therefore, generally conceded. But, as was to be expected, it has not been easy to synthesize ideas and tactics.

It does not require analytical sophistication to find valid reasons for reluctances, conflicting interests, and methodological distrust. The scientific temperament of the laboratory researcher, the therapeutic zeal of the clinician, and the mathematical detachment of the biostatistician seem predestined to experience a heavy dose of marital maladjustment. The recent mass production of poorly conceived and uncritically reported clinical studies on drug therapies has undoubtedly been detrimental to the cause of multidisciplinary progress. But poor performance on anyone's part is no justification for total rejection. We need to concentrate our attention on the methodological aspects of clinical psychopharmacology. The concept of pharmaco-psychiatry stems from Kraepelin. His attempt to lay the groundwork for an experimental-psychological approach to pharmaco-psychiatry encountered little interest at his time. A re-evaluation of Kraepelin's work in the light of current developments in pharmacological psychiatry indicates that "the spiral of scientific progress has returned to the position where, 60 years ago, Kraepelin formulated the inherent problems" (Mayer-Gross, 1957). Today the clinician still works without modern gadgets for objective measurement. His observational capacity and critical faculty for interpretation are his main tools. Since capacity and competence are highly individual matters, the clinician has come to be regarded by some as the weakest link in psychopharmacological research. The question now arises whether his investigative liabilities have attracted attention out of proportion to his assets.

Purpose and Nature of
Clinical Psychopharmacological Studies

In so far as clinical psychiatry is concerned, psychoactive drugs serve three major purposes. The first and most important is the therapeutic elimination or modification of psychopathological symptoms. Second, drug-induced mental changes are of diagnostic significance if latent phenomena can be transformed into manifest ones, as in the case of the various narcodiagnostic techniques with sodium amytal and similar drugs. And third, drugs capable of inducing psychotic states have become indispensable for experimental psychopathology.

The clinical study of drug effects depends on the proper identification of "targets" on which the drug exerts its action. A drug with therapeutic effects limited to headaches can only be assessed in patients with headache as a target for the drug's action. Amphetamine compounds have been prescribed for two unrelated purposes: to curb the appetite and to ameliorate depressed moods. The obese but emotionally harmonious patient experiences little, if any, mood change; he does not present a "target" for antidepressive action. A study of the antidepressive effects of this medication depends, therefore, on the proper selection of patients with dysphoria. Recognition and assessment of psychoactive effects in psychiatric patients require thorough knowledge not only of psychopathological states but also of the various circumstances under which they change. Without this knowledge, it is as easy to ascribe changes to drug effects which are in fact non-pharmacological in origin as to credit psychological factors with the production of changes which were determined solely by drug action.

Psychopathological states represent more than the sum total of their component symptoms. Since psychopathological states are characteristic for particular mental disorders, they must be evaluated in the context of the total clinical picture. Similarity of psychopathological states is, therefore, no indication of a common origin. This applies particularly to the controversy over whether drug-induced psychoses *resemble* or actually *are* schizophrenic psychoses. There is as yet no evidence that schizophrenia can be either produced or cured by means of any known specific chemical substance. The experimentally induced psychoses represent various kinds of exogenous psychoses which are clearly distinguishable from any endogenous disturbance like schizophrenia, in spite of superficial similarities (M. Bleuler, 1959).

Clinical experience with variation and variability of psychopathological states is a decisive prerequisite for psychopharmacological research. The differentiation between spontaneous, reactive, and treatment-induced changes has been of vital interest to psychiatrists for decades. The current emphasis, if not overemphasis, on social aspects of psychopathological behavior tends to obscure this fact. Eugen Bleuler introduced the chapter on therapy in his major contribution to our knowledge on schizophrenia, published in 1911, with these words of warning:

> Except for the treatment of purely psychogenic disorders, the therapy of schizophrenia is one of the most rewarding for the physician who does not ascribe the results of the natural healing processes of psychosis to his own intervention.

As an ardent advocate of early discharge from the hospital, he stated categorically:

> One should not wait for a cure. One can consider it an established rule that earlier release produces better results. . . . The only and often very practical criterion is the patient's capacity to react in a positive manner to changes in environment and treatment.

The potentialities of responses to many types of treatment as well as to highly varied social and administrative policies in hospitals of markedly different character and in countries of contrasting cultures have been explored and recorded for several decades. The value of this collective experience is enormous in providing information about constant and variable patterns of mental disorders. The substantial degree of constancy and similarity which points to intrinsic determinants of mental disorders is apt to be underestimated, if not deliberately ignored, in these times of sociological enthusiasm in the behavioral sciences. The acknowledgment of interaction of social, biological, and psychological variables does not make them a priori partners of equal causative significance in the evaluation of behavior, whether normal or abnormal.

The complexity of known and unknown interacting variables which pertain to psychopharmacological studies entails great risks when it comes to methodological standardizations. There is currently a tendency to contrast chiefly pharmacological and milieu-interactional aspects in experimental studies of psychoactive compounds.

From the clinical point of view, there remains the cardinal question whether we have objective methods which are sufficiently comprehensive to portray the multidimensional interactions between personality and psychopathology in the unique context of individuality. The problem of individual variation is mostly minimized in experimental design. Williams, who developed the concept of "biochemical individuality" (1956), calls attention to a crucial issue when he states: "The probable connection between variation in drug responses and biochemical individuality has not been generally recognized nor has any substantial amount of data been collected which is directly pertinent to this interpretation." In the light of the work of E. Kretschmer and W. H. Sheldon, it must appear anachronistic to dissociate drug effects from the aspects of individual differences. Both clinician and experimental psychologist must necessarily remain sensitive to the recognition of individual phenomena and variables which influence drug responses.

The development of specific criteria and sensitive controls for psychopharmacological research depends very substantially on clinical findings. Whether these are "impressionistic" or based on disciplined methods of observation and analysis cannot be resolved by theoretical argument.

Therapeutic Criteria for Neuroleptic Drugs

Delay developed the concept of "neuroleptic therapy" in order to lend specificity to the effects of drugs which have been classified as tranquilizers in the United States. According to this concept, the essential criterion for neuroleptic drugs is the aptitude to produce neurologic, autonomic, and psychological syndromes (Delay and Deniker, 1956). Initially, little was known about the pharmacological action of these compounds. What may be designated as the decisive clinical observation was the fact that neuroleptic compounds inhibit psychokinetic activity in a manner which involves changes in the functional state of the strio-pallidal system. These changes are manifested by symptoms which range from diminished initiative and mildly blunted affectivity to fully developed features of strio-pallidal syndromes. There was nothing in the pharmacological protocols pertaining to chlorpromazine and reserpine to alert the clinician to expect a neuropharmacological mode of action on the strio-pallidal system. It was indeed a most perplexing situation that two new compounds, chlorpromazine and reserpine, quite dissimilar in chemical structure, had in common the property to affect psychomotility functions and cause the syndrome of parkinsonism. Neuroleptic treatment was, therefore, conceived as being singularly effective for those psychopathological states which have in common hypermotility syndromes, abnormally increased initiative, and heightened affective tension. Neuroleptic treatment was not regarded as specific for specific mental diseases but as having specific effects on particular dysfunctions which occur in a great variety of mental disorders.

The emergence of psychomotility syndromes as therapeutic criteria necessitated a conceptual dissociation of diagnostic entities from psychokinetic behavior. It also made case selection the most important aspect with regard to success or failure of the treatment. Differences in case selection are, thus, primarily responsible for the discrepancies in reported observations and therapeutic results. Since potent neuroleptic compounds, through their inhibitory action on psychomotility functions, are specifically effective in reducing excitement and abnormal initiative, they are by virtue of this action useless, if not harmful, for patients with manifestations of energy deficits and affective retardation. In the early stages of my clinical investigations of chlorpromazine and reserpine, it quickly became evident that there existed a need for phenomenological analyses of behavioral and psychopathological symptoms in order to identify suitable therapeutic targets. I also found it impossible to determine borderlines between therapeutic degrees of reduced psychokinetic activity and the early manifestations of the parkinsonian syndrome. Neuroleptic drugs, it appeared, influence complex cerebral mechanisms which determine and alter psychomotor expression. The resulting reduction of psychokinetic activity may range from ordinary lassitude and passiveness to extreme parkinsonian rigidity (Freyhan, 1956, 1957a, b). The term "akinetic-avolitional syndrome" was applied by Fluegel to describe the motor and mental changes which are characteristic of neuroleptic action and are effective in influencing various psychotic conditions (Fluegel and Bente, 1957). Initially, however, many reported extrapyramidal manifestations in terms of toxic reactions. It took time and the development of still more potent compounds before it became more generally known that the effects on psychomotility constitute an integral part of the therapeutic function of neuroleptic compounds.

One may see more than a historical coincidence in the fact that these drugs made their appearance at a time of evolutionary changes in concepts on brain function. Hess (1954) demonstrated the functional integration of the diencephalon with the extrapyramidal motor system, referring to "diencephalic motor innervation." He regards the diencephalon rather than the cortex "as the true control organ of the body." Penfield and Jasper (1954) postulate the existence of a "centrencephalic system" as the highest level of functional integration. And Magoun's work contributes further support to the assumption of subcortical functional primacy. A meaningful interpretation of the neuroleptic effects presented itself within the framework of psychomotility referring to volitional, impulsive, and affective functions. Thus the development of drugs which influence functions of the sub-cortical systems created new therapeutic potentialities. What happens in neuroleptic treatment can be conceptualized as a temporary trans-formation of the patient's temperamental structure: an attenuation of impulsivity, initiative, and motor activity. Since consciousness and ideation remain virtually intact, it seems proper to speak of selective effects on the psychokinetic components of psychopathological states.

Clinical Investigations

Experience has shown that the preclinical data gathered in the laboratories are of limited informative and predictive value in so far as clinical effectiveness and applicability of psychoactive drugs are con-cerned. The rationale of clinical evaluations concerns the modi-fiability of particular symptoms which constitute what I call "target symptoms." The effectiveness of a psychoactive drug must then be measured in terms of its ability to reduce, alter, or eliminate these target symptoms. Patients were always selected on the basis of specified psychopathological symptoms which were clearly defined on the front sheet of the observational protocols. All final evaluations were based on kind and degree of the modification of these target symptoms. Details of my investigational procedures have been de-scribed elsewhere (Freyhan, 1959b). What is important here is to state that in this method all clinical observations, whether by re-search nurse or research physician, were unsolicited. In contrast to rating scales, which direct the observer's attention to predetermined items, great emphasis was placed on spontaneous and unrestricted observations. The range of observational faculties varies, of course, from individual to individual. Here, however, lies not only a limita-tion but also a great advantage. Many unexpected phenomena, be-havioral or somatic, will be recorded in the physician's and nurse's daily observational protocols if the initiative for comprehensive obser-vation is stimulated.

This approach, based on phenomenological analysis of kind and degree of modification of target symptoms, has led to the identification of differential modes of action of phenothiazine derivatives. Indica-tions of particular clusters of effects or action patterns were discerned which suggested a division into groups on the basis of their chemical structure. A distinction could be made between chlorpromazine-model compounds, having in common three carbons in a straight chain, prochlorperazine-model compounds with piperazine radicals at the end of the three-carbon straight chain; and a miscellaneous group of compounds which contain a side chain with more than three carbons. A comparative analysis of many phenothiazine derivatives and reserpine left little doubt about the concurrence of greater potency with higher frequencies of extrapyramidal manifestations. Compounds which failed to elicit extrapyramidal reactions showed the least favorable therapeutic results. Whereas chlorpromazine-model compounds have the higher incidence of drowsiness and lethargy, prochlorperazine-model compounds are least apt to diminish alertness. The incidence of extrapyramidal reactions is two or three times as high with prochlorperazine-model compounds. The latter are by far more potent, requiring very low doses to exert maximal effects in shorter time. But, while these summarized findings are of significance for therapeutic differentiation, they remain incomplete without a further analysis of the extrapyramidal reactions and their clinical and theoretical implications. So far, I have referred to parkinsonism, which is characterized by various degrees of rigidity, gait and postural abnormalities, a decrease of spontaneous motility, and other associated features. But our initial study of the effects of prochlorperazine had already revealed a variety of dyskinetic reactions which were as unexpected as they were clinically novel in connection with drug treatment (Freyhan, 1958). Dyskinetic manifestations, characterized by spastic contractions and involuntary movements occurring in various combinations, develop in a dramatic fashion during the initial phase of treatment with prochlorperazine-model compounds. They seem to be "borrowed" from the chapters in neurology texts on encephalitis and strio-pallidal disorders, except that the drug-induced syndromes are rapidly reversible.

Most surprising was the observation of still another extrapyramidal syndrome which is characterized by a compulsion to pace back and forth, an inability to sit down and keep still. Known as "acathisia" because of its occurrence in epidemic encephalitis and paralysis agitans, this syndrome was first observed with reserpine and later with far greater frequency as an effect of prochlorperazine-model compounds. If acathisia is mild, patients complain of a feeling of inner unrest, of pulling or drawing sensations in the extremities, chiefly in the legs. Once fully developed, acathisia manifests itself as an uncontrollable urge to pace back and forth. Since patients can neither sit down nor stay in bed, they are unable to sleep. In severe cases, this motor restlessness develops into states of frank agitation.

Acathisia has been mistaken for various psychological reactions. It was first described in the literature as "turbulence," as "paradoxical response," and it has also been psychodynamically interpreted as a break-through of anxiety.

Acathisia presents a classical example of the limitations of the rating-scale assessment of drug effects. The fact that the patient is "restless" will, of course, be recorded—provided the raters (often "trained aides") are good observers. But, as an isolated behavioral item, it will be, and has been, interpreted as mere evidence of psychotic behavior which the drug has failed to ameliorate. The clinically experienced observer, on the other hand, finds unmistakable evidence of a particular pattern of motor restlessness, highly uniform in its manifestations from patient to patient, which seems phenomenologically unrelated to the psychopathological picture. Manipulation of dosage and addition of antiparkinsonism medication proves effective in eliminating this syndrome. Animal and clinical experiments have since confirmed the property of the piperazine radical carrying phenothiazines to produce motor excitement (Lehmann and Csank, 1957; Delay, Deniker, Ropert, Eurieult, and Barande, 1958).

Our findings revealed, furthermore, essential sex differences in the incidence of extrapyramidal syndromes. For parkinsonism a male-female ratio of 1:2 prevails with most phenothiazine compounds as well as with reserpine. Dyskinetic manifestations, on the other hand, are more common in men. While the significance of this sex difference cannot be dealt with here, it provides many challenging questions about constitutional differences as well as case selection and sampling procedures.

As is obvious, the spectrum of neuroleptic effects includes akinetic and hyperkinetic manifestations as well. Unawareness of the differential effects has created much confusion. This is painfully clear if we contemplate the usefulness of the classification "tranquilizers." The reduction of multidimensional effects to a simple causal formula, such as the tranquilizer, entails dangers. Therapeutically, instead of the anticipated tranquility, there may be acathisia; instead of relaxation, parkinsonian rigidity. In "blind" studies, not only may compounds be rated ineffective because rating scales fail to reveal a decrease of pathological activity, but also the actual spectrum of neuropharmacological activity may remain unidentified. Clinical studies have demonstrated beyond doubt that the one-dimensional concept of "tranquilizers" should be replaced with a multidimensional concept of drugs which, by altering brain function in a variety of ways, may produce simultaneously dissimilar effects on personality functions.

The greater our knowledge of the differential effects of neuroleptic compounds or other psychoactive drugs, the easier will it become to find specific psychopathologic targets for therapeutic and experimental purposes. The recent search for effective antidepressive drugs has concentrated on compounds which block brain monoamine oxidase. The dependence of serotonin and norepinephrine metabolism on enzymic activity constitutes the backbone of the theory of a biochemical deficiency as basis for cause and treatment of depressive disorders. What this biochemical concept suggests is a two-dimensional model of depression as a deficit state of psychomotor or psychic energy which must be reversed by stimulating or energizing action. On purely clinical grounds, the question arises whether one can reduce the complex psychopathological variety of mood disturbances to simple pathophysiological antagonisms. There remains suggestive evidence that depressive disorders reflect multidimensional psychobiological changes. A depressive state, characterized by marked retardation of the psychic tempo and by poverty of thought and imagination, differs substantially from the picture of an agitated depression with despairing restlessness and tormenting ideation. Since both the retarded and the agitated depression are, at least empirically, distinctive entities, some doubt may arise as to a common biochemical origin.

The recent observation of Kuhn that imipramine hydrochloride possesses antidepressive properties is interesting, because this compound, which in its structural formula resembles the phenothiazine derivative promazine, was originally assumed to possess chlorpromazine-like effects. In this respect, it failed. A few of the schizophrenic patients, however, who responded with some improvement, had in common prominent symptoms of depression. On the basis of this observation, Kuhn began to treat patients suffering from depressive disorders. He then found that imipramine possesses markedly antidepressive properties. The best responses were obtained in cases "of endogenous depression showing the typical symptoms of mental and motor retardation, fatigue, feeling of heaviness, hopelessness, guilt and despair" (Kuhn, 1958). What must seem pharmacologically provocative is the fact that this compound is not reported to inhibit monoamine oxidase or to affect cerebral norepinephrine levels. The pharmacological data are as yet meager, and the nature of the drug's cerebral action has not been identified.

Our investigations of the antidepressive effects of imipramine, which are still in progress, support Kuhn's contention that imipramine is therapeutically effective. There is no evidence of a specific drug-induced psychoaffective syndrome. Neither euphoria nor psychokinetic stimulation is a regular concomitant of the drug's activity. Depressive apathy and kinetic retardation with feelings of hopelessness seem to be primary targets for imipramine treatment. Tentative as these results still are, they support the need for clinically oriented investigations that are based on psychopathological differentiation (Freyhan, 1959a). This aspect of psychopharmacological research may prove to be helpful in isolating multiple determinants of symptoms which "belong" to the same nosologic entities. In the absence of precise knowledge on the etiology of depressive or other mental disorders, the search for pertinent variables must remain wide open. Whether the clinician's observations yield impressions or valid data must then be determined by experimental methods.

On Controversial Aspects

Much recent controversy has been dedicated to the question whether psychopharmacological research should be "controlled" or "uncontrolled"; whether evaluations should be *a priori* "objective" or could still be valuable if "subjective." As happens so frequently when complicated matters are reduced to simple alternatives, this question transcends the realm of decision. Ideally, there is no problem. Only objective findings are scientifically valid. And only an investigative method which permits objective validation can be recognized as scientific. In an essay titled "Psychiatric Realities. An Analysis of Autistic Trends in Psychiatric Thinking," I commented on the danger of subjectivism (Freyhan, 1947):

> The psychiatrist should be the last to object to self-analysis and the first to struggle to achieve full insight into an attitude which Eugen Bleuler bluntly called "the autistic-undisciplined thinking in medicine." This thinking is either unconcerned with or unaware of fundamental realities. It permits subjective evaluations and presuppositions to displace objective disciplined thinking. In the case of psychiatry, there seems to be a preoccupation with positivistic ideologies which manifest a reaction to fear of therapeutic limitations.

A competent clinician must feel as frustrated and irritated by bias, by semantic obscurities, and by plain negligence on definition or descriptive detail as does the experimental psychologist or biostatistician. The promiscuous generalization of selected observations of personal interest has been, and still is, a major obstacle to progress in clinical science. For a long time, evaluations of psychiatric therapies, somatic and psychological, was the private and privileged task of the therapist. Only recently have psychiatric affairs been subjected to the examination and critique of scientists from other disciplines. If the demonstration of methodological deficiencies brings about a thorough reorganization of evaluation methods, psychiatry will profit immensely.

But, if the criticism is to be corrective, and I refer now specifically to the psychiatrist's role in psychopharmacology, we must take a close look at some of the proposed remedies. There are not only naive methods of clinical empiricism; there is also the threat of a naive faith in technical objectivism. Standardized investigational procedures and large-scale controlled studies have been recommended to put drug evaluations on a "scientific" basis. Could it be the case now that too much emphasis is placed on the structure of research while too little attention is given to analyzing the clinical soundness of essence and content?

A systematic review of the literature concerned with evaluations of drug effects in clinical populations reveals a close similarity of findings between those clinical and experimental investigations which were conducted under similar circumstances with regard to patient selection and dose requirements. The concept of "controlled studies" implies an arrangement sufficiently sensitive to provide information relevant to the purpose of the study. But an often unbelievable amount of time, energy, and money is being spent on testing hypotheses with objective methods which are, nevertheless, quite impotent.

Let me construe an imaginary example of a controlled study which is actually typical for many of the reported investigations. Let us call this study "A controlled clinical study of compound X treatment in chronic schizophrenia." The introduction briefly surveys various clinical reports, often contradictory, and emphasizes the need for an objective evaluation. Ample space is given to a description of research design. There is a careful elaboration of environmental variables and of methods to evaluate them by experimental procedures. New rating scales are introduced which are to portray global behavioral changes on an item-by-item basis. There may even follow a description of the special training program which was offered to psychiatric aides so that they might assume the responsibility for observing the patients and marking the rating scales. Medication schedules will have been carefully predetermined with regard to minimum and maximum doses, drug periods and placebo intervals. Needless to say, only the pharmacist knows the code and everyone else operates blindly. Finally, there is a statement on case selection. Patients were chosen according to diagnosis and length of hospitalization. Chronicity is defined as two or more years of continuous hospitalization. From the comments it may be quite apparent that the patients were "regressed" or "backward patients" and had not responded to previous treatments. Or the authors chose random sampling and arranged for only-drug and only-placebo samples. But whatever the specifications, the entire approach is objective and experimental. Thus the stage is set for obtaining valid information that will permit scientifically justified conclusions.

What can this type of investigation achieve? It will supply an answer to the question whether the particular schizophrenic patients selected under the particular circumstances of the inquiry, and under the administration of the particular dose regime provided, manifested changes in terms of the items contained in the rating scale. There will be little, if any, information about the spectrum of psychoactive effects of the compound; nor will the results be relevant to the treatment of chronic schizophrenia. Why, one must ask, should "chronicity" be assumed to be a therapeutic target, since there are as many discrepant behavioral variations in chronic as in acute patients? Why should the drug be expected to have the same effects on the dull and apathetic as on the agitated and disturbed patient? Should the suspicious and ill-nourished individual respond in the same manner to the same drug as the aggressive person in robust physical condition? Thus the study is directed at an entity, chronic schizophrenia, regardless of drastic differences in symptomatology and other pertinent variables.

Furthermore, the majority of the patients may have received drug quantities far below the therapeutic level for periods too short to produce behavioral changes. Since dose schedules were pre-arranged, the chances are (and there is an abundance of examples in the literature) that the authors did not, in fact, conduct an objective study of compound X at all. Whatever compound X is capable of achieving could not be determined with the procedure applied. Since the investigators are unaware of the deficiencies of their approach, they will arrive at certain conclusions. These are based on the statistical evidence of the presence or absence of group differences. If the drug group did not differ from the non-drug group, the mean results may still obscure significant data pertaining to those few patients who happened to be the only suitable candidates for treatment with compound X. But, even if the dose levels were adequate and if a significant change were measurably ascertained, the results still will not pertain to "chronic schizophrenia" but to particular patients whose behavioral characteristics remain unidentified. Thus the scientific value of the entire investigation remains limited.

It is precisely for this reason that experimental investigations cannot be substituted for clinical explorations. It must remain the clinician's task to find out what it is that the drug does to whom. In this endeavor, neither is he infallible nor does he proceed under the spell of what has been somewhat ambivalently called intuition. Disciplined observational faculties, the ability for abstraction, and the knowledge to apply the appropriate frame of reference are more desirable ingredients for a clinical investigator than skill for imaginative speculation. That there has been a liberal display of the latter can hardly be denied by anyone who is conversant with the history of psychiatry. Application of statistical methods, use of refined psychological test batteries, and dedication to the cause of interprofessional relations are not alone the answer to better psychopharmacological research. The recent tendency to think about psychopharmacological research in terms of large-scale testing centers implies the distinct danger that clinical discrimination may become the victim of sample engineering. In the light of present knowledge, it would seem to be entirely premature to reduce the number of actual or potential psychobiological variables to the minimum, which seems to be an operational requirement for large-scale investigations.

An effort has been made in this chapter to develop a better understanding of the clinical point of view in psychopharmacological research. At the present stage of knowledge, more harm than good will come from puristic insistence on objective methods. Objectivity is not accomplished by rigid rejection of clinical observation and evidence. It has to be the clinical investigator's goal to discover drug effects, to identify crucial variables of action and interaction, and to conceive hypotheses. And there his contribution ends. But only thus can productive evidence be sought and achieved.

R E F E R E N C E S

Bleuler, Eugen. *Dementia praecox or the group of schizophrenias.* New York: International Press, 1950.

Bleuler, M. Neuropharmakologische Hypothesen in ihrer Bedeutung fuer die Schizophrenielehre und die allgemeine Psychopathologie. Paper read at First int. meeting of Neuro-Psychopharmacology, Rome, Sept. 8–13, 1958. In

P. B. Bradley, P. Deniker, and C. Radouco-Thomas (Eds.), *Neuro-psychopharmacology.* Amsterdam: Elsevier, 1959.

Delay, J., and Deniker, P., Le traitement des psychoses par une méthode neurolytique derivée de l'hibernotherapie (Le 4560 R. P. utilisé seul en cure prolongée et continué). *C. R. Congr. Médecins alienistes neurol.* 1952, 1–6.

Delay, J., and Deniker, P. Chlorpromazine and neuroleptic treatments in psychiatry. *J. clin. exp. Psychopath.*, 1956, 17, 19–24.

Delay, J., Deniker, P., Robert, R., Barande, R., and Eurieult, M. Syndromes neurologiques engendrés par un nouveau neuroleptique majeur, le 7843 R.P. (Phenothiazine piperazinée et sulfamidée). *56th Congr. Psychiat. Neurol.*, Strasbourg, July 21–26, 1958.

Fluegel, F., and Bente, D. The akinetic-avolitional syndrome; its significance for psycho-pharmacological research. *German med. Monthly*, 1957, II, 51.

Freyhan, F. A. Psychiatic realities; an analysis of autistic trends in psychiatric thinking. *J. nerv. ment. Dis.*, 1947, 106, 482–92.

Freyhan, F. A. Comments on the biological and psychopathological basis of individual variation in chlorpromazine therapy. *L'Encéphale*, 1956, 45, 913–919.

Freyhan, F. A. Psychomotility and parkinsonism in treatment with neuroleptic drugs. *Arch. Neurol. Psychiat.*, 1957, 78, 465–472. (a)

Freyhan, F. A. Psychomotilitaet, extra-pyramidale Syndrome und Wirkungsweisen neuroleptischer Therapien. (Chlorpromazine, reserpine, proclorperazine.) *Nervenarzt*, 1957, 28, 504–509. (b)

Freyhan, F. A. The neuroleptic action and effectiveness of proclorperazine in psychiatric disorders. *Amer. psych. Ass. psychiat. Res. Rep. 9*, 1958, 32–45.

Freyhan, F. A. The pharmacological modification of mental depressions with imipramine. Paper read at First int. meeting on Neuro-psychopharmacol., Rome, Sept. 11, 1958. In P. B. Bradley, P. Deniker, and C. Radouco-Thomas (Eds.), *Neuro-psychopharmacology.* Amsterdam: Elsevier, 1959. (a)

Freyhan, F. A. Therapeutic implications of differential effects of new phenothiazine compounds. *Am. J. Psychiat.*, 1959, 115, 577–585. (b)

Hess, W. R. *Diencephalon:autonomic and extrapyramidal functions.* Vol. III. *Monographs in biology and medicine.* New York: Grune & Stratton, 1954.

Kuhn, R. The treatment of depressive states with G22355 (imipramine hydrochloride). *Am. J. Psychiat.*, 1958, 115, 459–464.

Lehmann, H. E., and Csank, J. Differential screening of phrenotropic agents in man:psychophysiologic test data. *J. clin. exp. Psychopath.*, 1957, 18, 222–235.

Mayer-Gross, W. Kraepelins Arzneimittelstudien und die pharmakologische Psychiatrie der Gegenwart. *Nervenarzt*, 1957, 28, 97–100.

Penfield, W., and Jasper, H. *Epilepsy and the functional anatomy of the human brain.* Boston: Little, Brown, 1954.

Williams, R. J. *Biochemical individuality.* New York: Wiley, 1956.

What does the clinician want to know about psychoactive drugs?

Problems about the modes of action and possible usages of psycho-active drugs are extremely complicated. The study of these problems has met with difficulties that go beyond those for any other types of pharmaceuticals. This is apparent from the thousands of papers that have been published on the action of only a limited number of such compounds with relatively little substantial increase in our understanding of their action upon which the clinician can depend when prescribing them. He still has to rely on rather vague hunches, and most of the time he is in the process of learning by trial and error. Indeed, despite the numerous studies, we can claim little progress in our understanding of the causal chain that starts with the introduction of chemical compounds into the body and ends with the complex, hard to describe changes in the patient's behavior and his experience of himself and his environment.

Some of the findings have made us realize the extreme complexity of every attempt to measure human behavior, and the placebo effect has made us aware that the drugs alone are not the only factors responsible for the behavioral changes that follow administration. The suggestive elements induced by the attitude of people in the environment, as well as by the personal meaning that a particular method of drug administration has for a patient, play fundamental roles in the ensuing behavioral changes. These variables have made exhaustive studies of individuals of questionable value, and have forced us to resort almost exclusively to studies of large numbers of people, which give a means of controlling the variables mentioned. They involve, however, disadvantages inherent in statistical methods, such as the

possibilities that many important factors simply cancel each other out
without the experimenter's knowledge, and that important qualitative
material escapes attention. The clinician, after all, is interested in
more than statistical generalities, such as that chlorpromazine alleviates anxiety in 57 per cent of anxiety neurotics. He wants to know
how the particular patient under treatment will respond to such a
drug. He wants to know in detail what possible meaning to the patient such drug administration can have, and how the physiological
changes it brings about will be interpreted and integrated by the patient into a new pattern of behavior.

Much difficulty arises from the fact that any drug given to a human
being is a new force added to an existing balance of forces. A central aspect of an organism is its organization—how all its component
forces interact to form a unitary totality. In the human being we
speak of integration instead of organization, to indicate that with the
introduction of self-awareness a new level of complexity and variability of organization has been introduced. Hughlings Jackson has
emphasized how the human organism will try to form a new sort of
integration if, for instance, as a result of trauma, part of the old
organization no longer functions. The same is true when a drug is
administered. Knowing the tremendous complexity of the balance of
forces that human integration represents, we can easily see the difficulty in predicting behavioral changes that may result from the introduction of chemical compounds into this balanced system. The
effects of such a drug are dependent both on its chemical structure
and on the characteristics of the balance to which it is added. On
such a basis we can try to understand why a drug given to one patient may have a tranquilizing effect, while the next patient will respond with a panic reaction to the same dose of the same drug.

The Clinician's Questions

It is almost impossible to apply to the human organism the findings
obtained in animal experiments with psychoactive drugs. We often
cannot even transfer experience obtained with one patient to another.
What questions do we want to ask about the drugs that have become
so important in psychiatry? Lack of specificity in the questions we
can ask indicates the relatively primitive state of the clinician's
thoughts about the psychoactive drugs today. Basically he wants to
know: "What does what? When? To whom?" Even though some
of the theories use the terminology of energy changes in the brain,
they do not really concern physiological factors. Rather, the energetic

formulations are metaphors that simply cloak fundamentally psychological phenomena in the terminology of the physical world. It is, therefore, not surprising that we find many psychoanalytically oriented psychotherapists reluctant to use psychoactive drugs. Implicit in the use of drugs to influence behavior is the admission that a narrowly psychodynamic framework is insufficient. This appears to be enough justification for many a clinician to neglect the psychoactive drugs. On first sight, the physiologic frame of reference seems most suitable for a rational approach to questions about psychoactive agents. However, we have only to look at such facts as, for example, the placebo effects to realize that this framework alone allows us to see only part of the total. Man is not a body from which emanates a strange epiphenomenon called "mind," and man is not spiritual being with a material burden called "body." Man is a complete, unitary, existing being. The clinician's current impasse concerning psychoactive drugs certainly does not arise from lack of data. We can hardly open a psychiatric journal without coming across a paper dealing with this area. The real stagnation lies in the insufficiency of our conceptualizations.

Advantages of a
Phenomenological Approach

The Western European existentialist psychiatry devotes much attention to the problem of form versus content. The underlying assumption is that the disease process makes a specific form of psychopathology possible (for example, the delusion), whereas the specific content of the delusion is dependent on the personal history of the patient. Minkowski (1933), in France, introduced the notion of "trouble générateur." He proposed that underneath the immediate symptomatology, the particular content of the patient's thinking and his way of experiencing, lies a fundamental disturbance that generates the apparent symptomatology. At present we have no guarantee that the factors Minkowski suggested as "troubles générateurs" are indeed the most essential. It may be fruitful to employ this method of investigation in an attempt to determine which fundamental factors are affected by drugs. This is done to some extent at present, though rather crudely. The number of papers describing supposedly basic drug-sensitive factors, such as anxiety and hyperactivity, is extensive. Possibly, however, more fundamental factors could be found through existentialist or phenomenological methods. If we search the literature, we find that such attempts to separate form from content have resulted in a number of suggestions. Rumke (1956) mentions the following possible "form categories" of mental functioning: (1) acceleration versus retardation; (2) excitation versus paralysis; (3) regulation or integration versus disintegration and disorganization; (4) evolution in time ("l'allure temporelle"); (5) hypertonia versus hypotonia; (6) level of psychological tension (Janet); (7) vital mood ("die vitale Stimmung"); (8) instincts; (9) rhythm of psychic life.

These categories are mentioned here as examples of possible starting points for research such as we propose. The categories mentioned certainly have not been rigorously established as fundamental coordinates along which all basic changes in psychic functioning take place. It is very unlikely that they are a set of unrelated variables. Nevertheless here might be an approach that, if undertaken conscientiously and carefully, could prove valuable.

In a paper on drugs and behavior Skinner (1958) recently criticized the research that has been done by psychiatrists on the psychoactive drugs. He suggested that most of it did not go beyond the adjectival description of changes in behavior and stressed the necessity of breaking up behavior into convenient pieces, rigidly defining the variables operationally, and studying these pieces separately. This is a highly desirable goal. However, Dr. Skinner neglects to name the convenient pieces into which we may break up behavior. One sometimes despairs of ever finding such convenient pieces of behavior, except perhaps in Skinner's pigeons. The phenomenological approach, therefore, seems as yet the most suited to help us. It cannot give us final answers, but the phenomenological (or naturalistic, taxonomic) phase of research must precede the quantitative approach, which must then determine whether our clinical hunches are indeed of practical value.

Impact of Tranquilizers on Psychiatric Practice

Therapists must constantly question beyond apparently benevolent motivations in prescribing drugs and wonder about the relationship-attenuating effects of the maneuver. They have to consider factors aside from their consciously desired effect—factors associated with unconscious magical, erotic, guilty, or retaliatory fantasies on the part of the giver *and* the receiver.

Let us examine the indirect effects of the advent of tranquilizing drugs. In 1950 there was an enormous need for something new in the psychiatric therapeutic armamentarium. Something that would cure or alleviate mental disease and consequently arouse public interest in mental health problems. Somehow society had to be administered a bitter pill of awareness of the growth and size of the problem of mental ill health. The world had just begun to recover from a terrible war and seemed to be constantly on the brink of another. Alarmingly and insidiously, all the symptoms of mental illness, neurosis and psychosis, juvenile delinquency and crime were increasing; but public recognition of this fact was clouded by culturally accepted denials and rationalizations. Whether the response was totally realistic or not, the advent of drug therapy has effectively increased public awareness of, and involvement in, mental health problems. Unfortunately, the hoped-for rapid emptying of state hospital wards and mass rehabilitation of the chronically ill was a wishful exaggeration of the much less dramatic truth, but people did feel that something was happening, and something good. There was a gradual change of attitude that permitted the acceptance of emotional illness as being like any other form of sickness. No longer was there the end-of-the-road inevitability of an anonymous death in an institution. Partly as a consequence, more money is now being spent on public education and research in mental health problems than ever before.

What has this to do with what the therapist wants to know about drugs? Quite obviously the practitioner who prescribes a psychoactive drug is not primarily interested in public health problems. The drug, however, has been developed, tested, and presumably found to be efficacious during a time of great enthusiasm for psychopharmacology. Both the practitioner and the patient will undoubtedly have been involved in the contemporary shift in attitudes toward mental health problems, and this will have some effect on the patient's response to the drug.

Psychiatric patients, particularly those seen in general psychiatric practice, have more clearly preformed ideas of what sort of treatment to expect than patients seen by other practitioners. The determinants of these ideas are multiple, involving social class and occupation as well as the individual's view of his own therapeutic needs and how he can satisfy them. The judicious use of drugs cannot be determined by knowledge of drug action alone; it must take account of the particular significance that drug prescribing and taking has to the particular patient. In some carefully planned programs the giving of drugs has been an integral part of the total therapy, but the capsule of love without understanding can become the bitter pill of rejection. We have yet to learn of a study where the attitudes of patients to drug taking has ever been considered, let alone evaluated. We are well aware of the placebo response and of the various diligent manipulations of double-blind studies, of large samples, and of controls, but we are critical and suspicious of evaluations that do not even begin to cope with the uniqueness of human beings.

It is an interesting observation that, in spite of the profuseness of available studies of any new drug, many psychiatrists prefer to reserve their decision about the effectiveness of a psychoactive drug until after they have observed the results in their own patients. This, we feel, is more than the exercise of a professional prerogative, it is a necessity dictated by the considerable difficulty there is in finding conclusive responsible accounts giving concisely the indications for use and the effects of the drugs and showing that a drug does produce more "good effects" and less "bad reactions" than its predecessors.

The Questionnaire to Psychiatrists

To answer the question as to what the clinician wants to know about drugs, we decided to resort to a questionnaire. Clearly, if we queried only our immediate associates, we could not expect their questions to be wholly representative. So we took at random from the directory of the American Psychiatric Association one hundred names. We sent each of these psychiatrists a letter explaining the purpose of our inquiry and a questionnaire intended to elicit three types of information. We asked for a description of his practice; then the amount and nature of the drugs he prescribed; and, finally, what he wanted to know about these drugs. Our questions were only leaders and certainly were not intended to (nor in fact did they) limit the replies. We did not want primarily to make a statistical study of the replies, but wished to gain insight into the significant problems concerning drugs from psychiatrists in as many varied practices as possible. This was accomplished: we had 56 replies, from psychiatrists in private practice, community clinics, state hospitals, private sanatoria, and teaching centers.

The following are the questions we asked and the distributions of replies.

Total number of questionnaires sent out	100
Number returned	56
Number returned and completed	54

Question 1. Description of practice.

A. Private	31
B. Clinic	16
C. State hospital	6
D. Others	6

(Some had both private and other practices, hence the overlap. "Others" included full-time researchers (on psychoactive drugs), teachers, and a military psychiatrist.)

Question 2.   Do you prescribe drugs?

Yes	42
Yes (qualified)	9
No	3

(Qualified "yes" respondents stated that drugs were prescribed in their clinic practice, but never or rarely in their private practice. "No" respondents included a full-time teacher and two whose practice was limited to psychoanalysis.)

Question 3.   Do you prescribe sedatives, tranquilizers, antidepressants?

A. Sedatives	40
B. Tranquilizers	28
C. Antidepressants	20

Question 4.   Do you prescribe drugs for an indefinite period?

Yes	10
No	41

(No respondent in private practice answered "yes." The 10 positive replies included the 6 in state hospital practice. The other 4 had clinic appointments.)

Question 5.   Are you prescribing more drugs than one year ago?

Yes	0
No	26

(Eight said "much less"; 10 said "about the same"; 6 did not answer.)

Question 6.   To what proportion of your patients do you prescribe drugs?

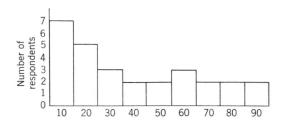

Figure 1.   Percentage of patients for whom drugs were prescribed.

(Twenty-nine replied.   Doctors at state hospitals and clinics more frequently prescribed drugs for a higher proportion of patients.)

Question 7.   How do you choose the drugs you prescribe?

    A. Observation of own results   12
    B. Result of studies reported in journals   16
    C. Other means (please state)   6

(Invariably the respondents who reported "other means" said "through personal communications." Drug house circulars or visits of "detail men" were not mentioned.)

Question 8.   Do you feel you have available adequate information about drugs?

    A. Yes   16
    B. No   32
    C. Did not answer   6

Question 9.   Do you think drugs are advertised and marketed before adequate proving?

    A. Yes   28
    B. No   16

Question 10.   Do you know the cost of drugs you prescribe?

    A. Yes   12
    B. No   12
    C. Some idea   11

Question 11.   Is the price likely to be important in your practice?

    A. Yes   6
    B. No   32

Question 12.   Do your patients ever specifically request drugs?

    A. No   0
    B. Sometimes   36
    C. Frequently   6
    D. Did not answer   12

Miscellaneous Questionnaire Comments

Our covering letter explained that the questions related only to psychoactive drugs that were specifically prescribed for psychological reasons. Hormones and anticonvulsant drugs were not to be included. We invited our respondents to use the questions only as a guide and not to be limited in their replies. Many named the drugs they frequently prescribed. Perhaps the most impressive feature was that none of the respondents was using more drugs than a year previously, in spite of the availability of many more psychoactive compounds. Many were using less, and some had stopped using them. Why was this? Some had become fearful of the adverse reactions, particularly leukopenia and liver damage. Some feared the addictive potentialities. Many stated that they were unable to discern improvement in their patients to support the information they had received on the drug, and that any risk incurred would not justify continued use. We observed that even those who continued to use psychoactive drugs only used three or four, though over 40 were on the market (Wortis, 1958). Almost invariably, one of the earlier developed phenothiazine derivatives or *Rauwolfia* compounds was preferred.

We asked these psychiatrists where they gained information about drugs. None credited the drug house circulars with any value at all, although we cannot believe that all our colleagues are beyond their influence. Some regarded Madison Avenue techniques as offensive and scarcely within the realm of ethical advertising, feeling that some of the displays and exotic claims should be kept for reducing pills. While many referred to articles in competent medical journals, there was obvious dissatisfaction when contradictory or equivocal evidence appeared. As we have indicated, the majority used drugs that were, within their own experience, satisfactory for their purpose—usually one of the older preparations. We noted a persistent attitude of contention and suspiciousness toward the drug companies. Some observations about research workers who were subsidized by free allocation of drugs or financial support from drug houses were not sufficiently circumspect for us to repeat. It was felt that many of the circulars contained definitely misleading information, quoting reports out of context or playing up small-sample short-term studies and minimizing or completely neglecting adverse effects.

The respondents repeatedly asked questions about research methodology, practically every aspect being considered. Could we presume the competence of the research worker? Would not the various orientations preclude many aspects of comparisons in the various tests? Did not the different groups of patients in different situations selected by doctors using, not improbably, different diagnostic criteria make cross-study comparisons impossible? And what was being tested for? Is the drug an anti-anxiety, antihallucinatory, antischizophrenia, or anti-mental illness agent? The latter area of questioning is eminently important because what the psychiatrist wants to know is directly relative to what he wishes the drug to do. Is he looking for a specific symptom response or a total clinical response? Is the medication the total therapy or an adjuvant part of the therapeutic program? From the many varied questions it is quite apparent that the fundamental problems of drug action and possible usage have not yet been answered despite the enormous research investment that has been made.

Conclusion

In this chapter we have discussed some of the questions that have been asked repeatedly by a group of psychiatrists, and we have elaborated some of the reasons why progress in making accurate descriptions of drug action is limited. Possibly in the next few years we shall see newer methods of psychiatric research that will enable us to look at the psychoactive drugs in a new perspective. Perhaps in our search for "peace of mind" we shall hesitate before imposing complete chemical annihilation of feelings. There is everything to commend a drug that alleviates suffering and permits an acquiescence that makes possible reintegration. But what would we be without any anxiety, without any fear, and without any guilt? In searching for the meaning of our new therapeutic agents we have a responsibility that goes beyond the present, beyond ourselves, and beyond the immediate results of our ingenuity.

REFERENCES

Minkowski, E. *Le temps vecu.* Paris: J. L. L. D'Artrey, 1933.
Rumke, H. C. Quelques remarques concernant la pharmacologie et la psychiatrie. In *Colloque international sur la chlorpromazine et les médicaments neuroleptiques en therapeutique psychiatrique.* Paris: G. Doin et Cie., 1956, 39–43.
Skinner, B. F. Drugs and behavior. Paper read at Annual Meeting, Amer. Asso. Adv. Sci., Washington, D.C., Dec. 1958.
Wortis, S. B. A list of some of the newer drugs used in psychiatric practice. *Am. J. Psychiat.,* 1958, 115, 169.

A psychoanalytic approach
to the pharmacology
of psychological processes

I shall begin with two disclaimers. The first is a simple acknowledgment that psychoanalysts have as yet made little contribution to our knowledge of pharmacotherapy either in the neuroses or in the psychoses. Therefore, as a psychoanalyst, I cannot bring you interesting, challenging, or even illustrative data or results. A few scattered clinical clues or challenging observations are no substitute for systematic observations.

Secondly, while it is our responsibility as analysts to participate in basic research in this area, it would be premature and would lead us astray if we were to plunge into applied research on pharmacotherapy. I would regret it were our efforts caught up in the competitive struggle among the drug houses to be the first to produce the most effective happiness pill. Therefore, I am not going to discuss comparative therapeutic scores. To evaluate therapeutic results before we have established clear criteria of basic change is to violate an elementary principle of scientific method.

Fallacies in Evaluating Effects
of Drugs on Neurotic Process

The criteria of change which are used currently seem to me to be fallacious. For instance, it may be of some limited interest from the

Portions of this chapter are reprinted, with permission, from Chapter XII of Psychopharmacology, Harry H. Pennes, Ed., New York: Hoeber-Harper, 1958, in the series Progress in Neurobiology, S. R. Korey and J. I. Nurnberger, Eds.

point of view of short-term symptomatic improvement to record correlations of drug intake with ensuing fluctuations in manifest neurotic
symptomatology, or with fluctuations in the concurrent play of conscious emotions which forms a contrapuntal accompaniment to the
sour melody of neurotic symptoms.   But, from the point of view of
understanding the impact of these same drugs on the neurotic process
itself, such correlations may be actively and seriously misleading.
Any sequence of dreams will show incessant fluctuations, with respect
both to their ideational content and to their concurrent affective states.
Yet the *dreamer* himself has not changed.   No one would be so naive
as to assume that such fluctuations indicated basic changes either in
the underlying personality or in the stream of dynamic processes of
which each dream is a phasic expression.   Precisely the same is true
of that chronic waking dream which we call the neurosis.   In both,
there are continuous changes in surface manifestations which result
from the impact of surface forces.   From such changes alone we are
not entitled to conclude that there have been any deeper alterations.

Therefore, the first challenge which analysts must accept is to help
in providing criteria of change in the dynamics of the personality and
of the neurotic process.   Once we are able to describe such criteria
with precision, and as soon as the experimental and clinical psychologists arm us with devices by which to estimate quantitative changes
even approximately, we will have taken that critical forward step
without which any fundamental understanding of the psychodynamic
influence of pharmacologic agents is impossible.

In the absence of more basic criteria, we would be wise at this
point to consider the impact of pharmacologic agents not on the symptoms of the crystallized neurotic state, nor even on the neurotic
process as a whole, but on various individual ingredients in the neurotic process.   This makes essential an attempt to characterize these
ingredients, a step which may itself be an essential prerequisite to the
recognition of more specific criteria of change.   Furthermore, since we
must ask at what point in the evolution of the neurotic process
pharmacologic agents exercise an influence, a clear description of the
successive steps in this process will also be essential for our purpose.
It is only to the first of these that I invite your attention, this chapter
being too brief for a full discussion of both.   I hope that such a
formulation may in the long run be a useful and clarifying contribution from the psychoanalytic study of the personality and of the neurotic process to the methodology of studying pharmacologic agents.

The psychoanalyst may not offer answers, but he can ask some essential and relevant questions.

I have already indicated that the more usual approach begins at the other end of the chain, asking to what extent the patient's symptomatic disturbances are increased or decreased by drugs, whether these symptomatic disturbances consist of thoughts, actions, feelings, or any combination of these. Because this attitude is deeply entrenched, I shall indicate more fully the reasons for my conviction that such changes are unsatisfactory as indices of change.

1. In the course of the therapeutic process, increases in all symptoms occur at least as frequently as do decreases, because both are necessary phases in the interaction between illness and treatment. While all observations of changes in symptoms are valid observations, it is misleading to use them immediately as a basis for concluding that any change means either an improvement or a worsening in the underlying condition. Many examples of both could be given from everyday practice by different individuals, using various techniques.

2. Moreover, subjective descriptions are not always easy to secure. Patients themselves are often in doubt about their self-observations, and observers of any one case will differ about the value of any patient's subjective report.

3. Similarly, observers differ about the value of any counting devices, or their interpretation. Do changes in the frequency of the washing in a hand-washing compulsion measure the severity of the neurotic process? Or does it measure rather the struggle that the man puts up against it? Or the amount of suffering which he experiences because of his symptom, or which he experiences through the unresolved problems which he displaces onto the symptom?

4. In any effort to estimate the influence of a pharmacologic agent on the end products of the neurotic process, one must ask whether drugs affect the intensity of the neurotic process itself or the extent to which the patient suffers from the secondary and tertiary consequences of his neurosis. One man with an agoraphobia may remain closeted in his room; another may range the world with relative freedom but with incessant inner torment, since his greater freedom of mobility may require acts of major heroism at every step. Will a drug increase or decrease the agoraphobia itself? the underlying conflict? the phobic avoidance? or his discomfort if he resists his own neurotic tendency to avoid open spaces? When the same patient may change from the

imprisoned way of handling his neurosis to the second, it may well be said to constitute a healthier way of life. This is surely true; but the question is whether the neurotic process itself is different when secondary elements in the situation determine the extent to which the neurosis will imprison the patient (Kubie, 1957).

5. Does the impact of drugs alter the inhibitory influences which emanate from a neurotic process, or alternatively its facilitating influences, without changing the underlying process itself? This is another distinction to bear in mind, if we are to understand at what point in the process any drug has exercised its influence.

6. Similar questions must be asked as to whether it is possible to use *affective* symptoms as criteria of the neurotic process itself. If we answer this hastily we are likely to oversimplify the problem. The severity of the emotional disturbance which at some point is stirred by every neurotic process usually depends not so much upon the nature of the process itself as upon the nature of the penalty which it exacts. Thus, for many years an individual with a compulsive work drive may pay a small price for it, e.g., a little loss of sleep, or neurotic headaches, or occasionally some disturbance in his family relationships or in his friendships. These will be more than balanced by the rewards which accrue to him through his neurotic drive. Yet, ultimately, the time comes, often late in life, when the failure of the work drive to achieve its unconscious goals will precipitate the patient into a depression or other major disturbance. At what point in this slow build-up do we appraise the impact of drugs on the evolution of this Odyssey of the Neurotic Process?

Or consider the life history of the individual with a rigid compulsion always to play the role of the benefactor. If he is fortunate enough to have grateful beneficiaries, his neurosis will cost him relatively little for years. But, when the time comes, as it surely will, that his beneficiaries (be they family, friends, or associates) exploit him, leave him, turn on him, reject the implicit domination; or, apart from this, when the time finally comes that the failure of his benevolence to attain its unconscious goals finally takes its toll, then suddenly his benevolence turns to gall and wormwood. Overnight this can precipitate a switch from benignity to a state of embittered, resentful depression. Where in this life history shall we look for the impact of tranquilizers?

Or, taking a more banal example, the man with a height phobia who lives on a flat plain is peaceful until the exigencies of his job require that he work high up in the Rockies. Shall we study the effect of tranquilizers when he is on the plains or on the peaks? Or in transit

from one to the other? The same neurosis accompanies him every-
where; but the symptomatic toll varies. Are we exploring, then, the
impact of the tranquilizers on the basic process or on the moments
when the tax collector comes around to collect his payments?

Or what of the woman with a claustrophobia who lives a happy life
as a newspaper reporter, always on the go, always foot-loose and free,
who marries a man she loves and has a child for which she has longed,
and who only then is confronted for the first time by the inescapable
consequences of her claustrophobia, which precipitates her into stormy
secondary conflicts over her marriage and over her newborn child?
One such patient plunged into panic, depression, and alcoholism. The
neurotic process had been lurking all along; but its emotional price increased at every step in its evolution. Where do we evaluate the
effects of tranquilizers on such a neurotic process? And, unless we
identify and differentiate these things clearly, how can we compare
results of one drug with another, or even of any one drug from patient
to patient?

Obviously, under such complex circumstances as these, and they
are inherent in every neurosis, it is impossible to use the emotional
status of a patient in an offhand and unthinking fashion as a criterion
of change in the neurotic process itself. It is possible, none the less,
to estimate the impact of a pharmacologic agent on emotional states if
(and this is a big *if*) one first makes certain that the conditions under
which the emotions are generated have not altered during the process
of observation. Relevant consideration of the role of affects in the
neurotic process is more fully discussed elsewhere (Kubie, 1952b;
Kubie and Glaser, 1952).

If these examples have made it clear why we cannot, without danger
of fallacious thinking, use the fluctuations either of symptomatic end
states or of their affective accompaniments as indicators of drug
effects, we can return to the question of what are some of the basic
ingredients in the neurotic process in which we can seek criteria of
change (Kubie, 1957).

Basic Ingredients
in the Neurotic Process

1. To me the most important single area to explore first is the
tendency which is most basic to the neurotic process, i.e., the repetition of behavior insatiably and in relatively unvarying forms (Kubie,

1954). The essence of the neurotic process is that in the neuroses the forces which converge to produce any pattern of behavior predetermine at the same time its obligatory repetition, irrespective of the immediate or remote consequences of the acts themselves, i.e., without regard to success or failure, pleasure or pain, rewards or punishments, etc. Does any drug increase the proclivity to obligatory repetition in one man and decrease it in another, or shift from one effect to the other in the same man under varying circumstances? In short, *does any drug either increase or decrease this repetitive tendency,* either the overall tendency toward obligatory repetition (the tendency of the central nervous system to go on doing whatever it is doing until and unless it is stopped), or else the repetitive tendency as it manifests itself in limited and specific areas? Consider the drunk who becomes a broken phonograph record: Do the tranquilizers increase or decrease this tendency?

2. My second consideration would concern the impact of any drug on the regressive phenomena which are inherent in the neurotic process: on the tendency to return to the past, to relive the sufferings, defeats, furors, guilts, and rages of the past, and to use again the patterns of behavior of the past. Do tranquilizers increase or decrease this tendency (to use quantitative terms), or alter the tendency qualitatively?

3. My third basic question is whether any maneuver (in this instance any drug) alters the central emotional position of the personality. In other connections (Kubie and Glaser, 1952; Kubie, 1952a, 1956b) I have tried to characterize this by various terms, such as an undifferentiated tension state or an undifferentiated affective potential, or level of preaffective tension. These can sometimes be recognized qualitatively, and even estimated quantitatively in subverbal animals. They can be modified by glandular, biochemical, electrical, and surgical means (Kubie and Glaser, 1952; Kubie, 1952a). And certainly one sees them unmasked in the banal everyday reactions to the pharmacologic influence of alcohol, where the same drug affects different men in quite different ways, or may alter any one man in different directions on different occasions—the differences with which all are familiar between the man who fights when he is drunk and who hates and distrusts everyone and becomes an isolationist, and the man who laughs and loves and becomes gregarious; the man who weeps into his beer in a crying jag; the man who becomes erotic and the man who becomes impotent, the man who becomes heterosexual and the man who becomes homosexual, or the man who, still under alcohol,

shifts from one of these phases to another. In a similar way other drugs can release or make manifest latent central affective positions. For later reference it must be borne in mind that these central affective positions are sometimes pleasant and sometimes unpleasant. But the release or unmasking of such latent affective positions within the personality (which is often mistaken for a more fundamental change) is only an unmasking. There are several important technical problems, therefore, which must be confronted: (a) How to distinguish between a mere unmasking of a concealed affective state and a quantitative change in its intensity, or a qualitative change. (b) How to determine whether the drug has any specificity when its effects seem to vary so widely from man to man or in the same man. (c) Whether any drug alters the thresholds of these affective positions, the levels on which they operate, or the extent to which they are expressed through conscious, preconscious, or unconscious aspects of psychologic function. (d) Whether such studies can be made with slow-motion pictures in color, thereby to study the expression of emotions visually, aurally, in facial change, in color, in voice, in posture, in gesture, and through movement analysis. These must be studied for their symmetry and for their asymmetry.

In further relation to the impact of these drugs on the affective component in the total constellation of the neurosis, we would have to distinguish between the impact of any pharmacologic agents on those underlying affective states which are pleasant and those which are unpleasant. One man spends his life yearning for and defending a central affective state of gentle euphoria and warm nostalgia; another spends his life warding off and defending against a painful central emotional position. It would be unrealistic to expect any chemotherapeutic agent or any procedure to produce identical changes in affective processes which are basically as dissimilar as these are, or in defensive maneuvers whose goal it is to preserve a comfortable and pleasant affective tonus, as contrasted with defensive maneuvers whose goal it is to ward off unpleasant affective states.

4. Closely related to this problem of central affective positions in the neurotic process, and the impact of pharmacologic agents upon them, is the question of the effects of drugs upon the thresholds at which such central affective positions can be triggered. It is one of the curious anomalies of psychiatric thinking that we have shut our eyes to what is probably the most common and banal single manifestation of the neurotic process: the universality of trigger mechanisms. Out of this universality we customarily recognize only the one which we call

the *phobia*, whereas actually there is no affective state that does not respond to trigger stimuli, and none which is not regularly triggered by stimuli which are wholly inadequate and inappropriate. That some of these are relatively benign does not make any the less certain the identity of the process with that of the typical self-diagnosing phobic reaction. I have in mind not only such triggered affects as laughter, elation, fear, depression, and rage, but also the triggers which put us to sleep and wake us up, the triggers which induce other forms of dissociation and of reintegration, the triggers which touch off obsessional-compulsive furors, etc.

Some of these form an integral part of the pattern of our daily and nightly living. Because they are constantly with us like the air we breathe, and because of the confusion in our minds between frequency and normality, we fail to recognize the deeply psychopathologic nature of many of them. Think of such examples as the furor of compulsive candy eating which can be touched off in the patient who has been dieting faithfully but who in a gingerly experiment takes one piece of chocolate; or the furor of compulsive smoking touched off in someone who has given up smoking if he takes one puff on a cigarette; or of the same trigger effects on the compulsive pimple squeezer, the compulsive nose picker, the compulsive nail biter, all compulsive furors or patterns of activity whose execution yields no inherent gratification, except the escape from the acute and intolerable displeasure at delay or interference.

In these, as in other triggered responses which may or may not at the same time gratify an impulse, the trigger sets in motion a chain reaction. This is familiar to all of us, yet its significance is neglected. Far more light can probably be shed on the relation of pharmacologic agents to the neurotic process by studying the impact of the drugs on the chain reactions to trigger mechanisms in just such common, everyday, banal psychopathologic phenomena as these, than by studying their effects on the more intricate and complex disturbances of the fully developed neurosis, or even on the so-called experimental neurosis in animals. (This does not imply that I would not be interested in studying their effects on the repetitive patterns which John Lilly and others have been studying at the National Institute of Mental Health, e.g., in monkeys with implanted electrodes who learn to stimulate their own brains. To use these animals as testing devices might help to determine whether or not the drugs have any effect on the threshold of repetitive patterning.)

For emphasis, I want to repeat that no study of affective states and affective components in the neurotic process will be meaningful which leaves out of account the impact of these drugs on the thresholds of trigger reactions, both in sleep and in the waking state.

5. There are still other aspects of the emotional component in the neurotic process to be studied, such as the extent to which all behavior, or special forms of behavior, are emotionalized, and the effects of drugs upon this. It is a truism that we can have emotion without content, and content without emotion. We can have behavior in what is called cold blood, or we can have behavior which is suffused with intense feeling. This aspect of the dissociation or integration of affect with thought or of affect with behavior is a central theme in our understanding both of the maturation of conduct and of the effects of insight on psychopathology; yet it is an area in which the influence of the pharmacologic agents has been slighted. This is curious, in view of the importance of the issue for our theoretic conceptions of both the neurotic process and the therapeutic process. We speak glibly of gaining and of communicating insight at various levels of psychotherapy; and we add that, if it is to be effective, such insight must be invested with emotion. While we do not know how universally valid such a generalization may be, it is a working hypothesis worth exploring; and in that exploration the impact of pharmacologic agents should play an important role.

6. Next in order comes the fundamental question: Does a drug increase or decrease the tendency toward disruption of the symbolic representation of experience? Does the drug shift the expression of the inner state along the symbolic spectrum in the direction of its preconscious and conscious expression and representation? Or does it shift the inner state toward the masked expression of unconscious processes through disguising symbolic usages? This issue is of significance in any comparison of the tranquilizers with the action of those drugs which produce schizoid delirious reactions. Obviously, it is easier to ask these questions than it is to devise the techniques by which they are to be answered with precision. It is none the less useful to pose the questions. Until we do so we are not likely to think in terms which will lead to the development of the necessary techniques. Detailed consideration of the ways in which psychoanalytic techniques form a model for meticulously controlled studies of free associations as a basis for an investigation of the interrelationships of conscious, preconscious, and unconscious processes will be found in earlier studies (Kubie, 1953; 1952a).

7. The preceding, in turn, is related to many other critical issues,

such as the effects of the drugs on the rigidity versus the modifiability of patterns, especially in relation to the relative roles of conscious, preconscious, and unconscious processes in their determination.

A central focus of my own interest would be on the influence of any pharmacologic agent on the continuous concurrent interplay among conscious, preconscious, and unconscious processes in every moment of life, as these are manifested in every aspect of normal function and of the neurotic process. Relevant here are the detailed discussions of the role of the study of free associations, of the transference situation, and of the careful restriction of all controllable variables in such work (Kubie, 1953, 1952a).

8. The recent work of Fisher (1956, 1954) and of Marsh and Worden (unpublished) must lead to a study of the influence of the tranquilizers and other pharmacologic agents on the threshold to and the role of preconscious perceptions, on their reproductions in dreams and in automatic writing or drawing, and on the threshold of direct autonomic responses to preconscious percepts.

9. This would lead to a study of the influence of these pharmacologic agents on sleep (Kubie, 1953, 1952a). It is not enough to specify sleep without breaking it down into its several operational components, such as the influence of drugs on the effectiveness of the triggers which precipitate people into sleep and which waken them, on the duration of the preparatory period before this takes effect, on the directions in which the psychologic processes move in sleep. Here one would have first to differentiate between those who in sleep return to a pleasant central emotional position and those who return to unpleasant positions, and whether this is a consistent characteristic of some individuals, or dependent on the affective quality of the residue of each previous day's experience. With this as a baseline, one could then go on to study the influence of the tranquilizer on the psychotherapeutic or psychonoxious influence of the sleep process itself, i.e., whether the subject wakens sicker than he was when he went to sleep (and in what sense) or healthier.

10. In conclusion, I must add that all of this highlights again the importance of equipping psychiatry with institutes for basic research. This opens up wide horizons for basic research which will require multidisciplinary teams of scientists (Kubie, 1956b).

I have not tried to minimize the difficulties of basic scientific work in this field. Rather, without any pretense of having exhausted all the possibilities, I have tried to list some of the most persistent current fallacies which distort much of the current clinical investigations and to indicate some of the legitimate foci for critical and immediate research on a few of the basic ingredients in the neurotic process and its affective concomitants.

Potentialities of Pharmacological Approach

Up to this point, my discussion of the pharmacology of psychotherapy has been skeptical and critical. Let me now balance this, in so far as I can, by reviewing the therapeutic potentialities which may be expected to emerge out of the pharmacological approach to the therapy of the neuroses and psychoses. Certain definite therapeutic gains, more modest than the exaggerated claims of the popular press, have been recorded since the introduction of drugs; and more can be anticipated.

Actually the story of this trend began long before the so-called tranquilizers, with the introduction of sedatives. Their wise use saved many a life and many a mind during the unusual stresses of World War II; and what was true under those special circumstances is in lesser degree true in the difficulties that arise in civilian life as well. Their early use can sometimes abort a serious breakdown by improving sleep and damping the pressures of unmanageable affects during waking hours. Furthermore, one of the most vulnerable moments in the incipient stages of an illness occurs during the daily transitions between waking and sleeping. Consequently any combination of medications will be useful which makes that transition as nearly instantaneous as possible, and which can secure for the patient as profound and unvarying a "depth" of sleep as possible, and which finally will bring the patient swiftly through the transition from deep sleep back to full alertness. Clinical details of the treatment of such disturbances were described in a brief "Manual of Emergency Treatment of Acute War Neuroses," published in *War Medicine* in 1943 (Kubie, 1943b).

The prolonged use of smaller doses of sedatives to lessen the tension with which individuals live and to raise their threshold against startle reactions is also a regimen so old as to require no special description here. The slower-acting barbiturates and bromides were used for these purposes long before the modern tranquilizers came into the picture. The underlying assumption was that they lessened both cortical activity and also the play of impulses arising in the cortex on those deeper centers which implement affective states.

All of this, however, is palliative at best. A more specific step was taken when medications were used in an effort to facilitate communication between patient and physician about topics which were painful to talk about. In principle this also is not new. "In vino veritas" was not a discovery of narcoanalysis. In the *Varieties of Religious Experience,* William James (1902) speaks of the "Anesthetic Revelation." Years later, especially during World War II, attempts were made to use general anesthetics for the same purpose: e.g., ether, chloroform, mixtures of nitrous oxide and oxygen, and carbon dioxide inhalations. Then the more rapidly absorbed and more rapidly oxidized barbiturates were employed for the same purpose: some by intramuscular injection, others by intravenous injection. Marijuana and its synthetic derivatives and analogs have also had their vogue. Unfortunately, however, in almost all this work the pressure for immediate therapeutic results corrupted the investigations. Consequently, when the therapeutic magic failed, as was predictable and predicted, people turned their backs on drugs and forgot that the necessary basic investigations had not yet been undertaken. The task remained to explore the role of drugs in the induction of controlled and communicative states of partial dissociation, and in shifting the relative roles of conscious, preconscious, and unconscious processes in their incessant symphonic interplay in all human behavior (Kubie, 1943a, b; 1945; Kubie and Margolin, 1945).

Even more basic questions are opened up by the recent development of tranquilizing and energizing drugs. Here the hope has been that—either by elevating or decreasing the general level of activity of the nervous system; or by raising or lowering the threshold of the response to stimuli; or by altering the intensity of the responses to triggers; or by lessening the violence of the automatic and recurrent return to central emotional positions; or by shortening the duration of reverberating circuits; or by altering the vulnerability to such circuits—one could bring such patients within the range of effective psychotherapy, or make it possible for them to exercise their own controlling devices and thus lessen their vulnerability to illness.

You will note that the theoretical assumptions which underlie each of these concepts are too simple. Actually, they are hardly to be dignified with the name "theories." They are, rather, figures of speech and allegories drawn from what is known of the physiology of the isolated nerve or of the relatively simple spinal reflex. No one yet has shown to what extent such concepts as "thresholds," "levels of activity," "spread" of "excitatory" or of "inhibitory" processes are valid, when applied to the central nervous system as a whole. Nor is it clear to what extent these are valid concepts to use for describing or explaining psychological disturbances. The various ingredients which enter into the neurotic potential, the neurotic process, and the neurotic state have already been described, and they will serve us better as hypothetical units for us to investigate (Kubie, 1956a, 1958a, b).

It is also a matter of great interest that there are a number of drugs, such as alcohol, metrazole and lysergic acid (LSD-25), which can produce transient facsimilies of psychotic states, some of which in certain respects are at least as reminiscent of schizophrenia as is the dream process. Yet we have long known that acute war stress can do the same thing, and also that an intensification of neurotic or psychotic symptomatology can occur during psychotherapy. It is an odd commentary on human prejudice that, when such simulations of illnesses are produced by drugs, the fact is greeted enthusiastically as a scientific advance, whereas if these same states occur as transient episodes during the course of psychotherapy the event is condemned.

It is not difficult to understand why the induction of disturbances by drugs is welcomed and the induction of similar disturbances by psychological methods is shunned. Not only does the drug hold out the always elusive hope for an organic shortcut to the solution of mental illness, but drugs also reactivate even in the sophisticated some of the feelings which the child has about potions, potions for good and potions for ill, the magical potions that change men into beasts and beasts into fairy princes. These fairy tales of childhood color and shape the conscious thoughts and feelings of the child, are then repressed and reappear in disguised forms in adult years. The idea that words alone can be equally potent seems far more dangerous and threatening and humiliating. Therefore people shrink from it.

However this may be, the question remains, what evidence is there that lasting gains have resulted from the introduction of these more modern drugs? It is too early to say. The picture is full of contradictions, which make definite conclusions impossible. There can be no doubt that in understaffed and overcrowded state hospitals there has been a sharp reduction in the duration of periods of violent disturbance and also in the degree of unchecked violence among disturbed patients. Consequently there is much greater ease of handling and less need for mechanical restraints. Paralleling this has been a sharp reduction in the use of electroshock. All of this is welcome. On the other hand, in smaller, private hospitals which are adequately staffed, where there is a high ratio of doctors to patients, and where it is possible to give patients more individualized attention of all kinds, including intensive psychotherapy, better medication, and better sleep, no such dramatic change has resulted from the introduction of tranquilizers.

Under the influence of drugs, we may also see the disappearance of violent and flagrant delusional ideas. Yet these may then be replaced by subtler distortions in the personality. For example, a mother who had had paranoid delusions that people were attempting to injure her and her children, to control her thoughts and theirs, and to subvert them, no longer had any such delusions. Yet she remained hostile, aloof, and suspicious, distrusting the children's explanation if they came home from school a few minutes late, uneasy, and critical of their friends. Her paranoid psychosis had been replaced or masked by a paranoid personality.

The urgency of the demand for an immediate cure has caused people to lose sight of the amount of careful, objective, self-critical research which is necessary. Furthermore, it has been almost forgotten that, even if these drugs should prove therapeutically ineffectual, they would still be valuable research implements, but only if the experiments are appropriately planned not for quick cures but to bring basic facts to light.

Once the exaggerated claims are forgotten, we shall be able to settle down to a quiet attempt to use tranquilizers and stimulants for objective and controlled research, introducing them cautiously in the course of psychotherapy of the neuroses and the psychoses, in the private office, in the outpatient department, and in the psychiatric hospital (Kubie, 1956b). It is a truism that in research on psychotherapy hope always plays too large a role, and hope does not make of the scientist an objective observer. For this reason the best tests use a "double-blind" technique. Drugs must be administered in a disguised form so that the results are independent of suggestion or anticipation. Otherwise, unconsciously the patient will attempt either to simulate health or to simulate disease. He will attempt either to pretend that he is well or to sabotage any possibility of good results. And without the help of blinders the observer is equally prone to see not what occurs but what he hopes or fears. This is still a field for the most careful, cautious, objectively controlled investigation, not a field for claims.

Actually, research at even more basic levels is needed before the time for applied research will be at hand (Kubie, 1953). For instance, until we have established criteria of change, criteria which can be tested and demonstrated objectively, subjective impressions of change are not likely to lead us along the path that we are trying to pursue.

This, of course, is only an initial step in the basic research which should be done before any claims are made about either the immediate or the long-run influence of drugs on the neurotic or the schizophrenic processes. It is impossible to exaggerate the importance of giving top priority to such basic preliminary investigations.

R E F E R E N C E S

Fisher, C. Dreams and perception: the role of preconscious and primary modes of perception in dream formation. *J. Amer. Psychoanal. A.* 1954, 2, 389.

Fisher, C. Dreams, images, and perception: a study of unconscious-preconscious relationships. *J. Amer. Psychoanal. A.* 1956, 4, 5.

James, W. *The Varieties of Religious Experience.* London: Longmans, Green, 1902.

Kubie, L. S. The use of induced hypnagogic reveries in the recovery of repressed amnesic data. *Bull. Menninger Clinic,* Sept.–Nov. 1943, 7 Nos. 5, 6, 172–182. (a)

Kubie, L. S. Manual of emergency treatment for acute war neuroses. *War Med.,* Dec. 1943, 4, 582–598. (b)

Kubie, L. S. The value of induced dissociated states in the therapeutic process. *Proc. roy. Soc. Med.* 1945, 38, 681.

Kubie, L. S. Review of *Narco-analysis* by J. S. Horsley. *Psychosom. Med.,* Jan. 1946, 8, No. 1, 65–66.

Kubie, L. S. Problems and techniques of psychoanalytic validation and progress in California Institute of Technology, Pasadena. In E. Pumpian-Mindlin (Ed.), *Hixon Lectures on the scientific status of psychoanalysis.* Palo Alto, Calif.: Stanford Univer. Press, 1952, 46–124. (a)

Kubie, L. S. The place of emotions in the feedback concept. In H. Von Foerster (Ed.), *Trans. Ninth Conf. on Cybernetics.* New York: Josiah Macy Jr. Found., 1952, 48–72. (b)

Kubie, L. S. Psychoanalysis as a Basic Science. In F. Alexander and H. Ross (Eds.), *Twenty years of psychoanalysis.* New York: Norton, 1953, 120–144.

Kubie, L. S. The fundamental nature of the distinction between normality and neurosis. *Psychoanal. Quart.* 1954, 23, 167.

Kubie, L. S. Some unsolved problems of psychoanalytic psychotherapy. In F. Reichmann and J. L. Moreno (Eds.), *Progress in psychotherapy.* New York: Grune & Stratton, 1956, 87–102. (a)

Kubie, L. S. An institute for basic research in psychiatry. *Bull. Menninger Clin.,* 1956, 20, 281. (b)

Kubie, L. S. Social forces and the neurotic process. In A. Leighton (Ed.), *Explanation in social psychiatry.* New York: Basic Books, 1957.

Kubie, L. S. The neurotic process as the focus of physiological and psychoanalytic research. (Read in part before the Roy. Soc. Med., London, Sept. 1957; *J. ment. Sci.*, 1958, 104, 518–536.) (a)

Kubie, L. S. *Neurotic distortion of the creative process.* Porter Lectures, Ser. 22, Lawrence, Kan.: Univer. of Kansas Press, 1958, 151. (b)

Kubie, L. S., and Glaser, G. Affectivity and psychosurgery. In *Proc. second Res. Conf. on Psychosurg.*, June 1950. Washington, D. C.: Government Printing Office, 1952. (U. S. Publ. Hlth. Serv., Publ. No. 156.)

Kubie, L., and Margolin, S. G. The therapeutic role of drugs in the process of repression, dissociation, and synthesis. *Psychosom. Med.* 1945, 7, 147.

Marsh, J. T., and Worden, F. G. Perceptual approach to personality. *Psychiatric Res. Rep.* No. 6, Amer. Psychiat. Ass., October, 1956.

PART II

Experimental
Procedures
and
Results

Experiments on Animals
of Potential Application
to Human Subjects

Some applications of conditioned "fear"

For a number of years, part of our research program has been devoted to studying the effects of selected drugs and other experimental variables on the emotional behavior of rats. In much of this work a conditioned emotional response (CER) of the "fear" or "anxiety" type has served as the behavioral indicator. We concentrated upon this, rather than upon the more complex experimental neuroses, in the interests of simplicity. Furthermore, the CER is of interest in its own right because it exemplifies that fundamental, perhaps primitive kind of learning that occurs when a stimulus acquires new functional, psychological properties through being paired with another stimulus already of importance to the experimental subject.

The conditioned emotional response is established by a few pairings of a signal (the CS or conditioned stimulus) with brief, unavoidable electric shocks (the UCS or unconditioned stimulus) to the feet. The method, in general, follows that employed many years ago by Watson and Rayner (1920) to condition the child, Albert, to fear a rat. The method also has many similarities to classical conditioning, except that the animal is unrestrained and the CS is presented for three to five minutes before it is reinforced at termination with the UCS.

For purposes of analysis and control, we have often superimposed this conditioning on operant lever pressing for food or water reward, by giving CER conditioning trials during runs in the lever-pressing apparatus, following the general procedure outlined by Estes and Skinner (1941) in their study of quantitative properties of anxiety. In the lever apparatus the CS acquires the power to evoke an emotional disturbance sufficiently strong to reduce or stop completely the output of lever pressing for food or water reward. It is important to note that the CS has this suppressant effect on the lever response even though the shocks have been paired only with the termination of the CS and no lever response ever has been "punished" with shock. If the CER conditioning takes place in the grill box (a chamber without any lever), the CS acquires the power to reduce or stop completely the output of the "exploratory" behavior rats normally show in that apparatus. The CS does this by evoking an overt reaction of the same topography as observed when the CER is elicited in the lever apparatus—the assumption of a tense crouching or "freezing" posture, usually accompanied by defecation. Though conditioning and testing of the CER in the lever apparatus requires a little more time and effort than such conditioning in the grill box, the extra expenditure is usually well repaid by gains in sensitivity and ease of quantitation. Also, the data from tests in the lever apparatus can be used to determine whether the changes in the CER produced by the drug or other experimental procedure are specific and selective for that conditioning or represent only expressions of somatic debilitation or generalized "amnesia" (Hunt and Brady, 1951; Brady and Hunt, 1951; Hunt, Jernberg, and Brady, 1952; Hunt, 1956, 1957).

The ease of establishing the CER and of controlling its strength experimentally, together with its ostensible relevance to human emotional disorders, favored its use as an indicator in numerous studies of conditioning and of the effects on behavior of electroconvulsive shock (ECS), tranquilizing drugs, and cerebral ablations. To give a few examples, ECS weakens the CER temporarily, but not by producing a generalized "amnesia" or somatic debilitation (Hunt and Brady, 1951; Brady and Hunt, 1951; Brady, 1951). Additional ECS convulsions or experimental extinction of the CS through non-reinforcement, after the main series of ECS, prevent the CER from returning (Brady, Stebbins, and Hunt, 1953; Hunt, Jernberg, and Brady, 1952). The effect of ECS appears to be blocked if the convulsions are blocked by ether anesthesia (Hunt, Jernberg, and Lawlor, 1953) or phenurone, though the anti-epileptic drug dilantin and the stimulant amphetamine appear to augment the attenuating effects of ECS on the CER (Hunt and Beckwith, 1956). Taking advantage of the precision with which the strength of the CER could be manipulated by varying conditioning parameters such as number of trials and intensity of the UCS, Goy (1953) was able to show that the latter is much more important than the former in determining the resistance of the CER to attenuation by ECS.

As would be expected, both meprobamate (Hunt, 1957), and reserpine (Brady, 1956) weaken the CER, though reserpine has much the greater effect. Chlorpromazine, in heavy doses, interferes markedly with both the expression and extinction of the CER, but only slightly with acquisition (Hunt, 1956; Jernberg, 1957). With modification and extension of these techniques to encompass instrumental avoidance, Halasz (1959) was able to show that chlorpromazine, in moderate doses, facilitates extinction of avoidance and conditioned fear in the cat. Finally, large bilateral lesions in the hippocampus in the cat appear to weaken instrumental avoidance to an auditory cue, but leave the conditioned fear that underlies it (or an independently established CER) largely intact (Hunt, Diamond, Moore, and Harvey, 1959).

Theoretical Implications

The CER has an appealing face validity as an animal analog of human psychiatric disorder. Through learning, a neutral signal acquires the power to evoke an intense emotional disturbance, a disturbance greater than that which the reinforcing shocks could evoke initially (Estes and Skinner, 1941; Hunt and Brady, 1951). Extrapolation to the human case should be restrained and guarded, however. The counterpart of the CER, if there is one in human psychopathology, is traumatic neurosis rather than psychoneurosis, because conflict (particularly intrapsychic conflict, if one can speak of that in animals) does not appear to play a critical role in the development of the CER and its symptomatology. The theoretical specifications for psychoneurosis demand a situation where stimuli arising from the subject's impulses to action (or responses) have become dangerous, through conditioning, so that these stimuli, when they appear, evoke an emotional disturbance that interferes with the output of that behavior which would eliminate the source of the stimuli. Rats ordinarily handle a conflict situation that meets these specifications by developing normal avoidance behaviors and no more than a normal amount of emotional disturbance (Hunt and Brady, 1955; Hunt, 1959). A brief summarizing statement of just what CER conditioning does to change a rat's behavior may be helpful to those who would employ the technique in other contexts. To call the CER "conditioned suppression," as some do when discussing results from the lever apparatus, is misleading. It is not the suppression of lever pressing that is conditioned; the suppression occurs because the rat is doing something else, that something else being evoked by the CS. However, it is equally incorrect to say that the emotional responses as such—the "freezing" and defecating—are conditioned, as reflexes, to the CS. Under other testing circumstances, after CER conditioning, the CS can evoke behavior of a quite different topography, escape. Rather, we now think of CER conditioning as endowing the CS with conditioned aversive properties, as a function of its pairing with primary aversive stimuli, the shocks. Whether the CS "rewards," "punishes," evokes escape, or paralyzes the rat with fear will depend upon the experimental arrangements and upon the contingent relations between the animal's behavior and the onset, duration, and termination of the CS (Hunt, 1959).

The numerous applications to human problems of this sort of conditioning of stimuli are either well known or easy to anticipate. Its use in experimental psychopathology, where it can serve to gauge the intensity of reaction to anticipated unpleasant events as well as to indicate the effects of treatment procedures on such anticipations, is but one. The possibility that the CER can be used to distinguish between anticipated pain and "actual" painful stimulation suggests an application to the study of analgesics and subjective pain, in which expectancy is such an important component. Something similar to CER conditioning has been used occasionally for many years to explore the sensory and discriminative capacities of very young children and impaired or uncooperative individuals. Also, a variant of CER conditioning is one of the methods used in the study of stimulus generalization. Polygraphic lie detection and investigation of emotionally toned experience capitalize on the fact that ordinarily neutral stimuli can acquire special response-evoking properties as a result of experience. Here the conditioning has taken place before the tests and during those experiences that have traumatized the person or have given him "guilty" knowledge. This listing does not begin to cover all the possibilities, of course, but it does give a picture of the range of applications to which simple conditioning can be adapted in drug and other behavioral research with human beings.

R E F E R E N C E S

Brady, J. V. The effect of electro-convulsive shock on a conditioned emotional response: the permanence of the effect. *J. comp. physiol. Psychol.*, 1951, 44, 507–511.

Brady, J. V. The assessment of drug effects on emotional behavior. *Science,* 1956, 123, 1033–1034.

Brady, J. V., and Hunt, H. F. A further demonstration of the effects of electro-convulsive shock on a conditioned emotional response. *J. comp. physiol. Psychol.,* 1951, 44, 204–209.

Brady, J. V., Stebbins, W. C., and Hunt, H. F. The effect of electro-convulsive shock on a conditioned emotional response: the effect of additional ECS convulsions. *J. comp. physiol. Psychol.* 1953, 46, 368–372.

Estes, W. K., and Skinner, B. F. Some quantitative properties of anxiety. *J. exp. Psychol.,* 1941, 29, 390–400.

Coy, R. W. The effect of electro-convulsive shock on a conditioned emotional response: the relation between amount of attenuation and strength of the conditioned emotional response. Unpubl. doctoral dissertation, Univer. of Chicago, 1953.

Halasz, M. The extinction of intercurrent avoidance and appetitive responses under chlorpromazine. Unpubl. doctoral dissertation, Univer. of Chicago, 1959.

Hunt, H. F. Some effects of drugs on classical (type S) conditioning. *Ann. N. Y. Acad. Science,* 1956, 65, 258–267.

Hunt, H. F. Some effects of meprobamate on conditioned fear and emotional behavior. *Ann. N. Y. Acad. Science,* 1957, 67, 712–723.

Hunt, H. F. Effects of drugs on emotional responses and abnormal behavior in animals. In J. O. Cole and R. W. Gerard (Eds.), *Psychopharmacology.* Washington D. C.: N.A.S.—N.R.C., No. 583; 1959, 268–283.

Hunt, H. F., and Beckwith, W. C. The effect of electro-convulsive shock under phenurone, dilantin, and amphetamine medication on a conditioned emotional response. *Amer. Psychologist,* 1956, 11, 442. (Abstract)

Hunt, H. F., and Brady, J. V. Some effects of electro-convulsive shock on a conditioned emotional response ("anxiety"). *J. comp. physiol. Psychol.,* 1951, 44, 88–98.

Hunt, H. F., and Brady, J. V. Some effects of punishment and intercurrent "anxiety" on a simple operant. *J. comp. physiol. Psychol.,* 1955, 48, 305–310.

Hunt, H. F., and Diamond, I. T. (with R. Y. Moore and J. A. Harvey). Some effects of hippocampal lesions on conditioned avoidance behavior in the cat. In *Proc. XV int. Congr. Psychol.* Amsterdam: North Holland Publ. Co., 1959, 203.

Hunt, H. F., Jernberg, P., and Brady, J. V. The effect of electro-convulsive shock on a conditioned emotional response: the effect of post-ECS extinction on the reappearance of the response. *J. comp. physiol. Psychol.,* 1952, 45, 589–599.

Hunt, H. F., Jernberg, P., and Lawlor, W. G. The effect of electro-convulsive shock on a conditioned emotional response: the effect of electro-convulsive shock under ether anesthesia. *J. comp. physiol. Psychol.,* 1953, 46, 64–68.

Jernberg, P. The effects of chlorpromazine upon the acquisition and loss of a conditioned emotional response. Unpubl. master's thesis, Univer. of Chicago, 1957.

Watson, J. B., and Rayner, R. Conditioned emotional reactions. *J. exp. Psychol.,* 1920, 3, 1–14.

Chapter 12 *Joseph V. Brady and Sherman Ross*

Testing drug effects
on controlled animal
and human behavior

One of the central attacks of our research program involves refinement of experimental control techniques in order to yield "behavioral profiles." We expect that, from the relatively extensive profiles we plan to collect, contrasts will emerge among the many classes of pharmacological agents with more or less known central effects. As the breadth of such drug-behavior profiles increases and their empirical relevance to more general psychopharmacological problems becomes explicit, the comparative analysis of new and unknown compounds can proceed. Similarities and differences in the behavioral consequences of the compounds could be the basis for screening psychiatrically useful drugs. However, the administration of a new compound, whose mechanisms of action are not well understood, to an animal and observing some aspect of its behavior, whose mechanisms are not well understood, are unlikely to clarify either the pharmacological or the behavioral process.

We are studying each of several behavioral situations in the following three ways (1) standardization of the test situations to provide quantitative measurement techniques; (2) comparative evaluations of drug effects in different animal species and strains; and (3) development of behavior profiles of different drugs. Our program to date has involved a variety of species: rhesus monkeys, rats, mice, pigeons, and human subjects.

The research described was published in J. V. Brady. Animal experimental evaluation of drug effects upon behavior. Fed. Proc., 1958, 17.

It was supported in part by a research grant (M-1604) from the National Institute of Mental Health, USPHS, to the University of Maryland.

The conceptual framework for this experimental approach to the investigation of psychopharmacologic relationships rests upon a simple principle: the characteristics of an organism's behavior are to a considerable extent determined by what the environmental consequences of that behavior have been in the past. The animal laboratory has provided an opportunity for the systematic analysis of orderly relations among behavioral segments within this framework, and the term "operant behavior" (Skinner, 1938) has been used to refer to behavior which operates upon the environment in this fashion. The process of manipulating such behavior as a function of its environmental consequences has been termed "operant conditioning" and has been most effectively applied in our experimental program by attention to a few basic details.

First, we have selected for measurement and manipulation a response congenial to the animal, one that he can perform and immediately be in a position to repeat. Second, we chose an environmental consequence, or "reinforcement," appropriate to the particular experimental animal and strong enough to minimize the effects of many experimentally irrelevant variables. Finally, we limited the experimental environment to permit at least some reasonable degree of stimulus control and specification. The subject in these studies may be a thirsty rat pressing a bar in a small chamber to obtain a drop of water. Or he may be a monkey in a somewhat larger experimental box or a chair-type restraining device manipulating a lever to postpone a painful electric shock or obtain a sugar pellet reward. Programming all these experimental procedures and recording the animal's behavior is accomplished automatically by timers, magnetic counters, cumulative work recorders, and associated relay circuits. Thus we place some arbitrary sample of behavior under experimental control so that it may be investigated as a function of a wide variety of operations including neurophysiological manipulations, "emotional disturbances," and drug administrations.

Initially, our efforts were directed toward the use of such operant conditioning techniques for reliably producing and selectively measuring emotional behavior patterns in experimental animals, and investigating the effects of various drugs, particularly the tranquilizers, upon such affective responses. More recently, however, we have been extending our analysis to other types of drugs and developing a somewhat broader range of behavioral techniques. In approaching these problems, rats and monkeys have been deprived of solid food and liquids for 24 hours or more and then trained to press a bar for a

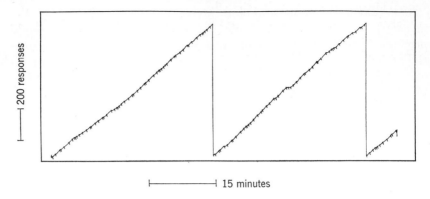

Figure 1. Sample cumulative response curve for a monkey showing the stable lever-pressing rate maintained by a variable interval sugared orange juice reward. The oblique pips on the curve indicate the aperiodic delivery of the reward after a response. The recorder can also be seen to reset to the baseline after 900 responses.

water or food reward. First, the animals received a portion of the reward every time they pressed the lever (continuous reinforcement), but they were rapidly shifted to a schedule on which the bar press produced the reward only aperiodically (variable interval reinforcement, average once per 60 seconds).

Figure 1 shows a record produced by a monkey pressing a lever on such a variable interval reward schedule during daily experimental sessions lasting several hours or more. This record was obtained using a cumulative work recorder which consists of a kymograph moving paper horizontally at a constant rate (eleven inches per hour) and a pen which moves vertically across the paper by a small increment each time the animal presses the lever (900 lever responses per five inches). The pen automatically resets to 0 whenever a complete vertical excursion of 900 responses has been made. This cumulative curve, then, indicates how many lever responses the animal made, and the pips on the curve indicate when a response was rewarded on the variable interval reinforcement schedule. The slope of the curve provides a direct measure of the animal's lever-pressing rate over time.

When the lever-pressing rates for all animals had stabilized on such a variable interval schedule, a conditioned emotional response (CER) of the "fear" or "anxiety" type was superimposed upon the bar-pressing behavior according to a modification of a basic procedure previously described in some detail (Brady and Hunt, 1955). A clicking noise was presented at regular intervals during the lever-pressing session and permitted to continue for a fixed period of time. Each time the clicking terminated, a brief painful electric shock was delivered to the animal's feet through the grill floor of the lever-pressing apparatus. Figure 2 illustrates the behavior pattern which develops after several sessions on this procedure for a monkey receiving alternate five-minute periods of click and no click during lever-pressing for the variable-interval sugared orange juice reward. With the pain shock following each five-minute click, virtually complete suppression of the lever-pressing behavior is apparent during the clicking (indicated by the offset sections of the cumulative curve), although the stable lever-pressing rate is maintained throughout the five-minute intervals between emotional conditioning trials.

After several experimental sessions with shock following every click presentation, all animals were shifted to a schedule which provided only occasional shock on termination of the clicking. Although the clicking noise continued to be presented at regular intervals for fixed five-minute periods (three minutes with the rats), the pain shock followed termination of the click on only one-third to one-half of the presentations. The effect of this procedure is shown in Fig. 3 for a rat receiving the three-minute click presentations every seven minutes during lever pressing for a variable-interval water reward. The short

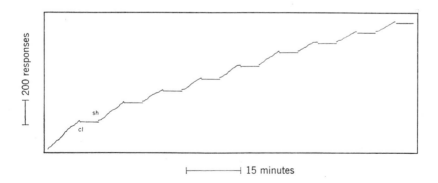

Figure 2. Sample cumulative response curve for a monkey showing complete suppression of lever pressing during repeated click presentation. Each click period (indicated by the offset sections of the curve marked "cl" for the click and "sh" for shock) was terminated contiguously with pain shock.

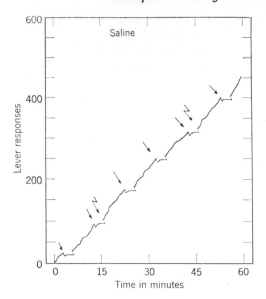

Figure 3. Sample cumulative response curve for rat AA-26 showing the development of a stable conditioned suppression pattern on the 30 to 50 per cent pain-shock-pairings procedure. The short offset sections of the curve mark the duration of the three-minute click periods, the straight arrows indicating click onset and the broken arrows indicating shock on the two trials when it was administered.

offset sections of the curve mark the duration of the click period, the straight arrows indicating click onset and the broken arrows indicating shock on the two trials when it was administered. A marked depression in lever-pressing rate is still apparent during the click periods as compared to the seven-minute intervals between emotional conditioning trials, but the suppression is by no means so complete as that observed during earlier training stages when shock was administered after each click presentation (Fig. 2). When this stage of training is reached, however, the ratio of the number of lever responses during the click periods to the number of lever responses during the periods without click has been found to remain stable (showing no consistent trend) during more than 100 experimental hours for such animals.

Since this procedure involved some stable and reproducible degree of control over an aspect of the animal's response repertoire ostensibly related to "emotional" or "affective" processes, it was decided to explore the effects of tranquilizing agents upon this behavior. In

addition to suggesting an approach to the evaluation of any so-
called "emotional" effects which the drug might be expected to have,
this technique of superimposing the conditioned suppression pattern
upon a stable baseline of on-going lever-pressing activity appeared to
provide a concurrent control for more generalized, non-specific behavior and motor disturbances and malaise. And, indeed, results
obtained with both the rat and the monkey have been most revealing
in this regard (Brady, 1956). Figure 4, for example, shows the effects
of reserpine upon the behavior of a monkey, after daily administration
of 0.75 mg. per kg. for one week. Although the overall lever-pressing
rate is depressed more than 50 per cent by comparison with the normal
rate for this same animal, as illustrated in Fig. 2, the conditioned suppression of responding during the five-minute click periods (indicated
by the offset sections of the curve) has been virtually eliminated. The
animal under the influence of this drug continues to respond throughout the five-minute click presentations at the same rate as during the
five-minute intervals between conditioning trials, even though the
pain shock is paired with 30 to 50 per cent of the click terminations.

Essentially the same results were obtained with the rats, although

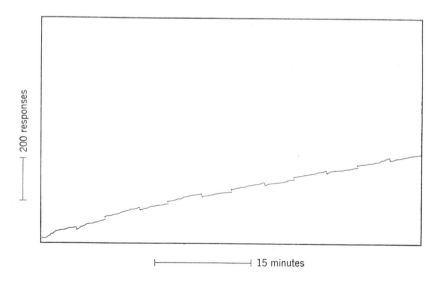

Figure 4. Sample cumulative response curve for a monkey showing the effect
of reserpine upon the conditioned "anxiety" response. The repeated five-minute
click periods are indicated by the offset sections of the curve and continue to be
paired with pain shock on 30 to 50 per cent of the presentations.

the time course for the appearance of the drug effect upon the CER varied to some extent in different animals. In an attempt to provide a quantitative description of these changes, comparisons, in the form of an "inflection ratio," were made between the number of lever responses during the auditory stimulus presentations and the number of lever responses during periods of equal duration immediately before the stimulus intervals. This inflection ratio was computed for all animals throughout the various phases of the experiment, and it indicated how much and in which direction the "emotional" stimulus, during the periods when it was presented, changed the output of lever responses (see Hunt, Jernberg, and Brady, 1952, for a more complete discussion of this measure). The "inflection ratio" expresses the difference in output between the non-stimulus and stimulus segments of the curve as a fraction (percentage in decimal form) of the output during the non-stimulus segment. (The "inflection ratio" is expressed by the formula $(B - A)/A$, where A is the number of lever responses made before the stimulus, and B is the number made during the stimulus.) Complete cessation of the lever pressing during the click stimulus appears as a ratio of -1.00, essentially unchanged output appears as a ratio of around 0.00, and a 100 per cent increase in output appears as a ratio of $+1.00$.

Figure 5 shows the changes in strength of the CER (expressed in terms of the inflection ratio) throughout the course of the experiment for three rats treated with the drug. During the six-day control period prior to the first reserpine series, the mean inflection ratios for all animals remained fairly stable at values around $-.75$, indicating a marked but incomplete suppression of lever responding during the click presentations, as illustrated by Fig. 3. Even when daily administration of 0.2 mg. per kg. of reserpine was begun after the experimental session on the sixth day, little change in the strength of the CER could be discerned for several days. After three or four days on the drug, however, some animals (i.e., rat AA-26, Fig. 5) began to show an increased rate of responding during the click periods, even though the rate in the absence of the stimulus was actually somewhat depressed in all animals as a result of the reserpine administration. And, indeed, within a week to ten days on this repeated daily drug regime, all but one of the six rats in this group had begun to respond to the reserpine treatments in this fashion. The change in inflection ratio values toward 0.00 during the first reserpine series indicated on Fig. 5 shows this drug effect on the CER for three typical animals. The obvious variability in drug-action time course is interesting and

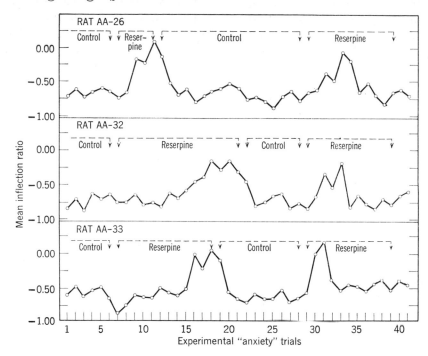

Figure 5. Changes in the strength of the conditioned "anxiety" response for three rats as a function of repeated reserpine administration.

worth noting, however, even though no ready explanation is available. A few animals (e.g., rat AA-26, Fig. 5) showed a relatively rapid, abrupt response to this drug dose, some (e.g., rat AA-32, Fig. 5) showed a relatively slow and gradual response, others (e.g., rat AA-33, Fig. 5), a slow but abrupt response, and still others (one rat, not shown), no response at all within a fourteen-day treatment period.

Withdrawals of the drug during the control period of seven days or more between treatment series resulted in a rapid reversion to the stable pretreatment inflection ratio values for all animals, as illustrated in Fig. 5. When the second drug series was administered with a high initial reserpine dose (1 mg. per kg.), however, the effect reappeared somewhat more rapidly and abruptly, as indicated by the inflection ratio changes toward 0.00 for the three rats represented in Fig. 5 between experimental trials 29 and 32. As the reserpine dose was progressively reduced to 0.5 mg. per kg., however, and then continued at

0.1 mg. per kg. (only half the chronic 0.2 mg. per kg. dose administered during the first reserpine series), a corresponding increase in the strength of the CER was observed. For the three animals represented in Fig. 5, the inflection ratio values can be seen to revert rather abruptly to the pretreatment values several sessions before the daily 0.1 mg. per kg. of reserpine treatments were discontinued. Either the chronic low dose of the drug was insufficient to prevent reappearance of the CER (maintained throughout the experiment with the 30 to 50 per cent shock pairings procedure), or some adaptation to the drug had resulted from the administration procedures utilized in this study. Of course, it is also possible that some interaction or combination of these two effects could account for the observed changes.

In the monkey, too, a repeated treatment course similar to that used with the rats was followed with essentially the same results. Withdrawal of reserpine after the initial response was followed by the rapid and abrupt reappearance of the CER, while readministration of the drug quickly brought back the lever-pressing rate during presentation of the click stimulus. Again, however, some reduction in the magnitude of this effect was observed with repeated administration of the 0.5 mg. per kg. chronic dose used during the second drug series, although a change in some of the pain shock contingencies makes the latter finding in the monkey difficult to interpret. Only one of the rats among this group of CER animals failed to show any significant change in the strength of the emotional response as a function of the two series of repeated reserpine doses.

Experimentation with Human Subjects

The general applicability of such techniques, developed in the animal laboratory, to the evaluation of pharmacologic effects upon human behavior is presently under investigation in at least three separate laboratories, and the results thus far obtained appear encouraging. Skinner, Solomon, and Lindsley of the Behavior Research Laboratory at Metropolitan State Hospital, Waltham, Massachusetts (1954), have been studying the behavior of a hospitalized psychiatric population over the past few years, utilizing the general principles embodied in the application of "operant conditioning" methods described above. They have developed relatively stable behavior baselines, using several reinforcement schedules, not only in patients with various psychiatric syndromes, but in a healthy normal population as well. Against these baselines, work has now begun toward an analysis of the behavioral changes related to drug administration, particularly in the clinical psychiatric groups. In closely related work with a normal human population, Peter Dews and William Morse of the Pharmacology Department at Harvard Medical School have undertaken to analyze the effects of drugs on certain temporal and discriminative aspects of behavior through the medium of some of the reward scheduling techniques. Specifically, differential reinforcement of low response rates by providing for the delivery of the reward for a response only after an interval of time has elapsed since the *last response* have been found to distinguish quite sensitively among various drug effects in a medical student population. Finally, Donald Bullock at the Psychological Service of the Institute of the Pennsylvania Hospital in Philadelphia has initiated an assessment program involving certain tranquilizers with psychiatric patients studied via a "multiple schedule" approach similar to that described above. Using both "fixed-interval" (reward delivered for a response made only after a fixed interval of time has elapsed since the last reward) and "fixed-ratio" (reward delivered only after a fixed number of responses) reinforcement schedules, Bullock has begun to analyze some operationally definable behavioral effects following the administration of some of the "milder" tranquilizers in the meprobamate class. Clearly, the first steps of transition have been taken from the animal experimental laboratory to the use of operant behavior methods for a more refined analysis of drug effects or human beings.

REFERENCES

Brady, J. V. A comparative approach to the evaluation of drug effects upon affective behavior. *Ann. N. Y. Acad. Sci.*, 1956, 64, 632–643.

Brady, J. V. Comparative psychopharmacology: animal experimental studies on the effects of drugs on behavior. In J. O. Cole and R. W. Gerard (Eds.), *Psychopharmacology.* Washington, D. C.: National Research Council, 1959, 46–63.

Brady, J. V., and Hunt, H. F. An experimental approach to the analysis of emotional behavior. *J. Psychol.*, 1955, 40, 313–324.

Dews, P. B. Studies on behavior I. Differential sensitivity to pentobarbital of pecking performance in pigeons depending on the schedule of reward. *J. Pharmacol. exp. Therap.*, 1955, 113, 393–401. (a)

Dews, P. B. Studies on behavior II. The effects of pentobarbital, methamphetamine, and scopolamine on performance in pigeons involving discriminations. *J. Pharmacol. exp. Therap.*, 1955, 115, 380–389. (b)

Dews, P. B. Modification by drugs of performance on simple schedules of positive reinforcement. *Ann. N. Y. Acad. Sci.*, 1956, 65, 268–281.

Herrnstein, R. J., and Morse, W. H.   Selective action of pentobarbital on component behaviors of a reinforcement schedule.   *Science,* 1956, 124, 367–368.

Hunt, H. F., Jernberg, J., and Brady, J. V.   The effect of electroconvulsive shock (ECS) on a conditioned emotional response: the effect of post-ECS extinction on the reappearance of the response.   *J. comp. physiol. Psychol.,* 1952, 45, 589–599.

Skinner, B. F.   *The behavior of organisms: an experimental analysis.*   New York: Appleton-Century-Crofts, 1938.

Skinner, B. F., Solomon, H. C., and Lindsley, O. R.   A new method for the experimental analysis of the behavior of psychotic patients.   *J. nerv. ment. Dis.,* 1954, 120, 403–406.

Skinner, B. F., Solomon, H. C., and Lindsley, O. R.   New techniques of analysis of psychotic behavior.   *Ann. Tech. Rep. No. 3.*   Waltham, Mass.: Metropolitan State Hospital, 1954.

Chlorpromazine and the discrimination
of response-produced cues

The effect of drugs on an organism's discrimination of its own be-havior, or the sensory feedback from this behavior, is a major problem in psychopharmacology. Few studies of the problem have been made, however, and still fewer methods devised for its solution. We have many procedures that yield measures of sensitivity to differences in wavelength, intensity, or other properties of exteroceptive stimula-tion, but practically none for dealing effectively with proprioceptive, or response-produced, stimuli.

The techniques to be described here had their immediate origin in studies of the effect of tocopherol (vitamin E) upon operant behavior in anoxia (Berryman and Mechner, 1960); Keller, Berryman, and Mechner (1960). Conceptually, they derive from several sources, in particular from the problem of double alternation (Hunter, 1922; Schlosberg and Katz, 1943) and related tasks (Masserman, 1946; Carey, 1951) in which subjects react correctly only on the basis of cues resulting directly from their own behavior.

Our basic procedure, described more fully by Mechner (1958), is one in which a thirsty white rat has two levers available to him within a small response chamber. Reinforcement, with water, is provided when the animal makes a certain "criterion" number of depressions of one lever, followed by a single additional depression of the other. He may exceed the criterion on the first level by any number of responses and still be reinforced after switching to the second, but a failure to

This work was supported in part by United States Public Health Service Grant M-1421.

make the required number results in his not being reinforced, and he must start all over again.

In this situation, where relevant exteroceptive cues are absent, the subject cannot discriminate except on the basis of cues derived from his own behavior. Evidence for such a discrimination (or the lack thereof) can be most conveniently obtained by recording the distribution of the number of times the animal makes one, two, three, or more depressions of the first lever before moving to the second. (A number of responses on one lever, followed by a response on the other, is spoken of as a "run." The distribution just mentioned is thus a distribution of run lengths.)

Such a distribution, obtained with a criterion of eight responses on the first lever, is shown for a typical rat in Fig. 1. In this case, the distribution is symmetrical, with a mode of 8, a mean of 8.3, and a standard deviation of 1.7. It is approximately normal, with some tendency to skewness in the direction of the longer run lengths. More than 25 per cent of the runs are of the criterion length, 8.

Considered by itself, this sort of distribution does not guarantee discrimination. However, it has been shown by Mechner (1958) that the mean and variance of the distribution are closely related to the size of the criterion. The run-length distribution has a mode at, or slightly beyond, the criterion, and, the larger the criterion, the flatter is the form of the distribution.

Our procedure may also be thought of as a psychophysical method. In its essential characteristics it is related to the audiometric techniques of von Bekesy (1947), wherein the subject controls stimulus in-

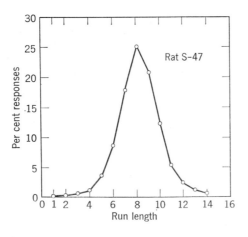

Figure 1. Distribution of run lengths for a criterion (k) of 8 or more responses. Data from a stable-state performance were cumulated over a 10-day period and converted to a percentage basis.

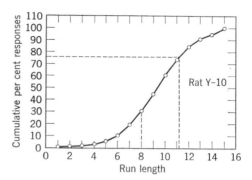

Figure 2. Psychophysical function derived from a cumulated run-length distribution.

tensity. In accord with this interpretation, a psychophysical function may be constructed, as in Fig. 2, and conventional psychophysical measures applied to its analysis. For example, note the 75 per cent difference limen (indicated by the dashed line) obtained in relation to the criterion (the dotted line).

A valuable measure can be derived from the run-length distribution by calculating the conditional probabilities of further responses—the probability of an animal's making n responses, having already made $n - 1$. Thus, if a rat has already made 7 responses on the first lever, what are the chances that he will make 8 responses, or more, before shifting? This measure can be derived from the *cumulative* distribution of run lengths. For instance, if the animal has made runs of 7 responses on 1000 occasions, but has gone beyond 7 (to 8, 9, 10, etc.) on only 500 of these, the conditional probability is 500/1000, or 0.5.

An illustration of such a function is shown in Fig. 3. Its shape indicates that, for this subject (S-47), the probability of an additional response remained close to 1.0 until the response number reached 6. Subsequently this probability drops off rapidly. Beyond 11 responses a new process comes into play and the probability function rises.

The slope of this probability function, particularly the segment of it immediately above and below the criterion value, may be thought of as a measure of the quality of the discrimination. If the discrimination is "good," the function will show a steep slope; if it is "poor," the slope will be shallow. *Absence* of a discrimination would be represented by a *zero* slope.

The usefulness of our technique and measures in assessing the effects of a drug may be suggested by describing two simple experiments with chlorpromazine.

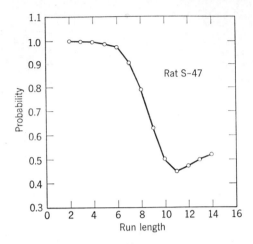

Figure 3. A conditional probability function showing changes (as run length increases) in the probability of an additional response given that a certain number of responses has already been made.

Experiment 1. The two-lever response chamber was employed and four male albino rats of Wistar strain were used as subjects. Water, provided in small quantities by a dipper mechanism, was used as reinforcement for the lever pressing. Experimentation began after the animal had spent two weeks on a deprivation schedule that gave access to water for one 15-minute period daily. (Food was freely available at all times.)

Initially the experimental sessions were one hour long and with only one lever present, alternately the right and left. At this stage all responses were reinforced. When moderately high rates of pressing were attained on each lever, the above-described discrimination procedure was introduced. In two daily sessions the criterion value on the first bar was moved up gradually from 2 to 10, the final value, and the session length was increased to two daily hours. No water was given to the animals except during this period, but food was available in the home cages.

This schedule was continued until the subjects had met a stability criterion based on the analysis of daily fluctuations in the run-length distributions. This stability, essential to any method in which experimental subjects are used as their own controls, is pictured in Fig. 4, which compares probability functions from the first and the second half of a 40-day experimental period for the same animal. The performance, as in the usual case of response-produced cue discrimination, shows remarkable stability.

Since there was adequate evidence of stable behavior, the subjects were given, on the following day, chlorpromazine,[1] 0.2 mg. per kg., injected intraperitoneally one hour before the experimental session. The sequence followed during a five-day period was Control 1, Drug 1, Control 2, Drug 2, and Control 3.

[1] Kindly supplied by Smith, Kline, and French as Thorazine.

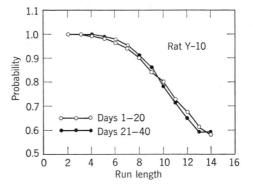

Figure 4. Comparison of probability functions based on data from the first and second halves of a 40-day period.

The results of this procedure are displayed in Fig. 5, which shows a segment of the conditional probability function (run lengths 8 to 12, inclusive) for the five days in question.   These data are for a typical rat, 0-8.

Several interesting observations emerge.   First, it may be seen that the initial administration of the drug (Drug 1) produces a noticeable deterioration of discriminative behavior.   This is indicated by the lowered slope of the conditional probability function when compared with the baseline performance (Control 1).   However, on the follow-

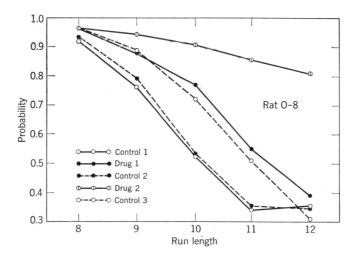

Figure 5.   Effects of chlorpromazine (0.2 mg./kg.) on a discrimination of response-produced cues.

ing control day, it is possible to recover this baseline record. The second day of drug treatment has a much greater effect than the first, the animal making a proportionally large number of runs well past the critcrion value. On the last day (Control 3), it is no longer possible to recover the baseline, although an improvement over the preceding drug day is obvious.

Results of this sort suggest a point of method. If a drug produces a change in behavior, it may also alter the probability that certain responses will be reinforced. If this is so, the subject may be reinforced more (or less) frequently than during his stable-state sessions. This, in turn, may itself alter the animal's performance, by way of differential reinforcement. We might then ask: Is the failure of an animal to return to his baseline level of behavior the result of *continuing* effects of the drug, or is it the result of slow extinction of the new behavior acquired through the change in reinforcement contingencies? Further study would be required to answer this question.

It is possible to say, however, that administration of chlorpromazine at the level of 0.2 mg. per kg. will initiate a considerable change in the discrimination of response-produced cues.

Experiment 2. Three albino rats were subjected to the same deprivation schedule and the same training procedures as described above, except that the criterion number of responses was in this case 8 or more. After this regimen had been maintained for approximately two months, as part of a study of variability, the animals were shifted to a schedule that required

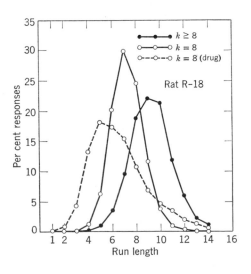

Figure 6. Proportional run-length distributions for a criterion of 8 or more, a criterion of exactly 8, and a criterion of exactly 8, with 0.5 mg./kg. chlorpromazine.

them to make *exactly* 8 responses before shifting from the first to the second lever.

The results of this restriction, for one animal (R-18), are shown in Fig. 6. Here it may be seen that, with the early criterion of 8 or more, the run-length distribution peaked in the region of 9 responses. When the criterion was changed to exactly 8, this mode shifted to 7 responses and a more leptokurtic distribution appeared.

Chlorpromazine (at 0.5 mg. per kg.), intraperitoneally injected one hour before the daily experimental session, produced greatly increased variance. The mode of the distribution shifted to 5, and there was an increase in the relative frequency of runs that fell either above or below the criterion. Results obtained with the other two subjects were substantially the same.

These two experiments show clearly that a discrimination of response-produced cues may be altered by administering a drug. But something else is suggested, at least in our first study: the direct effect of a drug upon behavior should not be confused with the derived effect. Research at this point is sorely needed, but alertness to such possibilities must be the rule in the development of psychopharmacological science.

R E F E R E N C E S

Bekesy, G. v. A new audiometer. *Acta Oto-laryngol.*, 1947, 35, 411–422.

Berryman, M., and Mechner, F. The establishment of a discrimination based on response-produced cues. *USAF Sch. Aviat. Med. Res. Rep.*, No. 55-13, 1960, in press.

Carey, J. P. Reinstatement of previously learned responses under conditions of extinction: a study of "progressive regression." Unpublished doctoral dissertation, Columbia Univer., 1951.

Hunter, W. S. The temporal maze and kinaesthetic sensory processes in the white rat. *Psychobiology*, 1922, 2, 1–17.

Keller, F. S., Berryman, R., and Mechner, F. The effects of tocopherol on behavior in anoxia. *USAF Sch. Aviat. Med. Res. Rep.*, 1960, in press.

Masserman, J. H. *Principles of dynamic psychiatry.* Philadelphia: Saunders, 1946.

Mechner, F. Probability relations within response sequences under ratio reinforcement. *J. exp. anal. Beih.*, 1958, 1, 109–122.

Schlosberg, H., and Katz, A. Double alternation lever-pressing in the white rat. *Amer. J. Psychol.*, 1943, 56, 274–282.

Drug effects on

experimental neuroses in animals

In animals with needle electrodes implanted in the central nervous system the following effects of various drugs were observed. Sodium amytal injected intravenously at a dose of 20 to 50 mg. per kg. diminished the electrical reactivity of the hypothalamus and contiguous diencephalic centers but not that of the frontal cortex; however, the direct injection of 10 to 30 mg. produced few effects at either site. Our studies revealed no specific or differential action of morphine sulfate either on the cortex or on the diencephalon. Metrazol, strychnine, Coramine, and picrotoxin produced much more marked analeptic effects when applied in minute amounts directly to the hypothalamus than when given in subconvulsive doses intravenously. The effects of these analeptic drugs could be counteracted by specific barbiturates.

Alcohol applied directly to central nervous tissue in low concentrations (0.01 per cent) may act as a mild stimulant; above 0.05 per cent it is definitely toxic. In systemic doses of 1 to 3 cc. per kg., alcohol diminishes cortical while sparing diencephalic activity; above these systemic concentrations, it inhibits CNS activity.

In subsequent studies these neurophysiologic approaches were displaced by prolonged and more comprehensive observations of (a) the spontaneous individual and social adaptations of the animal, (b) controlled learning behavior, (c) the effects of conflictful experiences in inducing neurotic and psychotic aberrations of conduct, and (d) the effects of various "psychotherapeutic" manipulations, including individual, physical, and social experiences, different methods of retraining, electrical or surgical interferences with brain functions, and the administration of various drugs.

In the past 10 years we have studied 142 cats and 43 monkeys from birth to adulthood. Preliminary control observations were made for 2 to 12 months of each animal's resting, feeding, sexual, exploratory and other spontaneous behavior patterns, its social relationships with cage and colony mates, and its interactions with members of other species, including the experimenters. Each animal was then trained in a special apparatus for 2 to 8 months to respond with maximal efficiency to specific visual, auditory, olfactory stimuli. The animal responded by pressing the appropriate one of two levers a required number of times before securing a pellet of food from a designated box, or being otherwise rewarded by fluids, warmth, sexual gratification, etc. The animals were also studied in groups of two or more at a time in various situations in and out of the laboratory to observe the effects of social frustration or collaboration on individual behavior, group dominance or submission, or other significant interactions.

We soon learned that without a fairly thorough knowledge of the "normal" ranges of behavior of an animal (including experimentally adaptive patterns such as "aggression" and "masochism") and their deviations under "normal" stress, the added effects of conflict, medication, operative intervention, etc., could not be accurately evaluated. With this more adequate background we could proceed as described below.

Production of Experimental Neuroses

These neuroses were evoked by subjecting our animals to a conflict between their previously learned patterns for securing a specific reward and a concurrently induced fear of the repetition of a disruptively traumatic experience while receiving the expected gratification. Physical deterrents effective for the cat included mild grille shock or air blast, or the sudden removal of bodily support. Such experiences were also moderately traumatic to the monkey. But the appearance of a toy rubber snake in the food box or the loss of a companion or of group dominance could be more effectively and significantly employed with this species. From 3 to 50 such conflictful experiences, presented irregularly at the time of food taking over a few days or weeks, produced in nearly all animals deviations of behavior sufficiently marked, generalized, and persistent to be termed experimental neuroses. These were characterized by physiologic manifestations of severe anxiety (e.g., mydriasis, horripilation, tachycardia), disorganization of learned skills, various skeletal, gastrointestinal, cardiorespiratory, and motor dysfunctions (e.g., asthmatic or cataleptic states), spreading phobias, stereotyped compulsions, and persistent social and sexual deviations: i.e., loss of group dominance or almost exclusive homo- or autoerotism. Some monkeys also showed deep anachronistic regressions, extreme or bizarre affectivity, and evidences of hallucinatory and delusional behavior such as unremittent searching and exploration of the cage or the recurrent seeking, chewing, and swallowing of imaginary food while refusing real food immediately available (cf. our motion picture, *Experimental Neuroses in Monkeys*).

Therapeutic Procedures

In succeeding series of experiments these neurotic (or psychotic?) animals were treated by a variety of techniques, among them (a) satiation of one of the conflict-arousing needs, (b) changes of "home" or "work" environments, (c) forced solution of the adaptational impasse, (d) group examples of "normal" behavior, (e) individualized retraining procedures, (f) the administration of various drugs, and (g) cerebral surgery and/or various forms of shock therapy. The following inferences were reached with regard to the pharmacologic and physical methods (f and g) of influencing total behavior.

Drugs. Alcohol in doses of 1 to 2 cc. per kg. affected learned adaptive skills so that those most complex and recently acquired were disorganized first, leaving preceding simpler patterns to be abolished only in severe intoxication; during subsequent recovery, the adaptive patterns were reacquired in their order of progressive complexity. When, therefore, traumatic conflicts induced highly complex neurotic behavior, alcohol also disorganized the complex inhibitions, phobias, regressions, etc., and thus temporarily permitted simpler adaptive patterns to emerge. About half of our animals, after experiencing such relief, became addicted to alcohol until their experimental neuroses were ameliorated by retraining or other therapeutic means. In slightly higher doses, alcohol impaired the perception and retention of disruptively conflictful experiences and thus was effective in preventing experimental neuroses.

Morphine and certain barbiturates also disorganized intricate adaptive patterns; however, our experiments were not designed to study the development of addiction to these drugs. *Mephenesin* produced virtually no therapeutically significant effects in our animals. *Reserpine, chlorpromazine,* and several other ataractic drugs when studied by our experimental methods were generally inferior to the barbiturates, alcohol, and morphine in relieving the acute manifestation of experimental neuroses in both cats and monkeys, whereas their undesirable side effects were more marked. The disorganizations of behavior produced by drugs were generally less pronounced in intact animals than in those with cortical injuries.

Electroshock also temporarily disorganized neurotic patterns and thus favored interim retraining or other therapeutic procedures. However, though electroshock when used moderately left relatively compensable impairments of adaptive capacity, the underlying deficits were in nearly all cases permanent.

Surgical lesions of various cortical regions or subcortical nuclei likewise produced the changes in behavior described under electroshock, though with more specialized neurophysiologic defects, such as greatly increased susceptibility to and disorganization under sensory isolation.

The effects of all manipulations and medications depended not only on their specific nature, intensity and timing, but also on complex combinations of factors comprising the genetic, physical, and metabolic constitution of the animal, its unique experiences, its material and social transactions during and subsequent to the procedure in question, and configurations of many other relevant influences, including the beliefs and interpretations of the observer.

R E F E R E N C E S

Masserman, J. H.   Effects of sodium amytal and other drugs on the reactivity of the hypothalamus of the cat. *Arch. Neurol. Psychiat.,* 1937, 37, 617–628.

Masserman, J. H.   The effect of strychnine sulphate on the emotional mimetic functions of the hypothalamus of the cat. *J. Pharmacol. exp. Therap.,* 1938, 64, 335–354.

Masserman, J. H.   Action of metrazol (pentamethylenetetrazol) on the hypothalamus of the cat. *Arch. Neurol. Psychiat.,* 1939, 41, 504–510.

Masserman, J. H.   Effects of morphine sulphate on hypothalamus of the cat. *Proc. Soc. exp. Biol. Med.,* 1939, 42, 315–317.

Masserman, J. H.   Effects of analeptic drugs on the hypothalamus of the cat. *Ass. Res. nerv. ment. Dis., Proc. 1939,* 1940, 20, 624–634.

Masserman, J. H.   Stimulant effects of ethyl alcohol in cortico-hypothalamic functions. *J. Pharmacol. exp. Therap.,* 1940, 70, 450–453.

Masserman, J. H.   *Behavior and neurosis: an experimental psychoanalytic approach to psychobiologic principles.*   Chicago: Univer. of Chicago Press, 1943.

Masserman, J. H.   Neurosis and alcohol. *Am. J. Psychiat.,* 1944, 101, 389–395.

Masserman, J. H.   *Motion picture films. Psychological cinema register catalogue.*   State College, Pa.: 1954, pp. 69ff.

Masserman, J. H. *Practice of dynamic psychiatry.* Philadelphia: Saunders, 1955.

Masserman, J. H. Experimental psychopharmacology and behavioral relativity. In P. Hoch and J. Zubin (Eds.), *Problems of addiction and habituation.* New York: Grune & Stratton, 1958, 110–148.

Masserman, J. H., Arieff, A., Pechtel, C., and Klehr, H. Effects of direct interrupted electroshock on experimental neuroses. *J. nerv. ment. Dis.,* 1950, 112, 384–392.

Masserman, J. H., and Heartig, E. W. The influence of hypothalamic stimulation on intestinal activity. *J. Neurophysiol.,* 1938, 1, 350–356.

Masserman, J. H., and Jacobson, L. Effects of ethyl alcohol on the cerebral cortex and the hypothalamus of the cat. *Arch. Neurol. Psychiat.,* 1940, 43, 334–340.

Masserman, J. H., and Jacques, Mary G. Effects of cerebral electroshock on experimental neuroses in cats. *Am. J. Psychiat.,* 1947, 104, 92–99.

Masserman, J. H., Jacques, M. G., and Nicholson, Mary R. Alcohol as a preventive of experimental neuroses. *Quart. J. Stud. Alcohol,* 1945, 6, 281–299.

Masserman, J. H., and Pechtel, C. Conflict-engendered neurotic and psychotic behavior in monkeys. *J. nerv. ment. Dis.,* 1953, 118, 408–411.

Masserman, J. H., and Pechtel, C. Neuroses in monkeys: a preliminary report of experimental observations. *Ann. N. Y. Acad. Sci.,* 1953, 56, 253–265.

Masserman, J. H., and Pechtel, C. The role of olfaction in normal and neurotic behavior in animals: a preliminary report. *Psychosom. Med.,* 1953, 15, 396–404.

Masserman, J. H., with Pechtel, C. The osmatic responses of normal and neurotic monkeys. *Ann. N. Y. Acad. Sci.,* 1954, 58, 256.

Masserman, J. H., and Pechtel, C. The role of drug therapies in current and future psychiatric practice. *Psychiatric Res. Rep.,* 1956, No. 4, 95–125.

Masserman, J. H., and Pechtel, C. How brain lesions affect normal and neurotic behavior. *Am. J. Psychiat.,* 1956, 112, 865–872.

Masserman, J. H., and Pechtel, C. Neurophysiologic and pharmacologic influences on experimental neuroses. *Am. J. Psychiat.* 1956, 113, 510–514.

Masserman, J. H., Pechtel, C., and Cain, J. Création de névrose expérimentales chez le chat par un traumatisme psychologique. *C. R. séances Soc. Biol.,* 1954, 148, 2041–2043.

Masserman, J. H., and Yum, K. S. Analysis of the influence of alcohol on experimental neuroses in cats. *Psychosom. Med.* 1946, 8, 36–52.

Wikler, A., and Masserman, J. H. The effects of morphine on learned adaptive responses and experimental neuroses in cats. *Arch. Neurol. Psychiat.,* 1943, 50, 401–404.

Effects of chlorpromazine, meprobamate, pentobarbital, and morphine on self-stimulation

In self-stimulation experiments the animal responds to an electric stimulus in the hypothalamus (which he applies to himself by pressing a bar) as though it were a positive reinforcement such as food or sexual stimulation (Olds and Milner, 1954). Contributing to the supposition that the stimulus activates centers normally involved in the positive reinforcement of behavior is the fact that the rate of the self-stimulation response is altered by sex or hunger drive, depending on the stimulus site (Olds, 1958a).

Experiments in which animals have been allowed to self-stimulate freely for long periods of time indicate that animals with hypothalamic electrodes self-stimulate to exhaustion, continuing for periods of more than 24 hours (Olds, 1958b). From this finding it appears possible that a positive feedback process is involved; a process, that is, which grows to a maximum and continues there. Such a process would constitute a danger to the organism because it would trap the animal in unidirectional behavior.

This suggests an alternative to the current notion that an excess of "sympathetic" activity underlies psychotic agitation (Brodie and Shore, 1957). We suspect that many episodes of psychotic agitation have quite a different etiology, namely, an excess of the positive feedback process subserving positive reinforcement mechanisms.

These studies were aided by grants to J. Olds from the Foundations' Fund for Research in Psychiatry, the United States Public Health Service, the Ford Foundation, and Wallace Laboratories.

This paper is reprinted, with permission, from the Journal of Pharmacology and Experimental Therapeutics, 1960, in press.

A series of pharmacological studies of self-stimulation have been made with a view to testing the corollary that chemicals which successfully control psychotic agitation may have in common the property of suppressing self-stimulation. Preliminary reports (Olds, Killam, and Bach-y-Rita, 1956; Olds, Killam, and Eiduson, 1957; Olds, 1959) have indicated that reserpine and chlorpromazine suppress self-stimulation and that pentobarbital and meprobamate do not. It has also been indicated that reserpine and chlorpromazine are differential in their effect on self-stimulation depending on electrode sites (Olds, Killam, and Bach-y-Rita, 1956; Olds, Killam, and Eiduson, 1957). No systematic study showing dose-response curves and statistical differences among different brain points and different drugs has yet been presented.

As the first such study, the present report substantially validates previous findings while correcting false impressions based on an insufficiently systematic canvass of brain points in earlier studies.

Data are presented on four compounds, chlorpromazine, morphine, meprobamate, and pentobarbital, injected by the intraperitoneal route. Reserpine has not yet been tested in these experiments because the group of test animals is used in a continuing investigation and reserpine in our laboratory has caused great variability in the subsequent data from a given animal.

Methods

SELF-STIMULATION. The general technique has been described previously (Olds and Milner, 1954). Each rat had a pair of silver electrodes implanted in the brain. These were silver wires, 0.01-inch diameter, insulated except for the cross section of the tips and placed 0.002 inch apart. The stimulus was a sine wave of 60 cycles per second varied between 0 and 50 μamperes r.m.s. in steps of 10 μamperes. For self-stimulation, animals were provided with a 4-inch pedal protruding into the short wall of a 5 x 11 x 10 inch box. Each lever press provided a stimulus train of a maximum duration of ½ second. Thereafter the lever had to be released and reactivated. For training, a 50-μampere current was used and animals were allowed to explore at random. A small source of light near the lever tended to increase the random lever pressing during this phase. Base-level lever pressing without current ranged from 10 to 50 responses per hour. The rate of lever pressing considered to be indicative of reward ranged from 500 to 7000 per hour. Training and testing sessions were composed of

6 consecutive 8-minute intervals. After the self-stimulation rate reached a stable level, using the 50-μampere training stimulus, electric current was varied successively within each block of 6 intervals: 0, 10, 20, 30, 40, and 50 μamperes.

Pharmacological tests were begun after it was clear that progressive changes were no longer occurring as a result of training, or from change in threshold following surgery, or from some consequence of stimulation itself. The general pattern for pharmacological tests was to compare self-stimulation scores for control days which preceded drug administration with self-stimulation scores achieved on days when animals had received intraperitoneal injections of the drug before testing.

Mapping tests and dose-response tests utilized two different groups of animals. In both cases chlorpromazine, meprobamate, pentobarbital, and morphine were tested in this order, with 13 days separating two drug tests on the same group.[1]

Groups of animals for mapping and dose-response tests are maintained in our laboratory in a fully trained condition and are carried through from one experiment to another. A given preparation is usually terminated when the electrodes become dislodged from the head. About one-fourth of the total number is so terminated in a month's time. While an operated replacement is maintained at all times for each animal in these groups, there is a training period of at least a month before the replacement animal can be used in tests. Therefore groups are normally at something less than 75 per cent of full strength for a given test.

MAPPING. Because preliminary tests showed a tendency for chlorpromazine to have successively greater effects for the same dose for 3 days if injected daily, and similar tests showed the opposite trend for meprobamate, mapping tests were made immediately after the third successive daily injection of the drug. Doses were 2 mg. per kg. for chlorpromazine, 7 mg. per kg. for morphine, 80 mg. per kg. for meprobamate, and 10 mg. per kg. for pentobarbital. For the mapping of effects, electrodes stimulating at points in the septal region, hypothalamus, and tegmentum were used. Some of these points produced

---

[1] If interaction is suspected here, it must be assumed that chlorpromazine 13 days earlier caused changed response to meprobamate; chlorpromazine 27 days earlier, and meprobamate 13 days earlier, caused changed response to pentobarbital; and so forth. As there were some new animals in each successive test (replacing drop-outs), it is possible to assert that such an interpretation of the differences between drugs finds no support.

rapid self-stimulation and very stable rates. Others produced slow self-stimulation with highly variable rates. Therefore the data for each animal were analyzed separately to find whether the drug treatment caused self-stimulation in a given interval to rise above or fall below the total range of control scores for that interval taken on the 12 days preceding the drug test. Such an analysis was made for each of the 4 suprathreshold electric-current intervals (20, 30, 40, and 50 μamperes) for each subject. Animals were scored +1 for each interval of augmentation, and −1 for each interval of diminution. Thus each animal could achieve a score ranging from +4 to −4, depending on the number of intervals during which the drug treatment caused an increase or decrease in self-stimulation rates. After these scores had been calculated, a frequency distribution was plotted for each drug showing the number of cases with various degrees of augmentation or diminution, or with no change. These cases were separated again to show whether the various degrees of augmentation or diminution came with electrodes in the septal region, the hypothalamus, or the tegmentum. The full strength of the group for these tests included 8 animals with electrodes in the septal region, 8 with electrodes in the anterior medial forebrain bundle of the hypothalamus, 8 with electrodes in the posterior medial forebrain bundle of the hypothalamus, and 8 with them in the tegmentum. Ordinarily, one or two animals in each group were missing from any given test. Thus there are 6 to 8 cases in each category for each drug.

DOSE RESPONSE. A group of animals with electrodes in the medial-forebrain bundle region of the hypothalamus was used. Self-stimulation rates in this group were very stable. For dose-response tests, the group was divided into four subgroups. Each subgroup received a different dose level. Injections were made on only one day. Doses for chlorpromazine were 1.0, 1.5, 2.0, and 2.5 mg. per kg. for morphine, 5.25, 7.0, 8.75, and 10.25 mg. per kg. for meprobamate, 80, 100, 120, and 160 mg. per kg. and for pentobarbital, 5, 10, 15, and 20 mg. per kg.

Mean self-stimulation rates for the various doses were plotted as percentage of control. Drug data were all taken on one day and plotted as percentage of the preceding control day. While animals were tested at all 6 levels, 0, 10, 20, 30, 40, and 50 μamperes, only the 30-μampere data were used in this analysis because they were the most stable; other data only told the same story in a less clear fashion.

CONTROL TEST. To find whether the differences between drugs were general differences in potency or specific differences in effects on self-stimulation, a second test was devised which would utilize the same response, yet bear no other relation to self-stimulation.

For this purpose an escape test was used. In this test, electric current was applied to electrodes implanted in dorso-medial or medial-lemniscus points of the midbrain tegmentum. Electric stimulation at these points produced in all cases a marked escape response, as if to intense pain.

In the escape test, electric current was repeatedly applied by a programmed stimulator. One-half-second trains were applied once every second. The animal, by holding a pedal down, could stop the stimulator for a period of 4 seconds. Then the stimulator started again and the animal had to release and press again for another 4 seconds of respite. The animal could not avoid the stimulus completely by releasing and repressing within the 4-second interval because, in such a case, the stimulator would be activated during the interval while the pedal was released.

Because of the 4-second delay used in this escape test, responding was often very regular, occurring once for every 4-second delay. As in the self-stimulation tests, there was a series of 8-minute intervals each day with electric current increasing from subthreshold through suprathreshold levels. The microampere series in this case was 14, 18, 22, 26, 30, and 34 μamperes for dorso-medial placements and 26, 30, 34, 38, 42, and 46 μamperes for medial-lemniscus ones. Once a threshold was achieved, responding became very regular, and drugs were mainly effective in causing a rise in threshold. However, they also sometimes caused changes in rates. The two effects were integrated by scoring animals on the basis of the total response output for the six 8-minute intervals.

A series of animals has been tested by this technique to locate the parts of the tegmentum yielding different kinds of escape and to find differential effects of drugs on the different kinds of escape. These data have been reported elsewhere (Travis and Olds, 1959). For present control purposes, dose-response curves are here presented for a group of 28 animals with electrodes in two tegmental locations. The group were divided into 3 matched subgroups each of which received a different dosage. The main purpose of these data is to indicate that chlorpromazine in the 1- to 2-mg. per kg. range is not more depressant than meprobamate in the 80- to 120-mg. per kg. range or pentobarbital in the 5- to 15-mg. per kg. range, and morphine in the 7- to 10¼-mg. per kg. range is about equal to meprobamate (80–120 mg. per kg.). The control tests thus provide a method for equating dosages across drugs and provide a basis for statistical comparison of different drugs. When we found one compound, X, more effective against self-stimulation than another, Y, we made statistical tests and claimed significance of the result only in those cases where our control test proved Y equally effective or more effective than X.

DOSAGES. The self-stimulation mapping tests were performed first, with doses of chlorpromazine at 2, morphine at 7, meprobamate at 80, and pentobarbital at 10 mg. per kg. These were selected from the literature as doses with moderate but definite effects on behavior (Berger, 1954; Miller, Murphy, and Mirsky, 1957; Ader and Clink, 1957; Verhave, Owen, and Robbine, 1959; Cook and Weidley, 1957). When great differences between drugs appeared in these early studies, four-step dose-response tests were undertaken from ¼ to full dose. Later, some higher doses were added to find the point of more or less complete inhibition of either self-stimulation or the escape response used for control. The doses presented in Figs. 2 and 3 are selected to give a more or less complete picture of the changes so far observed.

Results

MAPPING. Chlorpromazine (2 mg. per kg.) caused inhibitions in 81 per cent of the cases; morphine (7 mg. per kg.) caused inhibitions 68 per cent of the time; meprobamate (80 mg. per kg.), 32 per cent; and pentobarbital (10 mg. per kg.), 12 per cent. As for facilitation, meprobamate led the list causing significant increases in 39 per cent of the cases; pentobarbital in 25; morphine in 20; and chlorpromazine in none. As will be indicated below, placement proved an important determinant of the direction and intensity of the effects (see Fig. 1).

Turning first to the frequency of inhibitions and augmentations (Fig. 1), we find that chlorpromazine yields a bimodal distribution with most cases giving —3 or —4 inhibitions, but a much smaller group giving no effect. Morphine had a single mode at —1. Meprobamate produces a trimodal distribution: a small inhibited group has a mode of —3; a somewhat larger facilitated group has a mode of +2; and there is a still larger group, in which the drug had little effect, whose mode is 0. Pentobarbital had a single mode at 0; in fact, 15 of 24 cases were unaffected.

To a surprisingly large degree, the differences in effect from case to case could be accounted for by the gross differences in electrode placement (see Fig. 1). The outstanding finding in this connection

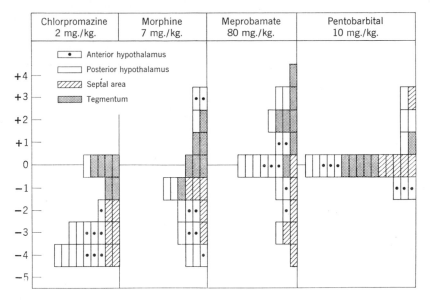

Figure 1. Increments and decrements in self-stimulation produced with electrodes in different parts of the brain. A frequency distribution of effects is given for each drug; each rectangle stands for one case. The ordinate indicates the extent of change produced by the drug. A drug is scored from +4 to −4, depending on the number of daily test intervals which it augmented (above the range of 4 preceding control days) or diminished (below the range of 4 preceding control days). Only the 4 suprathreshold intervals, at 20-, 30-, 40-, and 50-μampere settings, were used in this evaluation. Markings in rectangles indicate electrode placement according to the key. The differences between effects with electrodes in the tegmentum and effects with electrodes in the septal area were shown to be significant for meprobamate (.05 level), and chlorpromazine (.01 level), by the Mann-Whitney U-Test (1947).

was the significant difference between septal cases and tegmental ones for meprobamate, morphine, and chlorpromazine. Cases with septal electrodes always showed more tendency to be inhibited; those with tegmental electrodes showed more tendency to be facilitated.

With meprobamate, all but one of the tests with tegmental electrodes resulted in facilitation; all but one of the tests with septal electrodes showed inhibition. Cases with hypothalamic electrodes tended to fall between these two extremes, most of them being unaffected. Similar but less definite differences were found with mor-

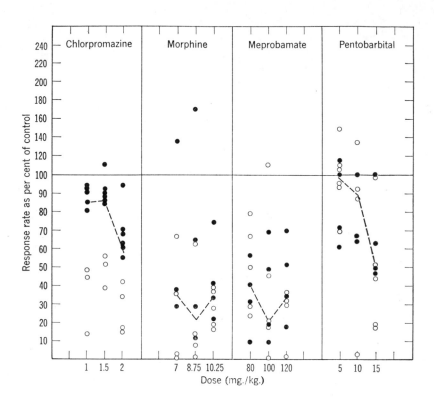

Figure 2. Dose-response curves: control test. The ordinate represents percentage increase or decrease in response rate caused by the drug in relation to the same test given the preceding day without the drug. Each point stands for one case. The broken lines connect the median points. Filled points stand for cases with electrodes in the dorso-medial tegmentum; open points stand for cases with electrodes in the medial-lemniscus region. The escape response output for six 8-minute intervals with current increasing in even steps (as described earlier) forms the basis for evaluation. The same bar-press response was used to turn this stimulation off as was used in self-stimulation tests to turn the current on. These data are presented here as a method of equating dosages only: they show chlorpromazine in the 1–2 mg./kg. range to be roughly equivalent to pentobarbital in the 5–15 mg./kg. range; morphine in the 7–10¼ mg./kg. range roughly equivalent to meprobamate in the 80–120 mg./kg.; and chlorpromazine certainly not below meprobamate in these ranges, so far as this tegmental escape test is concerned.

phine and chlorpromazine. With pentobarbital injections, however, cases with tegmental and septal electrodes were almost equally unaffected.

DOSE RESPONSE. The control data (Fig. 2) indicate that chlorpromazine (1–2 mg. per kg.) is not in this case more sedative than meprobamate (80–120 mg. per kg.) or pentobarbital (5–15 mg. per kg.). In fact, chlorpromazine in this range appears far less depressant than meprobamate, and about equal to pentobarbital. Morphine (7–10¼ mg. per kg.) appears about equal to meprobamate (80–120 mg. per kg.). These data are presented to permit a rough estimate of the relation between dosages in effects on a basic escape behavior. The main point is that in the quantities used, chlorpromazine is not more depressing on behavior than meprobamate.

The self-stimulation dose-response curves (Fig. 3) show that both chlorpromazine and morphine in these doses are significantly more depressant against self-stimulation than meprobamate or pentobarbital. The difference between the 1–2 mg. per kg. range for chlorpromazine and the 80–120 range for meprobamate is significant beyond the .01 level by the Mann-Whitney (1947) U-test. In view of the inversion of this relation in Fig. 2, this appears to indicate a significant difference between the two compounds in their modes of effect.

Doses of meprobamate and pentobarbital which have a 50 per cent tendency to antagonize escape do not have any systematic tendency to antagonize self-stimulation. In fact, there is a wide spread in the effects of these compounds on self-stimulation; raising the dosage to a point augments some cases of self-stimulation and inhibits others. The tendency to augment large numbers of self-stimulators continues up to the dose levels of 120 mg. per kg. for meprobamate, and 20 mg. per kg. for pentobarbital. That this tendency for meprobamate to augment some cases of self-stimulation while inhibiting others is not random is illustrated by the significant anatomical correlations of the preceding section.

The tendency to augment self-stimulation never appears with chlorpromazine; successive doses cause more and more inhibition up to 2 mg. per kg., and this dosage antagonizes self-stimulation almost completely. With morphine, 8.75 mg. per kg. antagonizes self-stimulation similarly. The 2 mg. per kg. dose of chlorpromazine has relatively mild effects on the escape response produced by stimulating the dorso-medial tegmentum.

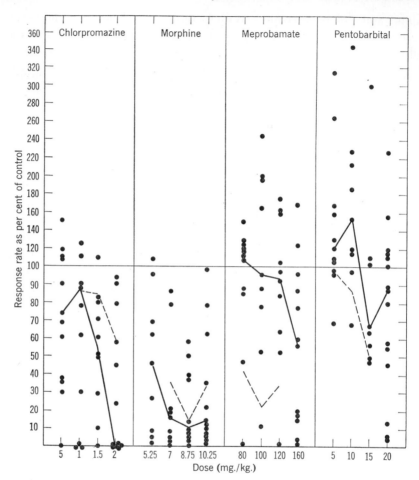

Figure 3. Dose-response curves: self-stimulation test. The ordinate represents percentage increase or decrease in response rate caused by the drug in relation to the same test given the preceding day without the drug. The solid lines connect the median points; the broken lines represent the medians of Fig. 2 for comparison. Each point stands for one case. All electrodes were in the medial-forebrain-bundle region of the hypothalamus. The self-stimulation output at 30 μamperes for 8 minutes forms the basis for evaluation. The same group of animals was run through the 4 drug tests in the following order: chlorpromazine, meprobamate, pentobarbital, morphine. At least 13 days separated any two drug tests; and animals which did not maintain stable control rates were replaced in the meantime. For a given dose-response test, the group was divided into four matched subgroups each of which received a different dose. Chlorpromazine in the 1–2 mg./kg. range had a significantly more depressing effect on self-stimulation than either meprobamate in the 80–120 mg./kg. range or pentobarbital

Discussion

RESERVATIONS. At the outset, a cautionary note is in order: although the self-stimulation response is matched in these experiments against an escape response, the latter to control for general behavioral effects, it is unwise at this point to interpret the outcomes in terms of selective effects on positive or negative motivation. The reason is that, besides the difference between the two kinds of motivating stimulus, another important difference exists: the self-stimulation test involves anticipatory responding—the pedal response occurs before the brain stimulus is applied; the escape test does not involve anticipatory responding—the pedal response occurs during application of the brain stimulus.

It is indeed tempting to suggest that self-stimulation is more like a classical avoidance response because of the anticipatory responding involved, and the control responses more like classical escape. In support of this view is the fact that our data, which suggest a specific effect of chlorpromazine and morphine on self-stimulation, but only a general effect of pentobarbital and meprobamate, present a striking parallel with those of Cook and Weidley (1957) which showed the same pattern of effects in relation to an avoidance response.

EFFECTS OF LOCUS. In the present case, a clear difference between chlorpromazine on the one hand and meprobamate and pentobarbital on the other is demonstrated in the effectiveness of mild doses against the self-stimulation response. The differential effects of chlorpromazine on various areas of the self-stimulation region reported earlier (Olds, Killam, and Eiduson, 1957; Olds, 1959) do not seem so important as this general tendency of chlorpromazine to inhibit self-stimulation when compared with meprobamate and pentobarbital.

A word about earlier discussions of localized effects, however, is relevant here. Chlorpromazine was reported (Olds, Killam, and Eiduson, 1957) to have a great effect on the rapid self-stimulation sites of posterior hypothalamus while having a much more moderate effect on the mild self-stimulation sites of the anterior hypothalamus.

---

in the 5–15 mg./kg. range; in both cases the Mann-Whitney U-test yielded a probability that the difference would occur by chance less than one time in a hundred. Similarly, morphine in the 7–10¼ mg./kg. range is significantly more depressing than meprobamate. No test of morphine against pentobarbital is made because morphine is also more depressing on both self-stimulation and control tests.

In those tests, anterior hypothalamic electrodes were placed in a boundary-line region between the medial forebrain bundle (which gives high rates) and the ventro-medial nucleus (which often gives escape responding). Thus response rates were low. In the present case, all hypothalamic electrodes were in the medial-forebrain-bundle region where response rates are high; but tegmental self-stimulation electrodes were on the boundary line between a self-stimulation system and a system yielding escape.

Our present speculation about the anatomical differences is twofold: (1) chlorpromazine has its depressant effect augmented by concomitant stimulation of the medial-forebrain-bundle–self-stimulation system, and therefore it has more effect in areas of more rapid self-stimulation; (2) meprobamate has a differential effect, inhibiting escape and avoidance tendencies in doses that do not similarly affect approach tendencies, and thus self-stimulation is augmented with electrodes in boundary-line areas. We also believe it possible that both meprobamate and pentobarbital may have their depressing effects counteracted by self-stimulation, accounting in another way for the differences between these drugs and chlorpromazine.

In relation to the hypothesis that the cases where meprobamate causes increases occur with electrodes in boundary-line areas, we may turn to earlier data (Roberts, 1958; Bower and Miller, 1958; Olds and Peretz, 1960) indicating that both in the hypothalamus and in the tegmentum there are places where the same electrode causes both self-stimulation and a tendency to escape at the same time. Particularly the animals with electrodes in these regions of "ambivalence" showed great augmentation in self-stimulation rate under meprobamate.

REFERENCES

Ader, R., and Clink, D. W. Effects of chlorpromazine on the acquisition and extinction of an avoidance response in the rat. *J. Pharmacol. exp. Therap.*, 1957, 121, 144–148.

Berger, F. M. The pharmacological properties of 2-methyl-2-*n*-propyl 1,3-propanedial discarbamate (Miltown), a new interneuronal blocking agent. *J. Pharmacol. exp. Therap.*, 1954, 112, 413–423.

Bower, G. H., and Miller, N. E. Rewarding and punishing effects from stimulating the same place in the rat's brain. *J. comp. Physiol. Psychol.*, 1958, 51, 669–674.

Brodie, B. B., and Shore, P. A. A concept for a role of serotonin and norepinephrine as chemical mediators in the brain. *Ann. N. Y. Acad. Sci.*, 1957, 66, 631–642.

Cook, L., and Weidley, E. Behavioral effects of some psychopharmacological agents. *Ann. N. Y. Acad. Sci.,* 1957, 66, 740–752.

Mann, H. B., and Whitney, D. R. On a test of whether one of two random variables is stochastically larger than the other. *Ann. Math. Statist.,* 1947, 18, 50–60.

Miller, R. E., Murphy, J. V., and Mirsky, I. A. The effect of chlorpromazine on fear-motivated behavior in rats. *J. Pharmacol. exp. Therap.,* 1957, 120, 379–387.

Olds, J. Effects of hunger and male sex hormone on self-stimulation of the brain. *J. comp. physiol. Psychol.,* 1958, 51, 320. (a)

Olds, J. Satiation effects in self-stimulation of the brain. *J. comp. Physiol. Psychol.,* 1958, 51, 675–678. (b)

Olds, J. Studies of neuropharmacologicals by electrical and chemical stimulation of the brain in animals with chronically implanted electrodes. In P. B. Bradley, P. Deniker, and C. Radouco-Thomas (Eds.), *Neuropsychopharmacology.* Amsterdam: Elsevier, 1959.

Olds, J., Killam, K. F., and Bach-y-Rita, P. Self-stimulation of the brain used as a screening method for tranquilizing drugs. *Science,* 1956, 124, 265–266.

Olds, J., Killam, K. F., and Eiduson, S. Effects of tranquilizers on self-stimulation of the brain. In S. Garattini and V. Chetti. (Eds.), *Psychotropic drugs.* New York: Elsevier: 1957, 235–243.

Olds, J., and Milner, P. Positive reinforcement produced by electrical stimulation of septal area and other regions of rat brain. *J. comp. Physiol. Psychol.,* 1954, 47, 419–427.

Olds, J., and Peretz, B. A motivational analysis of the reticular activating system. *Electroencephalog. clin. Neurophysiol.,* 1960, 12, 445–454.

Roberts, W. W. Both rewarding and punishing effects from stimulation of posterior hypothalamus of cat with same electrode at same intensity. *J. comp. Physiol. Psychol.,* 1958, 51, 400–407.

Travis, R. P., and Olds, J. Effects of secobarbital and pentobarbital on escape and avoidance behavior. *Amer. Psychol.,* 1959, 14, 430.

Verhave, T., Owen, J. E., and Robbine, E. B. The effect of morphine sulfate on avoidance and escape behavior. *J. Pharmacol. exp. Therap.,* 1959, 125, 248–251.

Effects of drugs on imprinting behavior

The general concept of imprinting is that it is an early experience which has a profound influence on the subsequent social behavior of an animal. Lorenz, a European ethologist and the first to study the phenomenon in detail (1935), postulated that the first object to elicit a social response from a young animal later releases not only that response but also related ones, such as sexual behavior. Lorenz also postulated that imprinting appeared to occur at a critical period early in the life of an animal.

We have carried out extensive studies, using chicks and ducklings, to determine the time of the "critical period" in these animals (Hess, 1957). This critical period lies in the first 32 hours after hatching with maximum effectiveness for an imprinting experience at the sixteenth hour after hatching. Not only is there a "critical period," but also the effectiveness of an imprinting experience is a function of the amount of effort expended by an animal in following an imprinting object (Hess, 1957). The temporal length of the imprinting experience does not in itself determine the strength of imprinting, but rather the distance for which the animal follows the imprinting object, or the effort expended in following. This relationship we summarized in a Law of Effort, which states that the strength of imprinting is equal to the logarithm of the effort expended, or $I_s = \log E$.

We became interested in finding what developmental and be-

The work described in this paper was supported in part by United States Public Health Service Grant M-776; by the Wallace C. and Clara A. Abbott Memorial Fund of the University of Chicago; and by the Wallace Laboratories, New Brunswick, New Jersey.

havioral trends were associated with the location of the critical period. One of these factors was fear. During the early hours of their lives, animals show no fear toward strange objects. Innate fear responses, however, later begin to develop, and at the same time the critical period for maximum effectiveness of imprinting also ends (Hess, 1959). These unlearned fear responses make imprinting impossible, since they result in an animal's avoiding a potential imprinting object instead of following it and making appropriate social responses toward it.

Therefore it seemed logical to reduce the emotional response in these young ducklings by the use of a tranquilizing drug. Meprobamate was chosen because of evidence that it would reduce emotionality without markedly depressing motility or coordination. Preliminary experiments with dosages of meprobamate resulted in a striking reduction of emotionality in the ducklings; they had no fear of strange objects or persons, even though they were at an age when marked fear is normally a certainty.

To obtain maximal information from this experiment, we then decided to test animals under the four following conditions: (1) drug at 12 hours of age, imprinting at 24 hours of age when the effect of the drug had worn off; (2) drug at 12 hours of age, imprinting at 14 to 16 hours of age, test when drug effect had worn off; (3) imprinting at 16 hours, test under drug later; and (4) drug at 24 hours, imprinting at 26 hours, test when drug effect had worn off. Between 20 and 30 animals were used in each group.

Control animals were given distilled water. Chlorpromazine and nembutal were used to obtain additional information. The results are shown in Table 1.

It is clear that, although meprobamate reduces fear or emotional behavior, it also renders imprinting almost impossible. But it does not disturb the effects of imprinting, as shown by the results of test 3. Chlorpromazine apparently allows a high degree of imprinting under all conditions, whereas nembutal reduces imprintability at all points except under the conditions of test 3. We might interpret the action of the drugs as follows. Assuming that meprobamate and chlorpromazine reduce neural metabolism (there is evidence that they do not affect general metabolism), we could expect the high imprinting scores at 24 hours of age (test 1), because slowing neural metabolism would extend the imprinting or sensitive period. This did not occur when we used nembutal or distilled water.

Reduction of emotionality must also be considered. In test 4 we

TABLE 1.   PER CENT OF POSITIVE RESPONSES MADE BY DUCKLINGS UNDER
DIFFERENT CONDITIONS OF TESTING AND DRUG ADMINISTRATION

Test	Control, H_2O	Mepro- bamate, 25 mg./kg.	Nem- butal, 5 mg./kg.	Chlor- promazine, 15 mg./kg.
1. Drug at 12 hours, imprint at 24 hours	14	54	31	57
2. Drug at 12 hours, imprint at 14–16 hours	62	8	28	63
3. Imprint without drug at 16 hours, test under drug	61	65	61	58
4. Drug at 24 hours, imprint at 26 hours	19	17	16	59

had little evidence of emotionality in the meprobamate and the chlor-promazine groups. Emotionality did occur in the control and in the nembutal group. The only way we can interpret the first result is to consider our Law of Effort, i.e., the strength of imprinting is a function of effort or of distance traveled. It may be that, since meprobamate is a muscle relaxant, meprobamate diminished muscular tension or proprioceptive impulses from the muscles and thus nullified the effectiveness of the imprinting experience. Since under the same circumstances we attained perfectly good imprinting in all cases with chlorpromazine, this notion becomes even more tenable.

To test this hypothesis, a congener of meprobamate, carisoprodol (Soma), which is primarily a muscle relaxant but has little or no tranquilizing effect, was used in an experiment with chicks. We imprinted three groups of chicks on three different occasions. In each instance one group was imprinted under the influence of meprobamate, another under carisoprodol, and a third group was given distilled water. The results in terms of test scores for strength of imprinting are shown in Table 2.

It is apparent that carisoprodol, like meprobamate, depresses imprintability, and to an even greater degree. This appears to confirm our hypothesis that the muscle-relaxing effect of meprobamate was responsible for the results we had obtained earlier. The fact that on every occasion we obtained the same rank-order relationship between the three groups lends confidence to the results even though they were based on small samples.

TABLE 2. AVERAGE TEST SCORES FOR IMPRINTING UNDER THREE DIFFERENT CONDITIONS IN THREE SERIES OF EXPERIMENTS

Test	H_2O	Meprobamate*	Carisoprodol†	Control
1	30.8	10.5	7.5	—
2	53.0	21.0	9.3	—
3	41.6	20.0	10.0	—
Average	41.2	16.3	8.7	40.8
Number	17	24	23	25

* Meprobamate is 2-methyl-2-*n*-propyl-1,3-propanediol dicarbamate.
† Carisoprodol is N-isopropyl-2-methyl-2-propyl-1,3-propanediol dicarbamate.

Thus we can see the possibility of using chicks or ducklings in drug-screening techniques. These animals are particularly useful in the investigation of the effects of drugs on unlearned fear. Findings on this can be obtained about three days after the animals are hatched. At this time their innate fear behavior toward strange objects is fully developed. By suitable measuring techniques, the effectiveness of psychopharmacological materials can be tested. It is also feasible to use simple conditioning procedures employing aversive stimulation so that the relative effects of psychoactive drugs on both learned and unlearned fear—fear behaviors of different origins—can be determined.

R E F E R E N C E S

Hess, E. H. Effects of meprobamate on imprinting in waterfowl. *Ann. N. Y. Acad. Sci.*, 1957, 67, 724–732.

Hess, E. H. Two conditions limiting critical age for imprinting. *J. comp. Physiol. Psychol.*, 1959, 52, 515–518.

Lorenz, K. Z. Der Kumpan in der Umwelt des Vogels. *J. Ornith.*, 1935, 83, 137–214, 289–413.

Objective Assessment
of Normal
Human Behavior

Psychomotor tests in drug research

Psychomotor tests are frequently used to study the effects of procedural, environmental, or physiological variables on human performance. The assumption is often made that such measures are especially susceptible to performance facilitation or performance decrement. Besides, psychomotor behavior somehow seems a more "uncontaminated," less ambiguous, and more direct measure of performance than is, let us say, verbal, conceptual, or even perceptual behavior. Most often, the experimenter can observe clocks or counters or he can obtain continuous records on some kind of moving tape. All this inspires confidence in the experimenter that he knows what he is measuring. In addition, such tasks frequently have a great deal of "face validity" and intrinsic interest to the subject as well as to the experimenter.

Some recent examples of the use of such measures in programmatic research include the work of Brozek and associates (1955) on the effects of caloric and water deficits in diets; Gorham and Orr (1957, 1958) in their studies of stress, especially fear; Bass, Hurder, and Ellis (1955) on physiological stress; and the Army Quartermaster Corps on the effects of extreme temperatures (Teichner and Wehrkamp, 1953; Teichner and Kobrick, 1954; Dusek, 1957). Many other examples could be cited.

This chapter will describe some problems and issues in the use of psychomotor tests in laboratory research with drugs.

Two primary motivations seem to inspire experimenters in their choice of tasks in this area. The more prevalent is the desire to discover a performance which will show *some* behavioral consequence of

273

experimental manipulation. This is often no easy matter. In studying "psychological" stress the selection of tasks is often carried one step farther. The experimenter may define a situation as stressful only in so far as performance decrement is demonstrated. Consequently, he may use only those tasks which are "stress sensitive." The circularity inherent in these difficulties, fortunately, need not concern us here.

I have elected to emphasize a second, less often used, rationale for choosing experimental tasks. This is where there is interest in the task itself, as a variable about which to make generalizations. The experimenter is interested in the interactions between drug variables on the one hand and task variables on the other. Provided there is some good criterion for choosing a given task, the fact that it exhibits no performance alteration under drugs is no cause for rejecting it. One can say simply that drug A, B, or C facilitates or depresses performance in tasks X and Y, but not Z. This kind of statement, of course, has limited value unless one knows what each of the tasks X, Y, and Z measures. It is precisely this kind of problem to which experimentalists have given insufficient attention; yet this is an essential problem if one is to generalize findings from one task to another. Later I shall describe what is known about the abilities which psychomotor tasks measure and the kinds of tests likely to tap these abilities.

A Brief History of
Psychomotor Test Development

Early tests of mental functioning were largely sensori-motor in nature. Galton (1883) identified such performance with "intelligence." Similarly, Cattell (1890) constructed "mental tests" which included measures of grip strength, rate of arm movement, and reaction time, along with simple sensory and memory measures. It was actually Binet (Binet and Henri, 1895) who first concluded that tests of sensori-motor skills have little relation to "general mental functioning." Consequently, to Binet goes credit for separating out at least two gross classes of human abilities (Fleishman, 1957c). Although the concept of "general intelligence" or "G" is still with us (less in the United States than in certain other countries), few today are willing to postulate a general ability embracing both psychomotor and intellectual classes of skills.

MOTOR ABILITY TESTS FOR CHILDREN. Many "intelligence tests" for children, including the Stanford-Binet test, contain tasks which involve motor components. In fact, many investigators view tests for young children not so much as evaluations of intelligence as of general developmental level. Because the most observable developments in young children are in motor facility, these tests have included many motor skill types of items.

Thus the Gesell Development Schedule (1940) includes among its tests at the 15 months age level: turns book pages, puts pellet in bottle, climbs stairs, initiates drawing stroke, places cubes in cups. Examples of items included in the 72 months level test are: jumping from a 12-inch height landing on toes, advanced throwing, standing on each foot alternately, walking the length of a 4-inch board.

The Merrill-Palmer Scale (Stutsman, 1931) contains predominantly sensori-motor items. Examples are throwing a ball, pulling a string, crossing the feet. The California scale (Bayley, 1933) (ages 1 to 18 months) covers postural and motor development, manipulation of objects, perception, attention, naming objects, the motor items being predominantly in the lower ages.

A test developed by Oseretsky in Russia in 1923 received attention in various countries. This test, known as the Oseretsky Tests of Motor Proficiency, was edited by Doll (1946) in the United States from a Portuguese adaptation. The tests were designed especially for use with feeble-minded children and children with motor disorders. They covered "all major types of motor behavior from postural reactions and gross bodily movements to finger coordination and control of facial muscles." There were six tests for each age which served as indices of "general coordination of hands," "motor speed," "simultaneous voluntary movement," and the "ability to perform without superfluous movements." Materials used included matchsticks, wooden spools, thread, paper, boxes, balls, sieves. Examples of the tasks are "thread a spool (5 years)," "wrinkle forehead without other movements (8 years)," "walk a line two meters long (7 years)."

There are a number of other individual performance tests for children such as the Pittner-Patterson, Cornell-Cox, and the Arthur Point scales of performance. However, these performance tests are not tests of motor skill. They are, essentially non-verbal scales of mental ability involving perceptual, spatial, or "insightful behavior."

ADULT PSYCHOMOTOR TESTS. As indicated above, earlier tests of psychomotor skills were of the simplest kind. Between 1920 and 1940 most of the research on motor skills remained confined to such tests. Laboratory investigations were conducted on such problems as the specificity of simple motor abilities, with some small-scale attempts to identify factors underlying individual differences in these abilities. Thus studies by Robert Seashore and his co-workers (1940, 1941, 1942, 1951), Reymert (1923), and Campbell (1934) indicated that in fine motor skills the sense employed is of moderate significance, the musculature employed is of slight significance, and the pattern of movement involved is likely to be the most important factor. Moreover, the investigators largely concluded that motor skill factors are relatively few and very narrow in scope (Buxton, 1938; Muscio, 1922; Perrin, 1929; R. H. Seashore, 1930, 1940; Seashore, Starman, Kendall, and Helmick, 1941; Seashore, Dudek, and Holtzman, 1949). In general, these early studies showed simple motor skill tests to have low correlations with each other. We shall see later that this was largely a function of the choice of measures and restricted range of skills investigated. It remained for subsequent research to exploit these relationships more thoroughly.

With the possible exception of certain dexterity tests, test batteries of special aptitudes during this era seldom included motor skill measures. Robert Seashore pioneered an attempt to develop a more comprehensive motor skills battery. This was called the Stanford Motor Skills Unit (Seashore, 1928), and it contained six tests of representative types of motor performances. It included: (a) the Koerth Pursuit Rotor, to measure accuracy in following with a stylus a small target moving rapidly in a circle; (b) the Miles Speed Rotor, to measure speed of rotary arm, wrist, and finger movements in turning a small drill; (c) the Brown Spool Packer, to measure precision in reproducing rhythmic patterns on a telegraphic key; (d) the Motor Rhythm Synchrometer, to measure precision in reproducing rhythmic patterns on a telegraphic key; (e) the Serial Discrimeter, to measure speed in making discriminating reactions to signals which change as fast as they are reacted to correctly, and finally (f) speed of tapping a telegraph key. These tests, described in 1928, were the forerunners of psychomotor tests dealing with more important types of psychomotor performances.

This era was characterized by an increasing number of validation studies of motor ability tests in field settings. A large number of these studies indicated zero or low correlations between simple motor ability tests and proficiency in more complex motor skills such as typing (Walker and Adams, 1934), machine shopwork (R. H. Seashore, 1951), and winding machine operation in knitting mills (S. H. Seashore, 1931). High validities were found in a number of studies for simple steadiness tests in predicting rifle marksmanship (R. H. Seashore and Adams, 1933; Humphreys, Buxton, and Taylor, 1936; Spaeth and Dunham, 1921). Finger and manual dexterities tests were shown on occasion to have some validity for watchmaking, electrical fixture and radio assemblies, coil winding, packing and wrapping, and certain kinds of machine operation. The United States Employment Service is one agency which employs simple motor ability tests in their comprehensive test batteries. Two of these, Manual Dexterity and Finger Dexterity, involve pegboards and assembly-type tasks. Two others, purporting to evaluate motor coordination and motor speed, are paper-and-pencil tests (e.g., tapping in circles). Actually, recent research by us has shown that the latter tests measure neither "motor speed" nor "motor coordination" as such.

The assumption underlying simple motor ability test development was that it should be possible to develop a battery of simple motor tests which would indicate likelihood of success in a more complex psychomotor skill. So strongly was this belief held that failures in prediction have often been attributed to faulty techniques, such as lack of reliability of the measures used. However, in most cases, the real cause was failure to sample the relevant psychomotor abilities.

World War II provided the impetus for developing more complex tests of psychomotor ability. The most extensive program of this type was conducted in the United States Air Force psychology research program (Melton, 1947). Some of the most critical jobs in the Air Force depended upon psychomotor skills of a complexity never before investigated. Outstanding examples were the tasks of pilot, gunner, and bombardier.

The apparatus tests employed varied in complexity from simple pegboards to complicated mechanical and electronic devices. The complex apparatus tests developed were shown to have substantial validity for predicting later proficiency in these jobs (Fleishman, 1956b; Melton, 1947). Recent research with these tests in other countries (e.g., France, England, Belgium, and the Netherlands) has confirmed the validity of certain of these psychomotor tests for predicting pilot proficiency. Some representative tests used in these programs can be usefully described. More complete descriptions (with pictures) of these and other psychomotor tests may be found eleswhere (Fleishman, 1956b; Melton, 1947).

THE COMPLEX COORDINATION TEST. The examinee must make ap-

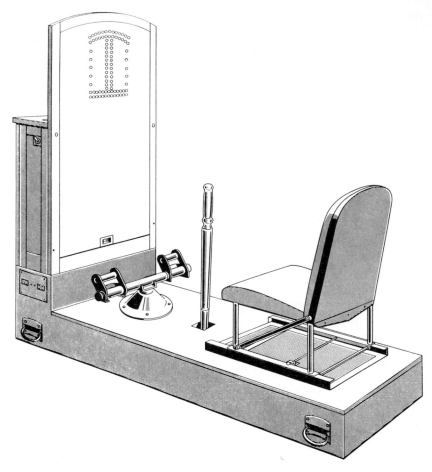

Figure 1.   The Complex Coordination Test (from Gagné and Fleishman, 1959).

propriate control adjustments of stick and pedal controls in response
to successively presented patterns of visual signals (Fig. 1).   The
task is to "match" the position of stimulus lights in each of three
dimensions by coordinate movements of these controls.   The score is
the number of completed matchings in an 8-minute period.   A validity
coefficient of .45 was achieved for this test in predicting subsequent
flying proficiency.

THE RUDDER CONTROL TEST.   This test has been another consistent
predictor of pilot success.   The examinee sits in a mock cockpit

arrangement (Fig. 2). His own weight throws the seat off balance unless he applies correction by means of coordinated pedal adjustments. The score is the amount of time the apparatus is correctly aligned. The test takes 15 minutes to administer and has a validity of .40 for pilot selection.

The reader may infer that these tests are valid because they seem to represent a miniature job sample of certain aspects of the pilot's job. However, this is only a small part of the answer. Many tests thought to duplicate what seemed to be important aspects of the pilot's job failed to achieve any prediction.

The reason the Complex Coordination Test and the Rudder Control Test are valid predictors is that between them they sample three of the underlying abilities which are crucial to pilot success (Fleishman, 1956b). The identification of these underlying abilities is a product of fundamental research which is described later. It is enough to say the resemblance of the task itself to the pilot's job is incidental to the fact that the Complex Coordination Test measures a spatial orientation factor and two psychomotor factors, while the Rudder Control Test measures these same two psychomotor factors. These factors have been identified as Control Precision and Multiple Limb Coordination (defined below).

ROTARY PURSUIT TEST. Now let us consider several other psychomotor tests found valid for pilots which do not resemble the pilot's job

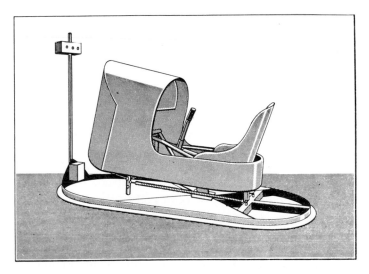

Figure 2.   The Rudder Control Test (from Gagné and Fleishman, 1959).

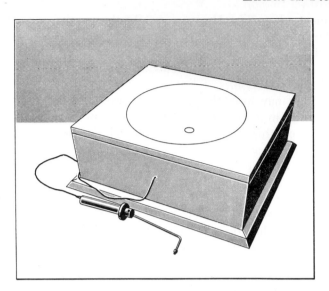

Figure. 3.   The Rotary Pursuit Test (from Fleishman, 1956b).

at all.   These tests tap the human abilities measured by the Rudder Control Test and the Complex Coordination Test.   An example is the Rotary Pursuit Test, which was used in the U. S. Air Force Battery for over 10 years (Fig. 3).   This test resembles a phonograph turntable.   The disk revolves at a speed of 60 rpm.   The examinee's task is to keep a stylus in contact with a small target embedded near the edge of the disk.   The score is the amount of time the stylus is on target in five 20-second periods.   The Rotary Pursuit Test does not resemble the task of aircraft pilot, but it does measure the Control Precision factor, which apparently accounts for its stable validity.

THE TWO-HAND COORDINATION TEST.   This is another example of a test which in no way resembles the pilot's task, but which is valid none the less, because it measures relevant abilities.   In this test, one lathe-type control handle moves a target follower to the right and left, while the other control handle moves it to and from the examinee.   By proper coordinate movements of both hands, the examinee can move the target follower in any direction.   During the test he must keep the target follower on a visually perceived target as it moves along an irregular pathway.   During World War II, scores on this test were found related to success in bombardier and flexible gunnery training as well as to pilot proficiency (Melton, 1947).

There are other examples of such tests; the interested reader may learn of them elsewhere (Fleishman, 1954b, 1956a; Melton, 1947). These kinds of measures obviously produce some unique test construction, maintenance, and scoring problems. (For a discussion of these, see Fleishman, 1953; Melton, 1947.) It is only in postwar research that we have been able to determine why some psychomotor tests predict and others do not. This is related to our investigation of fundamental dimensions of psychomotor abilities.

Recent Fundamental Research on Psychomotor Abilities

In 1953 Fleishman reviewed the limited number of existing factor analytic studies of psychomotor abilities and found considerable agreement among them as to the few factors identified up to that time. A major difficulty in explorations of this aptitude area is the administrative problem involved in constructing and assembling large batteries of psychomotor devices. We have been able to do this in recent research, and we feel that we have made progress in isolating and defining the important dimensions of psychomotor abilities (Fleishman, 1954a, 1956b, 1958a, b; Fleishman and Hempel, 1954a, 1956).

The primary approach in these studies has been to score the performance of the same individuals on a large variety of especially designed psychomotor performance tasks in the laboratory. For the most part, in any particular study, these tasks are constructed with a view to certain definite hypotheses about the organization of abilities contributing to performance on these tasks. It then remains to verify or modify these hypotheses through analysis of the correlation patterns obtained among these tasks. The techniques of factor analysis are applied to the intercorrelations in order to delineate more precisely the possible common abilities underlying these performances. The purpose is to define the fewest independent ability categories which might be most useful and meaningful in describing performance in the widest variety of tasks.

Thus far, we have investigated more than 200 different tasks administered to thousands of subjects in a series of interlocking studies. From the patterns of correlations obtained, we have been able to account for performance on this wide range of tasks in terms of a relatively small number of abilities. Moreover, in subsequent studies, our definitions of these abilities and their distinctions from one another have become more clearly delineated. As a result of these studies it should be possible to specify the best tests to measure each of the abilities identified.

We have made some interesting discoveries. For example, we find that there is no such thing as general physical proficiency (Hempel and Fleishman, 1955) or general psychomotor skill (Fleishman, 1954a) or general manual dexterity (Fleishman and Hempel, 1954a). Rather, each of these areas breaks up into a limited number of unitary abilities.

Psychomotor Ability Components

We turn now to a description of some of the more important ability factors identified.

CONTROL PRECISION. This factor is common to tasks which require fine, highly controlled, but not overcontrolled, muscular adjustments; primarily, large muscle groups are involved (Fleishman, 1958b; Fleishman and Hempel, 1956). This ability extends to arm-hand as well as to leg movements. It is highly important in the operation of equipment where careful positioning of controls, by the hands or feet, is required. It is most critical where such adjustments must be rapid but precise. This ability is measured by the Complex Coordination Test (Fig. 1) and the Rudder Control Test (Fig. 2) previously described, but the Rotary Pursuit Test (Fig. 3) is a purer measure of it. In earlier studies this factor has also been called Psychomotor Coordination I and Fine Control Sensitivity. The present term has emerged, and the generality and limits of the ability have been sharpened through successive studies.

MULTIPLE LIMB COORDINATION. This is the ability to coordinate the movements of a number of limbs simultaneously. It is best measured by devices involving multiple controls (Fleishman, 1958b; Fleishman and Hempel, 1956). The factor has been found common to tasks requiring coordination of the two feet (e.g., the Rudder Control Test described above), two hands (the Two Hand Pursuit and Two Hand Coordination Tests), and hands and feet (the Plane Control Test and the Complex Coordination Test). Thus far, a pure measure of this factor has not been developed, since it is difficult to partial out the Control Precision factor from such tasks. The tests mentioned, however, are heavily "loaded" with this factor.

RESPONSE ORIENTATION. This ability factor has been found common
to visual discrimination reaction psychomotor tasks involving rapid
directional discrimination and orientation of movement patterns
(Fleishman, 1958b; Fleishman and Hempel, 1956; Fleishman, 1957a,
b). It appears to involve skill in making the correct movement in
relation to the correct stimulus, especially under highly speeded conditions. In other words, "given this stimulus, which way should I
move?" Thus, where the first ability represents skill in controlling
movements and the second ability component above represents skill in
coordinating movements, this factor appears to emphasize the selection
of the appropriate response which is independent of either precision
or coordination. This factor may be measured by such tasks as discrimination reaction time tasks or other tasks involving rapid differential reactions to different stimuli which appear in rapid sequence.
The Discrimination Reaction Time Test (Fig. 4) and the Direction
Control Test used in Air Force research (Fleishman, 1954b; 1957) are
good measures of this factor. In a sense, this ability is a kind of
motor spatial ability. The purest measures of this factor do not
involve any spatial components in the stimulus aspects but only spatial
components in the response aspect. For example, the purest test
developed recently presents the subject with two colors of light appearing in the same little window and two kinds of sound. The lights

Figure 4. The Discrimination Reaction Time Test (from Fleishman, 1954a).

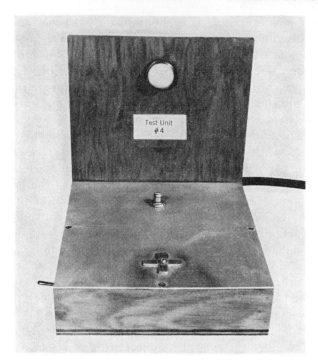

Figure 5.   A Reaction Time Test.   The switch on the left converts the test
from visual to auditory reaction time.   (From Fleishman, 1954b.)

may be red or green, and the sound may be a bell or a buzzer.   These
stimuli come on at approximately four-second intervals, and the
subject may have to respond to a green light, a red light, a bell, or a
buzzer in some random sequence.   For a green light he pushes a
right hand-lever forward; for a red light, a left hand-lever; for a
buzzer, a right foot-pedal; for a bell, a left foot-pedal.   The score is
the cumulative reaction time over 40 such reactions.

   REACTION TIME.   This represents simply the speed with which the
individual is able to respond to a stimulus when it appears (Fleishman, 1953, 1954a, 1958b; Fleishman and Hempel, 1955).   There are
consistent indications that individual differences in this ability are
independent of the type of response required or whether the
stimulus is auditory or visual.   Once the stimulus situation or the
response situation is complicated to involve alternate choices, reaction
time is not the primary factor measured.   There is considerable

evidence, however, that reaction time does contribute to individual differences in more complex tasks, especially at high levels of proficiency in such tasks. Consequently, although initially this is not a critical ability, it appears that measures of the effects of certain factors on reaction time have considerable implications in generalizing to more complex tasks. The purest measures of reaction time appear to be obtained when the subject is required to keep finger on a button rather than to have him move his hand a number of inches to the button when the stimulus appears (Fig. 5).

SPEED OF ARM MOVEMENT. This represents simply the speed with which an individual can make a gross, discrete arm movement where accuracy is not required (Fleishman, 1957a, 1954a, 1958b; Fleishman

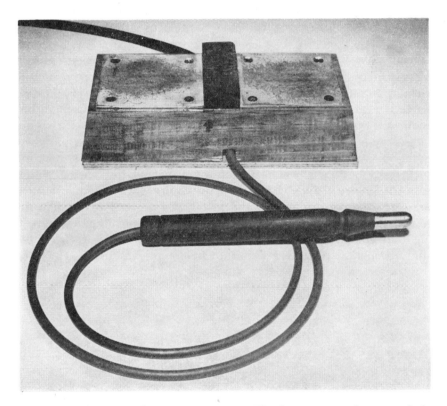

Figure 6. The Two Plate Tapping Test. The latest version has moved the plates 12 inches apart, providing a better measure of Speed of Arm Movement. (From Fleishman, 1954a.)

and Hempel, 1954b, 1955). There is ample evidence that this factor is independent of the reaction time factor. It is measured by tasks in which the subject must tap, alternately and as rapidly as possible, two metal plates with a stylus when these metal plates are placed more than six inches apart (Fig. 6). This factor has also been measured by tasks which require the subject to move his arm in multiple arcs as rapidly as possible past sets of photoelectric cells. Research has shown that this factor contributes variance in more complex kinds of tasks, primarily at high levels of efficiency achieved after continued practice on such tasks (Fleishman and Hempel, 1954b, 1955).

RATE CONTROL. This ability involves making continuous anticipatory motor adjustments relative to changes in speed and direction of a moving target or object (Fleishman, 1954a, 1958b; Fleishman and Hempel, 1955, 1956). A common feature of all the tasks which measure this factor is the element of pursuit which seems to be involved (see Fig. 7). Compensatory as well as following pursuit tasks load on this factor as do other tasks involving responses to changes in rate. Research has been conducted to discover if emphasis on this factor is on judging the rate of the stimulus as distinguished from skill on judging or estimating the rate of one's response. Thus in one study (Fleishman, 1958b) an apparatus test was used in which a target moved down through a slot. The subject was required to press a button when the target was expected to coincide with a set of reference points. The response required was a simple button-pressing response, ruling out the fact that rate was involved in the response. This task did not load on the Rate Control factor, suggesting that emphasis is, in fact, on the response aspect. In a further study a motion picture test of rate judgment was used. Here the

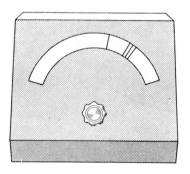

Figure 7. The Rate Control Test. The subject manipulates the knob to keep one line in coincidence with another as it deviates in direction and rate. (From Fleishman, 1954a.)

subject was required to extrapolate the course of a plane moving across the screen in front of him. Several tests of this type were used. The subject's response was simply to make a mark on an IBM answer sheet. Hence, again emphasis was on judging the rate of the stimulus and not on the response. The results showed that these motion picture tests did not load on the Rate Control factor which was common only to apparatus tests requiring an actual movement in relation to the changing direction and speed of the stimulus object. As indicated earlier, it has been found that either compensatory or following pursuit tasks give an indication of this ability.

MANUAL DEXTERITY. This ability involves skillful, well-directed arm-hand movements in manipulating fairly large objects under speed conditions (Fleishman, 1954a; Fleishman and Hempel, 1954a; Hempel and Fleishman, 1955). This ability appears to be involved in performance on tasks requiring tool manipulation, the assembly of large components, and the wrapping of packages. The Minnesota Rate of Manipulation Test, which is commercially available, is the most frequently used measure of this ability. However, improved measures of manual dexterity involving manipulation of larger blocks are under development.

FINGER DEXTERITY. This is the ability to make skillful, controlled manipulations of tiny objects involving, primarily, the fingers (Fleishman, 1954a; Fleishman and Hempel, 1954a; Hempel and Fleishman, 1955). It has been found important in small parts assembly tasks in wiring electrical circuits, in watchmaking, and in similar tasks involving primarily skillful finger manipulations. Measures of this ability which load highly on this factor are the O'Connor Finger Dexterity Test and the Purdue Peg Board.

ARM-HAND STEADINESS. This is the ability to make precise arm-hand positioning movements where strength and speed are minimized, and the critical feature, as the name implies, is the steadiness with which such movements can be made (Fleishman, 1954a, 1958a, b). This factor is measured by tasks which involve moving a stylus at arm's length through a slot without touching the sides, back, or bottom of the slot (see Fig. 8), as well as by tasks which require holding a stylus as steadily as possible in a small hole without hitting the sides. It has been found that the best measures of this ability allow the recording of the most minute tremors of the subject's arm or hand (Fleishman, 1958a). This ability has been found to be necessary

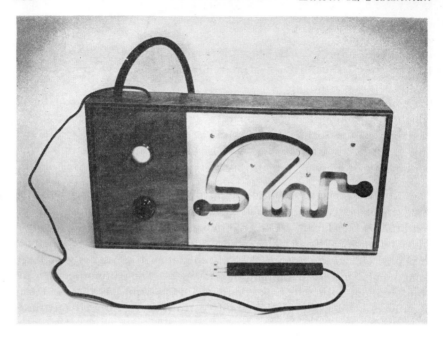

Figure 8.   The Track Tracing Test.   (From Fleishman, 1954a.)

for tasks involving needle threading, rifle marksmanship, and the stacking of small components one on top of the other.

WRIST-FINGER SPEED.   This ability has been called "tapping" in many previous studies through the years.   It has been used in a variety of studies, primarily because these are in the form of printed tests which are quick and easy to administer.   However, our research shows that this factor is highly restricted in scope and does not extend to tasks in which apparatus is used (Fleishman, 1954a; Fleishman and Hempel, 1954a).   It has been found that the factor is best measured by printed tests requiring rapid tapping of the pencil in relatively large areas. As a matter of fact, it has been found that loadings on this factor decrease as the size of the circle or square in which the pencil is to tap decreases.   In other words, as visual alignment and control become more essential to the task, tapping or wrist-finger speed seems less involved.   The name "wrist-finger speed" has been adopted rather than "tapping" because it appears that pendular, as well as rotary, arm movements may be included in this ability.

AIMING. This ability appears to be measured by printed tests which provide the subject with very small circles to place pencil dots in; there are a large number of circles and the test is highly speeded (Fleishman, 1954a; Fleishman and Hempel, 1954a; Greene, 1943). The subject typically goes from circle to circle, placing one dot in each circle as rapidly as possible. This factor has not been found to extend to apparatus tests; hence naming it "aiming" or, as other investigators have done, "eye-hand coordination" seems much too broad. It appears to represent a highly restricted ability; generalizations based on performance measures of this type must be considered highly tentative. As the counterpart of the tapping factor, it has been found that, as the size of the circles used increases, loadings on this factor drop systematically.

ABILITIES IN THE PHYSICAL PROFICIENCY AREA. Some mention should be made of the area of motor performance involving physical proficiency or more gross kinds of motor activities. There is much interest today in the measure of such physical capacities. Factor analyses of these tasks indicate that there is no general "athletic" ability, but that such abilities involve more basic components. Also, such skills appear relatively independent of the psychomotor abilities mentioned above. From the correlations among performances of athletic tasks, the following factor areas seem to emerge (Hempel and Fleishman, 1955).

The first area involves mainly *strength*. Thus far, strength of limbs and strength of trunk appear as separate factors. Strength of limbs can be measured by such tasks as chinning. Trunk strength appears measurable by situps and leg lifts. A general static strength is measurable by various dynamometer tasks. These indicate the maximum strain which can be exerted against a spring (e.g., by the grip). Such tests correlate with the amount of weight one can lift but not with the amount of chins or pushups one can do.

A second large area involves *flexibility* or suppleness of muscle groups. Factors of limb flexibility and trunk flexibility have been identified. Such tasks as toe touching (while standing) involve trunk flexibility, while limb flexibility can be measured by kicking height or leg bends. The critical feature here is the capacity of the muscle groups involved to resist distortion and to recover from this distortion repeatedly.

A third area has been called energy mobilization. This appears, at first, related to strength, and studies are under way to throw light on this relationship. For the present, however, it may be said that energy mobilization is exhibited in performances where exerting a maximum of energy at a given moment is critical. Examples of tasks which measure this ability are throwing a ball as far as possible, jumping as high as possible, and broad jump.

Balance abilities appear independent of the abilities already cited. Balance may be measured on such tasks as walking a rail and standing on one foot. Two additional factors, *gross body coordination* and *endurance,* also emerge from research. Gross body coordination appears independent of multiple limb coordination, since apparatus tests involving the latter sort of coordination do not correlate with athletic skill. Gross body coordination seems to emphasize the use of the entire body. Endurance has not been explored in detail mainly because of the practical problems involved in testing people continuously over lengthy periods.

Problems in the Use of
Psychomotor Tests in Research

The apparatus used to measure the abilities described may vary in complexity from simple pegboards (e.g., manual and finger dexterity) to complicated mechanical and electronic contrivances (multiple limb coordination). Paper-and-pencil measures, for the most part, do not sample the relevant psychomotor abilities. Tests requiring dotting in small circles, or tapping in large ones, do bring into play certain motor abilities, but, as has been pointed out, these are very specific abilities. Generalizations from experiments using such tasks (and there are a number) to statements about effects on "psychomotor performance" are apt to be misleading. Printed measures of response orientation have been devised, but these require making a differential response. In any case they are not so good as apparatus measures of this factor.

One other point needs clarification. Many printed tests do correlate with performance on apparatus tasks. The reason is that performance on psychomotor tasks may depend, in some degree, on non-motor abilities. Thus factor analyses of psychomotor tests often reveal a Spatial Orientation factor, and it is not surprising to find that the visual cues in such tests are often spatially arranged. Similarly, mechanical ability tests and perceptual speed tests sometimes correlate with psychomotor test performance. If the task instructions are complicated, a verbal factor may be revealed as a contributor. Research also indicates that this non-motor variance tends to drop out with practice on the psychomotor task, and usually at a fairly early stage of proficiency, while the common variance resulting from motor factors persists as a contributor to task performance (Fleishman, 1956a, 1957a; Fleishman and Hempel, 1954b, 1955; Parker and Fleishman, 1959).

Thus apparatus tests appear necessary whenever the primary interest of the experimenter is in the aspects of human responses having to do with coordination, dexterity, precision of control movements, speed of discriminative reactions, or responses involving kinesthetic cues. Some instrument is needed to provide the cues to be responded to, the means of response, the means for recording the speed, precision, and other relevant factors of that response. Often the test consists of a task unit (which the subject operates) and a control unit which contains the timing apparatus, counters, and switches which the experimenter uses to control the testing period. It is possible, for many purposes, to wire several task units into a single control console.

The most comprehensive review of problems which accompany the use of apparatus psychomotor tests has been presented by Melton (1947). He describes the pioneering use of these tests in the large-scale Air Force aircrew selection program, but much of the discussion is relevant to the experimental use of these devices.

The major difficulty with psychomotor devices, aside from their initial expense and construction, is the problem of maintenance. Calibration procedures must be carefully worked out and routine checks and preventive maintenance provided. If several models of the same test are used, care must be taken to ensure comparability of scores. A more serious problem is the maintenance of comparability of scores when the same piece of apparatus is used over a period of time. Thus a subject's scores on certain devices may decrease gradually simply because the scoring contacts are becoming dirty, pitted, or increasingly covered with carbon. If we are studying the effects of drugs on a "time on target" score we may find a depressing effect on performance when, in fact, the score decrement is a result of apparatus factors. A system of statistical control is needed to check on both inter- and intra-apparatus differences.

Another problem is lack of uniformity among examiners giving the same test or different models of a test. There is some evidence (Bilodeau, Goldbeck, and Reynolds, 1951) that the examiner is not an important source of variability, at least in situations where timing and recording errors are minimized. Studies on whether the number of subjects tested at one session influences individual test scores indicate negligible effect of this variable as long as the test instructions and procedures remain the same.

When several tests are to be given the same subjects, the order of presentation becomes a problem. An effect of presentation order was found in the case of only one test (Aiming Stress) in the Air Force research (Melton, 1947). However, some pretesting would seem to be in order before experimental studies are designed. Suitable intervals between tests should dissipate negative transfer effects, since most habit interference in motor learning is transitory in nature.

Psychomotor tests also present special problems in the determination of intra-test and test-retest reliability coefficients, since performance of subjects almost invariably shows improvement with practice on such tasks. A frequent procedure is the intra-test correlation where the total test period is divided into trials and odd versus even trial totals are correlated. If practice is continued over long periods, it may be desirable to ascertain such coefficients for early, intermediate, and advanced segments of practice (Parker and Fleishman, 1959). It is consistently found that such reliabilities increase with practice. The correlations between adjacent trials on psychomotor tasks are higher at late than in early stages of practice (Fleishman and Hempel, 1954b, 1955; Reynolds, 1952).

A Question of Research Strategy

In developing performance tasks to be used in the study of drug effects, the experimenter is often faced with a choice. On the one hand, he may seek a "work-sample" task which resembles an actual "job." Or he may use "simpler," more analytical tasks like some described above in our discussion of factors. Work-sample tasks seem to provide a more realistic basis for generalizing to a particular job. For example, a flight simulator might be used if one wants to generalize experimental results to flying skill. Or perhaps some more limited, but critical, aspect of the job could be studied in relation to drug effects (e.g., the "lock-on-target" phase of an interceptor mission). What kinds of generalizations can one make to other jobs from results with such a task? And, if a decrement or increment occurs in overall performance, what aspects of skill are most affected? The use of work-sample tasks in drug research may require prolonged periods of training for most groups of subjects, and the complexity of the task may make learning time prohibitive. Also, the "work-sample" nature of many of these tasks is often a delusion. There is always something about these tasks which is not like the real job, as any job incumbent will quickly point out.

The experimenter who uses simpler, more classical tests, like steadiness or tapping, has more control over his measures, and the learning period is relatively short. Furthermore, he is able to specify more accurately what he is measuring. If his tasks are described in the ability terms previously described, he may be more confident in his descriptions. However, he may feel dissatisfied that many of these tasks seem artificial. Also, decrement or increment may be harder to demonstrate, though this can often be alleviated by making the tasks more difficult while emphasizing the same factor.

An alternative solution is available. A good example is found in the recent stress research by Gorham and Orr (1957, 1958). In this study a standard task of the "work-sample" sort was developed; that is, the task was complex, seemed important, and required a number of skills, although there was no attempt to simulate an actual job. However, the task was developed to provide measures of the component abilities involved, in addition to a score on overall performance. Thus it was possible to obtain independent measures of such abilities as multiple limb coordination, rate control, response orientation, numerical ability, and vigilance. These workers found stressors to cause overall decrement in performance, but some skill components were more resistant to decrement than were others. Specific training procedures could be addressed to specific ability components. The potentiality of this type of approach has barely been explored, and its relevance to drug research seems especially clear.

Summary

Psychomotor tests are among the most frequently used devices in the study of human performance, and their use in drug research will undoubtedly increase. This chapter described some developments in this field of testing, with examples of tests previously used. Emphasis was on concepts and issues in this area. Special emphasis was given to a description of the different abilities psychomotor tests measure, with reference to the kinds of tests likely to tap these abilities. Problems associated with the uses of these tests were described. Wherever possible, laboratory tasks developed to measure human performance should provide for measurement of the relevant skill components. It would seem that such procedures would allow more dependable descriptions and generalizations about the effects of drugs on human skills.

R E F E R E N C E S

Bass, B. M., Hurder, W. P., and Ellis, N. Assessing human performance under stress. Dep. Psychol. La. State Univer., Contract No. AF 33(616)134. Final Tech. Rep., 1955.

Bayley, Nancy. *The California first year mental scale.* Berkeley, Calif.: Univer. of California Press, 1933.

Bilodeau, Ina, Goldbeck, R. A., and Reynolds, J. B. An exploratory investigation of the effect of the test administrator on subjects' performance. USAF Air Training Command, Human Resources Research Center. *Res. Note* P&MS 51–5, 1951.

Binet, A., and Henri, U. La psychologie individuelle. *Ann. psychol.*, 1895, 2, 411–463.

Brozek, J., Fleishman, E. A., Harris, S., Lassman, F. M., and Vidal, J. H. Sensory functions and motor performance during maintenance of survival rations. *Amer. Psychol.* 1955, 10, 502.

Buxton, C. E. The application of factorial methods to the study of motor abilities. *Psychometrika*, 1938, 3, 85–93.

Campbell, M. The "personal equation" in pursuit performances. *J. appl. Psychol.*, 1934, 18, 785–792.

Cattell, J. Mck. Mental tests and measurements. *Mind*, 1890, 15, 373–380.

Doll, E. A. (Ed.) *The Oseretsky tests of motor proficiency.* Minneapolis: Educ. Test Bur., 1946.

Dusek, E. R. Manual performance and finger temperature as a function of ambient temperature. Natick, Mass.: Quartermaster Research and Engineering Command, Tech. Rep. EP-68, 1957.

Fleishman, E. A. Testing for psychomotor abilities by means of apparatus tests. *Psychol. Bull.*, 1953, 50, 241–262.

Fleishman, E. A. Dimensional analysis of psychomotor abilities. *J. exp. Psychol.*, 1954, 48, 437–454. (a)

Fleishman, E. A. *Evaluations of psychomotor tests for pilot selection: the direction control and compensatory balance tests.* Lackland Air Force Base, Tex.: Air Force Personnel and Training Research Center, *Tech. Rep. AFPTRC-TR-54-131,* 1954. (b)

Fleishman, E. A. Predicting advanced levels of proficiency in psychomotor skill. In G. Finch and F. Cameron (Eds.), *Symposium on Air Force human engineering, personnel, and training research.* Washington, D. C.: N.A.S.-N.R.C., Pub. 455, 1956. (a)

Fleishman, E. A. Psychomotor selection tests: research and application in the U. S. Air Force. *Personnel Psychol.*, 1956, 9, 449–467. (b)

Fleishman, E. A. A comparative study of aptitude patterns in unskilled and skilled psychomotor performances. *J. appl. Psychol.*, 1957, 41, 263–272. (a)

Fleishman, E. A. Factor structure in relation to task difficulty in psychomotor performance, *Educ. psychol. Measmt*, 1957, 17, 522–532. (b)

Fleishman, E. A. Apports de Binet aux tests psycho-moteurs et developpement skilled psychomotor performances. *J. appl. Psychol.*, 1957, 41, 263–272. (c)

Fleishman, E. A. Analysis of positioning movements and static reactions. *J. exp. Psychol.*, 1958, 55, 13–24. (a)

Fleishman, E. A. Dimensional analysis of movement reactions. *J. exp. Psychol.*, 1958, 55, 430–453. (b)

Fleishman, E. A., and Hempel, W. E. A factor analysis of dexterity tests. *Personnel Psychol.*, 1954, 7, 15–32. (a)

Fleishman, E. A., and Hempel, W. E. Changes in factor structure of a complex psychomotor test as a function of practice. *Psychometrika*, 1954, 19, 239–252. (b)

Fleishman, E. A., and Hempel, W. E. The relation between abilities and improvement with practice in a visual discrimination reaction task. *J. exp. Psychol.*, 1955, 49, 301–310.

Fleishman, E. A., and Hempel, W. E. Factorial analysis of complex psychomotor performance and related skills. *J. appl. Psychol.*, 1956, 40, 96–104.

Gagné, R. M., and Fleishman, E. A. *Psychology and human performance.* New York: Holt, 1959.

Galton, F. *Inquiries into human faculty and its development.* London: MacMillan, 1883.

Gesell, A., et al. *The first five years of life.* New York: Harper, 1940.

Gorham, W. A., and Orr, D. B. Research on behavior impairment due to stress. Washington, D. C.: Amer. Inst. for Res., Contract AF 41(657)-39 Rep., 1957.

Gorham, W. A., and Orr, D. B. Research on behavior impairment due to stress. Experiments in impairment reduction. Washington, D. C.: Amer. Inst. for Res., Contract AF 41(657)-39 Formal Rep., 1958.

Greene, E. B. An analysis of random and systematic changes with practice. *Psychometrika*, 1943, 8, 37–52.

Hempel, W. E., and Fleishman, E. A. Factor analysis of physical proficiency and manipulative skill. *J. appl. Psychol.*, 1955, 39, 12–16.

Humphreys, L. G., Buxton, C. E., and Taylor, H. R. Steadiness and rifle marksmanship. *J. appl. Psychol.*, 1936, 20, 680–688.

Melton, A. W. (Ed.) Apparatus test. *AAF Psychol. Program Rep.* Vol. 4). Washington, D. C.: U. S. Government Printing Office, 1947.

Muscio, B. Motor capacity with special reference to vocational guidance. *Brit. J. Psychol.*, 1922, 13, 157–184.

Parker, J. F., and Fleishman, E. A. The prediction of advanced levels of proficiency in a complex tracking task. Arlington, Va.: Psychological Research Associates, Contract AF 41(657)-64, 1959.

Perrin, F. A. An experimental study of motor ability. *J. exp. Psychol.*, 1929, 4, 24–57.

Reymert, M. L. The personal equation in motor capacities. *Scand. Scient. Rev.*, 1923, 2, 177–194.

Reynolds, B. The effect of learning on the predictability of psychomotor performance. *J. exp. Psychol.*, 1952, 44, 189–198.

Seashore, R. H. Stanford motor skills unit. *Psychol. Monographs*, 1928, 39, No. 2 (Whole No. 178), 51–66.

Seashore, R. H.   Individual differences in motor skills.   *J. gen. Psychol.*, 1930, 3, 38–66.

Seashore, R. H.   Experimental and theoretical analysis of fine motor skills. *Amer. J. Psychol.*, 1940, 53, 86–98.

Seashore, R. H.   Work and motor performance.   In S. S. Stevens (Ed.), *Handbook of experimental psychology*.   New York: Wiley, 1951.

Seashore, R. H., and Adams, R. O.   The measurement of steadiness: a new apparatus and results in marksmanship.   *Science*, 1933, 78, 235.

Seashore, R. H., Buxton, C. E., and McCollom, I. N.   Multiple factorial analysis of fine motor skills.   *Amer. J. Psychol.*, 1942, 53, 251–259.

Seashore, R. H., Dudek, F. J., and Holtzman, W.   A factorial analysis of arm-hand precision tests.   *J. appl. Psychol.*, 1949, 33, 579–584.

Seashore, R. H., Starman, R., Kendall, W. E., and Helmick, J. S.   Group factors in simple and discriminative reaction times.   *J. exp. Psychol.*, 1941, 29, 346–349.

Seashore, S. H.   The aptitude hypothesis in motor skills.   *J. exp. Psychol.*, 1931, 14, 555–561.

Seashore, S. H., and Seashore, R. H.   Individual differences in simple auditory reaction times of hand, feet, and jaws.   *J. exp. Psychol.*, 1941, 29, 342–345.

Spaeth, R. A., and Dunham, G. C.   The correlation between motor control and rifle shooting.   *Amer. J. Physiol.*, 1921, 56, 249–256.

Stutsman, Rachel.   *Mental measurement of preschool children*.   Yonkers, N. Y.: World Book Co., 1931.

Teichner, W. H., and Kobrick, J. L.   Effects of prolonged exposure to low temperature on visual motor performance, flicker fusion and pain sensitivity.   Natick, Mass: Quartermaster Research and Engineering Command, Rep. No. 230, 1954.

Teichner, W. H., and Wehrkamp, R. F.   Visual motor temperature effects.   Lawrence, Mass.: Quartermaster Climatic Research Lab. Rep. No. 198, 1953.

Walker, R. Y., and Adams, R. D.   Motor skills: the validity of serial motor tests for predicting typewriter proficiency.   *J. gen. Psychol.*, 1934, 11, 173–186.

Alterations in psychomotor functions and individual differences in responses produced by psychoactive drugs

Although a variety of psychoactive drugs have been studied in our laboratory, most of the work has been concerned with a comparison of the effects of chlorpromazine and secobarbital on behavior. We have not been interested in the therapeutic efficacy of drugs, but rather in the extent to which they cause alterations in performance. For the most part we have used single doses in normal volunteer populations. We have completed one experiment in a schizophrenic population comparing the effects of acute and chronic administration of chlorpromazine and secobarbital, and another investigating some physiological changes caused by chlorpromazine and secobarbital in normal and schizophrenic groups.

In an early experiment we compared the effects of chlorpromazine, secobarbital, lysergic acid diethylamide (LSD), and meperidine (Kornetsky, Humphries, and Evarts, 1957) on speed of addition, speed of copying digits, the digit symbol substitution test, the pursuit rotor, visual discrimination, and tactual perception. In order that comparison could be made between the various drugs, the scores for each test were converted to a per cent of the control score, and the mean per cent score for each drug was obtained (Fig. 1). Although this mean per cent score does not tell which functions were most affected, it does give some overall comparison of the relative psychological impairment caused by each of the drugs. In addition to the objective performance tests mentioned above, subjects were given a symptom questionnaire (Abramson, Jarvik, Kaufman, Kornetsky,

This work was done at the National Institute of Mental Health, Bethesda, Maryland.

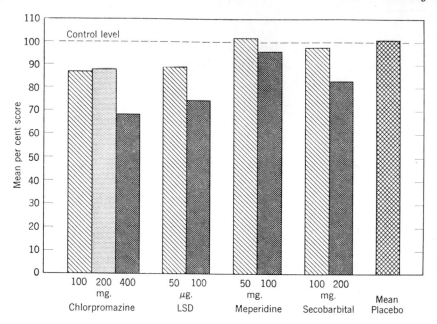

Figure 1. Mean per cent overall score for each drug. (Kornetsky, Humphries, and Evarts, 1957.)

Levine, and Wagner (1955). This questionnaire gives a quantitative estimate of the subjective effects of the drugs. Figure 2 shows the mean number of symptoms reported by the subjects during a four-hour period after the drugs were given.

Generally, there seems to be fair agreement between the group means of the objective and subjective effects of these drugs. For ex-

TABLE 1.   CORRELATIONS (ρ) BETWEEN OBJECTIVE (OVERALL SCORE) AND SUBJECTIVE (SYMPTOM QUESTIONNAIRE) EFFECTS OF THE VARIOUS DRUGS

	LSD		Meperidine		Secobarbital		Chlor-promazine
Placebo*	50 μg.	100 μg.	50 mg.	100 mg.	100 mg.	200 mg.	200 mg.
.46	.39	− .36	− .03	.12	.53	.66†	.54

* Mean of two placebos.
† $p < .05.$

ample, LSD caused the greatest mean objective impairment as well as the most symptoms, and meperidine the least. However, for a given drug the interindividual correlations are low. Table 1 shows that only with 200 mg. of secobarbital was there a significant correlation between objective and subjective effects. The lack of significant correlations between these two types of measures suggests that there may be little relationship between the subject's symptoms and the degree to which he is actually impaired by a drug. A similar phenomenon was observed in the effects of LSD (Kornetsky, 1957). There was no significant correlation between the physiological effects and reported symptoms, but with one exception there were significant correlations between physiological effects and performance scores (Table 2).

Some investigators (Kovitz, Carter, and Addison, 1955; Shaten, Rockmore, and Funk, 1956) studying the effects of chlorpromazine in

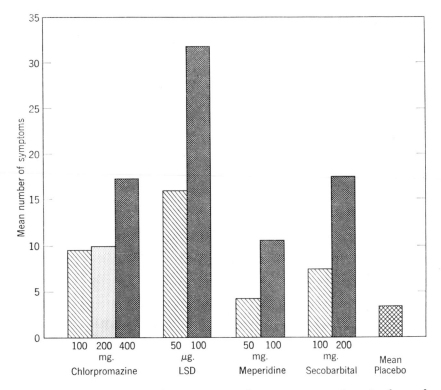

Figure 2. Mean number of symptoms on the symptom questionnaire for each drug (Kornetsky, Humphries, and Evarts, 1957).

TABLE 2.   COEFFICIENTS OF CORRELATION BETWEEN PHYSIOLOGICAL
AND PSYCHOLOGICAL EFFECTS OF 100 MICROGRAMS OF LSD

	Blood Pressure	Pulse	Respiration	Temperature
Objective performance scores	.65*	.68*	−.03	.86†
Subjective psychological symptoms	−.12	−.51	−.15	.42

* $p < .05$.
† $p < .01$.

schizophrenic patients have generally concluded that chlorpromazine either improves, or does not significantly impair, performance.   Our contrary results with similar tests of performance in normals may arise from differences between normals and schizophrenics, or from dif-

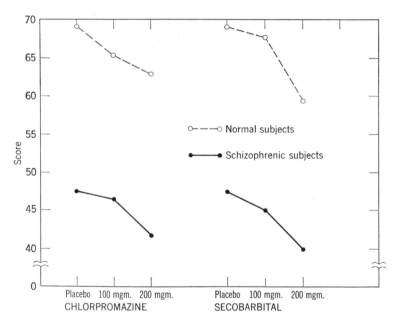

Figure 3.   Comparison between schizophrenic and normal subjects after acute administration of chlorpromazine and secobarbital on the digit symbol substitution test (Kornetsky, Pettit, Wynne, and Evarts, 1959).

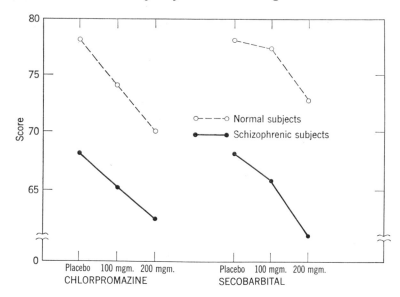

Figure 4. Comparison between schizophrenic and normal subjects after acute administration of chlorpromazine and secobarbital on tapping speed (Kornetsky et al., 1959).

ferences between chronic and acute administration, or from both. Two experiments completed in our laboratory shed some light on this problem.

In the first experiment single doses of 100 and 200 mg. of chlorpromazine and 100 and 200 mg. of secobarbital were administered to 12 normal volunteer subjects (Kornetsky and Humphries, 1958). In the second experiment the same drugs and dosages were administered to 12 chronic schizophrenic patients (Kornetsky, Pettit, Wynne, and Evarts, 1959). At the completion of the acute study the schizophrenic patients were put on a regimen of six weeks of chronic drug administration. This six-week period consisted of two weeks on each of the three treatments (chlorpromazine, secobarbital, and placebo). In the first week of each drug treatment the dose schedule was 100 mg. twice a day; in the second week, 200 mg. twice a day. Both experiments made use of the double-blind technique, and subjects always received the same number of identical capsules. Of the various procedures used in these experiments, data were obtained from both the schizo-

phrenics and the normal subjects on the following tests: the digit substitution test, tapping speed, the pursuit rotor, and tachistoscopic
threshold.

Figures 3 through 6 show the mean scores of both the schizophrenic
and the normal subjects on the various performance tests 90 minutes
after the administration of single doses of the two drugs. As can be
seen, the response of schizophrenic patients is similar to that of normal
subjects after chlorpromazine and secobarbital on the digit substitution test and on the tapping speed test. However, there are marked
differences between the two groups in their response to chlorpromazine on the pursuit rotor and tachistoscopic threshold tests, but no
difference between the two groups in their response to secobarbital
on these same two tests. Though there was divergence between
normal and schizophrenic subjects on the tachistoscopic and the
pursuit rotor tests caused by 200 mg. of chlorpromazine, a smaller

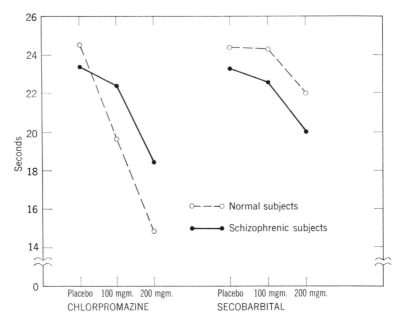

Figure 5. Comparison between schizophrenic and normal subjects after acute
administration of chlorpromazine and secobarbital on the pursuit rotor (Kornetsky
et al., 1959).

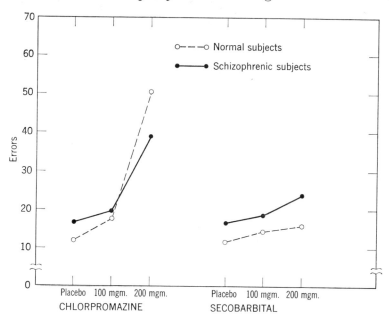

Figure 6. Comparison between schizophrenic and normal subjects after acute administration of chlorpromazine and secobarbital on tachistoscopic threshold (Kornetsky et al., 1959).

dose (100 mg.) did not cause a significant deficit in performance of the patients on any of the tests, while it did cause a significant deficit in performance of the normal subjects on tapping speed and the pursuit rotor.

Although differences found between schizophrenic and normal subjects in their responses to chlorpromazine would account for some of the discrepancies between our earlier results obtained with normal subjects and other investigators' results with schizophrenics, they certainly cannot account for all. More striking is the effect of chronic administration of chlorpromazine and secobarbital when compared to acute administration in the schizophrenic sample. Figures 7 through 10 compare the effects on performance of acute administration of chlorpromazine and secobarbital with the effects of chronic administration of these same drugs. At the end of two weeks of chronic administration of chlorpromazine, the morning dose of 200 mg. did not

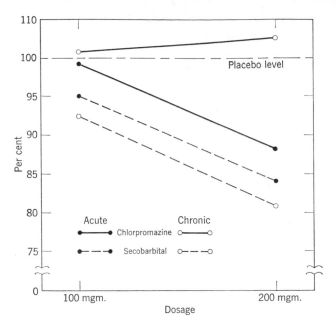

Figure 7. Comparison of acute and chronic administration of chlorpromazine and secobarbital plotted as per cent of placebo score on digit symbol substitution (Kornetsky et al., 1959).

cause a significant amount of impairment in the performance of the subjects. In fact, the results suggest that there is some tolerance to the drug even after only four days of 100 mg., twice daily. On the other hand, the administration of secobarbital at this dose level for this short a period did not produce any evidence of tolerance.

The differences between the response of schizophrenics and the response of normals to chlorpromazine suggested further work comparing normal and schizophrenic subjects' response to chlorpromazine. In an experiment on the hypnotic effect of chlorpromazine and secobarbital in normals it was found that when chlorpromazine was given to the subjects at 7 P.M. there was still marked postural hypotension at 7 A.M., but there was no postural hypotension after secobarbital. Since this effect was so marked in normals, the experiment was repeated using 12 chronic schizophrenics (Vates and Kornetsky, 1958). The schizophrenic patients exhibited no postural hypotension 12 hours after chlorpromazine administration. Table 3 shows the difference

TABLE 3.   COMPARISON OF DIFFERENCES BETWEEN SUPINE AND
STANDING BLOOD PRESSURE IN NORMALS AND SCHIZOPHRENICS*

| | Placebo | | Chlorpromazine | | | | Secobarbital | | | |
| | | | 100 mg. | | 200 mg. | | 100 mg. | | 200 mg. | |
	Norm.	Sch.	Norm.	Sch.	Norm.	Sch.	Norm.	Sch.	Norm.	Sch.
Diastolic	10.0	4.7	1.1	4.75	−21.7†	3.85	3.7	5.2	9.5	6.25
Systolic	1.8	1.3	−6.9‡	.9	−38.8‡	3.0	−3.2	3.4	2.5	3.8
Pulse	19.3	9.5	27.5	14.7	41.8‡	17.0	20.7	13.8	19.0	11.3

* Negative score occurred when standing reading was lower than supine reading.
† $p < .01$ between normal and schizophrenic subjects.
‡ $p < .02$ between normal and schizophrenic subjects.

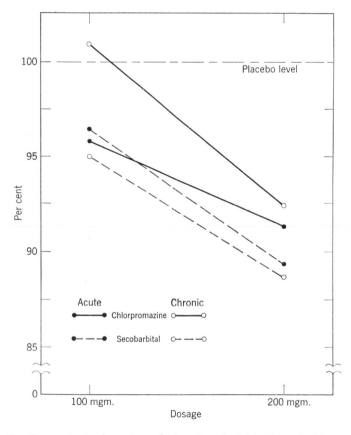

Figure 8.   Comparison of acute and chronic administration of chlorpromazine
and secobarbital plotted as per cent of placebo score on tapping speed (Kornetsky et al., 1959).

between supine and 60-second standing blood pressure and pulse rate in normals and schizophrenic patients. Although these results suggest a difference in the autonomic responsivity between normals and schizophrenic patients after chlorpromazine administration, there are factors that were not controlled in any of these experiments and preclude any interpretation at the present time. There was a mean difference in age between the normal and schizophrenic subjects of 14 years, and most of the schizophrenic patients were smokers while only two of the normal subjects smoked. Thus the question is unanswered whether these differences are due to the disease process itself, to the

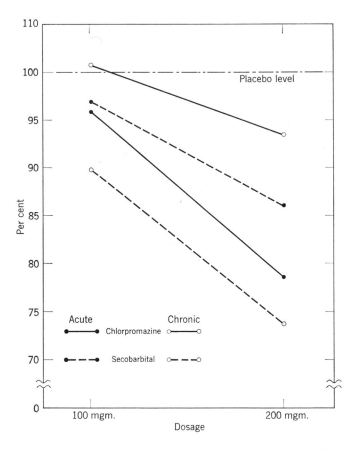

Figure 9. Comparison of acute and chronic administration of chlorpromazine and secobarbital plotted as per cent of placebo score on the pursuit rotor (Kornetsky et al., 1959).

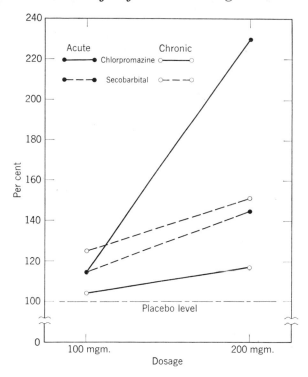

Figure 10. Comparison of acute and chronic administration of chlorpromazine and secobarbital plotted as per cent of the placebo error score on the tachistoscopic threshold test (higher score indicates poorer performance) (Kornetsky et al., 1959).

lack of response of this particular sample of patients to therapeutic measures, or to some alteration in the physiology of the schizophrenic patient not primarily related to the disease process, but conditioned by it.

All our experiments have indicated a discrepancy in effects on performance between 200 mg. of secobarbital and 200 mg. of chlorpromazine. (For more details see Chapter 29.) When the two drugs are administered to either normal or schizophrenic subjects, secobarbital produces greater impairment than chlorpromazine on subjects' performance on the digit symbol test, while chlorpromazine makes for poorer performance than secobarbital on tapping speed, the pursuit rotor test (see Figs. 3 through 5), and the continuous performance test (CPT) (Mirsky, Primac, and Bates, 1959). In our laboratory we have found that the effects of extended sleep deprivation (Kornetsky, Mirsky, Kammen, and Dorf, 1959) are similar to those of chlorpromazine while the effects of meprobamate are more like those of secobarbital on the digit substitution test and the CPT.

Individual Differences

One might expect that the effects of a psychoactive drug as measured by any performance test would vary between subjects. If subjects could be equated in performance before the administration of the drug, any variance obtained could be attributed to the differential action of this drug on the performance of the subjects. If we assume that our performance test is both a valid and a reliable indicator of drug response, this variation in response between subjects could be attributed to something intrinsic to the subjects. The variability between subjects would be dependent on the drug only to the extent that the drug is necessary to interact with this intrinsic individual variable. If, now, the same subjects were to be given several other drugs under similar experimental conditions, the response of the subjects would again vary around the mean effect of each of the drugs. This varia-

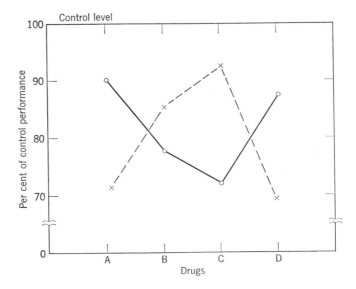

Figure 11. Significant drug × subject variance, and no significant subject variance. Solid curve, subject I; broken curve, subject II.

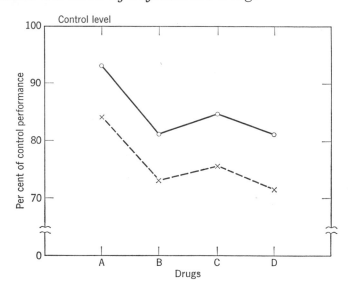

Figure 12. No significant drug × subject variance, and significant subject variance. Solid curve, subject I; broken curve, subject II.

tion in response around the mean response to each of the drugs may or may not be mutually independent. That is, the subject most affected by one drug may be the same subject most affected by the other drugs, but this is not necessarily so.

In order to illustrate better the possible types of interactions that might be obtained in an experiment where the same subjects are given a number of different drugs, the following hypothetical models are presented. For simplicity the models used involve only two subjects. Figure 11 indicates a hypothetical result of the effects of four drugs on the performance of two subjects. In this case there would be significant subject × drug interaction variance and no significant subject variance. On the other hand, if the subject most affected by drug A is most influenced by drugs B, C, and D, respectively, and the subject least affected by A is least influenced by the other drugs, there would be no drugs × subject interaction. However, there would be significant subject variance, as illustrated in the hypothetical case in Fig. 12.

Another possible result of an experiment where the same subjects are tested after the administration of a number of psychoactive drugs would be one in which there would be both significant subject variance independent of initial level and a significant drug × subject

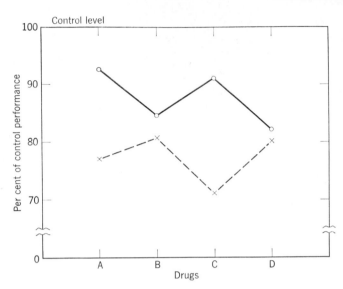

Figure 13.   Significant drug × subject variance, and significant subject variance. Solid curve, subject I; broken curve, subject II.

variance.   A result such as this is illustrated in the hypothetical model in Fig. 13.   In this situation there is a tendency for the same subjects to have relatively greater responses to all drugs, as well as for some subjects to be relatively more affected by some drugs than by others. Experimental evidence suggesting this to be the case is given in three experiments conducted in our laboratory, each on a different group of normal volunteer subjects.

In our first experiment (Kornetsky, Humphries, and Evarts, 1957) the analysis of variance gave a significant F ratio not only for drugs but for subjects and subject × drug interaction.   This result fits the model as illustrated in Fig. 13 and indicates that some subjects were more impaired than others on all the various drug treatments.   However, since the drug × subject interaction was significant, it also indicates that the subject responsivity was not linear, some subjects being also relatively more affected by some drugs than others.   To test further the responsivity or reaction pattern of the subjects, the Kendall coefficient for concordance (Kendall, 1948) was computed.   This yielded slight but positive evidence for the presence of a phenomenon of this type ($w = .35, p < .01$).

In another experiment (Kornetsky and Humphries, 1958) 12 normal subjects received 100 and 200 mg. of both chlorpromazine and seco-barbital on separate days. The partial correlations between all the various drug treatments were computed with the subjects' initial control scores partialed out. The mean correlation on the various tests used are shown in Table 4. They are all in the predicted direction, and, although not large, they support the hypothesis that the responder to one drug is also the responder to others.

TABLE 4.   MEAN PARTIAL CORRELATIONS OF ALL EXPERIMENTAL
TREATMENTS FOR EACH TEST

	Tapping Speed	Hand Steadiness	Digit Symbol	Pursuit Rotor	Tachistoscopic Threshold
Mean	.516	.570	.512	.439	.120
Range	.237–.680	.286–.894	.064–.848	.015–.785	.348–.663

In order to test this hypothesis further, a third experiment was completed. Fourteen subjects were tested on the continuous performance test (CPT) (Rosvold, Mirsky, Sarason, Bransome, and Beck, 1956) after 200 mg. of chlorpromazine and 15 mg. dextro-amphetamine (Kornetsky and Mirsky, unpublished data). The latter drug was administered after 64 hours of sleep deprivation. It was predicted that those subjects most impaired by chlorpromazine would be most stimulated by dextro-amphetamine. Thus there would be a negative correlation between the scores of the subjects after chlorpromazine administration and the scores after dextro-amphetamine when the effects of sleep deprivation were partialed out. The results supported the hypothesis: the obtained correlation between the effects of chlorpromazine and those of dextro-amphetamine was —.48 ($p < .05$ on a single-tailed test). Although this correlation is not high, it was in the predicted direction, suggesting that the intrinsic variable or variables that account for responsivity to drugs is the same for both depressants and stimulants.

What variables contribute importantly to this drug responsivity? In man we have found no suggestion that the important variable is body weight, although fat distribution may account for some of the variance. There is some evidence both from our studies (Kornetsky and Humphries, 1957) and from those of others that personality probably plays an important role in drug response; however, it is unlikely that personality factors can account for all this variance.

Further studies are currently planned to determine if with more carefully controlled experiments, we can raise the level of correlation between responses of subjects to various drugs, and if similar phenomena occur in animal drug studies.

R E F E R E N C E S

Abramson, H. A., Jarvik, M. E., Kaufman, M. R., Kornetsky, C., Levine, A., and Wagner, M. Lysergic acid diethylamide (LSD-25). I. Physiological and perceptual responses. *J. Psychol.*, 1955, 39, 3–60.

Kendall, M. G. *Rank correlation methods.* London: Charles Griffin & Co., Ltd.; 1948, 80.

Kornetsky, C. Relation of physiological and psychological effects of lysergic acid diethylamide. *Arch. Neurol. Psychiat.*, 1957, 77, 657–658.

Kornetsky, C., and Humphries, O. Relationship between effects of a number of centrally acting drugs and personality. *Arch. Neurol. Psychiat.*, 1957, 77, 325–327.

Kornetsky, C., and Humphries, O. Psychological effects of centrally acting drugs in man. Effects of chlorpromazine and secobarbital on visual and motor behavior. *J. ment. Sci.*, 1958, 104, 1093–1099.

Kornetsky, C., Humphries, O., and Evarts, E. V. Comparison of psychological effects of certain centrally acting drugs in man. *Arch. Neurol. Psychiat.*, 1957, 77, 318–324.

Kornetsky, C., Mirsky, A. F., Kammen, E., and Dorf, J. E. The effect of dextroamphetamine on behavioral deficits produced by sleep loss in humans. *J. Pharm. exp. Therap.*, 1959, 127, 46–50.

Kornetsky, C., Pettit, M., Wynne, R., and Evarts, E. V. A comparison of the psychological effects of chlorpromazine and secobarbital in schizophrenics. *J. ment. Sci.*, 1959, 105, 190–199.

Kovitz, B., Carter, J. T., and Addison, W. P. A comparison of chlorpromazine and reserpine in chronic psychoses. *Arch. Neurol. Psychiat.*, 1955, 74, 467–471.

Mirsky, A. F., Primac, D., and Bates, R. Effect of chlorpromazine and secobarbital on the continuous performance test. *J. nerv. ment. Dis.*, 1959, 128, 12–17.

Rosvold, H. E., Mirsky, A. F., Sarason, I., Bransome, E. D., Jr., and Beck, L. H. A continuous performance test of brain damage. *J. consult. Psychol.*, 1956, 20, 343–350.

Shaten, L., Rockmore, L., and Funk, I. C. Responses of psychiatric patients to massive doses of thorazine. II. Psychological test performance and comparative drug evaluation. *Psychiat. Quart.*, 1956, 30, 402–416.

Vates, T., and Kornetsky, C. A comparison of some physiological changes in normal and schizophrenic subjects twelve hours after chlorpromazine administration. Paper read at Fall meeting of Amer. Soc. for Pharm. Exp. Therap., 1958.

Chapter 19   *Donald W. Fiske*

The situational test as a method
for studying drug effects

Situational tests would seem, at first glance, to be highly desirable techniques for studying the effects of drugs on behavior. A comprehensive approach to psychopharmacology must include investigation of drug effects on natural, everyday behavior outside the laboratory, as well as on specific psychological functions, such as psychomotor performance and perception. Situational tests are intended to provide lifelike settings and tasks closely approximating those encountered in the normal course of a person's living. Flanagan (1954, p. 462), in introducing a symposium on such tests, refers to the use of "typical" situations in which a person will respond "spontaneously and naturally," yielding a "standard" sample of behavior. Situational tests are a compromise between observations of daily life and observations in highly controlled experimental or testing conditions. Unfortunately these tests suffer many of the major limitations of both these extremes on the continuum of experimental control.

Just what is a situational test? The definition offered in the dictionary by English and English (1958, p. 504) is: "a measure of a person's reaction to a situation that requires an actual adaptive response, rather than a mere 'test' response. The situation may be contrived by the examiner but must be recognized as posing a real problem to be solved, independent of its status as a test." The key word is "real": the ideal situational test would evoke natural behavior which would not be affected by the subject's knowledge that it is a test. While the effects of such knowledge can be minimized, rarely if ever can they be eliminated.

Situational tests are of two kinds. Some are measures of perform-

313

ance on a particular function. Examples are tests of ability to drive an automobile with simulated controls and roadway (such tests have been used in drug studies: e.g., Marquis, Kelly, Miller, Gerard, and Rapoport, 1957; Melander, 1957; Loomis and West, 1958; Kelly, Miller, Marquis, Gerard, and Uhr, 1958a, b; Miller and Uhr, 1959; Uhr, Pollard, and Miller, 1959) and the Leaders' Reaction Test and the Field Performance Test for combat infantrymen (cf. Weislogel, 1954). (See Chapters 20, 21, 22.) Tests of the second kind are designed to provide a sample of behavior from which judgments can be made of some abilities, such as leadership or physical ability, of some needs or drives, and of effectiveness. In this variety the subject usually interacts with other persons who may be other subjects (as in the Rochester drug studies; cf. Nowlis, 1953) but may be stooges, as in the Construction Test reported in the *Assessment of Men* (USOSS Assessment Staff, 1948, pp. 102–112), or may be the investigators (as in the study of adrenolutin by Hoffer, 1957). In this class may also be placed those contrived experimental procedures in which the subject believes he is exchanging messages with other subjects but is actually receiving a series of messages predetermined by the experimenter.

Tests of the first kind are primarily work samples which measure ability or achieved skills. They present few problems if the test is highly structured and is administered to one subject at a time. However, it must be emphasized that, even though such tests closely resemble on-the-job tasks, their validity, i.e., the degree of association between the test scores and actual job performance, must always be demonstrated empirically. Since they are given as tests, the performance of subjects is affected by the test situation and especially by the subject's knowledge that he is being tested.

The Continuum
of Experimental Control

In psychological measurement the intelligence test represents the extreme of firm experimental control. A person taking such a test knows that his ability is being assessed, knows that objective criteria for correct responses exist, and agrees to do his best. Ordinarily, the subject has practiced repeatedly the functions tapped by intelligence tests, though perhaps not with the particular content in the test. Moreover, most subjects are familiar with the experience of being tested; if they are not, the scores may not be dependable, as recent attempts to introduce such tests to other cultures have shown. Also, the experimenter cooperates with the subject by making the physical and motivational conditions optimal for maximum performance.[1]

At the other extreme of experimental control there is everyday behavior under free, lifelike circumstances. Such behavior is not ordinarily used as immediate data in research studies. While ratings by laymen may be collected, and while the subject may be asked to report on his own behavior, direct observation by professionally trained observers is rare with adult subjects, and objective scoring of free behavior is generally not possible. The reason is obvious: everyday behavior is largely determined by immediate circumstances and by recent experiences, factors which are so different for different persons that no meaningful comparisons can be made.

Between these extremes fall personality questionnaires, projective tests, and situational tests, in order of decreasing experimental control. Note that experimental control is composed of several parallel continua referring to the degree of specification of (a) the task and the goal to be sought, (b) the focal stimuli (e.g., test items), and (c) the responses permitted. Situational tests provide a sharp contrast to intelligence tests in these respects. Although a task is specified for the subject in a situational test, there is no assurance that he will exert optimal effort to complete the task, and he inevitably has other goals in the situation, such as making a favorable general impression on the experimenter. If other subjects are present, he may also be concerned with maintaining congenial relations with them or with seeking personal prominence or dominance. The external stimuli to which the subject is expected to respond are the few materials (if any) provided by the experimenter and the unpredictable, almost fortuitous behavior of the other subjects. The range of responses permitted is almost unlimited. In contrast, intelligence tests provide explicit stimuli and alternative responses, the latter being implicit or explicit in the task.

The diversity of possible responses in situational tests makes it necessary to use observers to transform the subjects' behavior into scores. Thus the measurements must be judgments. Even highly structured situational tests require judgments as to the occurrence or non-occurrence of responses prejudged as desirable or undesirable. (For an example of the limitations associated with the use of observers, see Nowlis and Nowlis, 1956, p. 351.)

[1] These ideas on the contrast between measuring ability and measuring personality have been developed jointly with John M. Butler.

The degree of experimental control produced by specifying task, stimuli, and response alternatives is of crucial significance because it is related to the observed reliability of psychological measurements. Higher degrees of control are found to be associated with higher internal consistency of responses on a given occasion and with greater stability of responses on retest after a period of time. Human behavior is variable, but experimental controls exercise constraints on this variability (cf. Fiske, 1957).

Intelligence tests and some achievement tests have very high indices of reliability, in terms of both stability and internal consistency. Interest inventories and personality questionnaires show a wide range of reliabilities. Most of the measures derived from relatively unstructured projective tests have limited reliability. In general, high reliability is found when the subject has clear criteria for selecting his response to the problem, task, or item. The investigator can, of course, maximize the reliabilities of scores by ensuring that the problems are appropriate for the population of subjects and by utilizing standard psychometric techniques in developing his instrument.

The significance of reliability in measurements of drug effects should need little elaboration. If the behavior being studied is variable from time to time, the isolation of any effect of a drug will be more difficult. In studies involving repeated measurements of the same subjects, the variance of the differences between drug and control conditions will be increased by such instability of behavior. Similarly, in studies utilizing separate groups, intraindividual variability will contribute to error variance.

Since situational tests ordinarily utilize limited experimental controls, investigators using them must anticipate a large amount of irrelevant or error variance associated with such variability. They will have difficulty in demonstrating the existence of small effects, especially when there are individual differences in reactions to a drug.

This discussion of experimental constraints should not be taken as an argument that behavior in responding to intelligence tests is less complex than behavior in a situational test—all behavior has complex determination. Yet the two differ with respect to motivational patterns. In intelligence testing, the motivational pattern is relatively stable in each subject throughout the test period. It is also relatively similar from one person to the next, since the desire to do well is pre-eminent and the capacity to solve at least a minimum number of the test problems is present in most subjects.

In a situational test a subject's motivational pattern may change during the test session, and it is ordinarily different from that of other subjects. The comparison may be highlighted by an examination of the factors in a situational test which affect a subject's behavior.

First, the subject is present for a purpose. He may have been ordered to attend, offered money, or given some other incentive. A related consideration is the subject's perception of the examiner: his feelings may be positive or negative, he may feel respectful or superior, and so forth. Such reactions will affect his behavior even if the experimenter leaves the room after the testing begins. Then there is the subject's reaction to the task. Does it have inherent interest for him? Does it give him an opportunity to utilize some special knowledge or skills?

Most important are the subject's responses to the others in his group. In addition to his interactions with the several individuals, analogous perhaps to those with the experimenter, there are his specific reactions to their acts. These are in part a function of the personalities of the particular persons with whom he happens to be placed (cf. Haythorn, 1953).

The analysis of behavior in groups has revealed several major dimensions, of which two are particularly well established: sociability and individual assertiveness (cf. Carter, 1954; Borgatta, Cottrell, and Mann, 1958). In so far as a group situation evokes different degrees of these traits in different subjects, any general effects of drugs may be obscured.

The influence of the group setting on observed reactions to drugs must not be minimized. On the one hand, if all members receive the same drug, the apparent influence may be greater than the true effect, since there may be facilitation. The observed influence of alcohol on one person will be magnified when the others in the group are also influenced by it. On the other hand, the apparent effect of a drug on a subject may be low when others are given different treatments: the group tone or atmosphere exercises a major constraint on the subject's dispositions (cf. Nowlis and Nowlis, 1956, pp. 350–352).

The effect of a drug must be added to all the other potent influences. If the dosage is strong, effects may be identified readily. If the dosage is moderate, they will be more difficult to isolate.

Using Situational Tests in Drug Studies

Situational tests are appropriately used to assess the operational effectiveness of a person rather than his maximal potential. Outside the experimental room, a person's performance is ordinarily below his maximum because he cannot sustain top effectiveness over long periods of time and in the presence of competing stimuli and motives. Effectiveness in day-to-day functioning is a product of three groups of determinants: aptitude, motivation, and adequacy of self-guidance mechanisms. Performance in situational tests is similarly determined (cf. Fiske, 1954). A high level of performance is achieved only when the subject has the requisite skills, is well motivated, and has an appropriate degree of control over competing dispositions and over his instrumental acts.

The effects of a drug on maximal potential and on the strength of a specific motive can often be assessed by simpler, more standardized techniques than situational tests. More elaborate procedures are required to observe effects on complex tasks involving competing behavioral tendencies. For example, Loomis and West (1958) mention that simple tests were not sensitive to the effects of small amounts of ethyl alcohol, but a simulative automobile-driving apparatus was. In most of daily life, a human being cannot continuously apply himself to maximizing a single outcome but must seek a balanced course of activity that yields many different outcomes, that is now aimed at one and now at another outcome as external situations and intraorganic conditions change. Even in carrying out a given task that requires more than a few minutes to complete, a person must differentiate between the several steps in its planning and execution and attend to the step appropriate at each stage of the process. This is the paradigm that a situational test simulates. The crux is the temporal sequence of activities: Does the person shift his attention and effort at the appropriate moments so as to perform the task completely and efficiently—that is, with suitable expenditures of energies and within a reasonable period of time?

In designing a situational test the investigator must first specify the exact nature of the function he wishes to study. This may be the capacity to maintain adequate performance on several simultaneous tasks, such as keeping several dial readings within designated limits, or continuing to apply his own efforts and those of his subordinates to the task at hand without neglecting the interpersonal needs of those involved. Again, the function may be to discriminate the relative importance of several subtasks, or to maximize output on a continuing task but shift to interjected problems as they arise.

The planning of the procedure must include consideration of the scoring scheme. Since successful performance will ordinarily be composed of several diverse outcomes, the investigator must work out a satisfactory plan not only for scoring each facet of the complex activity but also for determining the equivalence of different profiles of achievements on the several component parts. Since the task or tasks in a situational test rarely have obvious and universally accepted criteria for the ideal solution, the instructions must communicate to the subject the experimenter's criteria.

The preceding discussion is oriented primarily toward the performance or work-sample variety of situational tests. The other, less structured form has potentially. broader application but greater difficulties in its objective utilization. The two kinds have much in common, and a number of the points made earlier apply to the second kind also.

Situational tests aimed at sampling general behavior are concerned chiefly with the motives or needs manifested by the subject, with their strength, and with the extent to which the subject is able to attain his goals. It will be immediately evident that objective, rigorous measurement of behavior in such tests is difficult if not actually impossible. The raw behavior observed or recorded must usually be interpreted by a judge as to quality or kind of motive or motives, quantity or strength of each motive, and effectiveness, either from an impersonal viewpoint or from the frame of reference of the subject's goals. The less structured the test, the greater is the variety of observed behavior and the greater are the problems of obtaining high interobserver agreement. There is also the question of the stability of judgments over several samples of such behavior from the same subject.

For studying the effects of drugs on behavior, loosely structured situational tests may provide a number of hunches or leads which can be checked by more systematic investigations. Objective determinations of drug effects, especially with small to moderate dosages, are difficult to make with such tests because the number of diverse influences on the observed behavior and the range of individual reactions to the total situation create appreciable obstacles.

On the other hand, it should be possible to design situational tests which would permit the assessment of drug effects on a single motive, on the adequacy of the instrumental behavior seeking to achieve a given goal, or both. Such tests would involve a substantial amount of experimental control. In fact, they would probably be better described as complex experiments rather than situational tests. The ideal test would provide identical stimuli and setting to all subjects and yet be realistic. Such a test could involve no direct interaction

with other persons. Interpersonal behavior can be observed only at
the cost of reduced rigor in experimental control. The critical and
stressful discussion used by Hoffer (1957) appears to have been a
satisfactory technique for his purpose because the effects of adrenolutin
were quite marked. It is obvious, however, that the level of induced
stress would not be constant for all subjects (assuming that there
was some method of estimating the level). Furthermore, it would
be dangerous to assume that the stress would be equivalent on both
first and second administrations for each subject, especially with the
probable interactions between subject, order, and presence or absence
of drug (cf. Campbell, 1957).

Underlying much of our discussion is a fundamental dilemma concerning research on the effects of drugs on behavior. The greater
the degree of experimental control, the more the behavior is con-
strained by the conditions and the less opportunity there is for
limited dosages of drugs to have much effect. People under the influence of alcohol or anoxia show a remarkable capacity to deal
adequately with some tests and problems by exerting great effort and
mobilizing their resources. In such circumstances the effect may, of
course, be a reduction of the subject's ceiling, of his performance at
the limit of his capacity. It may also be detectable with problems
that require continuous application of attention and effort.

On the other hand, while less structured situations may provide
more opportunity for a drug to have an effect, they reduce the possibility for systematic, objective assessment of such effects.

The resolution of the dilemma depends upon the experimenter's
interests and resources. The experimental conditions should be as
controlled as possible to permit manifestation of the function being
studied. Small groups of subjects and repetition of the test under
drug and placebo conditions is to be preferred whenever repetition
has little effect, i.e., when the function is a highly practiced one or
when extensive practice can be provided. More commonly, it will be
desirable to obtain a large number of subjects and assign them
randomly to the different experimental conditions. The latter procedure avoids the assumption that two trials of the same procedure
are equivalent or that two forms of the test are interchangeable.

Inference from Situational Tests

The problem of determining the equivalence of two sets of conditions raises the issue of validity, of the extent to which the ex-

perimenter can generalize his findings beyond the specific testing conditions. When an investigator has completed a study of the effect of a drug on a complex task, he is faced with the task of interpreting and drawing inferences from his findings. If the results are negative, he may reasonably conclude that "Drug D does not affect performance on Task T, at least under the conditions of this experiment."

If the results are positive, he can state, with a specified risk of being in error, that "Drug D can affect performance on Task T," or "There is at least one task (T), such that Drug D affects performance on it." While such a conclusion may be of considerable importance because it establishes a connection between the drug and behavior, the crucial problem remains that of interpreting the finding. The question of how the drug works cannot usefully be asked until more is known about the test. Of what psychological capacity or disposition is it a valid measure?

This question implies two others: Does it measure the function which it appears to measure? Is the drug's effect associated with the relevant function or with some irrelevant factor in the total test situation?

These questions cannot be answered if the experiment has used only one test procedure. They require that several parallel procedures be employed with the same experimental population. This approach has been called "convergent and discriminant validation" (Campbell and Fiske, 1959). Its essence is the joint application of several procedures, each measuring the same set of variables, functions, or traits. It is necessary that the several procedures utilize different methods, or at least that there be no methodological element common to all methods.

In drug research, this approach would involve the application of several multidimensional procedures under drug and no-drug conditions, using appropriate experimental techniques to control order, bias, and other factors. The resulting set of comparisons would first be examined for consistency of effect over methods for each function. If the methods provide a reasonably representative sampling of the domain delineated by a given trait-concept, then a set of negative, or mostly negative, findings would permit the dependable conclusion that Drug D does not affect Trait T. If the results were mostly or wholly positive, then, in the ideal case, it might be concluded that D affects T. Even in the ideal case, however, this conclusion might be premature; the investigator should take into account all his other findings. Suppose that significant effects were obtained for all or most functions as measured by all the procedures. The more useful interpretation would be that the drug affected some function underlying all the specific functions tested. To give an extreme example, the drug might, by central blocking or by disruption of all integrative behavior, prevent the evocation of any appropriate behavior.

A frequent outcome would be the finding that the drug affected some measures of the function but not others. One possible interpretation, which probably could not be tested with the given set of results, would be that the drug affected one aspect of the function but not another, i.e., that the function as previously conceived was complex. Another possibility could be tested: that the drug's effect was associated with one or more methods in addition to, or instead of, any association with the function. To explore this lead, the homogeneity of the several results for each method would be determined. For example, if Method 1 showed drug effects for all functions it measured and Method 2 showed none, it would be safe to infer that the drug's effect was related to some part of the specific situation used in Method 1.

As an illustration, suppose that in both methods a group of subjects worked together on a task, the task being a verbal discussion for Method 1 and a physical assembly for Method 2, the functions being motivation, cooperation, contribution to the solution, and assertiveness. The drug's effects on these several traits as measured by Method 1 might stem from the fact that it interfered with the subjects' capacity to maintain their attention on the problem in the absence of visible task-related stimuli. Note that the question is not "Does the drug have an effect?" but rather "Does it have an effect on a given trait or only on that trait as measured by that method?" Psychological measurement involves trait-method units in each of which a particular trait content is joined to a method of measurement which is not specific to that content.

More generally, the problem has two facets: (a) It must be established that a test measures a given function. This can be done by demonstrating that it covaries with another independent measure of that function, or that its profile of relationships with drugs and other variables is similar to that of other measures of that function. (b) It must be established that the test discriminates the given function from others. This can be accomplished by showing that the test's measure of that function covaries more with other measures of it than with measures of reputedly different functions, or that its profile of relationships has more similarity to those for other measures of that function than to profiles for measures of different functions using the same general method.

While the problem is general in psychological measurement (cf. Campbell and Fiske, 1959), it is especially acute for situational tests. There is reason to believe that much of the variance of measures of behavior in a situational test is specific to the test, and even to particular aspects of the test conditions. For example, in reviewing one of the most intensively studied situational tests, the Leaderless Group Discussion, Bass (1954) reports that correlations between test and retest at a different time range from .90 down to .39, as a function of intervening conditions, changes in group composition, and other variables.

Conclusion

While situational tests are designed to evoke reactions to realistic problems as opposed to responses to test stimuli, they are still tests and subjects respond to them as such. The more naturalistic setting used in situational tests permits greater variability in the behavior of different subjects but also permits greater variability in the behavior of a single subject, both within one test session and over repeated sessions. Thus the reduced level of experimental control which characterizes situational tests is a weakness in so far as it reduces reliability of measurement. It can also be construed as an advantage in so far as it permits a broader range of psychological determinants to affect the observed behavior.

The measurement of effectiveness in dealing with complex problems, one form of situational test, is an extension of the more common work-sample techniques and achievement testing. The other form of situational test uses a less structured situation to provide an opportunity for estimating the kind and strength of the subject's motives and the effectiveness of his goal-directed behavior. It is most suitable for exploratory purposes.

Results from both forms of situational test face the critical problem of validation. Are the obtained measures correlated with other methodologically distinct measures of the pertinent function? Do they differentiate between that function and other, irrelevant ones? To what extent are the measures determined by reactions which are specific to the particular method, to the unique situation? While validity is a central problem in all psychological measurement, it is of crucial importance in situational tests.

The researcher studying the effects of drugs on behavior should use situational tests principally for exploratory purposes. To avoid using a poorly understood technique to investigate a relatively unknown area, he would be wise to limit himself to situational and other procedures whose success in assessing specific psychological functions has been appropriately demonstrated. But the promise of the situational test in psychopharmacology is sufficient to justify in the future much more than the present sporadic use of it.

REFERENCES

Bass, B. M.   The leaderless group discussion. *Psychol. Bull.*, 1954, 51, 465–492.

Borgatta, E. F., Cottrell, L. S., Jr., and Mann, J. H.   The spectrum of individual interaction characteristics: an inter-dimensional analysis. *Psychol. Rep.*, 1958, 4, 279–319. (Monogr. Suppl. No. 4.)

Campbell, D. T.   Factors relevant to the validity of experiments in social settings. *Psychol. Bull.*, 1957, 54, 297–312.

Campbell, D. T., and Fiske, D. W.   Convergent and discriminant validation by the multitrait-multimethod matrix. *Psychol. Bull.*, 1959, 56, 81–105.

Carter, L.   Evaluating the performance of individuals as members of small groups. *Personnel Psychol.*, 1954, 7, 477–484.

English, H. B., and English, A. C.   *A comprehensive dictionary of psychological and psychoanalytical terms.* New York: Longmans, Green, 1958.

Fiske, D. W.   Why do we use situational performance tests? *Personnel Psychol.*, 1954, 7, 464–469.

Fiske, D. W.   The constraints on intra-individual variability in test responses. *Educ. psychol. Measmt*, 1957, 17, 317–337.

Flanagan, J. C.   Some considerations in the development of situation tests. *Personnel Psychol.*, 1954, 7, 461–464.

Haythorn, W.   The influence of individual members on the characteristics of small groups. *J. Abnorm. soc. Psychol.*, 1953, 48, 276–284.

Hoffer, A.   Adrenolutin as a psychotomimetic agent. In H. E. Himwich (Ed.), *Tranquilizing Drugs.* Washington, D. C.: Amer. Ass. Adv. Sci., 1957, 73–100.

Kelly, E. L., Miller, J. G., Marquis, D. G., Gerard, R. W., and Uhr, L.   Personality differences and continued meprobamate and prochlorperazine administration. *Arch. Neurol. Psychiat.*, 1958, 80, 241–246. (a)

Kelly, E. L. Miller, J. G., Marquis, D. G. Gerard, R. W., and Uhr, L.   Continued meprobamate and prochlorperazine administration and behavior. *Arch. Neurol. Psychiat.*, 1958, 80, 247–252. (b)

Loomis, T. A., and West, T. C.   Comparative sedative effects of a barbiturate and some tranquilizer drugs on normal subjects. *J. Pharmacol. exp. Therap.*, 1958, 122, 525–531.

Marquis, D. G., Kelly, E. L., Miller, J. G., Gerard, R. W., and Rapoport, A. Experimental studies of behavioral effects of meprobamate on normal subjects. *Ann. N. Y. Acad. Sci.*, 1957, 67, 701–710.

Melander, B. *Psychotechnological investigation of car drivers in model equipment.* Stockholm: A/B Kabi, Research Division, 1957.

Miller, J. G., and Uhr, L. An experimental study of the behavioral effects of carbethoxysyringoyl methylreserpate (Singoserp). *Toxicol. appl. Pharmacol.*, 1959, 1, 534–544.

Nowlis, V. The development and modification of motivational systems in personality. In J. S. Brown, et al., *Current theory and research in motivation: a symposium.* Lincoln, Neb.: Univer. of Nebraska Press, 1953, 114–138.

Nowlis, V., and Nowlis, H. H. The description and analysis of mood. *Ann. N. Y. Acad. Sci.*, 1956, 65, 345–355.

OSS Assessment Staff. *Assessment of men.* New York: Rinehart, 1948.

Uhr, L., Pollard, J. C., and Miller, J. C. Behavioral effects of chronic administration of psychoactive drugs to anxious subjects. *Psychopharmacologia*, 1959, 1, 150–168.

Weislogel, R. L. Development of situational tests for military personnel. *Personnel Psychol.*, 1954, 7, 492–497.

Behavioral toxicity as measured

by tests of simulated driving

and of vision

The complex psychomotor and decision-making skills, such as those involved in driving an automobile, and the simple visual functions are probably among the most important for successful performance of day-to-day activities. Tests measuring these two aspects of behavior, employed as checks against possible behaviorally toxic effects of psychoactive drugs, have been used in a number of experiments conducted in the Mental Health Research Institute and the Department of Psychology of the University of Michigan. First, we shall briefly describe the instruments used (for a more complete description, see Marquis, Kelly, Miller, Gerard, and Rapoport, 1957). Then we shall summarize our findings with respect to these tests, and some of the pertinent results from other tests included in the same experiments.

Driver Test

The American Automobile Association's Driver-Trainer is used. The trainer consists of two parts: the complete controls of a conventional-shift automobile and a treadmill-like belt, about 10 feet long, painted to resemble a winding road, which extends away from the front of the control unit. A model car, operated by the subject, rests

Work reported in this chapter and in Chapter 23 was supported in part by research grants from: the Office of the Surgeon General, United States Army, Contracts DA-49-007-MD 575 and DA-49-007-MD 684; United States Public Health Service Grant M-1871; the U. S. Food and Drug Administration; Ayerst Laboratories; Ciba Pharmaceutical Products Inc.; Merck, Sharp and Dohme; Wallace Laboratories; and Whitehall Pharmacal Company.

on the belt. The subject's job is to keep the car on the road and to brake the car whenever a red stop light appears.

The subject is given trials as follows: 20 revolutions of the belt at a fixed low speed, 20 revolutions at a fixed high speed, and 20 revolutions at a speed controlled by the subject. Six reaction-time determinations are interspersed irregularly through the first two trials.

Accuracy, or proficiency, of driving in this situation is measured in terms of the ability of the subject to keep the car on the road. Three accuracy scores are obtained: at the fixed low speed, at the fixed high speed, and at the variable speed controlled by the subject. A "speed" score is also obtained, indicating the time required for each trial when the subject is controlling his own speed. During this phase of the test the subject is asked to drive as rapidly and as accurately as he can. In addition, a derived score is figured—the ratio of the difference between the accuracy score at low fixed speed and the accuracy score at subject-controlled speed, divided by the time score. This speed-accuracy ratio, which indicates the degree to which speed is sacrificed for accuracy, or vice versa, may be interpreted as a measure of judgment. The seven scores on the Driver Test thus consist of three accuracy scores, one speed score, one judgment score, and two reaction-time scores.

Vision Tests

Vision tests are conducted using the Bausch & Lomb Optical Company's master-model Ortho-rater, a device designed to test various visual functions with distance and illumination controlled.

Acuity is determined for both far and near vision; depth- and color-perception scores are determined for distant vision only. Vertical and lateral phorias for both near and far vision are also measured. Phoria scores indicate the relative posture or muscular balance of the eyes in relation to each other under conditions of controlled accommodation.

Experimental Findings

We first examined the acute effects on normal subjects of double-the-normal doses of meprobamate, dextro-amphetamine sulfate, meprobamate plus alcohol (2 oz., 80 proof), and alcohol alone. There was some evidence of unsteadiness under alcohol. No behavioral toxic effects were found for the other three treatments, as compared with placebo (Marquis, Kelly, Miller, Gerard, and Rapoport, 1957).

We next tested for chronic effects, using a more extensive battery on normal subjects (in an own-control design), after 21 to 28 days of meprobamate (1600 mg. per day) or prochlorperazine (20 mg. per day). Fifty-one behavioral measures were taken after each drug treatment; 68 personality variables were scored from a battery of personality tests. The very large number of significance tests run (153 t-tests for drug effects, plus 2400 tests of significances of correlations between personality variables and drug effects) led to a certain number of significant findings. But, as these were not clearly more than might have been expected by chance, it was concluded that no dependable drug effects had been found (Kelly, Miller, Marquis, Gerard, and Uhr, 1958a, b).

The effects of acute administration of benactyzine were examined on driving and vision tests, along with other behavioral tests, including the PSI (see Chapter 23). Four groups of six patients—obsessive compulsives, anxiety neurotics, reactive depressives, and normal controls—were compared. Because of the small number of subjects tested, only suggestive results could be obtained. There may have been some indication of improved performance, especially among the obsessive-compulsive patients, under benactyzine (Smith, Uhr, Pollard, and Miller, 1958).

The effects of chronic administration of meprobamate, and of "Tranquil" (essentially a triple-bromide preparation) were examined on a group including 24 anxiety neurotics and 12 normals. Behavioral measures, psychiatric assessment ratings, self-report ratings, and peer-report ratings were collected. On behavioral tests, some indications of slowing of reaction times in driving, plus improved time estimations under distraction, were found for meprobamate in dosages of 1600 mg. daily. Tranquil appeared to lead to a more general impairment of performance on driving. Psychiatric assessment and peer ratings gave a number of indications of decreased anxiety and tension under meprobamate, as contrasted with a slowing and dulling component under Tranquil (Uhr, Pollard, and Miller, 1959).

Acute effects of meprobamate were again examined on both the driving and the vision tests, and on simple behavioral tests performed under experimentally aroused stress. Meprobamate slowed reaction time and decreased accuracy on the driving test, with dosages of 800 mg., double the usual clinical dose. It also led to a raised level of galvanic skin resistance during the stress situation, and to feelings of diminished activity (Uhr and Miller, 1960a, b). Emylcamate in 800-mg., but not in 400-mg., doses brought about slowing of reaction time, along with feelings of greater calmness and relaxation than either 800 mg. of meprobamate or placebo. The usual clinical dose of emylcamate is not greater than 400 mg.

Other experiments have examined the effects of several non-psychoactive drugs on these and batteries of other tests, as checks into questions of possible behavioral toxicity. Miller and Uhr (1959) tested the behavioral effects of chronic administration of a reserpine-related hypotensive drug, carbethoxysyringoyl methylreserpate (Singoserp) on hypertensive patients. Uhr and Miller (1960c) examined the effects of a new antihistamine, isothipendyl hydrochloride (Theruhistin), said not to produce the typical side effect of this type of agent, drowsiness.

REFERENCES

Kelly, E. L., Miller, J. G., Marquis, D. G., Gerard, R. W., and Uhr, L. Personality differences and continued meprobamate and proclorperazine administration. *Arch. Neurol. Psychiat.*, 1958, 80, 241–246. (a)

Kelly, E. L., Miller, J. G., Marquis, D. G., Gerard, R. W. and Uhr, L. Continued meprobamate and procloperazine administration and behavior. *Arch. Neurol. Psychiat.*, 1958, 80, 247–252. (b)

Marquis, D. G., Kelly, E. L., Miller, J. G., Gerard, R. W. and Rapoport, A. Experimental studies of behavioral effects of meprobamate on normal subjects. *Ann. N. Y. Acad. Med.*, 1957, 67, 701–710.

Miller, J. G., and Uhr, L. An experimental study of the behavioral effects of carbethoxysyringoyl methylreserpate (Singoserp). *Toxicol. Appl. Pharmacol.*, 1959, 1, 534–544.

Smith, G. W. J., Uhr, L., Pollard, J. C., and Miller, J. G. An exploratory study of the behavioral effects of Suavitil (benactyzine hydrochloride). *Univer. Mich. med. Bull.*, 1958, 24, 402–407.

Uhr, L., and Miller, J. G. Behavioral toxicity of emylcamate (Striatran). *Amer. J. med. Sci.*, 1960, 240, 197–203. (a)

Uhr, L., and Miller, J. G. Experimentally determined effects of emylcamate (Striatran) on performance, autonomic response, and subjective reaction under stress. *Amer. J. med. Sci.*, 1960, 240, 204–212. (b)

Uhr, L., and Miller, J. G. Experimental study of the behavioral effects of isothipendyl hydrochloride (Theruhistin). M. H. R. I. Preprint, 1960. (c)

Uhr, L., Pollard, J. C., and Miller, J. G. Behavioral effects of chronic administration of psychoactive drugs to anxious subjects. *Psychopharmacologia*, 1959, 1, 150–168.

Some effects of
oxanamide on normal behavior

Two experiments are reported concerning the effects of moderate doses of oxanamide on six behavioral variables involved in complex acts such as driving (Kristofferson and Cormack, 1958). The behavior measures are similar to those employed by Marquis, Kelly, Miller, Gerard, and Rapoport, (1957) and include: (1) steadiness, or total time off target in a Whipple-type apparatus; (2) rate of tapping during a five-minute period; (3) accuracy of steering, slow speed; (4) accuracy of steering, fast speed; (5) brake reaction time, slow speed; and (6) brake reaction time, fast speed. The last four measures were made with the A.A.A. Driver-Trainer in two 15-minute periods.

Experiment I used 16 subjects in a double-blind design, with a single 800-mg. dose of oxanamide versus placebo. Each subject served as his own control, counterbalanced, and tests began 50 minutes after taking the tablets. Experiment II comprised four conditions: (1) no treatment; (2) 2 oz. of 100-proof bourbon whiskey; (3) 400 mg. of oxanamide four times a day for two days, last dose one hour before testing; and (4) placebo control on condition (3). Each of the 24 possible sequences of the four conditions was assigned at random to one subject.

No significant differences were obtained in Experiment I, and no trend was found in the pattern of differences. In Experiment II, of the six scores four were "poorer" for alcohol than for no treatment, 1 was poorer for drug than for no treatment, and 1 was poorer for alcohol than for placebo. In all these differences, significance reached

This research was supported by a grant-in-aid from the Wm. S. Merrell Co.

the level of $p = .05$. As in Experiment I, no trend appeared in the differences between drug and placebo and no difference approached significance.

There is no basis in the results of these experiments for concluding that oxanamide produces a greater decrement in performance than does a matching placebo.

On the other hand, it has been shown that the measures used are sufficiently sensitive to detect the toxic effects on behavior of drinking a single two-ounce dose of whiskey. At least some of this effect may be a "placebo" effect. The procedures have also been shown to be sufficiently sensitive, when interpreted as a pattern, to pick up the placebo effect of the placebo control on the drug.

If one wishes to arrive at a conclusion concerning the possible effects of oxanamide on driving, it is of utmost importance to realize that the behavioral measurements made in these experiments are only a small sample of one of several behavioral domains relevant to driving. Such factors as risk-taking behavior, and others of equal importance to driving, have not been sampled as yet.

R E F E R E N C E S

Kristofferson, A. B., and Cormack, R. H. Some effects of Quiactin on normal behavior. *Clin. Res.*, 1958, 6, 416.

Marquis, D. G., Kelly, E. L., Miller, J. G., Gerard, R. W., and Rapoport, A. Experimental studies of behavioral effects of meprobamate on normal subjects. *Ann. N. Y. Acad. Sci.*, 1957, 67, 701–711.

Two experiments on psychoactive drugs using a simulated auto-driving device

Sedation in the form of impaired mental acuity and motor response is a pharmacological action common to many drugs. When the degree of sedation is moderate to intense, conventional simple reaction-time tests, visual acuity tests, and pointer pursuit tests are excellent tools for measuring this action of drugs. When the degree of sedation is mild, these tests may not be sufficiently sensitive to detect impairment of function. Previous experience of the authors indicates that such tests are relatively insensitive to mild alcohol-induced sedation in human subjects, although subjective symptoms are present. An attempt to develop a practical and sensitive test for evaluating subtle degrees of drug-induced sedation resulted in the development of a simulated auto-driving device.

The apparatus required that the test subject perform multiple acts simultaneously. It included a conventional automobile steering wheel, and brake and accelerator pedals which could be operated in the way a standard automobile is driven. The steering apparatus was arranged to operate a model auto mounted over a translucent moving nylon belt which was 150 feet long and 30 inches wide. On the surface of the entire length of the belt was a continuous opaque strip, 1 inch wide, which simulated a road bed. As the belt moved beneath the auto, the road bed moved randomly but smoothly from side to side, simulating moderate to severe curves. In order to stop the movement of the belt, it was necessary for the subject to apply foot pressure to the brake pedal.

When the auto was not centered over the road the "time off the road" was accurately recorded by a photoelectric cell device, and the signal light above the auto was illuminated, indicating to the subject that the auto was off the road. Cumulative interval timers were arranged to record the summated elapsed times between the appearances of a red light and application of foot pressure to the brake pedal, and between the appearances of an amber light and the release of foot pressure on the accelerator pedal.

The amber, red, and green lights were automatically illuminated in the following sequence: green 12 seconds, amber 3 seconds, green 12 seconds, red 3 seconds, which was repeated so that each amber and each red light was illuminated eight times for 3 seconds' duration during the four-minute test period.

Subjects were thoroughly trained before starting the study. Each one was repeatedly tested at two-day to weekly intervals until his control ability reached a plateau of overall efficiency, so that repeated tests gave scores which did not vary more than 20 per cent. This usually required 5 to 10 training tests.

Two studies were performed using the simulated driving apparatus. The first (Loomis and West, 1958a) consisted of a study of the influence of alcohol on performance. The second study (Loomis and West, 1958b) was concerned with the influence of a barbiturate and some tranquilizer drugs on performance. Similar procedures were used in each of the studies. The double-blind method was employed in the second study. The five drugs were: placebo (corn starch), 200 mg.; secobarbital sodium, 100 mg.; chlorpromazine hydrochloride, 50 mg.; meprobamate, 400 mg.; and phenaglycodol, 300 mg. All subjects received the drugs in the same order of administration, and an interval of one week was allowed to pass between tests with the various drugs.

Impaired performance was evident when the blood alcohol concentration was at 0.05 per cent, a level at which gross clinical symptoms of sedation may be minimal or absent. In the presence of a blood alcohol concentration of 0.15 per cent, performance had decreased to approximately one-third of the control values (summated time off the road plus reaction times for proper response to red lights and to amber lights).

In the second study there were significant differences among the effects of the five drugs, among the subjects, and among the trials. Analyses by the *t*-test showed that neither the placebo nor phenaglycodol produced a significant effect. Chlorpromazine produced impairment of performance after a delayed onset. Meprobamate impaired performance two hours after the first dose and one hour after the second.

Secobarbital produced a prompt intense impairment of performance, which continued throughout the remainder of the day.

R E F E R E N C E S

Loomis, T. A., and West, T. C.   The influence of alcohol on automobile driving ability.   *Quart. J. Stud. Alcohol,* 1958, 19, 30–46. (a)
Loomis, T. A., and West, T. C.   Comparative sedative effects of a barbiturate and some tranquilizer drugs on normal subjects.   *J. Pharmacol. exp. Therap.,* 1958, 122, 525–531. (b)

Drugs and human information processing: perception, cognition, and response

In the literature of human experimental psychology are studies with various apparatuses, often electronic, designed to measure behavior—especially specific functions of perception and cognition—which have a high degree of precision and reliability. We have both adapted to purposes of personality evaluation under normal or psychopharmaceutical stress conditions tests already in existence and made new tests of our own for special purposes. The following are some of the tests which our research group have been using in drug studies.

Tanner-Swets Auditory Perceptual Battery

This complex electronic apparatus was constructed by Tanner and Swets to instrument investigations in terms of their statistical decision-theoretical approach to auditory signal detection. Tones, background noise, and decision conditions can be varied by the experimenter. We have run four thoroughly trained subjects on it under drugs. Each of these subjects, after normative trials, was given, on different days, single doses of 400, 800, and 1600 mg. of meprobamate, 15 mg. of dexedrine, 100 mg. of phenobarbital, 200 mg. of phenoglycodol, and placebo under double-blind conditions, and tested while under the influence of the drug. A careful analysis of these data indicated no systematic discoverable trends in either the sensory, perceptual, memory, or decision-making variables measured by this procedure.

Work reported in this chapter was supported by grants as noted in Chapter 20.

Visual Perceptual Test

This apparatus presents a small round target on a dim background with precisely controlled variable brightness. There are four time periods indicated by sounds, and during one the light is turned on for one centisecond. The subject is required to say in which period the light appeared, even if he must guess. Kristofferson had already run many subjects on this apparatus in order to establish norms for their behavior. We then ran 16 other subjects on the equipment under 400, 800, and 1600 mg. of meprobamate and placebo. One trial was carried out before the drug was taken, and six at half-hour or hour intervals after administration of the drug, which was done under double-blind conditions. This perceptual test showed slight statistical tendencies of unknown practical importance toward decreased acuity under meprobamate, but no clear-cut evidence that the functions measured by it were systematically affected by the levels or durations of the single dosages of drugs used (Miller, Marquis, Platz, Clay and Uhr, 1960).

The PSI Apparatus

This apparatus is sometimes referred to by The Psychological Corporation as the Logical Analysis Device. The test was developed by Dr. E. Roy John, Dr. Horacio Rimoldi, Mr. Stanley F. Molner, and the author about 1952 (John, 1957; John and Miller, 1957).

In this test a network of electronic elements is arranged so that relationships can be established between various elements. These relationships correspond to operations of Boolean algebra. The set of relationships imposed on the network is equivalent to a set of logical constraints.

The subject is required to determine an order of pressing three specific buttons out of a circle of nine, which will elicit a specific output from the network (light a tenth, central light on the board). He is given some clue to the solution by a central template with arrows from various lights to others, showing which lights are related to which others. In order to determine this pattern, the subject must analyze the relationships within the network. To do this it is necessary to push various buttons, lighting the lights contained in each button in certain orders. Lighting these lights sequentially activates other lights, demonstrating their logical relationships. The order and combinations in which buttons are pushed, i.e., the pattern by which information is sought, gives the experimenter evidence on the process of analysis used by the subject to obtain information and to synthesize this information into a solution of the problem.

The mode of presentation is as a "problem box." The subject is familiarized with the box by using a detailed example. Changing plug-in problem boards permits rapid and flexible alteration of problems, i.e., of the relationships of the network. Performance is automatically recorded.

Eighteen indices are derived in scoring performance on this apparatus. Each of the first ten is divided into five subscores calculated for the five major stages in the solution of such problems: (a) from the beginning to the first lighting of the center light; (b) from this first lighting to closure, when the subject could have observed or inferred all the necessary facts to solve the problem; (c) from closure to solution, which is two consecutive lightings of the central light, pushing one or more of the three specified buttons only, and with no unnecessary pushes; (d) closure to the point where the subject shifts from analytic to synthetic treatment of the problem; and (e) from this analytic-synthetic shift to solution. The eighteen scoring indices are: (1) number of questions in each stage of solution; (2) number of time periods for each stage; (3) rate of asking questions in each stage; (4) percentage of all questions falling in each stage; (5) percentage of time periods in each stage; (6) number of repeated questions in each stage; (7) complexity of questions asked in each stage; (8) percentage of synthetic questions in each stage; (9) non-fact-yielding questions asked in each stage; (10) unique questions asked in each stage; (11) total questions; (12) total time periods; (13) total "impossible moves" or errors; (14) percentage of questions asked before the analytic-synthetic shift; (15) number of shifts from analytic to synthetic questions; (16) number of analytic questions after the analytic-synthetic shift; (17) ratio of analytic to synthetic questions; (18) shifts from questions involving only the specified three buttons to other buttons.

Factor analytic studies of group PSI performance have been conducted, and factor analyses of individual performances are now being carried out by us. The primary factors of PSI performance which this work has so far revealed are: number of trials to first lighting of the central light; number of trials from lighting of the central light to closure; number of trials from closure to solution; time per trial; and number of complex moves.

F. Horvath and Uhr are now also correlating each PSI index with the following scores on other tests: ACE test, L scale; ACE test, Q scale; an arithmetic test; the Moore Eye-Hand Coordination Test; an eye-blink test; the Stroop Color Word Interference Test; the Semantic Differential Test; and a self-report check list, as well as level of education and field of major study. Previous evidence (John, 1957) has indicated that students in certain fields of major study perform quite differently from students in others.

Using the 18 PSI scoring indices, a number of questions have been studied: (1) the extent to which a given individual performs consistently from problem to problem; (2) the means and standard deviations of performances on each of these indices; (3) the effect on these means and standard deviations of increasing the complexity of problems in a stipulated way; (4) comparative performance of various different populations on two problems of different complexity.

Rapoport and Gyr (1958), working with other members of the Mental Health Research Institute, have developed a precise method for measuring the information content of each problem. In addition, various sorts of alternates for problems II, III, and IV of the PSI apparatus have been devised by us, and the electronic networks for these have been constructed. One sort of alternative problem simply substitutes certain button-light combinations on the machine for others, but this spatial reorganization is the only change. Another sort of problem has the same amount of information content and complexity as problem II, III, or IV but differs in the order in which information must be collected for solution, and not merely in spatial reorganization.

These alternative problems are being used in studying transfer of training effects from one problem to another, as well as for analyzing the effects of alterations in problem complexity on the problem-solving process. The alternative equivalent problems have been also used for repeated testing of individual subjects under stress and non-stress conditions.

Because of the novelty of the PSI apparatus, much effort has been required to develop the most useful techniques of administration and scoring, and to establish norms for performance on it both by individuals and by groups. It has been given to several hundred individuals and groups, because we considered this step essential before we undertook extensive drug and stress research with it. We have, however, done some of the latter sort of investigation.

Research previously done by us indicated that alcohol in sufficient dosages (more than $1\frac{1}{2}$ oz.) affects PSI performance, but we have not yet been able to handle all the problems involved in measuring these effects. We have also conducted two other researches on the PSI using drugs. In one (McLaughlin and Miller, 1960) we administered a PSI problem to 150 prisoners all of whom were suffering at the time from the physiological stress of headache. They were divided into three groups; 50 received two Anacin tablets, 50 received two aspirin tablets, and 50 received two placebo tablets, 15 minutes before testing. The medication was given under double-blind conditions. In this study 23 scores were obtained from each PSI performance, and only one score showed a significant difference among the groups at the .05 level. (Out of this number of scores one such significance might, of course, be expected by chance.) This finding was that the shift from analytic to synthetic thinking on the PSI occurred in significantly fewer moves under placebo than under either Anacin or aspirin.

Smith, Uhr, Pollard, and Miller (1958) conducted an exploratory study on the effects of benactyzine on groups of six anxiety neurotics, six compulsives, six depressives, and six normals. Tentative trends of improvement under benactyzine, especially by the compulsive group, were found. But, because of the small numbers tested, no statistical evaluations were attempted and results were considered simply suggestive for future research.

Our third drug research with the PSI apparatus involved 50 normal subjects to whom we administered one problem the first day after they received instructions, and then two problems the next day to ensure a good baseline of normal performance, before measuring their problem-solving ability on two problems after the administration of a drug on the third day. We divided the 50 subjects into five groups: 10 received 1 mg. of hyoscine; 10 received 2.5 mg. of Sernyl; 10 received 800 mg. of meprobamate; 10 received 15 mg. of dexedrine; and 10 received placebo. These data are now in process of being analyzed.

The Pi Apparatus
Patterned Motor Response Test

The subject in this test, developed by us, is seated before a semi-circle of eight clear plastic disks shaped like door knobs and containing white lights which can glow through the disks. The disks are arranged at arm's length from the subject. His problem is to hit them as soon as they light, thus extinguishing the lights. The temporal pattern of appearance of the lights is automatically controlled by electronic equipment, and the performance of the subject is automatically recorded. A wide range of temporal sequences and patterns of appearance of the lights can be presented to the subject, from very simple patterns to very complex.

Pretests conducted with the Pi apparatus under normal conditions, and under the stressors of weight on the arm and various dosages of alcohol, indicated the following: (1) A reasonably good fit to a straight line is obtained when the square root of the distance covered by the arm is plotted against the time required to traverse such a distance. This suggests that the arm moves with constant average acceleration. (2) The test is stress-sensitive, distinguishing significantly between the stresses of weight, alcohol, no alcohol, and no weight. (3) The variable altered by weight and alcohol is the effort required to overcome initial inertia, rather than the acceleration.

In an effort to apply the sort of drug stress most likely to produce effects upon the motor variables measured by the Pi apparatus, we conducted tests on it with three subjects under Anectine chloride (diacetylcholine chloride). This substance briefly paralyzes skeletal muscle by blocking nervous transmission at the myoneural junction, somewhat like curare. We gave doses up to about 60 mg. by slow intravenous drip, testing the subject during the infusion. No change in performance could be measured, however, up to the time generalized paralysis developed. We therefore decided that the Pi apparatus was not so promising as some of our other tests, and we have not continued to use it.

Complex Reaction Time Apparatus

The display of this test developed by Kornblum is eight neon bulbs at the eight cardinal points on the periphery of a circle 3 inches in diameter. At the center of the circle is a red neon light serving as a fixation point. All the lights are shielded with opaque tape to avoid cross-illumination by stray lights. The circle is mounted on a piece of masonite 2 feet square, painted black, which is hung 4 feet from the subject at eye level against a black cloth backdrop. Immediately behind the subject's chair and above his head is a 7½-watt bulb which illuminates the display. The visual angle subtended by the circle is approximately 3.5 degrees, so all the lights can easily be seen and identified from the fixation point without eye movement. Each light is named according to its clockwise order in the circle beginning with "1," the light at 12 o'clock. In order to minimize differences in the mouth movement time between responses, the name of each light is preceded by the vowel "b." The responses are thus: bun, boo, bee, bour, bive, bix, beven, beight. The display control and response recording are done by a Hunter interval counter, a Dynac preset counter, and a Hewlett-Packard oscillator. The experimenter and control equipment are in one room while the subject is in another, wearing earphones, observing the display, and speaking through a microphone.

After a two-second warning period, one display appears, the illumination of any number of lights from one to eight, Display P. This display remains for a period, which can be altered by the experimenter. Then there is a "dead time" between displays, which can be altered. Then a second display, Display Q, appears until the subject makes a response. In the second display one light is on that was off before, or vice versa. The subject is instructed to respond as rapidly as possible with the number of the light which has changed state, knowing in advance how many alternatives there are. Subjects are tested for about an hour, during which period 300 to 360 observations are made.

Consider the case in which a trial consists of Display Q only, and the stimulus is one of four possible lights changing state. If, for a series of many trials, each stimulus light is chosen at random, so that each one changes state as often as any other and there are no dependencies between trials, the uncertainty in this display averaged over all the trials is 2 bits. Consider, then, another display, Display P, in which two of the four possible lights are on, and for a series of trials each possible pair appears randomly and as often as every other pair, and there are no dependencies between trials. Since there are six such possible pairs, the average uncertainty in Display P is 2.59 bits. Now suppose Display P and Display Q are presented sequentially. A trial begins with a ready signal, followed by a pair of lights going on, and this in turn by either one of the two lights going off or one of the remaining two going on. Since the subject's task is to respond to that single light which changed state at the onset of Display Q, he is forced to have processed the information in Display P at the time it was presented. The total uncertainty in both decisions leading to the response is therefore 4.59 bits. A sizable number of different stimulus situations are possible with this apparatus, and the amount of information processed in making the decisions in each of the situations can be calculated as in the example above.

Three subjects were thoroughly trained and run extensively to obtain detailed baselines for them under non-drug conditions in the various situations which can be established with this apparatus. They were then given each of the four drugs used also in our testing with the PSI apparatus—hyoscine, 1 mg.; Sernyl, 2.5 mg.; meprobamate, 800 mg.; and dexedrine, 15 mg.; along with a placebo. These were administered double-blind. They received each of these drugs for two days running. The first day they were given runs measuring their performances under the drugs with one to eight possible alternatives, so comparing the drug effects on a single aspect of reaction time. The second day they were given two sorts of runs: in the first there were six lights in Display P and one to five lights in Display Q. The duration of Display P was held constant at 0.1 second, and the subjects had a number of repetitions of the various possibilities in this situation. In the second sort of run there were six lights in Display P and four lights in Display Q, the duration of Display P again being held constant at 0.1 second, but the dead time was altered as follows: 0.050, 0.150, 0.300, 0.500, 1.0, and 1.5 seconds, in order to alter the duration of the memory trace of Display P. Data so far analyzed indicated that, on the first days' runs, reaction times under all drugs were slower than under placebo (Kornblum, in preparation).

The IOTA Apparatus
(Information Overload Testing Aid)

This equipment consists of a ground-glass screen about 3 by 4 feet in size on which stimuli are thrown by a Perceptoscope which can show movie film at rates from 1 to 24 frames a second (Miller, 1960). On the screen are eight vertical slots, 2 inches wide, in one or all of which can appear white dials with black arrows on them. The arrows may assume any of eight positions on the dial, like clock hands. The subject may be presented with a maximum of eight different positions in four different slots, and he is provided with 32 buttons representing each of these alternatives. A correct response involves pushing the button corresponding to the position of the arrow and the slot in which it appears.

The subject has several processes of adjustment available to help him handle very rapid inputs. If he simply does not process some of them, pushing no button, that is (1) an omission. If he pushes the wrong button in order to get on with the job, that is (2) an error. A foot pedal provides for (3) queuing or delaying responses—the subject may lower or raise opaque strips behind each of the slots. At the beginning of the test only the top square in each of the slots is open, but the subject may use his pedal to open up to eleven more squares below in each slot. The moving-picture film is made to move the arrow to successively lower positions until it has gone through all twelve and finally leaves the screen. In the meantime, other stimuli usually appear higher in the same slot. By pushing the pedal, the subject can give himself more time to respond to the stimulus before it disappears. He can (4) filter by attending only to arrows in certain positions and ignoring others. He can (5) approximate by pushing all buttons for a given slot if he sees an arrow but cannot remember the direction, or more than one button if he is uncertain of the exact position but knows it was one of two or more. He can (6) use multiple channels by pushing with two hands at once. He can (7) escape by refusing to continue. All seven of these processes of adjustment are possible on this apparatus.

The experimenter can increase the rate of input information by speeding the film, by increasing from two to eight the number of alternative positions for the arrows, by increasing the number of slots in use, or by altering the degree of regularity (redundancy) or randomness of the presentations.

In training runs, subjects were told not only how to operate the IOTA apparatus for high performance, but also how each of the processes of adjustment can be used. Then each subject received in a random order inputs with one, two, or four slots open; with arrows in 10, 50, or 100 per cent of the movie frames; and with speeds of 1, 2, 3, 4, 6, or 12 frames a second. These combinations were run with arrows appearing randomly in one of eight possible positions (or a three-bit decision each time an arrow appeared). They were also repeated with arrows appearing in each frame in one of four possible positions (a two-bit choice) with one slot open at speeds of 1, 2, 3, 4, 6, and 12 frames a second. Input rates varied from 0.8 to 240 bits a second. Three hundred frames were projected in each trial.

After these normative trials, four trained subjects were tested by Eckerman and Uhr on the IOTA under each of the four drug conditions and placebo mentioned above, those used in drug runs on the PSI apparatus and the Complex Reaction-Time apparatus. Each subject was run twice in a randomized order on each of the drugs. Eight runs a day were made, or sixteen under each drug. These data are now under analysis.

SCRAP Apparatus (Simple and Complex Reaction Apparatus)

This is a forced-pace, multiple-choice, button-pushing task, in some ways like one slot of a simplified IOTA task and in other ways like a continuous series of displays on the Complex Reaction-Time apparatus, appearing at several unvarying rates.   The display consists of a panel of eight white lights at the cardinal points of the compass in a circle about 4 inches in diameter.   The seated subject holds in front of him a response box on which are mounted eight buttons conveniently arranged for the four fingers of both hands.   Each of these buttons corresponds to one of the lights in the display, an effort having been made to locate them so as to maximize stimulus-response compatibility.   A punched paper tape fed into the control apparatus randomly programs one of the eight stimuli at various preset rates.   There are 400 stimuli per run.   The rates vary from one to seven lights per second.   The recording apparatus automatically records the stimulus, response, and the time interval between them on an eight-channel paper recorder. The record makes possible scoring of the following processes of adjustment (like those in the IOTA test): (1) omission, (2) error, (3) filtering, (4) queuing, and (5) multiple responses.

This apparatus has been constructed by W. Horvath and Foster. Norms are now being obtained and the data analyzed.

Tracking Apparatus

This equipment makes it possible to study rather precisely the combined sensory, decision-making, and motor behavior of a human being as a component in a closed-loop control or input-thruput-output system. The subject's transfer function can be accurately calculated under different conditions, since all the other variables in the system can be controlled by the experimenter.   The apparatus, designed and constructed by Foster, consists of six major parts:

1. Function Generator: a group of 20 low-frequency non-phase-locked R-C oscillators summed to give a random-appearing signal of adjustable band width and center frequency.
2. Computer: a 10-amplifier Sterling Model L-10 analog computer used to sum the signal from the function generator; to prepare it for display; to compute the "error"; and to average, integrate, and perform other operations on the signals present in the experiment.
3. Display: a dual-beam Dumont Oscilloscope Model 279; one beam is used as the target, and one as the cursor.
4. Control: a modified joy-stick for use by the subject in responding.
5. Recorder: a two-channel Ampex magnetic tape recorder of the F-M type; one channel to record the signal and the other, the error.
6. Data Reducer: a combination clock, commutator, and punch

driver to measure the frequency of the signal from the recorder and prepare a six-hole punched paper tape corresponding to such signals.

Because of the complexities of reducing analog data, we have built a digitizer for data reduction designed to accept data in either analog or digital form and punch it on paper tape. Analog information is recorded on a two-channel Ampex F-M tape recorder at 60 inches per second. This recording is played back at 7½ inches per second, giving an 8-to-1 time expansion. The carrier frequency is counted directly without demodulation for 0.1 second. This count is then punched at the rate of 20 digits per second. Five-hundreths of a second after the completion of one count, the value of that count is stored, the counter is cleared, and the other channel is sampled in the same fashion. Thus 0.15 second of recording time is consumed per sample, two samples plus code signals taking 0.50 second. The "real time" sampling rate is therefore 16 interlaced samples per channel per second. This gives a maximum frequency response for two-channel recording of 8 cycles per second, or 16 cycles per second for single-channel recording.

Digital data must be encoded as a staircase voltage with 0 represented by 135 volts and 9 by 55 volts. Any number from 2 to 12 points may be sampled with immediate or "on demand" recycling. The rate is 20 digits per second.

In recording data by the digital method, if discrete values of the signal are measured, the sampling rate must be twice the highest frequency expected. While an overall accuracy of 1 per cent should be more than sufficient, an incremental accuracy of ten times this, or 0.1 per cent, is to be desired. Where the probable spectrum of interest lies below 20 cycles per second, we can estimate that $(20 + 20) \times 3 = 120$ digits per second printing speed (punching speed) is required. A typical IBM summary punch can handle 133 digits per second. Once the data are encoded or punched on cards, analysis can be done on various models of computer. We plan in the near future to collect normative data in this tracking task, analyzing them under several of the rubrics which have been developed in the rather extensive literature on the experimental psychology of tracking. Among these are:

1. Time on target. This is a classical variable, having received much attention in work with rotary pursuit apparatuses. An arbitrary target size is selected and the percentage of time on target is measured.

A single number results from each trial, all data about frequency and amplitude being discarded.

2. Target size. The percentage of time on target is plotted against target size. No data regarding frequency of responses or transition probabilities are calculated.

3. Servo analysis. The response of the operator, considering magnitude and phase of his error at the fundamental frequency only, is extracted. All the fine detail in the response is lumped as "noise" and discarded.

4. Derivative analysis. The original function and its first two derivatives, computed by an analog computer, are measured, and an exponentially decaying weighting function is applied to average them for ease of interpretation.

5. Power spectrum analysis. This computes (as a function of time) the percentage of error at each possible frequency of response. Data about "harmonic distortion," resonant frequencies, and "noise distribution" can be obtained.

6. Autocorrelation. This, in effect, measures the predictability of the signal. It may be obtained by the Laplace transform of the power spectrum or directly by an "autocorrelator." One run is then made for each "delay time" desired. Auto- (more properly "serial") correlation has the desirable feature of being able to emphasize any "regularities" in a performance.

7. Amplitude-delay analysis. This type of data reduction gives the distribution of delays-between-recurrences-of-a-given-amplitude.

These forms of data analysis can give, from a single tracking record, accurate measures of diverse functions carried out by subsystems of the nervous system. For instance, the derivative analysis (4) can give an *average lag time* (which may correlate with the length of the neural path and number of synapses involved in the task); a measure of *error due to misperception of distance* (first derivative), which may be a function primarily of visual association areas; a measure of *error due to misperception of speed* (second derivative), and a measure of *error due to misperception of acceleration* (third derivative). (The last two may well involve cerebellar as well as visual functions.) Even if we cannot identify the anatomical subsystems involved, we can isolate functional subsystems by these methods. There is good possibility that such subsystems are differentially affected by various psychoactive drugs and other stressors, and for this reason we believe the tracking test has promise in our research field.

The Stroud Time Quanta Apparatus

Several years ago, equipment was constructed by Foster and Peretz to test Stroud's hypothesis that there is subjective quantization of time. It enabled us to present auditory stimuli at regular intervals, the duration of which could be varied by the experimenter. The first apparatus also had two visual stimuli, left and right bulbs which glowed at a fixed time after the auditory stimulus. This fixed time could be altered by the experimenter, as could the time between the glowing of the two bulbs. If Stroud's hypothesis is correct, when the two visual stimuli appear in sequence, with a certain constant phase relationship after the auditory stimulus (which is repeated at a regular, rapid rate), the order of the glowing of the two lights will be correctly perceived better than chance, but at other phase relationships it will not be perceived better than chance.

Preliminary tests failed to support Stroud's hypothesis, but it was felt that this was because the apparatus was inadequate. Construction of a new apparatus has been undertaken.

The Kay Apparatus

The display of this apparatus consists of ten lights, about ¾ inch apart, in a horizontal row. The subject sits with ten pushbuttons similarly arranged. The experiment begins when one of the lights in the display lights up. The control apparatus is so constructed that several problems can be inserted into it, the apparatus being so wired that the buttons that extinguish the lights vary from problem to problem. When one light is extinguished another light immediately goes on, and when that one is extinguished a third goes on; this continues until all ten lights have been extinguished—the end of one trial. Then the first light automatically lights again. The task is always to find out which button extinguishes which light, and to extinguish as many lights as possible in a given period of time. The apparatus was developed by Kay, and a duplicate has been constructed by us for use in stress and drug testing at the suggestion of Gerard.

In the simplest problem the ten buttons from left to right extinguish the ten lights from left to right in the same order. A more complicated problem reverses the direction, so that the buttons from left to right extinguish the lights from right to left, in regular order. More and more complicated patterns can be built into problems.

An automatic record is made of the total number of button pushes in a trial and the number of lights the subject has extinguished or the number of times he has gone through the ten-light cycle in the same period of time.

Miscellaneous Behavioral and Personality Tests

In several of our individual projects we also administered other behavioral tests and personality inventories, such as tests of figural after-effect, flicker-fusion, apparent motion, preferred tempos, continuous attention, line judgment, the Minnesota Multiphasic Personality Inventory, the California Personality Inventory, the Edwards Personal Preference Schedule, and Cattell's 16 Personality Factor Test (Kelly, Miller, Marquis, Gerard, and Uhr, 1958a, b; Miller, Marquis, Platz, Clay, and Uhr, 1960; Miller and Uhr, 1959; Uhr and Miller, 1960a; Uhr, Pollard, and Miller, 1959).

There were no striking drug effects on scores on these various instruments, however. In one study (Burnstein and Dorfman, 1959) it was found that human learning of materials with which anxiety normally interferes was speeded by meprobamate, and in another (Uhr, Clay, Platz, Miller, and Kelly, 1960) it appeared that meprobamate increased conditioning to a positive unconditioned stimulus in human beings but prochlorperazine did not. Meprobamate was also found to improve performance on a continuous attention test under experimentally aroused stress (Uhr, Platz, and Miller, 1960).

Self-Rating and Subjective Scales

Scales like the Semantic Differential and symptom check lists were also employed in some of our studies (Kelly, Miller, Marquis, Gerard, and Uhr, 1958a, b; Miller and Uhr, 1959; Uhr and Miller, 1960a, b, c). In some of the researches they indicated decreased anxiety or symptoms under meprobamate, decreased symptoms under Tranquil, decreased feelings of activity under meprobamate and high doses (800 mg.) of emylcamate, greater calmness and relaxation under 800 mg. of emylcamate, and increased feelings of activity under isothipendyl hydrochloride.

Stress Situations

So far we have worked with three sorts of stress situations: (a) experimentally induced; (b) illness-induced (headache); and (c) drug-induced (with psychotomimetics). We have used experimentally induced stress in drug research because this seems to be a good way to quantify positive actions of tranquilizers, sedatives, and similar compounds to measure improvements in performance under stress after the subject has received the drug. The stress apparatus we have built is a box in which sparks as threats of shock, actual shocks, blasts of air, and loud noises can be presented. Volunteers are subjected to such stressors while taking various pencil-and-paper tests. In one study (Uhr and Miller, 1960b) we found no effects of either 800 mg. of meprobamate or 400 or 800 mg. of emylcamate in altering performance on these tests under stress.

Headache is a physiological stressor which is often said to diminish efficiency. In our Anacin-aspirin investigation (McLaughlin and Miller, 1960) we found a few significant differences on specific test scores among the groups, but we did not obtain more than would be expected by chance, so none of the drugs measurably altered behavior under stress.

Using psychotomimetic drugs as stressors, Bakker has carried out pretests with several volunteers. He has so far observed only nine subjects on Sernyl and one on LSD. He has carefully recorded their behavior and given them psychiatric diagnostic interviews before, during, and after the drug took effect. He has begun to administer behavioral tests to such subjects in larger numbers and under controlled conditions.

Physiological Measures

Our general overall strategy has been to develop and refine the behavioral and psychological tests first, and then to correlate performance on them under normal and stress conditions with various physiological measures. We have planned to include in the latter some of the following: palmar sweat; electrical skin resistance of the palm (GSR); respiration rate; finger, face, and axillary temperature; heart rate, potentials, and rhythms; changes in finger and leg blood volume; systolic and diastolic blood pressure; stroke volume of the heart; pupillary diameter; stomach and lower bowel motility; salivary output; and selected muscle action potentials (Wenger, Engel, and Clemens, 1957).

We are now setting up such a physiological battery. In some of our completed studies (Uhr, Clay, Platz, Miller, and Kelly, 1960; Uhr and Miller, 1960b; Uhr, Platz, and Miller, 1960) we have begun to combine physiological and behavioral measures. We found previously that ordinary single doses of meprobamate do not affect performance on our Driving Battery, but they do significantly increase sweating on the palmar surface of the thumb under driving conditions. This was an unexpected finding. In later studies under the present program (Kelly, Miller, Marquis, Gerard, and Uhr, 1958a, b) we repeated this physiological test with better controls in subjects under chronic meprobamate and prochlorperazine administration and found no significant differences from when they were under placebo. We also have measured galvanic skin resistance in stress situations in patients under meprobamate, emylcamate, and placebo (Uhr and Miller, 1960b; Platz, Uhr, and Miller, in preparation). The first compound consistently raised the level of galvanic skin resistance, but the others had no effect.

Our general hope for the future is to continue in our attempts to identify the significant dimensions of behavior along which stress effects can be demonstrated when stressors, and especially psychoactive drugs, are applied; to develop precise, objective measures of these dimensions; to standardize and validate such instruments; and to test various populations with them under various sorts, magnitudes, and durations of stress—whenever possible, observing onset of and recovery from the stressor. We hope to incorporate the findings into a self-consistent conceptual scheme.

More specifically we intend to devote special attention to promising new instruments like the Complex Reaction Time apparatus and the IOTA apparatus—going through comparable extensive normative procedures similar to those we have applied to the PSI apparatus. Then we hope to conduct further drug and stress studies on these and other instruments, like the Tanner-Swets Auditory Perceptual Battery.

REFERENCES

Burnstein, E., and Dorfman, D. Some effects of meprobamate on human learning. *J. Psychol.*, 1959, 47, 81–86.

John, E. R. Contribution to the study of the problem-solving process. *Psychol. Monogr.* 1957, 18 (whole No. 447).

John, E. R., and Miller, J. G. The acquisition and application of information in the problem-solving process: an electronically operated logical test. *Behavioral Sci.*, 1957, 4, 291–300.

Kelly, E. L., Miller, J. G., Marquis, D. G., Gerard, R. W., and Uhr, L. Personality differences and continued meprobamate and proclorperazine administration. *Arch. Neurol. Psychiat.*, 1958, 80, 241–246. (a)

Kelly, E. L., Miller, J. G., Marquis, D. G., Gerard, R. W. and Uhr, L. Continued meprobamate and procloperazine administration and behavior. *Arch. Neurol. Psychiat.*, 1958, 80, 247–252. (b)

Kornblum, S. The effects of drugs on reaction time. In preparation.

McLaughlin, Q., and Miller, J. G. A test of the behavioral effects of Anacin. M. H. R. I. Preprint, 1960.

Miller, J. G. Future impact of psychological theory on personality assessments. In B. M. Bass and I. A. Berg (Eds.), *Objective approaches to personality assessment.* Princeton, N. J.: Van Nostrand, 1959, 204–215.

Miller, J. G. Information input overload and psychopathology. *Amer. J. Psychiat.*, 1960, 116, 695–704.

Miller, J. G., Marquis, D. G., Platz, A., Clay, M., and Uhr, L. The effects of meprobamate on visual sensory threshold and behavior. M. H. R. I. Preprint, 1960.

Miller, J. G., and Uhr, L. An experimental study of the behavioral effects of carbethoxysyringoyl methylreserpate (Singoserp). *Toxicol. appl. Pharmacol.*, 1959, 1, 534–544.

Platz, A., Uhr, L., and Miller, J. G. The effects of meprobamate on the galvanic skin response. In preparation.

Rapoport, A. A research study for the development of measurements of group stress tolerance. *Univ. Mich. ment. Hlth. Res. Inst. Rep.*, 1958.

Smith, G. W. J., Uhr, L., Pollard, J. C., and Miller, J. G. An exploratory study of the behavioral effects of Suavitil (benactyzine hydrochloride). *Univer. Mich. Med. Bull.*, 1958, 24, 402–407.

Uhr, L., Clay, M., Platz, A., Miller, J. G., and Kelly, E. L. Effects of meprobamate and prochlorperazine on positive and negative conditioning. M. H. R. I. Preprint, 1960.

Uhr, L., and Miller, J. G. Behavioral toxicity of emylcamate (Striatran). *Amer. J. med. Sci.*, 1960, 240, 197–203. (a)

Uhr, L., and Miller, J. G. Experimentally determined effects of emylcamate (Striatran) on performance, autonomic response, and subjective reaction under stress. *Amer. J. med. Sci.*, 1960, 240, 204–212. (b)

Uhr, L., and Miller, J. G. Experimental study of the behavioral effects of isothipendyl hydrochloride (Theruhistin). M. H. R. I. Preprint, 1960. (c)

Uhr, L., Platz, A., and Miller, J. G. Effects of meprobamate on attention under experimentally aroused stress. M. H. R. I. Preprint, 1960.

Uhr, L., Pollard, J. C., and Miller, J. G. Behavioral effects of chronic administration of psychoactive drugs to anxious subjects. *Psychopharmacologia*, 1959, 1, 150–168.

Wenger, M. A., Engel, B. P., and Clemens, D. L. Studies of autonomic response patterns: rationale and methods. *Behavioral Sci.*, 1957, 2, 216–221.

Drug postulates, theoretical deductions, and methodological considerations

Much of the experimental work in drug effects carried out at the University of London Institute of Psychiatry has been devoted to the study of certain deductions from a postulate which reads as follows: "Depressant drugs increase cortical inhibition, decrease cortical excitation and thereby produce extraverted behaviour patterns. Stimulant drugs decrease cortical inhibition, increase cortical excitation and thereby produce introverted behavior patterns" (Eysenck, 1957b). The terms used in this postulate are carefully defined (Eysenck, 1957a); both on the pharmacological and on the psychological side they refer to changes in the central nervous system. In this brief review, twelve deductions will be mentioned, although several others have also been tested; space does not allow a longer list.

Deduction 1. *Eye-blink conditioning will be facilitated by the administration of stimulant drugs and retarded by the administration of depressant drugs.* This deduction was tested by Franks and Laverty (1955), and by Franks and Trouton (1958), who found the predicted differentiation using dextro-amphetamine sulfate and sodium amytal as a stimulant and a depressant drug respectively, as well as a placebo. It had previously been shown (Eysenck, 1957b) that rate of conditioning was correlated with introversion both in normal and in neurotic subjects.

Deduction 2. *After-effects of the Archimedes spiral, being conceived of as physiological processes subject to satiation, will be shortened by the administration of depressant drugs and lengthened by the administration of stimulant drugs.* An investigation by

Eysenck, Holland, and Trouton (1957) has demonstrated that the predicted effects occur.   It has been found that, according to the hypothesis, after-effects of the Archimedes spiral are longer in introverts than in extraverts (Holland, in Eysenck, 1960).   There is also a report in the literature (Poser, 1958) showing that the predicted effects of drugs are to be found with other measurements of satiation, i.e. the kinesthetic figural after-effect measure.

Deduction 3.   *The suppression of the primary visual stimulus by the presentation of a subsequent stimulus will be facilitated by depressant drugs and made more difficult by stimulant drugs.*   The subject is presented intermittently with a bright red light, followed by a brief stimulation by a white light, followed in turn by black.   As the brightness of the red light is decreased, it disappears and a green light is seen instead.   As predicted, dextro-amphetamine sulfate lowers the threshold of the original red stimulus while amytal raises it (Eysenck and Aiba, 1957).   (See Chapter 34 for related work.)

Deduction 4.   *Continuous work will be facilitated by stimulant drugs and impeded by depressant drugs.*   Using the pursuit rotor, Eysenck, Casey, and Trouton (1957) showed that the predicted effects occurred during three five-minute work periods separated by two ten-minute rest pauses.   Similar results have been found by Treadwell (in Eysenck, 1960).   Ray and Wischner (1958) have shown that extraversion is correlated in normal university students with lower performance in continuous rotor work, while introversion is correlated with better performance.   (See also Chapters 18 and 37.)

Deduction 5.   *Nonsense-syllable learning will be facilitated by a stimulant drug and impeded by a depressant drug.*   Willett found that subjects under amytal needed more trials, subjects under dextro-amphetamine sulfate less trials, to learn to a criterion, although the differences were not significant (Eysenck, 1957b, 1960).   Anticipatory errors were increased by dextro-amphetamine sulfate and decreased by sodium amytal.   Contrary to prediction, there was a failure to observe a bowing of the serial position learning curve *greater* after sodium amytal, and *less* after dextro-amphetamine sulfate.

Deduction 6.   *Alternation behavior in rats, being due to satiation, will be increased by inhibitory drugs and decreased by stimulant drugs.*   Sinha, Franks, and Broadhurst (1958), using amytal, pipradol, and a placebo, studied alternation behavior in a simple T-maze where choice of the right or left turn was preceded by 0, 1, 2, or 3 previous right or left turns. They found, as predicted, that, where the number of previous turns was plotted against the proportion of contrary turns at the choice point, a sloped line was produced, and that the slope was significantly *increased* by amytal and *decreased* by pipradol.

Deduction 7. *Conditioned aversion behavior in the rat will be strengthened by stimulant drugs and weakened by depressant drugs.* Singh (1958) studied the effect of various drugs on the conditioned interference with Skinner box bar-pressing behavior produced by a flickering light which had been previously paired with a strong electric shock (conditioned emotional response). The prediction was borne out. (See Chapters 11, 12, and 35 for related work.)

Deduction 8. *Light thresholds on the perimeter, when taken after a depressant drug, will be reduced for ingoing stimuli and increased for outgoing stimuli.* H. Holland, using meprobamate, verified this deduction at a high level of significance (Eysenck, 1960).

Deduction 9. *Sensitivity on the perimeter will be decreased by depressant drugs.* Working with four-light intensities on the perimeter under standard conditions, H. Holland found a decrement in sensitivity under all conditions (Eysenck, 1960).

Deduction 10. *Performance on a visuo-motor task will be worsened by a depressant drug.* Using meprobamate, Treadwell tested subjects' ability to guide a stylus along a curved path by turning a handle; she found a significant decrease, as predicted (Eysenck, 1960).

Deduction 11. *Certain types of observable behavioral characteristics of extraversion will be increased in frequency of occurrence by depressant drugs.* Laverty and Franks (1956) have shown that some such observations can be reliably and verifiably made; the observations relate to number of movements made; reports of relaxation, drowsiness, and similar states; estimations of the passage of time; and self-rating on an extraversion questionnaire.

Deduction 12. *Conductivity on the psychogalvanic reflex (resting level) will be reduced by a depressant drug.* This deduction was tested by I. Martin (Eysenck, 1960) and was found to be verified at a high level of significance.

With the interesting exception of the bowing of the serial learning curve, all the predictions made from the postulate have been verified.

This prediction depends on the correctness of the Hull-Lepley hypothesis regarding the bowing effect, and a special experiment was carried out to test the truth of this hypothesis by comparing bowing effects under conditions of exposure (a) with and (b) without a pause between lists (Eysenck, 1959). That no differences in bowing were observed suggests that the Hull-Lepley hypothesis is in fact wrong, and that this accounts for the failure of our prediction, as well as for the failure of Hull (1935) to verify a similar prediction.

One of the outstanding problems raised by this attempt to describe behavioral effects of drugs in dimensional terms is related to the fact that the observed impairment in performance caused by depressant drugs might result either from an increase in I_R (reactive inhibition) or from a decrease in $_sH_R$ (stimulus-response Habit strength) produced by the drug; similarly, improvement in performance produced by a stimulant drug might be caused by an increase in $_sH_R$ or by a decrease in I_R. An experiment is being planned to investigate these alternative possibilities, using two designs.

DESIGN I

	1st Day	2nd Day
Experimental	Drug	Placebo
Control	Placebo	Placebo

This design depends on the well-known reminiscence effect, which in Hullian theory is a measure of the dissipation of I_R during the rest pause between the first day and the second day of testing. This effect may be used in the following manner to decide between the alternative hypotheses. Let us consider an experiment in which the experimental group is given a depressant drug on the first day. If this drug increases I_R, then the reminiscence effect for this group should be stronger than for the control group, and its performance on the second day should revert to the same level as that of the control group. If, however, the drug decreases $_sH_R$, then there should be no difference in reminiscence, but a decline in the performance of the experimental group on the second day, as compared with the placebo group. The same argument applies to the situation in which the experimental group is given a stimulant drug. If this drug merely decreases I_R, then the reminiscence effect should be smaller than that of the control group, and the performance of the two groups should be equal on the second day. If, on the other hand, the drug increases $_sH_R$, then the reminiscence effect should be equal to that of the control group, and there should be a superior performance of the experimental group on the second day. Thus the design can serve as a reasonably accurate measure of the effects of the drugs on $_sH_R$ and I_R separately. (A different group of subjects is, of course, required for each drug.)

DESIGN II
Spaced Practice

Stimulant	Group 1
Depressant	Group 2
Placebo	Group 3

The second design does not require two days of testing, but requires a rather larger number of subjects. Here the experimental paradigm relies on the use of spaced practice which, according to the theory, originates no I_R. If the stimulant drug increases $_sH_R$, then Group 1 should be superior to Group 2, as the two groups are working under conditions which do not produce I_R at all. If it decreases I_R, Group 1 should be equal to Group 3. Similarly, if the depressant drug decreases $_sH_R$, Group 2 should be inferior to Group 3; if it increases I_R, Group 2 should be equal to Group 3.

Both designs will be combined in the actual experiment, as follows.

DESIGN III
First Day

Drug	Spaced Practice	Massed Practice	Second Day
Stimulant	Group 1	Group 4	Group 4 (placebo)
Depressant	Group 2	Group 5	Group 5 (placebo)
Placebo	Group 3	Group 6	Group 6 (placebo)

On the second day of testing Groups 4, 5 and 6, half of each group will be tested under massed practice conditions, the other half under spaced practice conditions.

The tests to be used for this study will be (1) eye-blink conditioning, (2) pursuit rotor learning, and (3) nonsense-syllable learning. It is also planned to use verbal and perceptual conditioning tasks.

Another investigation is being pursued at the moment into certain predictions following from a second drug postulate linking the effects of *subcortical stimulant and depressant drugs* to the personality dimension of *neuroticism,* the hypothesis being that stimulant drugs increase and depressant drugs decrease neuroticism and affect in a predictable manner all the objective tests known to measure this dimension (Trouton and Eysenck, 1960). A beginning is being made with rats; using a compound design in which the ultimate measure is the amount of interference caused by a conditioned aversive response to bar pressing in a Skinner box. The conditioned stimulus is a flickering light previously paired with a strong electric shock. The design is complex not only because animals are being compared under different drug conditions but also because they are taken from our emotional and non-emotional breeding strains. This provides a check on the hypothesis by making it possible to predict that the behavior of both strains under the stimulant drug should shift in the direction characteristic of the emotional rats, whereas administration of the depressant drug should shift the behavior of both strains in the direction characteristic of the non-emotional rats. The design makes possible the study of interaction effects, and sex of the animal also forms a part of the analysis of variance design (Singh, 1960; Singh and Eysenck, 1960).

The third type of investigation planned relates to a third personality dimension being studied in detail, namely psychoticism (Eysenck, 1959a). The possibility is being investigated that the tranquilizers have a depsychoticizing action. Several large-scale factorial studies have been carried out in an effort to find the best objective tests of psychoticism, as well as of the separate schizophrenic and manic-depressive reaction patterns, and an empirical study is in progress to evaluate the effects of meprobamate and chlorpromazine on a selection of these tests.

Most of the investigations mentioned so far suffer from the difficulty that the time sequence for the particular drug effects is usually unknown, i.e., when the drug effect is maximal and what the slope of the curve relating time since administration and drug effect may be. It is also unknown whether there are individual differences in these respects and whether differences in dosage produce significant differences in the shape of these curves. A beginning in investigating these relationships is being made using meprobamate as the drug, and the Archimedes spiral after-effects and apparent movement thresholds as the variables under investigation.

Conclusion

It is hoped that these studies will throw some light on the suitability of a dimensional framework for the classification of drugs in terms of their behavioral effects. If successful, the result should also provide some confirmation of the validity of the dimensional framework in personality description, and the two sets of data should enable us to extend considerably the deductive power of the general theory in question. Experiments completed to date appear to give strong empirical verification for the drug postulates investigated.

R E F E R E N C E S

Eysenck, H. J. Drugs and personality. I. Theory and methodology. *J. ment. Sci.*, 1957, 103, 119–131. (a)

Eysenck, H. J. *Dynamics of anxiety and hysteria.* London: Routledge & Kegan Paul, 1957. (b)

Eysenck, H. J. Serial position effects in nonsense syllable learning as a function of interlist rest pauses. *Brit. J. Psychol.*, 1959, 50, 360–362.

Eysenck, H. J. *Experiments in personality.* London: Routledge & Kegan Paul, 1960.

Eysenck, H. J., and Aiba, S. Drugs and personality. V. The effects of stimulant and depressant drugs on the suppression of the primary visual stimulus. *J. ment. Sci.*, 1957, 103, 661–665.

Eysenck, H. J., Casey, S., and Trouton, D. S. Drugs and personality. II. The effect of stimulant and depressant drugs on continuous work. *J. ment. Sci.*, 1957, 103, 645–649.

Eysenck, H. J., Holland, H., and Trouton, D. S. Drugs and personality. III. The effects of stimulant and depressant drugs on visual after-effects. *J. ment. Sci.*, 1957, 103, 650–655.

Franks, C. M., and Laverty, S. G. Sodium amytal and eyelid conditioning. *J. ment. Sci.*, 1955, 101, 654–663.

Franks, C. M., and Trouton, D. Effects of amobarbital sodium and dexamphetamine sulfate on the conditioning of the eyeblink response. *J. comp. Physiol. Psychol.*, 1958, 51, 220–222.

Hull, C. L. The influence of caffeine and other factors on certain phenomena of rote learning. *J. gen. Psychol.*, 1935, 13, 249–264.

Laverty, S. G., and Franks, C. M. Sodium Amytal and behaviour in neurotic subjects. *J. Neurol. Neurosurg. Psychiat.*, 1956, 19, 137–143.

Poser, E. G. Kinaesthetic figural after-effect as a measure of cortical excitation and inhibition. *Amer. Psychol.*, 1958 13, 334.

Ray, O. S., and Wischner, G. J. Personality factors in motor learning. *Amer. Psychol.*, 1958, 13, 325.

Singh, S. D. A study of the constitutional and situational determinants of conditioned emotional response in the rat, and its modification by drugs.   Doctoral dissertation, Univer. of London, 1958.

Singh, S. D.   Conditioned emotional response in the rat: II. Effects of stimulant and depressant drugs.   *Acta Psychol.*, 1960.   (In press.)

Singh, S. D., and Eysenck, H. J.   Conditioned emotional response in the rat: III. Drug antagonism.   *J. gen. Psychol.*, 1960.   (In press.)

Sinha, S. N., Franks, C. M., and Broadhurst, P.   The effect of a stimulant and a depressant drug on a measure of reactive inhibition.   *J. exp. Psychol.*, 1958, 56, 349–354.

Trouton, D., and Eysenck, H. J.   The effects of drugs on behaviour.   In H. J. Eysenck (Ed.), *Handbook of abnormal psychology.*   London: Pitman, 1960.

Psychophysiological studies
of psychoactive drugs

The uniqueness of psychoactive drugs in altering symbolic processes and emotional capacities has limited the role of animal research with them, making human studies necessary. At the Massachusetts Mental Health Center, we have developed procedures for simultaneously examining in human subjects physiological, psychomotor, psychiatric, psychological, and subjective effects of phrenotropic agents. During the past few years we have completed a series of studies investigating: lysergic acid diethylamide (DiMascio, Greenblatt, and Hyde, 1957; DiMascio, Suter, Greenblatt, and Hyde, 1957), phenyltoloxamine, reserpine (DiMascio, Klerman, Greenblatt, and Rinkel, 1958; Klerman, DiMascio, Rinkel, and Greenblatt, 1959; Brown, DiMascio, and Klerman, 1960), meprobamate, secobarbital, and a placebo (DiMascio and Rinkel, 1959; Klerman and DiMascio, 1959; DiMascio and Brown, 1959; Klerman and Greenblatt, in preparation). Each of these agents has been examined at various dose levels.

Experimental Procedure

We employ a double-blind technique with each subject receiving, on separate days one week apart, a large single dose of one of the agents. Each subject is tested repeatedly, under different agents or different doses of the same agent, so that comparative effects in the same individuals can be noted.

The subjects are normal, male college students, paid volunteers, evaluated and screened by psychiatric interviews and psychological tests.

Polygraphic recordings of heart rate, muscle tension, respiration, skin temperature, galvanic skin response, blood pressure, and pupil size are made simultaneously and synchronously every two hours. In the interval between these physiological recording sessions, competitive paired-associate learning, serial addition, visuomotor coordination, steadiness, and speed of motor activity tests, a subjective symptom rating questionnaire, and the Clyde Mood Scale are administered over the course of the day. A psychiatrist interviews the subjects before a drug is administered, three to four hours later (near the peak effect period) and nine hours later at the end of the experimental day.

DRUG ACTION PROFILES. The technique of having repeated testing throughout the day allows for the determination of the temporal course of drug effects. For each drug and each parameter, the data at peak effect are converted into per cent deviation from the predrug level and graphed to give the "drug action profile."

RESULTS. From this compilation of information we were able to note that, although individual differences in reactivity to each of the drugs studied occurred, the psychophysiological data collected presented a consistent and characteristic pattern of drug action that allowed for differentiation of the various agents. Alterations in the "drug action profiles" which resulted from variations in dosage tended to be a matter of degree rather than of changed modality of action.

Study I.   Comparison of Phenyltoloxamine, Reserpine, and Placebo

In our initial study with tranquilizers we compared reserpine with an antihistaminic agent, phenyltoloxamine. (The latter compound, in a previous clinical study by an independent investigator, was noted to have beneficial effects on the same type of patients that could benefit by reserpine.) By our examining techniques we found that phenyltoloxamine had psychophysiological effects (predominantly cortical) on normal subjects that were quite different from those occurring after reserpine administration (subcortical and midbrain). Our results were interpreted as showing a similarity in the effects of phenyltoloxamine to these of meprobamate as well as of secobarbital, rather than to reserpine. We stated (and our statement was subsequently clinically corroborated) that this compound should not be of value in the treatment of psychotic states.

Study II. Role of Personality

In this study we chose from the group of volunteers subjects that could be classified, on the basis of psychological tests and psychiatric interview material, into one of two different personality types. Subjects falling into these two personality types showed differential responses to the drugs and to a placebo on three levels of observation— physiologic, behavioral, and subjective. We concluded that individuals whose personality was organized about active mastery of the environment (by athletic prowess, hostile outbursts, or extrapunitive acts) found sedative drug actions ego-threatening and therefore reacted with denial and negation of effects. In contrast, passive, intellectual, intrapunitive, and anxious individuals accepted more readily sedative drug actions and experienced great reduction of anxiety and tension. The hypothesis was also suggested from the data that the latter group of subjects, who also manifested anxiety over bodily health and had known histories of hypochondriasis, would react negatively to drugs which induce perceptible effects on autonomic and visceral functioning.

The necessity of an awareness of these personality mechanisms for the proper understanding of the effects of these drugs in clinical situations is obvious.

Study III. Role of Dosage

Next, a dosage study for phenyltoloxamine was completed in which we established that the most efficacious dose tended to be between 100 and 200 mg. Independent clinical studies subsequently revealed that 50 mg. three times a day is the most therapeutic dose.

Study IV. Comparisons of Phenyltoloxamine, Secobarbital, Meprobamate, and Placebo

We then did a study comparing the effects of phenyltoloxamine, meprobamate, secobarbital, and a placebo. There were two phases to the study, each drug being studied at two dosage levels. The analysis of these data is still in process, but our initial hypothesis that phenyltoloxamine is similar in action to both meprobamate and secobarbital tends to be substantiated. *At the lower dose, phenyltoloxamine resembled meprobamate* in that psychomotor coordination and activity were increased and mental tasks were performed more accurately and faster. There was a minimum of toxic or side effects at this dose of phenyltoloxamine. *At the higher dose, phenyltoloxamine resembled secobarbital,* since in comparison to meprobamate both produced more drowsiness, irritability, intellectual retardation, and loss of drive, as well as some impairment of psychomotor functioning. (Phenyltoloxamine was found in independent clinical trials to be of value in the treatment of neurotic states and to have strong sedative properties.)

Study V. *Determinants of Placebo Responses*

These studies revealed that physiologic, behavioral, and subjective changes were noted after placebo ingestion in all subjects. While we had previously noted that subjects with different personality types reacted differentially in magnitude and direction to the placebo, in this study it was found that the placebo responses of the subjects differed according to whether they were in the high or the low dosage groups. It was felt that this phenomenon resulted from the situational expectancies set up by experience with the active drugs in the study.

Future Plans

We now are examining the effects of four compounds (phenothiazines) from the same chemical group, but whose clinical action has been observed to differ. It will be useful to determine whether "drug action profiles" are more similar for drugs of the same chemical group or for drugs having similar clinical action. We also shall examine more intensely the relationship of personality characteristics to drug actions. Both tranquilizers and antidepressant compounds will be investigated in acute and extended dosage studies.

REFERENCES

Brown, J., DiMascio, A., and Klerman, G. L. An exploratory study on the effects of tranquilizers on competitive paired associates learning. *Psychol. Rep.*, 1958, 4, 583.

DiMascio, A., and Brown, J. Competitive paired associate learning: phrenotropic drug effects for their implications for P.A.L. theory. Paper read at the A.P.A. Meeting, September, 1959.

DiMascio, A., Greenblatt, M., and Hyde, R. A study of the effects of LSD: physiologic and psychological changes and their interrelations. *Amer. J. Psychiat.*, 1957, 114, 309–317.

DiMascio, A., and Klerman, G. L. Experimental human psycho-pharmacology: the role of non-drug factors. Paper read at Conference on Psychodynamic, Psychoanalytic, and Sociological Aspects of the Neuroleptic (Tranquilizing) Drugs of Psychiatry, Montreal, Canada, April 11-13, 1958. Published in G. J. Sawrer-Foner (Ed.), *Dynamics of psychiatric drug therapy.* Springfield, Ill.: Charles C Thomas.

DiMascio, A., Klerman, G. L., Greenblatt, M., and Rinkel, M. Psycho-physiologic evaluation of phenyltoloxamine, a new phrenotropic agent (a comparative study with reserpine and placebo). *Amer. J. Psychiat.,* 1958, 115, 301–317.

DiMascio, A., and Rinkel, M. "Drug action profiles" in normal human subjects (a methodological study for the assessment of phrenotropic agents: phenyltoloxamine, meprobamate, secobarbital, reserpine and a placebo). Paper read at the Society of Biological Psychiatry, April, 1959, in Atlantic City, N. J. Published in J. Wortis, M.D. (Ed.), *Biological psychiatry,* Vol. II. New York: Grune & Stratton, 1960.

DiMascio, A., Suter, E., Greenblatt, M., and Hyde, R. Physiological effects of lysergic acid Diethylamide: report of a detailed investigation in one subject. Presented in part at American Psychiatric Association in St. Louis, 1955. *Psychiat. Quart.,* 1957, 31, 57.

Klerman, G. L., and DiMascio, A. Dosage phenomena in the psychophysiology of phenyltoloxamine. Paper read at Bristol Laboratories Conference on P.R.N. in Syracuse, N. Y.

Klerman, G. L., and DiMascio, A. Differential effects of tranquilizers and placebo in normal subjects. Paper read at the Boston Society for Psychiatry and Neurology, April, 1959.

Klerman, G. L., DiMascio, A., Rinkel, M., and Greenblatt, M. The influence of personality factors on the effects of phrenotropic agents (an experimental procedure to integrate physiologic and psychologic action). Paper read at meeting of Society of Biological Psychiatry in May, 1958, at San Francisco. Published in Jules H. Masserman, M.D. (Ed.), *Biological psychiatry.* Vol. I. New York: Grune & Stratton, 1959.

Klerman, G. L., and Greenblatt, M. Personality and situational determinant of the placebo response. (In preparation.)

Comparative behavioral effects
of phenaglycodol,
meprobamate, and placebo

The study to be summarized (Reitan, 1957) was concerned with measuring possible adverse behavioral effects of phenaglycodol and of meprobamate. As a first consideration, the investigator felt a necessity to demonstrate that the behavioral testing procedures used were pertinent to the effects of the drug.

In order to show that the behavioral testing conditions were sensitive to adverse effects of the drugs, four times the customary clinical dose was administered to a group of twelve young, healthy physicians and medical students. These subjects were selected deliberately as the most reliable sample of individuals available. Each subject was tested three times (under each condition of medication) with a battery of psychological tests, a double-blind Latin square design being followed. Still another precaution was taken that probably should be followed routinely. Because an experimenter working with drugs gradually may become able to respond to minimal cues suggesting which medication the subject has received, the tests were given in a completely standard way by a technician who had no information whatsoever regarding the details of the experiment. The eight behavioral tests evaluated alertness, sustained attention, accuracy of visuomotor coordination, motor speed, reaction time, and problem-solving ability. Statistical comparison of the results obtained indicated significantly better performance on placebo than on either phenaglycodol or meprobamate.

Since it was thus demonstrated that the procedures and tests used were pertinent to the effects of the drugs in heavy doses, we were now in a position to obtain results under clinical conditions and with customary clinical doses. The same tests were therefore administered, according to the same experimental design, to a group of patients without positive physical findings who were suffering from neurotic disorders manifested principally by chronic somatic complaints. The results were consistently negative, indicating no reliable differences on any of the behavioral measures among the conditions of medication (placebo, phenaglycodol, or meprobamate). Thus while the behavioral measures had been shown to be pertinent to the adverse effects of the drugs under heavy dosages, no indications of behavioral impairment were present with clinical dosages for patients similar to those who might be treated in routine clinical practice.

Some Considerations of Method

The behavioral tests used in this type of experimental design should meet at least four criteria. They should have "face validity"; they should tap a variety of abilities; they should be relatively uninfluenced by positive practice effect on repeated administrations; and they should be the types of tasks that are particularly sensitive to any impairment of organic brain functions. The first two criteria probably need no elaboration.

Practice effect on repeated administrations of the behavioral tests represents a serious problem. Although the experimental design in this study was such that improvement from practice should have been distributed equally under the conditions of medication, one can have no assurance that this is actually achieved in small populations. A still more serious problem relates to the specific characteristics of statistical tests of significance. These tests are constituted typically of a ratio in which the numerator represents the estimated difference in results and the denominator represents the variance shown in the individual measurements. Any factor which contributes to the variance in results increases the size of the denominator and thereby decreases the likelihood of a given difference being significant. This problem is particularly acute in experiments with drugs, since one must anticipate that the effects of such transient and reversible influences will often be relatively slight in comparison with the aggregate of influences, genetic as well as environmental, that are known to affect the results obtained with psychological tests. The use of behavioral measures on which there is relatively little positive practice effect, therefore, represents a real advantage in evaluation of the effects of drugs.

The fourth criterion, that behavioral measures should be sensitive to organic brain dysfunction, is obvious if we assume that behavioral limitations effected by the drugs are the results of alterations of brain functions. Many years have been spent in the search for psychological tests specifically sensitive to structural brain damage, and only recently have promising results of cross-validation studies been published (Halstead, 1947; Reitan, 1955). The behavioral tests used in this study were selected on the basis of much experience in measuring the psychological effects of organic brain damage.

Finally, the selection of subjects may affect the variance estimate strikingly in intergroup comparisons. Most studies of the behavioral effects of drugs have used experimental groups composed according to criteria designed to make the sample at least somewhat representative of the population in question. The difficulty arising from the use of groups composed of patients is one concerning reliability of results obtained with behavioral measures. Many neurotic and psychotic patients, for example, cannot deliver consistent, high-level performance on successive examinations. Thus unreliability of performance may be another important source of variance sufficient to obscure as "statistically insignificant" real but small effects of a drug.

The necessity for showing that one's measuring instruments are appropriate and pertinent cannot be escaped. Such validity demonstration may be accomplished most effectively by using normal subjects. Even in studies proposing to demonstrate enhanced efficiency of behavior in pathological subjects after drug administration, the most reasonable approach in some instances may be to use normal subjects whose momentary efficiency has been impaired by experimentally induced stress or conflict.

R E F E R E N C E S

Halstead, W. C. *Brain and intelligence: a quantitative study of the frontal lobes.* Chicago: Univer. of Chicago Press, 1947.
Reitan, R. M. Investigation of the validity of Halstead's measures of biological intelligence. *Arch. Neurol. Psychiat.*, 1955, 73, 28–35.
Reitan, R. M. The comparative effects of placebo, Ultran, and meprobamate on psychologic test performances. *Antibiotic Med. clin. Ther.*, 1957, 4, 158–165.

Chemotherapy and pharmacodynamic
experimentation with schizophrenics

Our approach at first was clinical and very empirical, consisting of a series of therapeutic trials with hospitalized schizophrenics. But very soon we began to search for the cause of therapeutic improvements and other changes, and we started a series of experimental polygraphic and psychometric studies. We also tested serotonin, which is considered an intermediary chemical agent in the brain and may be involved in the mechanism of action of certain psychoactive drugs.

Clinical Observations:
Chemotherapy of Schizophrenia

Since 1953 we have concentrated on a technique of tranquilizer therapy by chlorpromazine combined with phenobarbital and promethazine to induce not a true and continuing sleep, but rather successive states of relaxation and drowsiness (Lafon, Duc, Minvielle, and Maurel, 1953): the cure of somnolency.

Afterwards we became interested in using both chlorpromazine and electroshock in certain cases, either for patients who were not responding to the course of drug therapy or to obtain a rather long lasting sleep following a shock therapy (Pelissier, Minvielle, and Dutarte, 1956). The results from similar use of reserpine were slightly worse, but none the less useful (Lafon, Duc, Abric, Pouget, and Comelade, 1956). Prochlorperazine gave us good results in those cases of schizophrenia which had not been helped by other treatments (Duc, Minvielle, and Danan, 1957).

Experimental Research

Three drugs were tested by polygraphic and psychometric methods: chlorpromazine, reserpine, and serotonin. The studies were most often done jointly and comparatively. Almost all the patients were schizophrenics.

POLYGRAPHY. 1. HEART TENSION MODIFICATIONS: THE SYMPATHOGRAM (Faurre, 1959). *Technique.* This method is described in detail elsewhere (Lafon and Faurre, 1955). It is based on the changes in pulse and in arterial pressure elicited by sympathetic (solar reflex, changes in orthostatic blood pressure) and parasympathetic (oculocardiac reflex, changes in blood pressure upon reclining) excitations as well as intravenous injections of atropine (Danielopolu's test for the determination of sympathetic and vagal tonus).

In this manner each of 15 schizophrenics was given four successive tests; the first without treatment, the second after intravenous injection of 25 mg. of chlorpromazine, the third after intravenous injection of 2.5 mg. of reserpine, and the fourth after intravenous injection of serotonin-creatinine sulfate. These patients had previously been unresponsive to treatment.

Results. Chlorpromazine brings about a tachycardia and a sharp decrease in blood pressure, as a result of a strong increase in sympathetic excitability and tonus. The parasympathetic effects are much less marked (Lafon, Duc, Minvielle, and Faurre, 1957a).

Reserpine lowers vagal tonus and curbs the excitability of the autonomic nervous system. Its action is clearly different from that of chlorpromazine; this can be explained (animal experimentation; clinical and EEG data from patients) by a different locus of action in the nervous system centers (Lafon, Boyer, Duc, Minvielle, and Pouget, 1956; Lafon, Duc, Minvielle, and Faurre, 1957a).

Serotonin's primary effect is to trigger a tachycardia; less often, it produces an increase in arterial pressure. These reactions are accompanied by clinical symptoms, such as a sensation of discomfort or of oppression in the chest, chills or hot flashes, or headaches. These aberrations are fleeting and never reach a disturbing degree (Lafon, Boyer, Duc, Minvielle, and Pouget, 1956; Lafon, Duc, Minvielle, and Faurre, 1957b).

2. MODIFICATIONS OF THE ELECTROCARDIOGRAM, OF RESPIRATION, AND OF THE EEG. The respiration, EEG, and EKG were also recorded at the same time that the blood pressure was recorded on the oscillograph.

Results. Intravenous injections of chlorpromazine (Pelissier, Minvielle, and Dutarte, 1956) at first speed the EEG and then produce slow waves. These are followed by waxing-waning phenomena and finally by a light sleep. In epileptics these changes are much more intense. Sleep is preceded by a period of facilitation and the epileptic abnormalities are exaggerated in the ten minutes following the injection (in 30 cases out of 34). These results suggest an effect on the non-specific formations of the brain stem, notably the reticular formation.

Reserpine does not noticeably change the EEG of schizophrenics in the dosages. This is in contrast to the facilitation which was found in epileptics (Passouant, Minvielle, and Cadilhac, 1957); a sleep trace, however, is not generally obtained in the second phase.

Serotonin (Lafon, Duc, Minvielle, and Faurre, 1957b) does not appreciably affect cerebral electrical activity. Although respiration rate changes in most cases, the changes are not systematic.

PSYCHOMETRY. TESTS USED. In this type of research we have had to limit ourselves to tests which demand a minimum amount of active participation on the part of the patient (responses by simple gestures, pencil marks, or single words). Furthermore, the test must be capable of being given on repeated occasions without practice effects. Finally, testing time must be short in order to avoid fatigue (Lafon, Boyer, Duc, Minvielle, and Pouget, 1956; Lafon, Duc, Boyer, Abric, and Pouget, 1956).

The psychological aspect of our investigation examined patients' overt behavior and cooperation during the tests; the rapidity and precision of attentive mechanisms; memory capacities; the efficiency of general intelligence; and characteristic differences in personality.

The battery of tests consists of the Zazzo "barrage of symbols"; the repetition of a series of numbers, forward and backward; Raven Progressive Matrices, and the Szondi test.

Results. The study with chlorpromazine was done on too small a number of cases to permit any conclusions to be drawn.

Reserpine, by single intravenous injection, slightly improves attention and sometimes gives rise to an outburst of aggression (Szondi). Over a longer period of time, in the course of regular treatment, attention becomes more efficient and its output improves. No changes are observed in memory or in general intelligence. The Szondi test frequently shows the release of strong affective feelings, which may indicate an attitude of withdrawal and fear of exteriorization of the aggression which tends to be released.

In general, reserpine causes a slight feeling of return to reality in schizophrenics. Their reactions become greater but also more labile. Although their intellectual efficiency is not altered, there are changes in their emotional states.

Serotonin sharply increases the output in Zazzo's test (diminution of omissions and errors). Similarly, there is an improvement in digit span. The scores on the Progressive Matrices are also better. On the Szondi test an outburst of aggression was clearly present in six out of ten cases. When administered to the same patients, the tests are much more conclusive after serotonin than after reserpine.

REFERENCES

Duc, M., Minvielle, J., and Danan, M.   Traitement de la schizophrenie par le 61-40 R.P. (proclorperazine).   Resultats cliniques et E.E.G. 55eme Congr. des alienistes et neurologistes de langue française, Lyon, Sept. 1957.

Faurre, L. E.   Exploration neuro-végétative générale et sympathogramme.   Thèse en pharmacie, Montpellier, 1959.

Lafon, R., Boyer, S., Duc, N., Minvielle, J., and Pouget, R.   Effets comparatifs de l'injection intra-veineuse de sérotonine et de réserpine.   Étude psycho-metrique, neuro-végétative et electroencéphalographique.   *Ann. med.-psychol.,* 1956, 114, 3, 463–367.

Lafon, R., Duc, N., Abric, J., Pouget, R., and Comelade, P.   Étude comparative de la chlorpromazine et de la réserpine dans les syndromes schizophreniques. *L'Encéphale,* 1956, 4, 368–371.

Lafon, R., Duc, N., Boyer, S., Abric, J., and Pouget, R.   Explorations psycho-logiques des malades traités par la chlorpromazine et la réserpine.   *L'Encéphale,* 1956, 4, 696–699.

Lafon, R., Duc, N., Minvielle, J., and Faurre, L. E.   Étude des effets végétatifs chez l'homme de la chlorpromazine et de la réserpine.   *Thérapie,* 1957, 12, 361–370.   (a)

Lafon, R., Duc, N., Minvielle, J., and Faurre, L. E.   Étude des effets végétatifs chez l'homme de la sérotonine.   *Thérapie,* 1957, 12, 371–375.   (b)

Lafon, R., Duc, N., Minvielle, J., and Maurel, H.   Cure de somnolence en pratique psychiatrique.   51eme Congr. des alienistes et neurologistes de langue française, Pau, juillet 1953.

Lafon, R., and Faurre, L. E.   Le sympathogramme.   Représentation graphique des résultats et de l'exploration analytique du système nerveux sympathique. *Ann. med.-psychol.,* 1955, 113, 1, 529–547.

Passouant, R., Minvielle, J., and Cadilhac, J.   Facilitation épileptique par la Réserpine.   55eme Congr. des alienistes et neurologistes de langue française, Lyon, septembre 1957.

Pelissier, H., Minvielle, J., and Dutarte, J.   Association chlorpromazine—electro-chocs en thérapeutique psychiatrique.   Observations cliniques et E.E.G. *L'Encéphale,* 1956, 4, 891–897.

Mental changes in psychopharmacology

The studies described in this chapter are typical of those possible in a hospital of 1200 patients, carried on by a minimal research staff, in this case one psychologist with a part-time assistant. They are cited more to illustrate problems of method than for the importance of the results; yet some of the findings are in new areas.

In the first study, 50 male patients in a closed ward were given chlorpromazine, 300 mg. three times a day for 18 weeks. An equal number of cases in a similar ward were administered placebos under what is optimistically called the double-blind procedure. Actually, within a week the psychiatric aides who were to rate effects knew which was the experimental ward.

A ward behavior scale of 12 trait-complexes, to be rated graphically according to degree of appearance from mild or ordinary to constantly excessive, was devised by Porteus. Ratings were quantified by position along a scale ranging from 0 to 6 inches. The terms used were suited to the understanding of aides. Aides were selected as raters on the basis of two premedication ratings of 100 patients given at two periods three weeks apart. To ensure a proper spread of ratings, the aides rated selected patients and also each other, so that they would realize that, with the exception of hallucinations, delusions, and possibly compulsive trends, the traits to some degree were characteristic of normal as well as of psychotic behavior. Any changes in rating in the premedication period had to be justified by actual evidence.

The premedication status was based on the average score of each patient on two ratings. His postmedication scores were plotted at three points, the average of the ratings for 3 and 6, the 9 and 12, and the 15 and 18 weeks. This was done to lessen the effects of fluctuations either in behavior or in raters' judgments. In all items but "asocialization," amelioration of symptom traits occurred, but at different times and rates. Sixty per cent of the experimental group and 11 per cent of the controls showed behavioral changes greater than 9 points (Porteus, 1956, 1957a, b).

Our experience led to the following methodological conclusions:

1. Administering placebos or no drug at all to one of two groups does not constitute an adequate control unless populations are large. In small hospital groups, cases should be first equated for suggestibility before they can serve as proper controls. We do not now know how to do this.

2. Fluctuations in specific behavior during medication are frequent, various degrees of improvement alternating with plateaus or temporary regressions. Rapid improvement occasions too favorable ratings, while plateaus become grounds for pessimistic judgments.

3. The most important factor is the training and supervision of raters. Pooling a number of raters' judgments yields only fictitious reliability.

In the second study Porteus and Barclay (1957) found that 22 patients suffered an average loss of 2.08 years or 15 test quotient points (usually called IQ), as measured on the Porteus maze. This is more than the loss recorded after frontal lobotomy (1.6 years) but less than the 3 years or more of Maze deficits apparent when a practice-free extension maze is used to measure losses.

To conform with the usual but dubious method of using controls drawn from an abnormal population, the study was repeated with 35 cases and 25 controls (Porteus and Barclay, 1957). The chlorpromazine group lost 1.89 years (13.5 T.Q. points), the controls 0.1 year. Twenty of the drug cases could be paired with 20 controls according to original Maze scores. The former lost 2.2 years (16 T.Q. points), while the latter *gained* 0.2 of a year.

From this experience we drew these further conclusions.

1. Research in small hospitals must be content with small numbers of cases, because of marked attrition. Changes in treatment or ward location, though sometimes necessary, seriously diminish the size of the study group.

2. The adequate equation of small groups is rarely possible. A single instance will suffice. Let us suppose that advanced age is a

factor in a project. Since senility and chronological age cannot be equated as regards mental decline, to use a hospital group averaging, say, 65 years to match with an experimental group of equal age is futile. Only if large groups were available would degenerative changes be balanced. Small control groups give the study only fictitious reliability.

3. Wherever possible, a research ward should be set up when stability of groups and constant psychological supervision is desired.

The repetition of the Maze after an interval of time revealed, as a by-product of our research, that it is possible to identify the performances of the same individual, using minimal data including only beginnings and endings of repeated Maze tracings in three test designs. This opened up a new dimension in Maze work—the area of subconscious memory of psychomotor reactions. If 90 per cent of all individuals are to this degree stimulus-bound and the consistency tendency can be expressed in a "similarities score," an obvious research project would be to measure the effect of psychoactive drugs on rigidity.

That drugs other than chlorpromazine cause similar Maze deficits is shown by a study by Bloom (1960). Twenty-two patients in separate groups were given a variety of psychoactive drugs. Before and after medication a number of tests, which had either proved sensitive or unaffected by psychosurgery, were applied. Of these, the only one which showed significant deficits was the Porteus Maze.

R E F E R E N C E S

Bloom, Bernard L.   Ataractic drugs and psychosurgery: psychological test parallels. 1960. (In press.)

Porteus, S. D.   Variations spécifiques du comportement sous l'effet de la chlorpromazine.   *Rev. psychol. appl.*, 1956, 6, No. 3, 187–202.

Porteus, S. D.   Maze Test reactions after chlorpromazine.   *J. consult. Psychol.*, 1957, 21, 15–21.   (a)

Porteus, S. D.   Specific behavior changes following chlorpromazine.   *J. consult. Psychol.*, 1957, 21, 257–263.   (b)

Porteus, S. D.   *The Maze Test and clinical psychology.*   Palo Alto, Calif.: Pacific Books, 1959.

Porteus, S. D., and Barclay, John E.   A further note on chlorpromazine: Maze reactions.   *J. consult. Psychol.*, 1957, 21, 297–299.

The use of psychoactive drugs
as a neuropsychological tool
in studies of attention in man

The primary purpose of the studies described in this chapter was to determine the relationship between attentive behavior and neural mechanisms. In this research, information gained from studies of the effects of psychoactive drugs upon the behavior of normal individuals has supplemented and supported interpretations of data gathered from patients with brain pathology. In addition, however, the drug studies have led to the formulation of hypotheses which may prove useful in dissociating from one another the behavioral functions required in the performance of various tests of attention, and in specifying the neural structures which mediate these functions. These studies also suggest that investigation of the differences in the behavioral effects of psychoactive drugs upon different psychopathological populations may help in the understanding of the fundamental nature of the disturbances in these groups.

Specifying the Neural Correlates
of the Deficit

The initial investigation in this series of studies of attentive behavior (Rosvold, Mirsky, Sarason, Bransome, and Beck, 1956) was based on the possibility of there being an association between impaired attention and hypersynchronous (high-amplitude) brain-wave activity. It was argued that, if hypersynchrony is associated with reduced vigilance or attention, as suggested by its presence in the normal electroencephalogram (EEG) of sleeping (and therefore inattentive) subjects, then the brain-damaged subject who generally shows either irregular bursts of hypersynchronous activity or a general hypersynchrony should exhibit impaired attention. In the case of the patient showing only intermittent bursts of such activity, only momentary lapses should occur. In order for a psychological test to reflect such lapses, it should provide a measure of omitted responses; otherwise, it would fail to detect the impaired attention. Thus the failure of the usual measures of attentive behavior (e.g., the Digit Span and the Digit-Symbol subtests of the Wechsler-Bellevue Scale) to show decline following brain damage (Mettler, 1949, 1952; Partridge, 1950; Petrie, 1952) might result from the fact that these tests do not provide a measure of the omitted responses, but only of those committed between lapses. In addition, these tests might not be of sufficient duration to reflect the behavioral effects of an appreciable number of lapses. The reduced vigilance associated with hypersynchronous activity would then not affect the score to any measurable extent.

On the other hand, a test which would require responses at specific points in time, regardless of the individual's readiness to respond (paced by the experimenter, in Broadbent's [1953] terms), and which would require performance over an appreciable interval of time, might

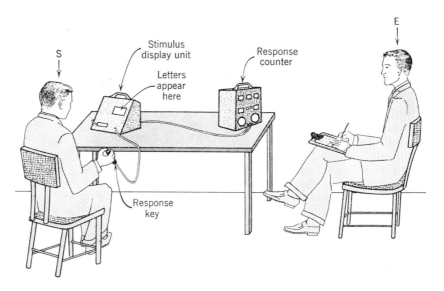

Figure 1. Semischematic view of the CPT apparatus currently used in studies of attention.

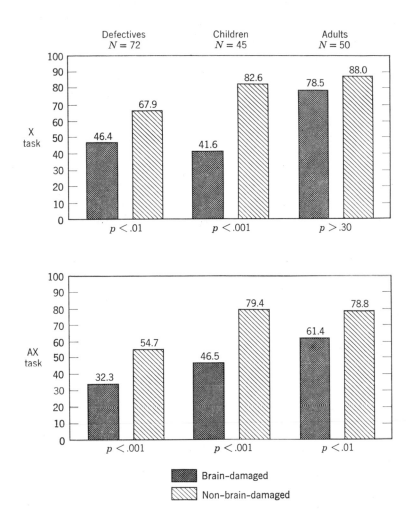

Figure 2. A summary of the results of the study by Rosvold et al. (1956). Three separate populations of individuals were studied, including in each case a subgroup with brain damage and a matched subgroup without brain damage. In each of the three populations, i.e., mental defectives, children of normal intelligence, and adults of normal intelligence, the subgroup with brain damage tended to perform more poorly on the X and AX tasks than the other subgroup.

reflect a deficit that other procedures would miss. Accordingly, the Continuous Performance Test (CPT) was designed to provide two such attention tasks, labeled X and AX. The subject watches for periods of 10 minutes a continuous display on which letters appear one at a time. He is instructed, in the first task, to press a response key whenever the letter X appears; in the second task, he is instructed to press whenever X follows immediately after the letter A. Figure 1 presents a semischematic view of the apparatus.

The results of the initial study (Rosvold, Mirsky, Sarason, Bransome, and Beck, 1956) using this technique, which are summarized in Fig. 2, suggested that individuals with brain damage did, in fact, perform more poorly than matched groups of persons without brain pathology. On the basis of these results, another study (Mirsky, Primac, Ajmone-Marsan, Rosvold, and Stevens, 1960) was undertaken with the intention of specifying more precisely the neural locus of the function involved in the test. In this study the location of the electroencephalographic abnormality, and presumably, therefore, the brain locus of the pathology determined the selection of the subjects. There were three groups of epileptic patients with foci of abnormality in either the frontal lobes, the temporal lobes, or the "centrencephalon," i.e., in subcortical structures which include the mesodiencephalic reticular formation (MRF) according to the formulation of Penfield and Jasper (1954). The results (Fig. 3) revealed that the patients with focal, presumably cortical abnormality showed no deficit on the CPT. Furthermore, on the basis of some unpublished observations, it can be said that unilateral frontal and temporal lobe cortical removals do not interfere with performance on this test. The patients with the "centrencephalic" abnormality, on the other hand, were markedly impaired on the AX task of the CPT, despite statistical matching with the focal groups in terms of IQ, age, frequency of seizures, duration of illness, and total amount of EEG abnormality. Thus the poor performance of the brain-damaged individuals in the initial study could be attributed to subcortical involvement in those patients.

The fact that in the second study only the centrencephalic patients performed poorly on this test of attention suggests that it is particularly sensitive to the effects of subcortical, probably MRF, dysfunction. Other studies suggest that involvement of the structures of the MRF may affect the functions of attention, alertness, and wakefulness. Lindsley, Bowden, and Magoun (1950) have shown that lesions in the area of the midbrain tegmentum will render animals

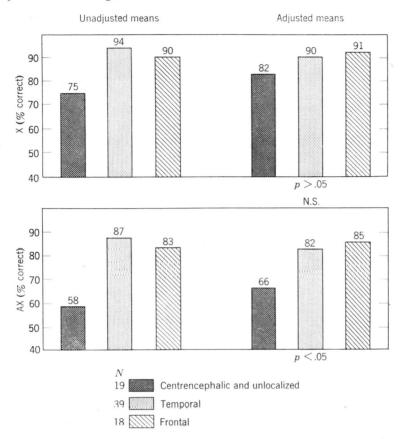

Figure 3. A summary of the results of the study by Mirsky et al. (1960). The raw (unadjusted) means and the multiple covariance-adjusted means of the three groups of epileptic patients on the X and AX tasks of the CPT are presented. In each case the centrencephalic group tended to perform more poorly than the other two epileptic groups. The scores of the temporal and frontal groups, in fact, do not differ significantly from the scores of the adult subgroup without brain damage (Fig. 2) in the study of Rosvold et al. (1956). Covariates: 1, age; 2, verbal IQ (W.B.); 3, performance IQ (W.B.); 4, memory quotient; 5, frequency of seizures; 6, duration of illness; 7, degree of abnormality (EEG).

permanently somnolent. Similarly, it is well known that lesions in the brain stem in humans may result in deep coma (Jefferson, 1952). Such evidence together with that from the present studies leads to the conclusion that the same neural structures are involved in coma and in impaired attentiveness. It may be that these behavioral changes are part of a continuum of impairment which corresponds roughly to the degree of involvement of the MRF structures.

The Nature of the Lesion

What is the nature of the lesion in centrencephalics? The fact is that necropsy material most often reveals no observable lesion in the brains of such patients, suggesting that the disorder results from some biochemical disturbance in the centrencephalon which is unaccompanied by obvious macroscopic or microscopic change (Penfield and Jasper, 1954). The usefulness of psychoactive drugs as a research tool in this context now becomes evident: a number of these agents produce temporary depression of the functioning of structures in the region of the MRF and thereby provide a means, perhaps, of producing for a brief period in the brains of normal individuals the kind of functional disturbance which may exist in the brain of the centrencephalic patient. Among those drugs which have been demonstrated to have a depressant action on brain structures in the region of the MRF are the barbiturates secobarbital, phenobarbital and pentobarbital, the tranquilizers chlorpromazine and meprobamate, and the psychotomimetic drug lysergic acid (LSD-25). If these drugs produce the same kind of impairment in normal individuals as is found in centrencephalic patients, then the argument that the deficit in the centrencephalic patient comes from a functional disturbance of this region of the brain is supported.

A number of studies were therefore undertaken to investigate the effects of these drugs on the CPT. With two exceptions, all these drugs in fact produced significant impairment in CPT performance of normal subjects. Figure 4 summarizes the results of those experiments in which significant impairment has been found, ranking the drugs in order from chlorpromazine, which produced the most impairment, to meprobamate, which produced the least impairment. Meperidine, which has only a minimal effect on subcortical structures (Wikler, 1950) has also been investigated; it was found to be without significant effect on the CPT (Primac, Mirsky, and Rosvold, 1957). No significant impairment was produced by LSD-25 (Primac, Mirsky, and Rosvold, 1957) or by phenobarbital (Townsend and Mirsky, 1960); we shall discuss later the lack of effect of these MRF-depressant drugs.

The dependence of the functions of sleep and wakefulness upon the integrity of structures in the MRF (Lindsley, Bowden, and Magoun,

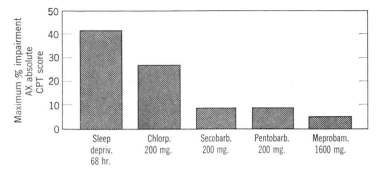

Figure 4. A summary of the studies in which significant impairment of the CPT performance of normal individuals has been found. The percentage impairment in each case is defined as the difference between the placebo and treatment scores divided by the placebo score (×100). The score presented for each treatment is the maximum percentage of impairment observed under the conditions of the experiment. The sleep deprivation scores are from Kornetsky et al. (1959); the pentobarbital scores from unpublished observations by Kornetsky and Mirsky; the chlorpromazine and secobarbital scores from Mirsky, Primac, and Bates (1959); and the meprobamate score from Townsend and Mirsky (1960).

1950) suggested another technique for producing temporary changes in this area of the brain in normal subjects. If it is assumed that prolonged sleep deprivation produces a functional impairment in this area of the brain (perhaps by altering the balance of humoral agents in the MRF) significant impairment in attentiveness should result and be reflected in CPT performance. Figure 4 shows the effect on CPT performance of 68 hours of sleep deprivation in a group of normal subjects; the amount of impairment is even greater than that produced by any of the MRF-depressant drugs which were employed to produce a functional change in the MRF. In addition, Williams, Lubin, and Goodnow (1959) and Kornetsky, Mirsky, Kammen, and Dorff (1959) have shown that sleep loss has a greater and earlier effect on CPT than on other tests.

The results of the drug and sleep deprivation studies indicate that agents which presumably produce a functional impairment of structures in the mesodiencephalic reticular formation can produce as much deficit in the CPT performance of normal individuals as is evident in patients with centrencephalic epilepsy. Therefore the interpretation that centrencephalic epilepsy is a functional, biochemical disturbance in the mesodiencephalic reticular formation would appear to be supported.

The Nature of the Deficit

The impaired performances of the centrencephalic patient and of the normal subject under the influence of MRF-depressant drugs appear to be similar. In each condition the deficit might be characterized as a series of irregular, momentary lapses in performance, resulting in errors of omission, rather than as a pervasive slowing of the capacity to respond, or as a tendency toward misidentification of the correct letter.

As was suggested in the rationale for the development of the CPT, such an episodic, phasic deficit might well be related to the abnormal electrical activity of the brain in these conditions. In order to demonstrate this relationship directly, techniques were developed for simultaneously recording a patient's responses on the CPT and the electrical activity of his brain. Figure 5 presents some sample recordings illustrating some of the phenomena which have been observed in the course of these investigations. The most frequent finding in the case of the centrencephalic patient (Fig. 5B) is that errors of omission on the CPT are coincident with the paroxysmal bursts of three-per-second spike and wave activity characteristic of this disorder (Penfield and Jasper, 1954). A similar finding was reported by Schwab (1939). However, errors of omission may also occur in the absence of observable discharge in the centrencephalic patient (error of omission to the right in Fig. 5C) and, curiously, in some patients coincident in time with what appears as EEG "alerting" or activation (Fig. 5D).

In contrast, there appears to be no effect on CPT behavior of the epileptic discharge activity recorded from patients with temporal lobe foci (Fig. 5E). Even when the abnormal electrical activity of patients with temporal lobe epilepsy is recorded from the cortex directly or from the depths of the temporal lobe, there is no measurable effect on CPT performance (Fig. 5F). This result supports the earlier findings of Mirsky, Primac, Ajmone-Marsan, Rosvold, and Stevens (1960) that temporal lobe patients are unimpaired on the CPT.

The simultaneous behavior-EEG recordings obtained from normal subjects under the influence of MRF-depressant drugs such as chlorpromazine or secobarbital have revealed little in the way of grossly observable punctiform EEG concomitants of errors of performance. In general, however, performance deteriorates as the EEG shows the characteristic changes accompanying the course of action of these various agents. Compare, for example, Figs. 5G and 5H, which show the performance of a normal subject before and after, respectively, administration of 200 mg. of chlorpromazine.

In summary, the simultaneous behavior-EEG records suggest that errors of omission on the CPT may accompany the characteristic electrographic abnormality of the centrencephalic patient, but that there is little effect of temporal lobe (presumably focal cortical) abnormality on CPT performance. Gross inspection of the records of the other conditions (i.e., chlorpromazine, secobarbital) in which some clear behavioral-EEG relationship might have been expected reveals little in the way of a punctiform relationship. However, the possibility that some less obvious relation between EEG patterns and errors of omission might exist is suggested by the coincidence of errors with flattening or activation of the record, as illustrated in Fig. 5D. A more refined analysis of the amplitude and frequency of the EEG record than it is possible to do with visual inspection might reveal some reliable electrographic change associated with errors. This possibility seems likely in view of the results of the sleep deprivation studies of Williams, Lubin, and Goodnow (1959) in which automatically recorded amplitude analysis of the EEG revealed a significant tendency for errors of omission on a continuous performance test to be associated with depressions of alpha. The relevance of such changes in the baseline or alpha activity to brain-stem functioning is suggested by the work of Garoutte and Aird (1958) which indicates that alpha activity is regulated by a central pacemaker in the region of the MRF. Moreover, that modifications in the baseline activity may in fact reflect abnormal activity of the brain-stem region is suggested by the study of Kreindler, Zuckermann, Steriade, and Chimion (1958) in which experimentally produced brain-stem convulsions in cats were noted at times to be without grossly observable cortical changes with the exception of a momentary flattening or "activation" of the background activity. Thus, for example, the errors of omission illustrated in Fig. 5H and on the right side of Fig. 5C may represent the behavioral accompaniment of abnormal paroxysmal brain-stem activity which is not reflected in gross changes in the scalp EEG.

Another line of investigation suggested by the similarity of the episodic nature of the deficit accompanying centrencephalic epilepsy, the administration of MRF-depressant drugs, and sleep deprivation is suggested by the discussion of Elkes concerning the transmitter role of acetylcholine in the central nervous system: "Its concentration is higher in the brain in sleep . . . and in anesthesia . . . than in wake-

(A)

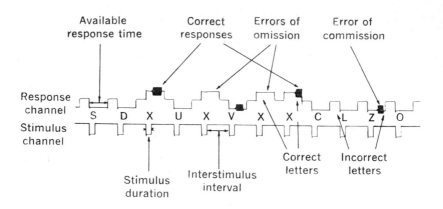

(C)

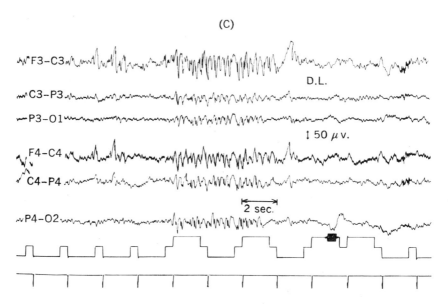

Figure 5. Representative samples of some of the phenomena which have been observed in studies employing simultaneous recording of CPT behavior and the EEG. A explains the scheme for coding CPT behavior used in B through H. The two bottom channels in each case are used to represent the stimulus display and the subject's responses; the top six channels are EEG. Letters requiring a

(B)

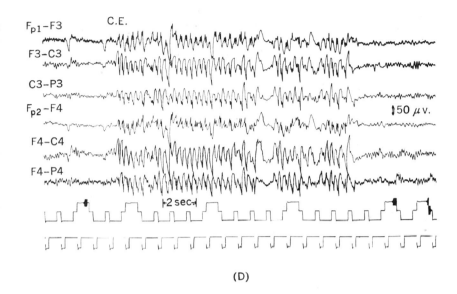

(D)

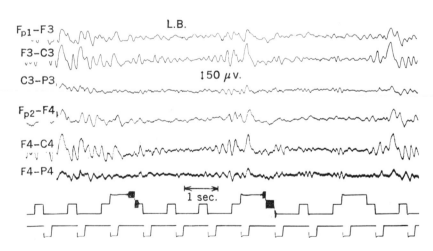

Figure 5 (Continued)

response (i.e., "X") cause an upward deflection of the baseline of the response channel; other letters produce a downward deflection of the baseline. Responses appear as heavy black signals on the response channel; those occurring at times other than during the available response time of a correct letter (i.e., "X") are

(E)

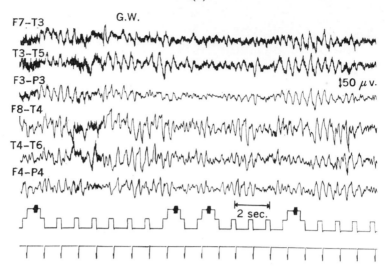

(G)

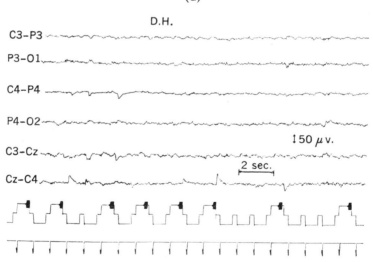

Figure 5   (Continued)

scored as errors of commission.   Each presentation of a letter appears as a downward deflection of the stimulus channel, the width of the deflection corresponding to the length of time the stimulus is presented to the subject.   The EEG

(F)

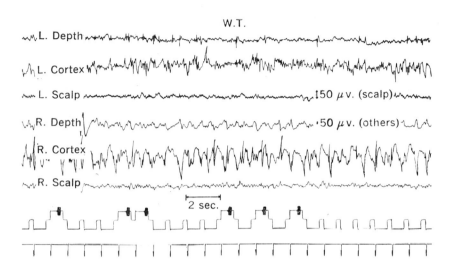

(H)

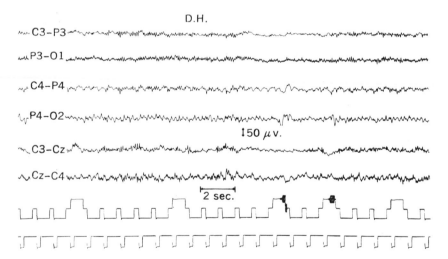

Figure 5 (Continued)

channel designations in B, C, D, E, G, and H correspond to scalp electrode placements as described by Penfield and Jasper (1954). The text provides a description of the individuals from whom these records were obtained.

fulness . . . . It shows a phasic variation in content following electrical stimulation . . . . Its precise state . . . has been implicated in the genesis of the epileptogenic discharge" (Elkes, 1958, p. 306). It may be that the fine balance of humoral agents which is probably required for efficient performance on a task such as the CPT is irregularly disrupted by abnormal chemical activity in the MRF of the centrencephalic patient and the drugged or sleep-deprived normal subject. In view of this, it would seem profitable to investigate the relationship between phasic variations in performance and in the concentration of humoral agents within the nervous system, perhaps by direct injection of substances such as acetylcholine into the brain of an animal performing on a task similar to the CPT.

Comparison of the Digit-Symbol
Substitution Test with the CPT
An Apparent Dissociation of Function

Kornetsky (cf. Chapter 18) has used the Digit-Symbol Substitution Test (DSST) quite extensively in the investigation of the effects of psychoactive drugs. Performance of this test, which requires the subject to write symbols beneath numbers in accordance with a predetermined code, necessitates sustained attentive performance, and attention to a visual "display." A *priori*, there would be little reason to assume that the CPT was tapping any fundamentally different behavior from that involved in the DSST. However, in view of the experimenter-paced nature of the CPT, as opposed to the non-paced nature of the DSST, it might be expected that the CPT would present a more sensitive measure of impairment in attentiveness than that provided by the DSST. This, in fact, was the rationale behind the design of the CPT (Rosvold, Mirsky, Sarason, and Bransome, 1956). The only evidence which might suggest *a priori* that this formulation is oversimplified is the fact that the correlation between the two tests, although significant, is low ($r = .375$ to $.410$) and the fact that CPT correlates less highly with Full Scale IQ ($r = .461$ to $.464$) than does DSST ($r = .673$ to $.697$, third highest correlation of the ten Wechsler-Bellevue subtests).

When the effects on these two tests of various agents which presumably affect the MRF are compared, it is apparent that there is no simple relationship between degree of deficit on the CPT and degree of deficit on the DSST. As Fig. 6 clearly shows, secobarbital,

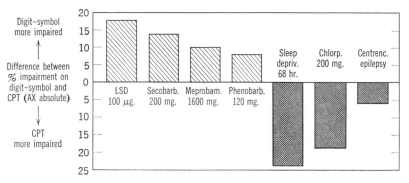

Figure 6. The several agents which impair DSST more than CPT (above the baseline) and those which produce the reverse effect (below the baseline). The percentages of impairment from which these differences were obtained in each case are defined as in Fig. 4, with the exception of the column representing centrencephalic epilepsy. Since there is no "placebo" score with which to compare the effects of the "treatment" (centrencephalic epilepsy), the percentages of impairment were obtained by comparison of the mean CPT and DSST scores of the centrencephalic patients with those of the temporal lobe epileptic patients in Mirsky et al. (1960). The data on which the other difference scores are based are from the following sources: LSD, Primac et al. (1957) and Kornetsky et al. (1957); secobarbital, Mirsky et al. (1959) and Kornetsky and Humphries (1958); meprobamate, Townsend and Mirsky (1960); chlorpromazine, Mirsky et al. (1959) and Kornetsky et al. (1957); sleep deprivation, Kornetsky et al. (1959); and phenobarbital, unpublished observations by Kornetsky and Mirsky.

phenobarbital, LSD-25, and meprobamate impair performance of the DSST more than of the CPT, whereas the reverse is true with respect to chlorpromazine, sleep deprivation, and, possibly, centrencephalic epilepsy. (As noted in a previous section, phenobarbital and LSD are in fact without significant effect on the CPT.) The apparent dissociation between the two classes of agents suggests that the two tests are not measuring precisely the same function and that the loci of the effects of the two classes of agents are different. The specific details of the analysis of the differences between the two tests are too lengthy for inclusion in this report; in brief, there are electrographic and neurophysiological similarities among the agents which affect the DSST more than the CPT, and among those agents which have the reverse effect. The difference between the effects of the two classes of agents on the two tests appears to come from the fact that the DSST is more sensitive than the CPT to the effects of agents (barbiturates, LSD, meprobamate) which have a major depressant effect on the cortex as well as upon subcortical structures (Brazier, 1954; Evarts, 1957; Pfeiffer, Riopelle, Smith, Jenney, and Williams, 1957). By virtue of its dependence on intact cortical functioning, the DSST might thus be viewed primarily as a cognitive test. On the other hand, the CPT is more sensitive to the effects of agents (chlorpromazine, sleep deprivation, centrencephalic epilepsy) which have their primary effects on subcortical, MRF structures (Unna, 1957; Bjerner, 1949; Penfield and Jasper, 1954). The CPT may thus be viewed primarily as a test of attentiveness or alertness.

This type of analysis suggests a way in which the available information about the neurophysiological effects of centrally acting drugs may aid in determining the locus of the structures which subserve the behavior measured by specific tests.

Implications for Psychopathology

Studies of the behavioral effects of centrally acting drugs, when viewed in the light of the neurophysiological evidence of their locus of action, may prove useful in investigating psychopathological states. For example, Kornetsky (see Chapter 18) has shown that schizophrenic subjects to whom chlorpromazine has been administered do not exhibit the same amount of impairment on some performance tests as do normal persons. Some preliminary observations suggest the same to be true of the effect of chlorpromazine on the CPT in schizophrenics. This suggests that the receptor sites, in the MRF for the effects of this drug are altered in the schizophrenic, and that it might be profitable to study schizophrenia as though it were a functional disturbance like centrencephalic epilepsy.

Study of the differences between the behavioral response of the schizophrenic and the normal individual to psychoactive drugs and other agents may possibly provide useful clues to understanding the fundamental nature of schizophrenia.

REFERENCES

Bjerner, B. Alpha depression and lowered pulse rate during delayed actions in a serial reaction test. *Acta Physiol. Scand.*, 1949, 19, Suppl. 65.

Brazier, M. A. B. The action of anesthetics on the nervous system. In E. D. Adrian and H. H. Jasper (Eds.), *Brain mechanisms and consciousness.* Springfield, Ill.: Charles C Thomas, 1954, 163–199.

Broadbent, D. E. Noise, paced performance and vigilance tasks. *Brit. J. Psychol.*, 1953, 44, 295–303.

Elkes, J. Drug effects in relation to receptor specificity within the brain: some evidence and provisional formulation. In *Ciba Foundation symposium on the neurological basis of behavior.* London: Ciba Foundation, 1958, 303–332.

Evarts, E. V. A review of the neurophysiological effects of lysergic acid diethylamide (LSD) and other psychotomimetic agents. *Ann. N. Y. Acad. Sci.*, 1957, 66, 479–495.

Garoutte, B., and Aird, R. B. Studies on the cortical pacemaker: synchrony and asynchrony of bilateral recorded alpha and beta activity. *Electroencephalog. clin. Neurophysiol.*, 1958, 10, 259–268.

Jefferson, H. Altered consciousness associated with brain stem lesions. *Brain*, 1952, 75, 55–67.

Kornetsky, C., and Humphries, O. Psychological effects of centrally acting drugs in man. Effects of chlorpromazine and secobarbital on visual and motor behavior. *J. ment. Sci.*, 1958, 104, 1093–1099.

Kornetsky, C., Humphries, O., and Evarts, E. V. A comparison of the psychological effects of certain centrally acting drugs in man. *Arch. Neurol. Psychiat.*, 1957, 77, 318–324.

Kornetsky, C., Mirsky, A. F., Kammen, E. K., and Dorff, J. E. The effects of dextro-amphetamine on behavioral deficits produced by sleep loss in humans. *J. Pharmacol. exp. Therap.*, 1959, 127, 46–50.

Kreindler, A., Zuckermann, E., Steriade, M., and Chimion, D. Electroclinical features of convulsions induced by stimulation of brain stem. *J. Neurophysiol.*, 1958, 21, 430–436.

Lindsley, D. B. Electroencephalography. In J. McV. Hunt (Ed.), *Personality and the behavior disorders*, New York: Ronald, 1944, 1033–1103.

Lindsley, D. B., Bowden, J. W., and Magoun, H. W. Behavioral and E.E.G. changes following chronic brain stem lesions. *Electroencephalog. Neurophysiol.*, 1950, 2, 483–498.

Mettler, F. A. (Ed.) *Selective partial ablation of the frontal cortex.* New York: Hoeber, 1949.

Mettler, F. A. (Ed.) *Psychosurgical problems.* New York: Blakiston, 1952.

Mirsky, A. F., Primac, D. W., Ajmone-Marsan, C., Rosvold, H. E., and Stevens, J. R. A comparison of the psychological test performance of patients with focal and non-focal epilepsy. *Exp. Neurol.*, 1960, 2, 75–89.

Mirsky, A. F., Primac, D. W., and Bates, R. The effects of chlorpromazine and secobarbital on the continuous performance test. *J. nerv. ment. Dis.*, 1959, 128, 12–17.

Partridge, M. *Pre-frontal leucotomy.* Springfield, Ill.: Charles C Thomas, 1950.

Penfield, W., and Jasper, H. *Epilepsy and the functional anatomy of the human brain.* Boston: Little, Brown, 1954.

Petrie, A. *Personality and the frontal lobes.* New York: Blakiston, 1952.

Pfeiffer, C. C., Riopelle, A. J., Smith, R. P., Jenney, E. H., and Williams, H. L. Comparative study of the effect of meprobamate on the conditioned response, on strychnine and pentylenetetrazol thresholds, on the normal electroencephalogram, and on polysynaptic reflexes. *Ann. N. Y. Acad. Sci.*, 1957, 67, 734–745.

Primac, D. W., Mirsky, A. F., and Rosvold, H. E. Effects of centrally acting drugs on two tests of brain damage. *Arch. Neurol. Psychiat.*, 1957, 77, 328–332.

Rosvold, H. E., Mirsky, A. F., Sarason, I., Bransome, E. B., Jr., and Beck, L. H. A continuous performance test of brain damage. *J. consult. Psychol.*, 1956, 20, 343–350.

Schwab, R. S. A method of measuring consciousness in petit mal epilepsy. *J. nerv. ment. Dis.*, 1939, 89, 690–697.

Schwab, R. S. *Electroencephalography in clinical practice.* Philadelphia: Saunders, 1951.

Townsend, A. M., III, and Mirsky, A. F. A comparison of the effects of meprobamate, phenobarbital and d-amphetamine on two psychological tests. *J. nerv. ment. Dis.*, 1960, 130, 212–216.

Unna, K. R. A review of the neurophysiological effects of psychotherapeutic drugs. *Ann. N. Y. Acad. Sci.*, 1957, 66, 777–783.

Wikler, A. Sites and mechanisms of action of morphine and related drugs in the central nervous system. *Pharmacol. Rev.*, 1950, 2, 435–506.

Williams, H. L., Lubin, A., and Goodnow, J. J. Impaired performance with acute sleep loss. *Psychol. Monogr.*, 1959, 73, 1–26.

Chapter 30   Enoch Callaway III and George Stone

Re-evaluating focus of attention

Some drugs make people less responsive to things occurring at the periphery of attention (Callaway and Thompson, 1953; Callaway and Dembo, 1958; Callaway, 1959). Drugs which have this psychological effect are also capable of increasing electroencephalographic arousal. Atropine, which can block or decrease electroencephalographic arousal, has the opposite effect (Callaway and Band, 1958). For example, atropine-treated subjects are more than ordinarily susceptible to interference from peripheral stimuli, yet they perform more efficiently than do control subjects when apparently irrelevant stimuli actually serve a useful function. Such findings led to the hypothesis that arousal is correlated with narrowed "focus of attention." This hypothesis allowed us to make some predictions, but the concept is far from satisfactory.

A recent book by Broadbent (1958) opens the way for re-evaluating the concept of focus of attention. The details of Broadbent's model are carefully worked out and supported by observations, but they can only be hinted at here. He considers that the human central nervous system has limited input channels and that the handling of sensory data can be effectively viewed in terms of information theory. The resulting model has some interesting characteristics which would seem to lead to a better interpretation of our experimental results. Several of the most important characteristics follow.

1. Information loading imposed by stimuli is a function of the size of the ensemble from which stimuli are expected to be drawn. For example: "We found much evidence that increase in the amount of

393

information per message made listening more difficult; in particular, when messages were chosen from a larger ensemble they interfered more even though they might be physically the same." (Broadbent, 1958, p. 41.)

2. The greater the overall information load, the slower are adaptive responses: "For example, Hyman [1953], working with visual reaction times found that as the ensemble of signals increased the reaction time went up, confirming the finding by Hick [1952] that reaction time was proportional to the information in the signal." (Broadbent, 1958, p. 85.)

3. The more subjectively probable a stimulus is, the more rapid will be the adaptive response to it. For example: "The probability of a listener hearing a word correctly varies with the probability of that word occurring in a particular situation." (Broadbent, 1958, p. 13.)

4. Incoming sensory data can be filtered to reject certain classes of stimuli. This filtering may operate according to a variety of criteria, but usually these criteria are physical properties such as position, sense modality, color, pitch, and form. For example: " . . . it is particularly hard to listen to one of two equally loud voices and becomes easier when the relevant one is fainter; this effect opposes the normal effect of signal-noise ratio." (Broadbent, 1958, p. 21.)

5. In addition to filtering, various other forms of coding can be used to reduce the overall information load. Thus: (a) Stimulus classes can be grouped and a whole set of stimulus possibilities can be lumped into one class. For instance, consider the usual process of lumping a number of stimulus possibilities as "background." This response has the effect of reducing ensemble size. (b) Stimuli are also probably more appropriately considered as sequences of events rather than as discrete instantaneous events. Reducing the sequence length considered reduces the number of stimulus classes that have to be considered. (c) A third important coding device might be called probabilistic coding. In conventional information theory, an ensemble of possible input classes imposes maximal information load if all classes are considered equally probable. When the classes can be considered in some hierarchy as to the probability of occurrence, then the information load is reduced. Thus: " . . . When Hyman altered the frequency of the signals instead of having them equally probable he found once again that this decrease in the average information per signal did give a decrease in the average reaction time." (Broadbent, 1958, p. 85.) This effect occurs in spite of an increased reaction time to the less likely signals.

This model has led us to re-evaluate some observations of the functioning of aroused or alerted people. Intuitively it would seem that the aroused individual tends to relinquish his probabilistic coding. Subjectively this would correspond to the feeling of "What now?" or "Anything may happen." Giving increased probability weighting to relatively unlikely events will increase the information load. If the information load is already close to the overload point, the aroused subject must either resort to filtering and other coding devices to reduce input or else run the risk of overload. We would therefore expect arousal to increase filtering and also lead to a reduction in the size of the probable stimulus ensemble considered. The latter could be accomplished either by grouping or by reducing the length of sequences considered.

It would seem that reducing the length of sensory sequences considered would not be a good strategy during periods of arousal. Longer samples of sensory data might be needed to make up for the greater uncertainty about expectation during arousal. Broadbent's book contains some evidence suggesting that input data reduction techniques applied during arousal do not include reduction of sequence length. The suggestive data come largely from experiments on conditioning and manifest anxiety.

The last point will need more experimental investigation, but at present our best prediction is that arousal will lead to: (1) reduced probabilistic coding (i.e., increased overall uncertainty with regard to the stimulus ensemble under consideration); (2) increased filtering (as in our previous concept of narrowed attention); and (3) reduced size of stimulus ensemble under consideration, accomplished by means of grouping.

Unfortunately, an ambiguity arises here. Extremely unlikely stimuli may be dropped out of consideration entirely by extremely aroused individuals instead of being considered as having heightened probability of occurrence. Because of this, in certain borderline cases we cannot predict *a priori* whether a particular stimulus possibility will be considered more than usually likely or will, on the other hand, be completely ignored. An additional difficulty arises because the probabilistic model makes no allowance for overall changes in levels of receptivity or responsiveness of the sensory and motor components of the system.

Nevertheless, the model does make some interesting predictions. A reduced ensemble of possible stimuli all considered more nearly equally probable than previously would imply a reduced ensemble of response possibilities all more nearly equally ready for expression than previously. This statement is analogous to the Hullian concept that increased drive elevates competing responses nearer to threshold. Thus the Broadbent model will generate Hullian predictions concerning certain effects of drive.

This model will also explain a number of other intriguing phenomena. For example, anxious people may show reduced flexibility but may at the same time have difficulty in maintaining set. This apparent paradox is resolved if one assumes that the total ensemble of expectancies is reduced (reduced flexibility), while all members of the remaining limited ensemble are treated as if they had more nearly equal probabilities of occurrence (thus, greater probability of shift in set).

The Broadbent model also handles narrowed attention, which Hullian theory fails to consider. For example, the pharmacologically aroused individual does better than an unaroused subject in naming the colors of inks used to print conflicting color names on the Stroop test (the names of colors are printed in inks of conflicting colors; e.g., the word "yellow" may be printed in red, blue, or green ink). This increased ability to ignore the distracting color names in calling off the actual colors was taken as evidence of narrowed attention. The Broadbent model would predict an increase in the filtering of interfering stimuli but would also give a supplemental explanation with an additional prediction. The printed word is the more probable stimulus for naming response, while color is a less probable one. The delayed processing of the less probable stimulus leads to the well-known tendency to read the word instead of naming the color. Arousal, by enhancing the expectancy of the less likely event, speeds the sensory processing of the color and so reduces color-word interference. If this explanation has any validity, then the arousal-increasing drugs should also speed the naming of colored spots (Stroop Card B). Analysis of our data shows that this is, in fact, the case and that scores derived by subtracting time for reading color alone from time for reading colors on words are less sensitive to drug effects than the sum of these two times.

Methamphetamine is one of the arousal-producing drugs used to narrow the focus of attention. According to the probabilistic coding hypothesis, this drug would increase uncertainty about expectation. In other words, if a set of events had unequal probabilities of occurrence, the relatively unlikely events would be dealt with as if their probability of occurrence had increased.

Amobarbital, on the other hand, gave some indications of broadening the focus of attention, and so might be expected to reduce uncertainty about expectations.

In an experiment of Brengleman (1958), subjects were presented figures made up of several geometrical forms, and were required to reproduce the figures or to recognize them at the end of 10 presentations. Subjects were tested after medication with dextro-amphetamine (similar to methamphetamine), amobarbital, and a placebo. Under the particular experimental conditions employed, recall was a relatively easy task. Since correct recall responses were the rule, they would be considered by the subjects as more likely than incorrect responses. Dextro-amphetamine should increase the subjective probability of unlikely events (i.e., make the subject suspect that the relatively rare incorrect responses had an increased probability of occurrence)—and in fact dextro-amphetamine was found to decrease certainty about adequacy of recall—without influencing the adequacy of recall itself. Amobarbital, on the other hand, increased certainty about adequacy of recall (i.e., caused subjects to give increased weighting to the more probable correct recalls).

With the more difficult recognition task, where correct and incorrect responses were almost evenly divided, both amobarbital and dextro-amphetamine reduced certainty about adequacy of recognition. This may represent a second sort of drug effect which amobarbital and dextro-amphetamine have in common, but our probabilistic coding hypothesis would make no prediction when the two sorts of events in a set had nearly equal probabilities of occurrence.

The concept of changed probability coding does not replace the concept that increased ability to filter out peripheral stimuli may also be playing a role in "narrowed attention." For example, Teitlebaum and Derks (1958) have studied the effect of amphetamine on the behavior of rats in an avoidance-type operant conditioning situation. Amphetamine appeared to limit the ability of the rat to make use of peripheral aspects of the conditioning situation while at the same time it increased responsiveness to the more central aspects of the situation. Thus " . . . they [the rats] were no longer discriminating the shock schedule or even the consequences of their responses, but were still performing the response that was appropriate to avoiding shock." This experiment would appear to demonstrate well a narrowed focus of attention in lower animals.

The Broadbent model makes some other interesting predictions which are being tested in our laboratory. Currently we are simultaneously recording polygraphic data and reaction times in human subjects. We vary the characteristics of the stimulus situation and can study a number of aspects of performance. By recording physiological variables and responses simultaneously, each response can be ranked according to the degree of "arousal" recorded at the moment of the response. In this way, use can be made of spontaneous fluctuations in arousal as a check on inferences made concerning the effects of drugs on "arousal."

Reaction-time experiments require data to be processed by the subject at once. Additional data can also be presented at the same time as the stimulus for a reaction-time response, processing of them being delayed until after the primary response. For example, the signal for a reaction-time response may have some characteristic that does not influence the response itself, but must be recorded by the subject after the response has been made. Both reaction-time stimuli and delayed response stimuli can be varied to alter information load and relevance of probabilistic coding. In this way we hope to study the actions of these hypothesized "filter" and probabilistic coding systems. Perhaps then we can see whether both drugs and spontaneous fluctuations in "arousal" influence these systems in predictable ways.

REFERENCES

Brenglemen, J. C.   *d*-Amphetamine and Amytal: II. Effect on certainty and adequacy of certainty in recall and recognition.   *J. ment. Sci.*, 1958, 104, 160–166.

Broadbent, D. E.   *Perception and communication.*   New York: Pergamon Press, 1958.

Callaway, E.   The influence of amobarbital and methamphetamine on the focus of attention.   *J. ment. Sci.*, 1959, 105, 382–392.

Callaway, E., and Band, R. I.   Some psychopharmacological effects of atropine: the preliminary investigation of broadened attention.   *J. Neurol. Psychiat.*, 1958, 79, 91–102.

Callaway, E., and Dembo, D.   Narrowed attention: a psychological phenomenon that accompanies a certain physiological change.   *J. Neurol. Psychiat.*, 1958, 79, 74–90.

Callaway, E., and Thompson, S. V.   Sympathetic activity and perception, an approach to the relationship between autonomic activity and personality.   *Psychosom. Med.*, 1953, 15, 443.

Hick, W. E.   On the rate of gain of information.   *Quart. J. exp. Psychol.*, 1952, 4, 11–26.

Hyman, R.   Stimulus information as a determinant of reaction time.   *J. exp. Psychol.*, 1953, 45, 188–196.

Teitlebaum, P., and Derks, P.   The effects of amphetamine on forced drinking in the rat.   *J. comp. physiol., Psychol.*, 1958, 51, 801–810.

Drug thresholds as indicators of personality and affect

The studies discussed below were stimulated by the hypothesis that individual differences in drug tolerance may reflect significant aspects of affect and personality. Two main steps were required to verify this hypothesis: (1) to devise objective and quantitative tests of specified drug effects; and (2) to show that these determinations vary significantly as a function of different affective states or personality patterns. It was possible to fulfill these aims by using barbiturates to determine sedation and "sleep" thresholds.

Sedation Threshold

PROCEDURE. Amobarbital is injected intravenously into human normal subjects or patients at the rate of 0.5 mg. per kg. per 40 sec. until well after speech is definitely slurred (Shagass, 1954). The frontal EEG is recorded simultaneously. The amplitude of fast activity (17 to 25 cycles per second), which is increased by amobarbital, is measured, preferably by means of an electronic integrator (Davis, 1956). A dosage-response curve is obtained by plotting fast frequency amplitude. This curve is usually S-shaped, and it contains a point of inflection which corresponds roughly in time to onset of slurred speech and perhaps more closely to onset of nystagmus to lateral gaze (Fink, 1958). The sedation threshold is the amount of amobarbital required to reach this inflection point.

RELIABILITY. The coefficient of correlation between thresholds determined on two occasions in 37 patients was .83. When 11 patients, who had shown significant clinical improvement at time of retesting, were excluded, the coefficient rose to .96 (Shagass, Mihalik, and Jones, 1957). These results indicated that the threshold is quite reliable and is sensitive to fluctuations in clinical status.

RESULTS IN NON-PSYCHOTIC SUBJECTS AND PATIENTS. Table 1 gives the mean thresholds and the percentage of above-average thresholds

TABLE 1. SEDATION THRESHOLD FINDINGS IN NON-PSYCHOTIC SUBJECTS AND PATIENTS

| | | Sedation Threshold (mg./kg.) | | |
Group	No. of Cases	Mean	S.E.	Per Cent 4 mg./kg. or more
Normal controls	45	3.09	0.11	15.6
Conversion hysteria	31	2.79	0.10	3.2
Hysterical personality	40	2.71	0.08	0.0
Mixed neurosis	54	3.40	0.10	35.2
Anxiety hysteria	22	3.91	0.18	54.6
Obsessive-compulsive	13	4.42	0.30	69.2
Neurotic depression	94	4.78	0.10	90.6
Anxiety state	54	5.27	0.12	98.1

for 45 non-patient control subjects and 308 patients diagnosed as psychoneurotic in a series of 750 consecutive psychiatric cases with technically valid tests (Shagass and Jones, 1958). Thresholds of the controls were intermediate between those of patients with hysteria and mixed neuroses and lower than those of all other psychoneurotic patients. Among the controls, higher thresholds were associated with symptoms of anxiety (Shagass and Naiman, 1955). In patients, the finding that thresholds increased in a gradient from hysteria to anxiety state supported the formulation that the threshold reflects the degree of manifest anxiety.

Another interpretation of the data in Table 1 is that the threshold reflects a personality trend along a hysterical-obsessional continuum, as the patients with neurotic depression and anxiety state were predominantly obsessional personalities. This is in accord with Eysenck's (1955) theory of introversion-extraversion as a personality dimension governing the clinical form of neuroses and reflecting quantitative variations in inhibitory potential. The prediction that the sedation threshold would be positively correlated with degree of introversion was confirmed in an experiment using the Gilford S and R scales to measure this personality dimension (Shagass and Kerenyi, 1958a). In the same study, ratings of hysterical-obsessional trend were also found to be correlated with the threshold.

It seems reasonable to formulate the results in non-psychotic subjects as indicating that the sedation threshold measures the activity of neurophysiological processes mediating anxiety in obsessional or introverted persons. This supposes that there are several processes mediating anxiety and that the process used is a function of personality pattern. This formulation accounts for decreases in the sedation threshold when anxiety is diminished (Shagass, Mihalik, and Jones, 1957).

RESULTS IN PSYCHOTIC PATIENTS. Table 2 gives the data for 350 psychotics. A formulation which seems to organize these results is

TABLE 2.   SEDATION THRESHOLD FINDINGS IN PSYCHOTIC PATIENTS

| | | Sedation Threshold (mg./kg.) | | Per Cent |
Group	No. of Cases	Mean	S.E.	4 mg./kg. or more
Organic psychosis	25	1.94	0.14	0.0
Psychotic depression	153	2.81	0.06	5.2
Paranoid state	12	3.00	0.16	8.3
Manic, hypomanic	10	3.45	0.29	40.0
Schizo-affective	16	2.84	0.19	6.3
Acute schizophrenia	19	2.66	0.17	0.0
Chronic simple schizophrenia	12	2.67	0.22	0.0
Other chronic schizophrenia	56	4.27	0.12	71.3
"Borderline" schizophrenia	47	4.70	0.17	83.0

that the threshold is inversely related to degree of impairment of ego functioning, in the gross sense of contact with reality. Thus the lowest thresholds were found in patients with organic psychoses, and the highest in the "borderline" schizophrenic group (Shagass, 1956). Thresholds in acute psychoses, either depressions or schizophrenias, were generally low. In schizophrenia, when symptoms had been present one year or more, thresholds were generally high (Shagass and Jones, 1958).

The low thresholds in psychotic depressions (manic-depressive or

involutional, agitated or retarded) permit one to differentiate these patients from those with neurotic depressions and anxiety states with a
high degree of accuracy (Shagass, Naiman, and Mihalik, 1956). The
sedation threshold predicted the outcome of convulsive therapy (Shagass and Jones, 1958) and it may point to unsuspected cases of depression (Kral, 1958).

"Sleep" Thresholds

PROCEDURE. Amobarbital or thiopental may be used. The injection, given as for the sedation threshold, is made without EEG recording and is continued to the point where the patient no longer makes
any observable attempt to respond to verbal stimulation. The judgment of the end point is not difficult (Shagass, Müller, and Acosta,
1959).

RESULTS. The correlation between the amobarbital "sleep" and
sedation thresholds was 0.66 (Shagass and Kerenyi, 1958b). In a
group of 201 patients the diagnostic relationships were similar for both
determinations, particularly regarding differentiating neurotic from
psychotic depressions.

The pentothal "sleep" threshold was applied to longitudinal study
of patients receiving electrotherapy (Shagass, Müller, and Acosta,
1959). It was shown that changes in the threshold were significantly
correlated with clinical evidence of affective change. Anger seemed
to produce marked increases in the threshold.

As no apparatus is required for the "sleep" threshold determination,
the evidence that it reflects affective changes and is related to psychiatric diagnosis makes it an attractive tool for investigation and clinical use.

Implications for Study of Drugs and Behavior

The results of these investigations leave little doubt that barbiturate
tolerance, as measured by threshold methods, reflects significant aspects of personality and affect. Kawi's demonstration (1958) that
alcohol and amobarbital sedation thresholds are positively correlated
is an indication that the threshold is not entirely dependent on the
specific drug. This may also be inferred from a previously noted
parallel between sedation threshold results and those obtained by
Pavlov in treating "experimentally neurotic" dogs with bromides

(Shagass, 1957). As barbiturates, alcohol, and bromides are all thought to be CNS. depressants, one might propose a "depressant threshold." However, a recent study of methedrine, a psychic energizer, suggested that excitant tolerance may be high in the same individuals who have high sedative tolerance (Shagass and Lipowski, 1958). Consequently it seems possible that there may be some general factor of cerebral resistance to drugs, which is related to personality.

It is tempting to ask whether one may be able to arrive at a classification of affective states by carrying out a few relevant drug threshold determinations. Such a classification might be meaningful in terms of diagnosis and indications for treatment. To answer this question, quantitative threshold methods for all types of psychoactive drugs, including tranquilizers and stimulants, will have to be developed. The main technical difficulty lies in discovering objective indicators of drug effects which are as specific as the effect of barbiturates on the EEG. It seems reasonable to expect that effort directed toward discovering such indicators will be rewarded. In our current research program we are attempting to study cortical potentials evoked in the intact human by sensory stimulation. It is hoped that the differential quantitative effects of drugs on these potentials will prove to be meaningfully related to personality and affect.

The great recent advances in neuropharmacology have intensified the need for methods which may be used to correlate behavioral and neural events. Drug thresholds may be used for this purpose, as there should be little difficulty in applying them to animals. One might then elucidate by animal studies the neurophysiological processes involved in human behavior which is correlated with the threshold.

R E F E R E N C E S

Davis, J. F. Low frequency analyzers in electroencephalography. Paper read at Instr. Soc. Amer., 1956, Paper No. 56-24-1.

Eysenck, H. J. A dynamic theory of anxiety and hysteria. *J. ment. Sci.*, 1955, 101, 28–51.

Fink, M. Lateral gaze nystagmus as an index of the sedation threshold. *Electroencephalog. clin. Neurophysiol.*, 1958, 10, 162–163.

Kawi, A. The sedation threshold. *Arch. Neurol. Psychiat.*, 1958, 80, 232–236.

Kral, V. A. Masked depression in middle aged men. *Canad. med. Ass. J.*, 1958, 79, 1–5.

Shagass, C. The sedation threshold. A method for estimating tension in psychiatric patients. *Electroencephalog. clin. Neurophysiol.*, 1954, 6, 221–233.

Shagass, C. Sedation threshold. A neurophysiological tool for psychosomatic research. *Psychosom. Med.*, 1956, 18, 410–419.

Shagass, C. A measurable neurophysiological factor of psychiatric significance. *Electroencephalog. clin. Neurophysiol.*, 1957, 9, 101–108.

Shagass, C., and Jones, A. L. A neurophysiological test for psychiatric diagnosis: result in 750 patients. *Amer. J. Psychiat.*, 1958, 114, 1002–1009.

Shagass, C., and Kerenyi, A. B. Neurophysiologic studies of personality. *J. nerv. ment. Dis.*, 1958, 126, 141–147. (a)

Shagass, C., and Kerenyi, A. B. The "sleep" threshold. A simple form of the sedation threshold for clinical use. *Canad. Psychiat. J.*, 1958, 3, 101–109. (b)

Shagass, C., and Lipowski, Z. J. Effect of methedrine on critical flicker fusion and its relation to personality and affect. *J. nerv. ment. Dis.*, 1958, 127, 407–416.

Shagass, C., Mihalik, J., and Jones, A. L. Clinical psychiatric studies using the sedation threshold. *J. psychosom. Res.*, 1957, 2, 45–55.

Shagass, C., Müller, K., and Acosta, H. B. The pentothal "sleep" threshold as an indicator of affective change. *J. psychosom. Res.*, 1959, 3, 253–270.

Shagass, C., and Naiman, J. The sedation threshold, manifest anxiety, and some aspects of ego function. *Arch. Neurol. Psychiat.*, 1955, 74, 397–406.

Shagass, C., Naiman, J., and Mihalik, J. An objective test which differentiates between neurotic and psychotic depression. *Arch. Neurol. Psychiat.*, 1956, 75, 461–471.

Preliminary results concerning the galvanic skin response as an indicator of drug effects

Few response measurements have been as widely used in both laboratory and clinical studies in physiology and psychology as the galvanic skin response (GSR). It reflects activity in the sympathetic nervous system and repeatedly has been shown to be a sensitive indicator of level of tension or "activation level." Many of the data supporting these statements are detailed in McCleary (1950), Lindsley (1951), and Woodworth and Schlosberg (1954). The latter two references, along with Duffy (1957) and Malmo (1957), elaborate the concept of activation level. Since the many diverse operations which affect activation level produce consistent changes in the basal electrical resistance of the skin and in the galvanic skin response, it would be expected that pharmacological agents such as the tranquilizers, which appear to reduce either level of tension or reactivity to stress, or both, would produce such changes also. Some experiments undertaken in this laboratory are designed to investigate this general hypothesis. One exploratory experiment and the directions being pursued currently will be described briefly.

The exploratory experiment consisted of two main parts, a period of relaxation followed by a period of reactivation and, subsequently, the performance of a simple task. A traditional lie-detection sequence was selected as the task.

Measurements of basal resistance level (BRL) were made four times during the procedure, once as soon as the subject was settled in the apparatus and had just been given the instructions to sit quietly, again five minutes later, and once more at eight minutes. Immediately after the eight-minute reading, additional instructions concerning the lie-detection procedure were read to the subject and, as soon as he acknowledged understanding of them, the final reading of BRL was made.

The lie-detection phase required the subject to select one of five blocks, each numbered from one through five. The subject noted the number of his selected block and placed it under a box. Selection of the block was at random and without knowledge of either the subject or the experimenter. The experimenter did not learn the identity of the selected block until the completion of the experiment. Instructions to the subject required him to answer either yes or no to all questions, but to answer all questions concerning the identity of blocks in the negative. Selection of the block by the subject was followed by a series of questions at approximately 20-second intervals. The first two questions were irrelevant and were inserted to minimize the series effects which are known to occur in this procedure. They were followed by five questions concerning the blocks, one each for the numbers one through five. Finally, an eighth question was asked which was a repetition of the question from the preceding five which gave the largest GSR. Questions were of the form "Did you take block number —?" The GSR was recorded after each question.

Both the GSR responses and the BRL's were measured with the "psychogalvanoscope" produced commercially by the Stoelting Company. Stainless steel finger electrodes were attached to the index and fifth fingers of the left hand after preparation of the surface by cleaning and the application of electrode jelly. With this instrument BRL can be measured to within 400 ohms apparent resistance, and the GSR to within 25 ohms.

Forty-two college students, all acquainted with the experimenter, participated as subjects. They were divided equally into drug and placebo groups on a random basis with double-blind control. All reported for drug administration one hour in advance of the actual starting time of the experimental procedure. The drug group received a single 400-mg. capsule of meprobamate, and the placebo group received an identical capsule of an inert substance.

The results will be discussed in three sections: (1) BRL during relaxation and reactivation; (2) overall GSR reactivity; and (3) success in detecting deception.

The four measurements of BRL for each group are given in Table 1, expressed as basal conductance levels relative to the level for the placebo group before relaxation. No differences between the drug and placebo groups are statistically significant. The changes in conductance with relaxation and reactivation are significant, e.g., comparing 0 and 8 minutes, conductance decreased for 19 of the 21 subjects in each group. Note the consistent pattern of changes, which is the same for both groups.

The analysis of overall GSR reactivity considered the total GSR responses to all eight questions in units of meter deflection, which is directly proportional to resistance. Mean responsiveness was 61.4 for the placebo group and 45.8 for the drug group. Because of the shape of the distributions, a test of significance was not computed. Variances were 1790 for the placebo group and 830 for the drug group. Six of the 21 subjects in the placebo group yielded scores greater than 100, while only one of the 21 who received the drug exceeded 100.

TABLE 1. BASAL CONDUCTANCE LEVELS BEFORE, DURING, AND AFTER RELAXATION EXPRESSED AS PERCENTAGE OF LEVEL FOR PLACEBO GROUP BEFORE RELAXATION

	Relaxation			
	0 min.	5 min.	8 min.	Reactivation
Placebo	100	85	79	106
Drug	111	97	92	117

GSR responses to the five critical questions were rank-ordered from high to low for each subject. A hit was defined as the case in which the rank order of the GSR to the question concerning the selected block was either one or two. In the placebo group 17 hits occurred for the 21 subjects, while in the drug group there were 11 hits out of 21. This difference is statistically significant. The probability of a hit, corrected for the chance probability of a hit, is .20 for the drug group and .68 for the placebo group. For the placebo group, the distribution of rank orders of GSR to the question concerning the selected block was highly different from chance expectancy ($p < .001$); for the drug group the same distribution could have been obtained by chance ($p = .25$).

These data justify no final conclusions. However, they do encourage further research, which we are undertaking at the present time. A number of refinements have been added. Permanent continuous records are now made with a Fels dermohmmeter. The drug dosage is increased over the minimal dose used above. The lie-detection situation has been redesigned to increase the involvement of the subject and the amount of information obtained per session while losing none of the interpretability of the method described above. A longer relaxation period is allowed and we are analyzing the records for sudden changes which occur during relaxation.

Of great interest is the possibility of using the method to study single individuals intensively. We have done only a little in this direction as yet, but the preliminary results suggest that the measurements can be made with sufficient repeatability to be useful in the search for individual differences in susceptibility to psychoactive drugs.

REFERENCES

Duffy, E. The psychological significance of the concept of "arousal" or "activation." *Psychol. Rev.* 1957, 64, 5, 265–275.
Lindsley, D. B. In S. S. Stevens (Ed.), *Handbook of experimental psychology.* New York: Wiley, 1951, Ch. 14.
McCleary, R. A., The nature of the galvanic skin response. *Psychol. Bull.,* 1950, 47, 97–113.
Malmo, R. B. Anxiety and behavioral arousal. *Psychol. Rev.,* 1957, 64, 5, 276–287.
Woodworth, R. S., and Schlosberg, H. *Experimental psychology.* New York: Holt, 1954, Ch. 6.

Drug effects and activation level

Recently Mitchell and Zax (1958) have shown that chlorpromazine increases basal skin resistance (BSR). Moreover Howe (1958) has shown that BSR is, at a high level of confidence, greatest for schizophrenics, least for chronically anxious, and intermediate for normals. These data from a conditioning procedure also show that schizophrenics for whom the galvanic skin response (GSR) did not become conditioned were more deteriorated clinically than those who were conditionable. In conjunction with another result of Mitchell and Zax's study (i.e., patients given chlorpromazine were less conditionable than control patients), these results suggest that the use of tranquilizing drugs should be undertaken with due regard to the level of autonomic function of the patient lest this level be altered in an undesirable direction.

Our research is an initial investigation of the effects of drugs on activation level during and preceding a moderate stress. It is also designed to appraise the long-term reliability of BSR adaptation of mental patients during stress.

The research population consisted of two groups of 16 patients each, one group being composed of 13 on various tranquilizers plus three on iproniazid, and the other group consisting of patients who did not receive drugs. The subjects had been chosen to equate the two groups approximately with respect to the following characteristics: age, sex, race, diagnostic category, duration of hospitalization, and degree of manifest agitation.

Reprinted, with permission, and with additions, from Science, 1959, 129, 784.

Silver electrodes, stabilized by reversing polarity every 3.1 seconds, were applied to the palms of each patient's hands. The patient reclined on a couch and was instructed to look continuously at a strobolux which delivered a large field of flickering light from a distance of 7 feet. The strobolux was turned on after a resting period of 10 minutes and remained on for 7 minutes. BSR readings separated by half-minute intervals were made during the following periods: (1) 0.5 to 1.5 minutes, the initial resting period; (2) 9 to 11.5 minutes; and (3) 16 to 17 minutes. After a three-day interval the procedure was repeated on each patient.

Two test-retest reliabilities were computed for the following scores, which were selected in advance of the data:

$$Q_1 = \frac{R_{17} - R_{10.5}}{R_{10} - R_{10.5}} \quad \text{and} \quad Q_2 = \frac{R_{17} - R_{10.5}}{R_{10.5}}$$

The subscripts denote the time at which the basal resistance, R, was measured. Q_1 is the amount of recovery of basal resistance from a low point one-half minute after the onset of flicker to the cessation of flicker 6.5 minutes later, expressed as a fraction of the initial lowering of basal resistance caused by the flicker. Q_2 is the same recovery or adaptation expressed as a fraction of the resistance at the low point, one-half minute after the onset of flicker.

Although Q_1 is highly recommended in the literature as a recovery quotient, its use gave insignificant reliabilities. The data strongly suggest that this is partly due to anticipatory activation during the second session. The use of Q_2, which is not influenced by anticipatory activation during the resting period of the second session (since its denominator is the BSR just after the onset of strobolux stimulation) gave rank-order correlations of .72 ($p < .01$) for both drug and control groups, and a total product-moment coefficient of .78 ($p < .01$) for the combined groups. In order to evaluate the elements contributing to the reliability of the ratio score, product-moment coefficients were computed for the following three measures: $R_{17} - R_{10.5}$, $R_{10.5}$, and the change in the former from session 1 to session 2 as compared with the change in the latter. The first two quantities yielded correlations of .73 and .66 respectively, both significant at the 1 per cent level of confidence. The correlation of changes in these two measures yielded an insignificant positive coefficient of .16.

A subsidiary experiment, an exploratory attempt at evaluating the validity of BSR measures of activation level, was conducted with data obtained from the above study. The data were converted to log conductance units in order to approximate a normal distribution. Casual clinical observations by the author and his associates on patients under the influence of tranquilizing drugs yielded general agreement that these patients were manifestly less active than those not receiving tranquilizers. It was then reasoned that the manifest validity of BSR should be reflected by a higher resistance level for patients on tranquilizers than for patients not receiving drugs. Hence the three patients on iproniazid were dropped from the study along with three patients randomly chosen from the control group. It is worth noting that it was necessary to replace two of the patients on tranquilizers because their resistances exceeded the ohm limit of the apparatus, a fact consistent with the results.

An analysis of variance was done comparing drug and control groups for the initial minute and one-half of the resting period and over session number. Interaction and session number were not significant. Drug versus control achieved an F value of 9.63, with the BSR level of the group receiving tranquilizers significantly raised ($p < .01$). A breakdown of this F by two t-tests, one for the first session which was significant beyond the 1 per cent level, and one for the second session which was not significant, suggested that anticipatory effects are important.

It was found also that the change in the BSR level during the first minute and one-half of the resting period from session one to session two did not differ significantly between drug and control groups. But the increase in BSR level over the relaxation period was significantly greater ($p < .05$) for the drug than for the control group.

It is concluded that the drug group was significantly less activated during the initial period of the first session. The significance of the t-test suggests that tranquilizing drugs tend to facilitate deactivation over a period when stress may well be anticipated.

Further research now in progress utilizes a continuously recording dermohmmeter in an autonomic conditioning procedure. A tranquilizer, central nervous system stimulant, or placebo will be given to each of three matched groups of chronic schizophrenics. The experimental procedure will involve conditioning the GSR to an auditory stimulus above absolute threshold but below the threshold of awareness, using a schedule of partial reinforcement.

R E F E R E N C E S

Howe, Edmund S.   GSR conditioning in anxiety states, normals, and chronic
    functional schizophrenic subjects.   *J. abnorm. soc. Psychol.,* 1958, 56, 183–
    189.
Mitchell, L. E., and Zax, Melvin.   The effects of ataractic therapy on condition-
    ing rate of GSR in a group of psychiatric patients.   Paper read at meet-
    ing of the Amer. Psychol. Ass., Sept. 1958, Washington, D. C.

Drugs and hypothalamic excitability

The clinical success of the mecholyl test (Funkenstein, Greenblatt, and Solomon, 1948) in the prediction of changes following electric shock treatment stimulated the neurophysiological experiments of Gellhorn (1957). Gellhorn's analysis indicated that the mecholyl test measures hypothalamic excitability by a central sympathetic reflex (CSR). Since other CSR's exist besides the blood pressure reaction to mecholyl, new fields for the development of tests of hypothalamic excitability significant in the study of mental disease were indicated. Quite separately from Gellhorn's formulation, investigations of sensory interaction in a Pavlovian conceptual framework (Kravkov, 1941) had established that differential spectral sensitization (DSS) to short versus long wavelengths is induced by autonomic arousal. A convergence of the two independent lines of investigation seemed possible with the assumption that sensory conditioning, or sensitization, by autonomic arousal provided an untapped reservoir of CSR's. The hypothesis that DSS is a central autonomic reflex and a potential measure of hypothalamic excitability was tested first on the clinical level. Depressed patients, on the average, show increased hypotensive reaction to mecholyl. Would DSS discriminate between depressed patients and normals? The correspondence between the two tests was examined on a physiological level. Hypothalamic sympathetic hyper-

This investigation was supported by research grants M-1520 and M-2060, from the National Institute of Mental Health, USPHS. The research was done with the technical assistance of Beverly Kaplan, my wife, and Jerry Schrader, student at the University of Kansas Medical Center, Kansas City, Kansas. The projected research plans are to be carried out at Lincoln State Hospital, Lincoln, Nebraska.

and hyporeactors selected by the criterion of the mecholyl test were examined on the DSS test.

DSS and Depression

SPECTRAL SENSITIVITY. Spectral sensitivity was measured by the brightness threshold of after-image disappearance (AID) of a hue's after-image, which is complementary in color. A vivid after-image was elicited by a Bidwell disk episcotister (Lehmann, 1950) and was extinguished suddenly as the experimenter gradually dimmed the light by sweeping the lever of a diaphragm over a scale calibrated in foot-lamberts (Kaplan, 1960a). The stimuli for the hues were Munsell papers colored blue, green, gray, and red. All were of the same brightness.

AUTONOMIC SENSITIZATION. There were 36 subjects. For each of them AID was first determined for each hue before any drug was administered. Then the subject received a pill. Six normals and six depressed patients each received one of three pills: a sympathomimetic (ephedrine sulfate, 25 mg.), a parasympathomimetic (neostigmine bromide, 15 mg.), or an inert placebo. After 45 minutes, a period of peak drug action as determined by a pilot study, AID under the drug was determined. A hue's AID before the drug minus its AID afterward was the measure of sensitization (Kaplan, 1960b).

TABLE 1. MEAN SENSITIZATION, IN FOOT-LAMBERTS, CAUSED BY AUTONOMIC AROUSAL IN DEPRESSED PATIENTS AND IN NORMALS

Drug	Stimulus Hue			
	Blue	Green	Gray	Red
Patient:				
Placebo	1.0	1.4	1.4	0.5
Neostigmine	1.8	1.7	1.7	1.9
Ephedrine	1.8	1.2	1.3	2.9
Normal:				
Placebo	0.4	0.5	1.3	1.6
Neostigmine*	5.1	5.0	2.8	1.8
Ephedrine*	−0.7	−0.4	1.6	1.1

* Difference between blue and green on one side of the spectrum and gray and red on the other is significant at the .05 level.

RESULTS. An analysis of variance of spectral sensitization following autonomic arousal for the four hues in the depressed patients and in the normals was performed. At the .05 level of confidence, the interaction between drugs and hues was significant for normals only, and it was significantly smaller for depressives than for normals. The significantly decreased interaction means that depression results in a loss of the differential characteristic of DSS. In depression, sensitization of all spectral wavelengths, long and short, is the same despite autonomic arousal. Table 1 presents the mean sensitization, in foot-lamberts, caused by autonomic arousal in depressed patients and in normals.

DSS and Hypothalamic Excitability

THE MECHOLYL TEST. The subjects were 83 male convicts who were not color-blind. Two groups of nine hypothalamic sympathetic hyper- and hyporeactors were selected by the criterion of a consistent hyper- or hypotensive reaction to each of three mecholyl tests with and without accessory quieting drugs, either sodium amytal, 200 mg. by mouth, or chlorpromazine, 100 mg. by mouth, one hour before the injection of mecholyl.

THE DSS TEST. The mecholyl tests were followed by tests of DSS. A DSS test score consists of the change, 45 minutes after neostigmine bromide, 15 mg., is taken by mouth, in the difference between AID measures of green and of red hue sensitivity. Fifteen minutes before neostigmine, on each of three separate days, the subject also received an accessory pill. The pill was either a placebo or one or the other of the quieting drugs used with the mecholyl tests.

RESULTS. Table 2 presents the mean DSS score in foot-lamberts for hypothalamic sympathetic hyper- and hyporeactors selected by the criterion of the mecholyl tests. The DSS test scores with the acces-

TABLE 2. MEAN DSS SCORE, IN FOOT-LAMBERTS, FOR HYPOTHALAMIC SYMPATHETIC HYPER- AND HYPOREACTORS

Hypothalamic Excitability	Neostigmine Bromide plus		
	Placebo	Amytal	Chlorpromazine
Hyper	−0.6	2.8	1.8
Hypo	2.5	1.2	3.7

sory placebo indicate that the mecholyl test hypothalamic sympathetic hyperreactors had a sympathetic balance (indicated by a negative DSS score), and the hyporeactors had a parasympathetic balance. This was confirmed at the .01 level of confidence by a binomial test (Siegel, 1956).

EFFECT OF QUIETING DRUGS. The accessory quieting drugs restored the appropriate autonomic balance of DSS for the hyperreactors who had displayed, in Pavlovian terms, an "ultra-paradoxical" sympathetic response despite a parasympathomimetic drug. Autonomic imbalance on the mecholyl test was measured by an excessive degree of hyper- or hypotensive reactivity. The point of excessive reactivity was determined objectively in a manner described by Gellhorn (1957). Quieting drugs aggravated autonomic imbalances on the mecholyl test, chlorpromazine increasing the severity of hyperreactivity and amytal transforming hyporeactors into hyperreactors. The aggravation of imbalances on the mecholyl tests by quieting drugs was a finding opposite that reported for other extreme blood pressure reactors (Schneider, 1955; Schneider, Costiloe, Yamamoto, and Lester, 1960) where the quieting drugs normalized the imbalances. The degree of divergence in the effect of the quieting drugs between correcting the visual test imbalances and aggravating the blood pressure imbalances may have been exaggerated by the experimental artifact of a population of convict volunteers. Gellhorn (1957) has shown that sociopaths, as a group, are characterized by central sympathetic hyperreactivity. Not only as a group as found by Gellhorn, but is it characteristic of all sociopaths, even those who superficially appear to be hyporeactors, to release latent central sympathetic hyperreactivity? Do quieting drugs release the sociopath from cortical inhibition instead of calming both cortical and subcortical processes together? Are psychologic personality patterns here modifying pharmacologic principles?

CONCLUSIONS. DSS is a visual test of hypothalamic excitability. The convergence at the hypothalamus of the DSS test and the mecholyl test is characterized by a divergence in the effect of accessory quieting drugs in altering autonomic imbalances on each test.

Divergence from the Hypothalamus

The divergent effects of accessory quieting drugs were associated with another interesting finding incidental to the main inquiry. The

mecholyl test required a severe degree of arousal, whereas the DSS
test required a mild degree. When the DSS test was administered
with the usual large blood pressure test dose of mecholyl, the differential characteristic of DSS was lost; sensitivity to all wavelengths
fluctuated. The same dose whose excessive magnitude obliterated
the differential characteristic of DSS, however, was required to produce an abrupt blood pressure drop and to elicit a central sympathetic
rebound of the blood pressure.

The differences between the two tests suggested the possibility of
two different kinds of hypothalamic autonomic reflexes. The DSS
test concerns the hypothalamic regulation of the autonomic balance
of functions above the hypothalamus. The mecholyl test concerns
the hypothalamic regulation of the autonomic balance of functions
below the hypothalamus. In addition to differing in the direction of
their regulation, the two reflexes also differ in function. A hypothalamic autonomic reflex like that affected in the DSS test differentially sensitizes to a stimulus gradient by a mild departure from
homeostasis, while a hypothalamic autonomic reflex like that activated
on the mecholyl test restores severely disturbed homeostasis. When
autonomic arousal exceeds a critical point, there may be an antagonism, called schizokinesis by Gantt (1953), between differential sensory and homeostatic visceral hypothalamic autonomic reflexes. Therefore we plan to find the threshold for each subject at which a
differential sensory reflex is inhibited by a homeostatic one, as the
strength of autonomic arousal is increased by autonomic drugs and
also as the degree of hypothalamic excitability is varied by quieting
drugs or stimulants.

This combined DSS test and mecholyl test will set the pattern for
associating sensory and visceral tests of hypothalamic autonomic
associating sensory and homeostatic tests of hypothalamic autonomic
reactivity. Sensory measures of autonomic balance regulated by
upward hypothalamic discharges may be developed from Pavlovian
studies of sensory interaction (London, 1954). For example, a test
of differential olfactory sensitization (DOS) could be constructed to
parallel the DSS test. The tests of differential sensory sensitization
resulting from autonomic arousal may be administered, one at a time,
not only along with the mecholyl blood pressure test but also with a
large battery of measures of effector organs whose autonomic balance
is regulated below the hypothalamus. Gellhorn (1957) has shown how
to apply the model of hypothalamic autonomic regulation not only
to blood pressure but also to respiration and other visceral functions.

Finally, an attempt may be made to extend the study of the regulation of autonomic balance beyond the hypothalamus to the cortex. In the case of the DSS test this means studying the effects of different doses of mecholyl upon electroencephalographic recordings during the intermittent photic stimulation used in the DSS test. These can be studied with an analyzer like that used by Walter. The after-image effects upon the rhythmic activity of the brain can also be evaluated by investigating the effects of after-images on EEG alpha waves. Jasper and Cruikshank (1937) came to the conclusion that "cortical rhythms may have pacemakers in the diencephalon which not only serve to synchronize the activity observed from various localized areas of the cortex, but which tend to cause a given external stimulus to be effective in suppressing the cortical rhythms only when it involves responses which are ordinarily associated with the autonomic division of the nervous system." In addition to studying the simultaneous effects upon brain activity of the intermittent photic stimulation and of the enduring after-image generated by the stimulation, their effects on retinal activity can be studied by electroretinography. A multichannel oscilloscope will record all the measures in a particular sensory test simultaneously with the measures from the combination of effector systems whose autonomic balances are regulated by downward hypothalamic discharges. This can elucidate the effects of different degrees of arousal on the central integration of autonomic balance.

A comparison will be made of the sensory and visceral autonomic tests in terms of different diagnostic categories, age, hypothalamic sympathetic hyper- or hyporeactivity selected by the criterion of the mecholyl test, the effects of quieting drugs and stimulants, and interactions among these variables.

R E F E R E N C E S

Funkenstein, D. H., Greenblatt, M., and Solomon, H. C. Autonomic nervous changes following electric shock treatment. *J. nerv. ment. Dis.*, 1948, 108, 409–422.

Gantt, W. H. The physiological basis of psychiatry: the conditional reflex. In J. Wortis, (Ed.), *Basic problems in psychiatry.* New York: Grune & Stratton, 1953.

Gellhorn, E. *Autonomic imbalance and the hypothalamus.* Minneapolis: Univer. of Minnesota Press, 1957.

Jasper, H. H., and Cruikshank, Ruth M. Electro-encephalography: II. Visual stimulation and the after-image as affecting the occipital alpha rhythm. *J. gen. Psychol.*, 1937, 17, 47.

Kaplan, S. D. Autonomic visual regulation. Part I. The afterimage spectral photometer. *Psychiat. Res. Rep.*, 1960, 12, 104–114. (a)

Kaplan, S. D. Autonomic visual regulation. Part II. Differential spectral sensitization to autonomic drugs in depression. *Psychiat. Res. Rep.*, 1960, 12, 115–118. (b)

Kravkov, S. V. Color vision and the autonomic nervous system. *J. opt. Soc. Amer.*, 1941, 31, 335–337.

Lehmann, H. Preliminary report on a device for the objective measurement of the negative afterimage phenomenon. *Science*, 1950, 112, 199–201.

London, I. D. Research on sensory interaction in the Soviet Union. *Psychol. Bull.*, 1954, 51, 531–568.

Schneider, R. A. The acute effects of reserpine and of amytal on central sympathetic reactivity. *Annals N. Y. Academy Sciences*, 1955, 61, 150–160.

Schneider, R. A., Costiloe, J. P., Yamamoto, J., and Lester, B. K. Estimation of central sympathetic reactivity using the blood pressure response to methacholine (mecholyl). *Psychiat. Res. Rep.*, 1960, 12, 149–160.

Siegel, S. *Nonparametric statistics for the behavioral sciences.* New York: McGraw-Hill, 1956.

The influence of predrug level of functioning on the effects of sedatives, tranquilizers, and stimulants on central autonomic function and reaction time

Interest has centered in our laboratory on the effects in man of sedatives or tranquilizers (amytal, chlorpromazine, reserpine) and a stimulant (phenidylate) on two aspects of autonomic function: central sympathetic responsivity (blood pressure response to mecholyl) and conditioning of the galvanic skin response (GSR); and psychomotor function (simple reaction time). It was found, as might be expected, that the first three drugs decreased central sympathetic reactivity (CSR), inhibited conditioning of the GSR, and prolonged the reaction time, and that the stimulant facilitated conditioning and shortened the reaction time. Of particular interest and perhaps of importance were the individual subject differences. By dividing the subjects in each study into two groups on the basis of their level of function on the control day—increased versus decreased central sympathetic reactivity subjects; good conditioners versus poor; and fast reactors versus slow—it became clear that the magnitude of change following drug administration was strikingly related to the predrug level of functioning. For example, chlorpromazine prolonged the reaction time most in those subjects who before drug administration were fast reactors, and altered the reaction time only slightly in the slow reactors. Our data, summarized below, lend support to the concept which has been referred to as the "law of initial values" (Wilder, 1950; Lacey, 1956; Mock, 1958).

The work reported here was materially aided in design and execution by J. Paul Costiloe, M. S., Research Associate, Departments of Medicine and of Psychiatry, Neurology, and the Behavioral Sciences, University of Oklahoma Medical Center.

Alterations in Central Sympathetic Reactivity Accompanying the Administration of Amytal, Reserpine, and Chlorpromazine

An estimate of a subject's central sympathetic reactivity (CSR) can be made by measuring, at intervals, his systolic blood pressure response to the intramuscular injection of 10 mg. of mecholyl (R. A. Schneider, 1955a, b). Gellhorn (1953) has demonstrated in animals that the fall in pressure in the carotid sinus initiates a reflex involving the sympathetic centers in the hypothalamus and brain stem and that efferent impulses cause both a neural and a humoral sympathetic discharge which return the blood pressure to its pre-mecholyl basal level. Funkenstein, Greenblatt, and Solomon (1948) have used this test clinically as an aid to prognosis with certain treatments in psychiatric patients. Three prototype curves are illustrated in Fig. 1.

Twelve ambulatory medical patients were given the mecholyl test on four successive days. No drug was given on the first day as a

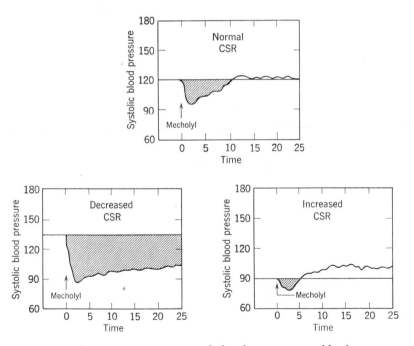

Figure 1. A schematic representation of the three prototype blood pressure response patterns seen after mecholyl administration.

control. One hour before testing on days 2, 3, and 4, 250 mg. of sodium amytal, 1.0 mg. of reserpine, and 100 mg. of chlorpromazine, respectively, were given by mouth. After the subject's basal blood pressure was established, the mecholyl was injected and the systolic pressure was recorded every minute for 25 minutes.

Results are given in Table 1. The subjects are grouped on the control day into those having normal, increased, or decreased CSR.

TABLE 1. CENTRAL SYMPATHETIC REACTIVITY (CSR) MEASURED 41 TIMES IN 12 SUBJECTS WITHOUT PREMEDICATION AND AFTER AMYTAL, RESERPINE, AND CHLORPROMAZINE

		CSR Relative to Control Day		
Subject	CSR Control Day	After Amytal (250 mg. by mouth 1 hr. before test)	After Reserpine (1.0 mg. by mouth 1 hr. before test)	After Chlorpromazine (100 mg. by mouth 1 hr. before test)
F.T.	Normal	Decreased	Decreased	Decreased
S.S.	Normal	Decreased	Decreased	Decreased
M.E.	Normal	Decreased*	Decreased	Decreased
I.C.	Normal	Decreased	Decreased†	—
T.J.	Increased	Decreased	Decreased	—
S.E.	Increased	—	Decreased†	Decreased
B.L.	Increased	—	Decreased	Decreased
H.N.	Decreased	Decreased	Increased	Increased
E.S.	Decreased	Decreased	Increased	Increased
P.L.	Decreased	Decreased*	Increased†	—
W.T.	Decreased	Decreased*	—	Increased
D.N.	Decreased	Decreased*	Decreased†	—

* 250 mg. intramuscularly 2 hr. before test.

† 2.5 mg. intramuscularly 3 hr. before test.

The CSR on the drug days represents the patterns relative to each subject's control day curve. The blanks indicate that tests were not performed on a given subject with a particular drug. After amytal, all 12 subjects showed decreased CSR irrespective of their control day pattern. However, after reserpine and chlorpromazine the resultant patterns appeared to be related to the control day classification. In all cases when the control CSR was normal or increased, the resultant CSR was decreased. However, when the CSR on the control day was decreased, the resultant CSR's were increased with one exception (D.N., after reserpine).

We interpret our findings as demonstrating, with the dosage and time intervals used, that the hypothalamus is depressed in all our subjects by amytal and is similarly depressed by reserpine and chlorpromazine in those subjects who before the drugs demonstrated normal or increased CSR. Why, in the present study, both reserpine and chlorpromazine led to an increase in CSR in subjects who had *decreased* CSR on the control days remains unexplained. J. A. Schneider, Plummer, Earl, Gaunt (1955) reported that reserpine reduces sympathetic activity by blocking centrally afferent stimuli which normally activate the autonomic regulating centers.

The Inhibiting and Facilitating Effects of Amytal, Chlorpromazine, and Phenidylate on the Conditioned Galvanic Skin Response

Forty subjects were divided into a control and three drug-treated groups (R. A. Schneider and Costiloe, 1957). With electric shock as the unconditioned stimulus, the GSR was conditioned to a light flash and then extinguished in all subjects the first day without prior drug administration. Twenty-four hours later the conditioning procedure was repeated, 2 hours after the subjects in the drug groups had received one of three agents (200 mg. of amytal intramuscularly, 50 mg. of chlorpromazine orally, or 30 mg. of phenidylate orally). On this second day the light alone was first presented to measure the degree of spontaneous recovery of the conditioned reflex, and then the subject was reconditioned. The effects of each drug were determined by comparing median difference scores (number of presentations of the light alone required to extinguish the conditioned response on the first day minus the number required on the second day) in the drug groups with the control group means.

The results are diagrammed in Fig. 2, in terms of median differences in conditioning. The extent of conditioning on the first day was not significantly different in the four groups. Reaction to the shock alone was not influenced by any of the drugs. In the amytal group spontaneous recovery at the start of the second day's experiment was significantly decreased as compared to the controls ($p < .01$) and there was a trend toward inhibition of reconditioning. In the group receiving chlorpromazine there was a non-significant tendency for decrease of spontaneous recovery but a significant decrease in re-

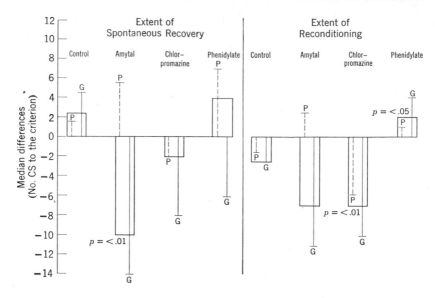

Figure 2. The effects of amytal, chlorpromazine, and phenidylate on spontaneous recovery and reconditioning compared to the no-drug control. The median differences were derived from intraindividual difference scores which were obtained by subtracting the number of conditioned stimuli required to reach the criterion of extinction for spontaneous recovery and reconditioning (both on the second day) from the number required to reach extinction of the GSR on the first day. Positive values indicate a gain, and negative values a loss, in extent of conditioning. The histograms represent the *group* medians, the interrupted vertical line the "poor" conditioners (P), and the solid vertical line the "good" conditioners (G), based on each subject's performance on the first day without drug. Statistical significances for group medians are based in each case on comparison with the control group.

conditioning ($p < .01$). In the phenidylate group spontaneous recovery was not affected, but reconditioning was facilitated significantly ($p < .05$). This retention of a learned emotional response was decreased in the amytal group, and the relearning of this response was inhibited by chlorpromazine and facilitated by phenidylate.

Modification of the Simple Reaction Time by Chlorpromazine and Phenidylate

Eight healthy volunteer male subjects (ages 24 to 40) took a simple reaction time test on two successive days (100 trials each) for practice

(R. A. Schneider and Costiloe, 1959). Then on four successive days four subjects received 100 mg. of chlorpromazine orally, and the remaining four received a placebo. Practice effects were controlled by a counter-balanced design. A week later the procedure was repeated and on two of the four days each of the subjects received 30 mg. of phenidylate orally. All drugs were administered in a double-blind fashion two hours before testing. Five dollars were offered each week to the subject who made the greatest improvement in reaction time. The reaction time was measured as the time interval between the onset of a light signal and the lifting of the subject's middle finger from a microswitch. The light signal was presented automatically by a

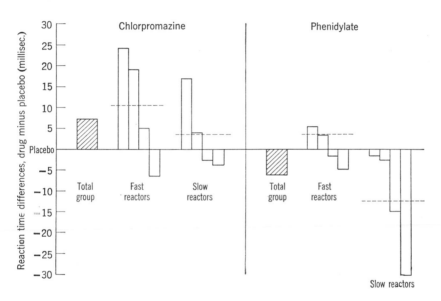

Figure 3. The effects of chlorpromazine and phenidylate on the simple reaction time. The same subjects received each drug. The mean reaction time differences, in milliseconds, were derived by subtracting each subject's placebo value from his drug value. Positive values indicate a prolongation, and negative values a shortening, of reaction time. The cross-hatched wide histograms represent the group findings, and the plain narrow histograms those for the individual subjects. For each drug the subjects were divided into those with short reaction times (fast reactors) and those with long reaction times (slow reactors). It will be noted that the fast reactors were slowed more than the slow reactors by chlorpromazine, and that the slow reactors were speeded up more than the fast reactors by phenidylate. The horizontal interrupted lines represent the subgroup mean values.

stimulus timer at intervals varying between 1.5 and 2.0 seconds. Each day's test consisted of 50 trials.

The results are presented in Fig. 3, and for both drugs are given as the difference in each subject's mean drug reaction time and his mean placebo reaction time in milliseconds. The group mean difference for chlorpromazine was 7.2 milliseconds, significant at the 8 per cent level. The "fast reactors" (based on placebo day means) tended to show the greater prolongation, but this was not statistically significant. For phenidylate the group mean difference was —5.6 milliseconds ($p < .08$). While not statistically significant, greater shortening was seen in the "slow reactors."

The physiologic explanation for these drug effects could be related to a decrease (chlorpromazine) or increase (phenidylate) in central excitability, as with the effect of these agents on conditioning. It is, of course, well known that many psychophysical factors influence the speed of reaction, such as motivation and set, and it is conceivable that psychoactive drugs affect these factors.

REFERENCES

Freeman, G. L. *The energetics of human behavior.* Ithaca, N. Y.: Cornell Univer. Press, 1948.

Funkenstein, D. H., Greenblatt, M., and Solomon, H. C. Autonomic nervous system changes following electric shock treatment. *J. nerv. ment. Dis.,* 1948, 108, 409.

Gellhorn, E. *Physiological foundations of neurology and psychiatry.* Minneapolis, Minn.: Univer. of Minnesota Press, 1953, 466–486.

Lacey, John I. The evaluation of autonomic responses: toward a general solution. *Ann. N. Y. Acad. Sci.,* 1956, 67, 123–164.

Mock, D. C., Kyriakopoulos, A., Clark, Mervin, Brandt, E. N., and Hagans, J. A. Observations on the law of initial values in therapeutic research: a study of the effects of diuretic agents. *Clin. Res.,* 1958, 6, 417.

Schneider, J. A., Plummer, A. J., Earl, A. E., and Gaunt, R. *Ann. N. Y. Acad. Sci.,* 1955, 61, 17.

Schneider, R. A. Central sympathetic reactivity in man as influenced by Amytal, Reserpine and Chlorpromazine. *Psychiat. Res. Reps.,* 1955, 1, 1–10. (a)

Schneider, R. A. The acute effects of reserpine and of Amytal on central sympathetic reactivity. *Ann. N. Y. Acad. Sci.,* 1955, 61, 150–160. (b)

Schneider, R. A., and Costiloe, J. P. *Am. J. med. Sci.,* 1957, 233, 418–422.

Schneider, R. A., and Costiloe, J. P. Unpublished data. 1959.

Wilder, J. The law of initial values. *Psychosom. Med.,* 1950, 12, 392.

Experimental studies
of the tranquilizer syndrome
by the method of conditioned reflexes

The researches carried out on tranquilizers at the Centre de Trait-ment et de Réadaptation Sociale of Villejuif, a suburb of Paris, have been inspired by the spirit of what is sometimes called "clinical psy-chology." That is, they involve a close and constant association of the clinic and various psychological testing methods. Observations and clinical impressions concerning the effects produced by different drugs have been ceaselessly submitted to as objective a study as possible of the modifications of psychic or psychomotor activity. The data of these studies in return led us to observe more attentively certain traits of behavior of patients under tranquilizers in work situations and in human relationships, notably in psychotherapy, but also at the hospital, in social, family, and marital life, and so forth. We have recently stressed (LeGuillant, Pariente, Huguet, and Bonnet, 1960) the fact that some patients are subject to disturbances which are more subtle and less well recognized than the classic disturbances which result from excessive doses of tranquilizers. These obscure and troublesome "coenesthetic states" appear to us to account, at least in part, for the resistance which is so often encountered to prolonged therapy and for the frequent and sometimes dramatic failure of these cures. Likewise the patients' tendencies to indifference, withdrawal, and inertia deprive them of the general psychotherapy which is avail-able in the services where they are treated, as well as of actual par-ticipation in individual or group psychotherapy.

The research methods which were used are common ones. They gain significance solely because of their continual association and contact with the clinic. In addition to the standard tests we used

427

Wechsler-Bellevue (which generally does not reveal significant alteration in intelligence), the Heuyer-Bailie test of fine motor abilities, and
a reaction time measure. Tremors were objectified by means of a
tremblcomctcr; a systematic study of handwriting was made.

These tests are repeated, not only in different periods in the treatments with tranquilizers, but when the patients are under the influence
of different doses of these drugs and after different alterations in their
situations: resumption of physical activity or of work or trips out of
the hospital, administration of various "antagonists," especially hept-
aminol chlorhydrate.

We have, thanks to these methods, distinguished two major types of
tranquilizer syndrome, often associated. The first, with psychomotor
symptoms predominating, is the better recognized, capable of going
as far as pseudo-Parkinsonian states. The other, with psychic symptoms predominating, is often unnoticed. In the first the greatest
changes are in voluntary movements—its spontaneity, its speed, its
precision, the fatigue which it involves, and so forth. In the second,
changes in test results are slight. Subjective influences dominate,
and they are expressed by more or less profound alterations in mood
and in tone.

One must always remember that, like the data from clinical observations, those of psychometric studies of tranquilizers often are limited
and of little significance, especially with regard to "psychic" reactions.
Frequently it is not easy to find evidence of, and especially to objectify,
effects, separating them from the manifestations of the symptoms of
the pathological state itself. The inadequacy of objective experimental techniques in statistical studies are especially evident in the
evaluation of something as complex as psychiatric therapy.

We also are trying to study what we call, along with the Pavlovian
school, "superior nervous activity" (SNA). We had envisaged initially
using the method of Ivanov-Smolenski. She experimentally produces, in man, through the use of verbal reinforcement, a conditioned
bond between a given sensory signal and a motor response. The
sensory signals may be simple or complex, differentiated or not, with
a positive or negative significance, this significance itself perhaps being
inverted. It seemed to us that we were dealing here with a method
capable of objectifying the different processes (excitation, inhibition,
lability, and so forth) and, through them, the state of the nervous
system.

However, the application of the method of Ivanov-Smolenski following the procedures of its author and her collaborators, notably

Povorinski (Ivanov-Smolenski, 1927; Povorinski, 1956) has led us to raise serious objections to the validity and significance of the experimental results, if not to the theoretical concept itself. We have the impression that consciousness in the adult leads not to conditioned reactions, but rather to voluntary responses to the ambiguous instructions, responses which are a function of the totality of the personality and of the experience of the subject.

Our technique has been modified in the light of these remarks. Preliminary instructions inform the subject of the task. Placed in a separate room, he must learn to differentiate lights which are successively illuminated before him and to respond to each stimulus by pressing rapidly one of two buttons, left or right. The spatial significance of the stimuli becomes elaborated little by little through colored lights which constitute the new reinforcement used by this technique, and whose significance (right or left) is known by the subject before the beginning of the test. The order of appearance of the signals, their relative frequency, the unchanging duration of each signal and of its reinforcement, and the variable rest periods are all determined in advance. Their temporal and spatial distribution is automatic, and identical for all subjects. In principle, the test is continued until the subject reaches the criterion of learning or a predetermined limit.

The following data are obtained: the latency for the different correct responses and the number of errors committed by the subject.

Our experimental group includes 100 patients who are as closely matched as possible on mental state and who have no noticeable deterioration of intellectual functions.

Our purpose is to compare their performances at four different phases of treatment: at the time of arrival, after three days of medication with tranquilizers, after the appearance of the tranquilizer syndrome, and after the correction of this syndrome by an appropriate "psychic energizer." The beginning of the tranquilizer syndrome is clinically recognized. In order to avoid sources of error, standard forms listing the principal complaints have been devised. They are filled out by the treating physician and are then collected by the experimenter. They make it possible to keep track of the clinical course during the experiment.

Theoretically the patients should be tested at these four phases of treatment. Practically, however, learning phenomena interfere and must therefore be cancelled out by experimental controls. The patients are divided into four subgroups. Each one of these is tested for the first time in a different phase of treatment. Comparisons can then be established among patients with the same amount of experience on the task, and the differences in their performance may be attributed uniquely to the action of the medication. This method eventually can be refined, notably by using other visual signals (geometric figures for example) involving progressively more difficult differentiations.

R E F E R E N C E S

Ivanov-Smolenski, A. G.   Études expérimentales sur les enfants et les alienes par la methode des reflexes conditionnés.   Traduc. française.   *Ann. medi.-psychol.*, 1927.

LeGuillant, L., Pariente, M., Huguet, H., and Bonnet, F.   Nouvelles perspectives dans l'étude clinique et experimentale du syndrome neuroleptique.   In P. B. Bradley, P. Deniker, and G. Radouco-Thomas (Eds.), *Neuro-psychopharmacology*.   Amsterdam: Elsevier, 1960, 586–592.

Povorinski, I. A.   La methode d'étude des reflexes conditionnés moteurs avec renforcement verbal.   Le compte rendu detaille a paru dans *Le Raison*, Deuxieme trimestre, 1956 (14).

Experimentally controlled stress
and drug effects

The psychological laboratory of the University of Washington, which is sponsored by the Department of Pharmacology, subscribes to the thesis that an experimental laboratory investigation of drug effects using human subjects under controlled conditions should be conducted subsequent to animal investigations and prior to clinical trials. It is contended that the effects of drugs on behavior can be more precisely defined and differentiated by experimental laboratory investigations than in clinical trials, and that the information provided by these investigations should result in more precise hypotheses about the effects of any given drug when clinical trials are conducted.

An example of an experimental laboratory investigation using normal subjects conducted here is a study which was designed to test the effects of 800 mg. of meprobamate, 50 mg. of chlorpromazine, 100 mg. of pentobarbital, and a placebo on a behavioral task performed under stress conditions (Holliday and Dille, 1958). Forty normal subjects were trained in the operation of a pointer-pursuit apparatus and were then randomly divided into four matched groups, and each group was randomly assigned a drug condition.

The testing procedure in the second session under drug conditions was exactly the same as the training procedure under non-drug conditions, except that stress conditions were introduced. The first two trials were unpunished. The subsequent ten experimental trials consisted of five punished trials and five unpunished trials, each trial being of three minutes' duration with one minute intervening between trials. The third, fourth, sixth, eighth, and eleventh trials were punished; punishment was randomly administered approximately 90 per cent of the time when the subject was off target. Punishment for errors in performance of the task was of three kinds: (1) a loud blast from an automobile horn, (2) a blast of air to the back of the subject's neck, and (3) shock to the finger. Both the sequence and the administration of the different punishing stimuli were random and automatically controlled. Subjects were unable to predict precisely on which trials punishment would occur; they were unable to predict whether punishment would result for any given error; they were unable to predict what punishing stimulus or combination of stimuli would occur on a punished error.

As in the report by Rodnick, Rubin, and Freeman (1943), who used a similar procedure, the intent was to induce stress and concomitant anxiety. Interest was centered particularly in the unpunished trials, which were regarded as conditioned-stress trials reflecting generalized anxiety and tension unobscured by the "startle" and distraction of the actual punishing stimuli on motor performance. The hypothesis was that the tranquilizing drugs would allow the subjects to perform more efficiently during the unpunished trials than would a placebo. The two dependent variables measured were the total time off target and the number of times off target.

Analyses of variance revealed that there were no significant differences between the drugs in regard to the performance of the groups on the first two control trials. Neither was there a significant difference between drugs for either dependent variable on the punished trials. With the exception of the chlorpromazine group, all groups showed a significant improvement in time on the punished trials. With the exception of the placebo group, all groups showed a significant improvement in number of times off target over the punished trials.

On the unpunished trials there were significant differences between the drug groups on both variables. All groups, with the exception of the meprobamate group, evidenced a strong tendency toward poorer scores over the unpunished trials on number of times off target. The meprobamate group showed a significant improvement over these trials. The meprobamate group was also the only group not evidencing a deleterious effect in total time off target.

In summary, before the introduction of the punishment variable, there were no significant differences in performance among the drug groups. After the introduction of the punishment variable, there were. The fact that there were no significant differences among the drug groups on the punished trials is important. All groups, when faced with an identifiable, concrete stimulus, were able to adapt, to show improvement in their scores on both dependent variables. However, in the absence of any actual punishing stimuli, significant differences in performance among the groups appeared. The anxiety engendered by the anticipation of punishment in the absence of any concrete punishing stimuli to which the subject might respond in an adaptive manner appeared to result in disruption in performance on the unpunished trials for the chlorpromazine, pentobarbital, and placebo groups. Only the meprobamate group was not affected. Hunt (1957) has indicated that meprobamate modifies a conditioned emotional response in animals.

With the exception that random, independent groups were used rather than matched groups and with a change in the apparatus to the extent that the motor-driven pointer was changed to make an unpredictable excursion, the experiment described above was repeated with the following drugs: meprobamate, an experimental tranquilizer, and a placebo. Significant differences among the drugs were obtained, the meprobamate group in this study performing as it had done in the first study.

We predicted (Holliday, 1959) that meprobamate, a muscle relaxant, would reduce the degree of muscular tension shown by stutterers. Two random, homogeneous groups of male stutterers read a prose passage twice with three weeks intervening between the two readings. Measures of the number of words stuttered upon and the mean blocking time were obtained, in addition to ratings of the degree of physical tension accompanying the act of speaking, the latter being the variable in which there was primary interest. Subjects in the meprobamate group were given 800 mg. three times a day for the period intervening between trials. Neither the placebo nor the drug group showed a significant change between the first and second trials in the number of words stuttered upon and the mean blocking time. The meprobamate group but not the placebo group showed a significant improvement between the first and second trials on the tension variable. Maxwell and Paterson (1958) carried out a clinical investigation related to this problem; they also concluded that meprobamate was useful in alleviating the tension of stuttering.

Not all the studies conducted in this laboratory have been smashing successes. We were once influenced by the criticism that the apprehension and tension engendered by the anticipation of punishment was not *"real* anxiety" to the extent that an elaborate study was designed involving environmental stress as a variable. The members of the freshman class in the Dental School were told that, as a part of their training in research, they were to participate in a study testing motor coordination. Prior to the motor task, the subjects were given either meprobamate (400 mg.) or placebo three times a day for one week.

On the testing day the Dean of the Dental School interrupted the assembled class and told them that he and the staff were totally dissatisfied with their performance, as a group, on the quarterly examinations. Reporting back their grades had been delayed, and they were informed that this was the reason. They were told that they had turned in the worst performance in the history of the Dental School, that there had apparently been some failure in the method of selection of the students, and that the staff felt that it could not, in good conscience, allow these students to continue studying without further evaluation.

The experiment was an absolute success in so far as producing stress was concerned. The students were later asked whether they had found the Dean's performance believable. Representative samples of their responses are: "I thought I was a goner." "My heart dropped about two feet." "He scared me to death."

Unfortunately, although the stress situation was effective, our results, partly because of unforeseen technical problems, were unclear. In summary, a control group that did *not* hear the Dean gave the highest manifest anxiety scores, followed by the meprobamate group. The stressed placebo subjects gave the least manifest anxiety and the best performance on a test of abstract reasoning.

R E F E R E N C E S

Edwards, A. L. *The social desirability variable in personality assessment and research.* New York: Dryden, 1957.

Holliday, Audrey R. The effect of meprobamate on stuttering. *Northwest Med.,* 1959, 58, 837–841.

Holliday, Audrey R., and Dille, J. M. The effects of meprobamate, chlorpromazine, pentobarbital and a placebo on a behavioral task performed under stress conditions. *J. comp. Physiol. Psychol.,* 1958, 51, 811–815.

Hunt, H. F. Some effects of meprobamate on conditioned fear and emotional behavior. *Ann. N. Y. Acad. Sci.,* 1957, 67, 712–721.

Maxwell, R. D. H., and Paterson, J. W. Meprobamate in the treatment of stuttering. *Brit. Med. J.,* 1958, 1, 873–874.

Rodnick, E. H., Rubin, M. A., and Freeman, H. Relations to experimentally induced stress. *Amer. J. Psychiat.,* 1943, 99, 872–880.

Meprobamate and laboratory-induced anxiety

This study derives from an earlier investigation (Pronko and Leith, 1956) which employed the delayed auditory feedback technique for precipitating a disintegration of manual and speech reactions. The aim then was to evaluate the role of preparedness in a panic situation. Three groups of subjects were used, a "sink-or-swim," a "planted leader," and a "response-prepared-in-advance" group. Subjects had to read aloud a set of instructions on a reading-rate controller. Results showed that the sink-or-swim group made the poorest performance with a mean of 4.55 correct responses. The planted leader and response-prepared-in-advance groups, (the first group had had the correct responses pointed out, and the second had had a practice run) gave mean correct responses of 8.1 and 9.3, respectively.

In the present experiment, our subjects were 51 beginning psychology students. Their instructions were comparable with those of the earlier sink-or-swim group. They were in a situation which required them to manipulate a set of dials and switches on a panel before them. A reading-rate controller was set behind the panel box. A pair of earphones permitted the subject to hear his own speech played back at a delay of 1.75 seconds. Shock to the wrist was threatened (but never used) if the subject stopped manipulating the switches or if he stopped reading aloud the instructions that directed him to make the panel adjustments. The reading pacer forced him to read at a rate of 150 words per minute.

The investigation reported here was supported by Grant MY-2328 from the United States Public Health Service.

Electrophysiological measures including the electromyogram (EMG), the galvanic skin response (GSR), and the heart rate (by EKG) were taken from the subject's left arm. The EMG's and GSR's were integrated and the EKG's which yielded the heart rate were added through a summating circuit.

The Problem

The specific problem investigated was whether, with suitable amplification of the individual's response configurations, meprobamate would influence behavior under stress as compared with control conditions of placebo or no drug (Pronko and Kenyon, 1959).

Dosage was set at two 400-mg. capsules of meprobamate or matching placebo capsules administered under double-blind conditions 35 to 45 minutes before the experimental session outlined above.

Results and Discussion

The overall pattern of results showed no consistent effects of the meprobamate, placebo or no-drug conditions. Average task times and number of correct panel operations under the three experimental conditions were not significantly different. This finding would appear to indicate that, for normal subjects under stress, meprobamate did not interfere with the simple motor task or with its speed of execution. In this respect our results are consistent with those of Marquis, Kelly, Miller, Gerard, and Rapoport (1957) and of Reitan (1957). (See also Chapters 20 and 26.)

In the GSR data a significant difference appeared only between the conditions of placebo and meprobamate. This would appear to be a drug effect, except that the meprobamate and no-drug conditions did not differ significantly.

Our results for muscle potentials give significant differences throughout, except when meprobamate is compared with the no-drug condition. This finding supports neither drug nor placebo effect and is discrepant with the findings of other investigations. However, since the latter were done with spastic and other types of biopathological conditions, the comparisons may not be relevant.

R E F E R E N C E S

Laties, V. G. Effects of meprobamate on fear and palmar sweating. *Fed. Proc.*, 1957, 16, 315. (Abstract)

Laties, Y. G.   Effects of meprobamate on fear and palmar sweating.   *J. abnorm. soc. Psychol.*, 1959, 59, 156–161.

Marquis, D. G., Kelly, E. L., Miller, J. G., Gerard, R. W., and Rapoport, A. Experimental studies of behavioral effects of meprobamate on normal subjects. *Ann. N.Y. Acad. Sci.*, 1957, 61, 701–710.

Pronko, N. H., and Kenyon, G. Y.   Meprobamate and laboratory-induced anxiety. *Psychol. Rep.*, 1959, 5, 217–238.

Pronko, N. H., and Leith, W. R.   Behavior under stress: a study of its disintegration, *Psychol. Rep.*, 1956, 2, 205–222.

Reitan, R. M.   The comparative effects of placebo, Ultran, and Meprobamate on psychologic test performances.   *Antibiotic Med. clin. Ther.*, 1957, IV, 158–165.

The dimensional (unitary-component) measurement of anxiety, excitement, effort stress, and other mood reaction patterns

The special characteristic of the measurement devices described in this chapter is that they are directed to states and traits which have first been demonstrated by exploratory, factor analytic research to be *unitary* dimensions of variation. That is to say, they are based on the functional response unities which exist naturally in the organism. This research demonstrates that some verbally similar dimensions of mood variation are functionally quite distinct, and that the mere existence of many traditional labels is no proof of there being many independent dimensions.

Prior to the work which has taken place along these lines, with increasing acceleration during the past five years, the methodologically more naive experimenter considered that it was sufficient to define his concept of a psychological state verbally, and then to set up, *a priori*, a particular variable, which, he asserted, in terms of the consistency of his theory, to be a measure of this concept. Thus, for example, many investigators defined anxiety in various ways, usually in conformity with the popular definition of anxiety, and then set up tests such as the trembelometer, questionnaire statements of experienced fears or nightmares, or measures of impairment of perception, to represent it. Without justifying this representation they proceeded to conclude that anxiety itself would be related to certain stimuli in the manner in which these particular measures proved to be related to the stimuli.

By the methodology here expounded, this is putting the cart before the horse. It is necessary first to demonstrate if one or more unitary patterns of anxiety exist, and what their forms may be. The mere fact that we popularly use one word certainly does not imply that there is a single functional unity. Nor does the fact that many clinicians distinguish several terms assure us that there are several distinct forms of anxiety, i.e., that a person should be measured separately on each, because he may be at quite different levels on the different forms. In short, regardless of whether we have a monistic or pluralistic view of anxiety, we are equally wrong if we depend on the mere word usage or subjective concepts to decide for us what the response patterns are. Instead, it is scientifically necessary to enter an experiment with a great number of alleged manifestations of anxiety, especially those collected in the semantic reference of our existing verbal labels, and to determine whether these manifestations of anxiety vary together, in a monistic way, or whether they split up into several distinct varieties of anxiety.

Thus, whereas the classical, brass instrument, univariate experimenter assumes that a single variable will stand for a single concept in his experiments, the newer, multivariate experimental approach, of which factor analysis is the principle methodology, makes no such assumption. It first explores the firmness of the ground under our feet by intercorrelating a lot of manifestations governing the whole area in which the experimenter is interested, and then discovers, by factor analysis, how many functionally unitary influences are required to account for the observed correlations (Cattell, 1952). Wundt, many years ago, neatly but arbitrarily defined dimensions of variation of mood in terms of excitement, pleasure-unpleasure, and so on. But it is strange, in view of the twenty or thirty years the newer methodologies have been available, that this arbitrary approach to defining moods and emotional states is still permitted in some experiments to be the pivot of important conclusions, e.g., about drug action. However, the more penetrating work of the last five years has introduced factor analysis, in ways which will be briefly described, and has already made considerable progress. In fact, some five or six dimensions of state variation can be reasonably accurately defined at the present time and measured by available test batteries (Cattell, 1957a; Rosenthal, 1955).

A Factor Analytic Model for Dimensionalizing Moods and Emotional States

The principal assumption of this model, which has so far fitted well to experimental facts, is that there are certain built-in reaction patterns in the organism which, once started, follow a certain pattern of combined physiological and psychological expression, though any such pattern may be triggered by a fair variety of different stimuli. What the stimuli are will depend upon the learning experiences of the particular individual, and the cultural setting in which he grows up. For example, the statement that one's bank account is overdrawn may be a stimulus for anxiety in our culture, but not in the Trobriand Islands, though the behavioral and physiological changes in anxiety may be much the same in both. A number of physiologists working in the field of stress and anxiety have perhaps been impressed rather more quickly than psychologists by the need to operate with a model of this kind. Thus Stewart Wolf (1958) recommends the conceptual separation of "causes" and "mechanisms," in avoiding contradictory conclusions in psychosomatics, and by these he means what we have called, respectively, *stimulus situations* and *unitary patterns of response, common to most people in our culture, each operating in response to a variety of stimuli*. In the experimental studies described here this pattern of response is at once an introspective mood, a change in behavior on various performance measures, and a collection of physiological changes.

Accordingly, the experimental approach capable of leading to positive results in terms of this model is one which factor analyzes a great variety of responses, and, after determining the number and nature of unitary response patterns, sets out by secondary experiments to discover what the particular stimuli are which set off each response pattern, and to what degree they affect it. For example, it should be possible to find for the average member of our culture a number of stimuli which typically are strongly associated with a particular response, and it would then be appropriate to call these "anxiety stimuli," if the *response* we are dealing with is anxiety, or "stress stimuli," if we are dealing with what we shall define below as the effort stress *response*.

Here, too, the procedure is just the converse of what has been practiced by many unfamiliar with this methodology. Such experimenters have first described a certain stimulus as a stress stimulus, and have then proceeded to assume that the response to it always is a stress response. In fact, research publications generalize about "the stress response" on no better grounds than that an arbitrary stimulus has been used which appears to the writers in question to be a pure stress stimulus. However, by the present conceptual approach, it will be quite uncommon for any actual response to a particular stimulus—in any given person or group of persons—to be a pure, unitary response pattern. Usually the subject will be reacting to a complex stimulus by a complex combination of several dimensions of response. For example, the news about a disappearing bank balance may evoke so much of an anxiety response, so much of a depressive response, and so much of, say, effort stress, in a single, combined, mood swing. By the model of factor analysis it is possible to analyze any such actual response neatly and quantitatively into the combination of responses that has gone into it, and to express, say, the response of the typical man in our culture to a particular life situational stimulus in terms of a "specification" equation, in which the response is described as the weighted sum of a number of distinct factors, i.e., independent dimensions of response (Cattell, 1952).

Dimensions of Anxiety

Let us see in more detail what the experimental approaches of this type have yielded in regard to measurement of anxiety, and its distinction from such related moods and affect reactions as stress, fatigue, and the adrenergic response. In a recent monograph (Scheier and Cattell, 1958b) a comprehensive experimental survey has been made of most variables that have been said to indicate anxiety. Indeed, no fewer than 814 variables were measured, together, in various overlapping sets of variables, on a sufficient population sample. The more simple conceptual approach to evaluating the validity of the various measures tried would be to get a single criterion score by pooling the scores of all 814 variables, and then to correlate each separate variable with the pool, to see which showed the maximum agreement and which is therefore the most concentrated measure of everything that is measured by the total group of alleged anxiety variables. However, the more sophisticated multivariate analytic approach is first to factor these variables and discover how many truly independent functional entities exist.

When this was done, it was found that several dimensions of change in response to threatening, unpleasant, nocive stimuli were necessary to account for the variance in all these variables. However, one direction of change stood out above all the others, and this deserves semantically to inherit the title of *the* anxiety factor. This factor has turned up independently in four different personality studies using objective personality tests (Cattell, 1957a). In accordance with the proposed scheme (Cattell, 1956) to identify factors by index numbers, so that, although they cannot be confused, they need not be immediately interpreted, it was styled *universal index #24*, henceforth UI 24. This UI 24 pattern is shown in Table 1.

TABLE 1. SUMMARY LIST OF BEST-CONFIRMED VARIABLES
LOADING ANXIETY AS A TRAIT

(UI 24 and F(Q)II)

---

1. Introspective, Questionnaire Variables
(Mean Loading from Six Experiments)

16 PF Factor		Average Loading
Q_4+	Ergic tension	$+.67$
$O+$	Guilt proneness or more super-ego	$+.60$
Q_3	Low self-sentiment development	$-.53$
$C-$	Low ego strength	$-.49$
$L+$	More protension	$+.45$
$H-$	More threctia	$-.32$
$M+$	More autia	$-.30$

2. Objective Test Variables

Identifying Master Index Number		
219	More willingness to admit common frailties	.38
211	More susceptibility to annoyance	.36
473	Fewer friends recalled	.28
108	Little confidence in skill in untried performance	.24

3. Physical and Physiological Variables

620	Increase of pulse rate in cold pressor test (or startle)	.60
623	Early onset of pulse rate change	.50 (1 study only)

It will be noted that this factor contained the principal questionnaire expressions of anxiety, as well as several physiological and general behavioral measures. What may appeal still more to the clinician is that it proved to be the only factor which simultaneously loaded the anxiety ratings made by different psychiatrists, i.e., whatever was *common* to psychiatrists' evaluations of anxiety was in this factor (Scheier and Cattell, 1958a).

This massive factor, covering changes of psychological performance and physiological response, obviously also covers most introspective, therapeutic interview responses about anxiety, as shown by its including every questionnaire factor that contains items about anxiety. Nevertheless one is at first puzzled by finding it related to *six* primary questionnaire personality factors rather than one—C (−), H (−), L, O, Q3 (−), and Q4 in the 16 PF Test (Cattell and Stice, 1957). The solution to this riddle appeared when independent research directed simply to discovering second-order factors (Cattell, 1956) among the simple structure (oblique factors found by repeated factor analysis of the total area of personality expression in the questionnaire, opinionnaire medium) revealed a curious alignment. There appeared in these data (dealing with the full "normal" personality range) a big second-order factor subtending some six primary factors. This second-order factor was confirmed to exist in children as well as in adults (Cattell, 1959; Karson and Pool, 1958). Finally, when studies were carried out in which the original *objective test,* UI 24, factor was measured along with these questionnaire factors, the statistical analysis revealed that they are identical. That is to say, a second-order factor found in the questionnaire realm is identical with a first-order factor found in objective, physiological, laboratory tests (Scheier, 1957). This simply means that for some reason introspective response is a more sensitive medium of perception and reveals different varieties, or sources, of what is essentially a common pattern of anxiety response.

Indeed, it turns out that the nature of the general personality factors which load the second-order general anxiety factor are such as agree closely with general clinical theory as developed by Freud and his followers. The largest factor is one which had originally been called ergic tension, 4, i.e., the level of stimulated but unsatisfied drive, which, according to clinical theory, might be expected to transform itself into anxiety, as in the transference neuroses. The second largest factor is ego weakness, C (−), defined according to the classical clinical conception of the ego. It has long been realized clinically that the amount of anxiety experienced by the individual is likely to be proportional to the weakness of the ego, when faced with difficulties in handling impulses, and stresses between the internal and external environment. The defense mechanisms are one expression of the strength of this anxiety, and in the present factor analytic research the correlations with the ego weakness factor offer proof of this dynamic explanation. Another of the six factors therein, the H (−) factor, labeled threctia, or constitutional susceptibility to threat (Cattell, 1957), has not entered into psychoanalytic theory, though it should be obvious that an individual of a constitutionally more timid disposition would, in general, experience a magnified form of whatever anxiety that another, less threctic, individual would experience from the same amount of conflict or threat. Some loading also is found in the L factor of paranoid personality (Cattell and Stice, 1957), though it is not clear whether this correlation expresses the tendency of paranoid persons to become anxious or of anxious persons to become paranoid. For this summary, since the purpose of this chapter is not to go into questions of the dynamics of anxiety, we shall say no more, except to point out that the functionally unitary structures found by factor analysis *do* correspond to meaningful concepts in general dynamic clinical psychology. Indeed, they provide a basis not previously available for verifying, by quantitative measurement, the theories that have been clinically entertained about anxiety.

Before we can inspect the other dimensions of variation that have been found akin to anxiety, and susceptible to confusion with it, let us ask if the above really gets hold of the pattern of anxiety as a *mood state* (or, at least, a state, conscious or unconscious). What we actually have so far is evidence that, when a lot of putative anxiety measuring devices are applied to a lot of people and intercorrelated, a single core factor of general anxiety exists, but this is a demonstration of a *trait* difference rather than a state difference. That is, it defines a dimension in which individuals differ from one another, and not necessarily the dimension of mood change within individuals. This is correct, for it is at least theoretically possible that the set of variables which change together when a person moves in and out of an anxious state are in some way different from the set of measures which change together when we compare anxious people with non-anxious people.

For anxiety, in the latter situation, might be some sort of characterological and relatively permanent feature, which would have different characteristics from a state. For example, possibly some of the autonomic response variables, which would show up strongly in a mood or state, could not be maintained homeostatically at a life-long level of high anxiety. Accordingly, it becomes necessary, in order to complete the research, to measure these variables on individuals, then to allow a lapse of time, to measure them again, and finally to correlate the *changes* in these variables. This can actually be done in two ways, which have become called, respectively, P-technique and Incremental R-technique. In the former, a single person is measured on, say, fifty variables repeatedly, for perhaps a hundred or two hundred days (P-technique thus means single *person* analysis). The correlatable series over the hundred or two hundred occasions, showing the way in which variables change together with the natural stimuli of everyday life, as they raise and lower anxiety from day to day, can then be correlated and factor analyzed. This gives the unique trait pattern of the individual, but we should expect, and we in fact find, that P-technique studies on different individuals yield recognizably the same fundamental patterns, though they may have some particular directions of investment in a particular individual. The Incremental R-technique, on the other hand, measures, say, two hundred persons at the beginning of the week and the same two hundred persons at the end of the week, on the same variables. Some of the individuals may be counted upon to have increased their anxiety through events in that period, whereas in others there will be a downward trend. The result is that, if these change scores are correlated and factor analyzed, as in the ordinary R-technique factor analysis (except that increments rather than absolute levels are being measured), a similar pattern should be found as for the central tendency among the P-technique studies, if anxiety really is, in every sense a unitary trait.

The actual upshot of such correlated P- and R-technique studies has been to show that the pattern of anxiety as a *state*, obtained from the P-technique and Incremental R-technique studies, is similar to the pattern of anxiety as a *trait*, derived from ordinary R-technique, individual difference studies (Cattell and Scheier, 1960). However, there are some important differences, especially of the kind one would expect from homeostatic principles. Let us inspect the pattern found for anxiety as a state (to be contrasted with anxiety as a trait, set out in Table 1) as shown in Table 2.

From the standpoint of psychophysiological research, and particularly of the study of psychoactive drugs, it is one of the beauties of P-technique that it brings out simultaneously the psychological and physiological aspects of a single reaction pattern. This does not mean that certain *single* physiological variables, e.g., the 17-OH-corticosteroid excretion level, may not be determined by more than one pattern, e.g., by anxiety, effort-stress, or the adrenergic response. But it does mean that there are certain *patterns* of physiological response that are shown by the evidence to align themselves with certain *patterns* of psychological feeling and behavior. These have considerable interest for the study of psychoactive drugs, because they give initial indications of possible chemical interactions in which to search for the

TABLE 2.   SUMMARY LIST OF BEST-CONFIRMED ANXIETY SENSITIVE
VARIABLES LOADING ANXIETY AS A STATE
[Incremental UI 24 and PUI 9 (−)]

1. Introspective, Questionnaire Variables
(Mean Loading from Six Experiments)

16 PF Factor		Average Loading
C −	More emotionality (ego weakness)	− .53
Q$_3$ −	Weaker self-sentiment	− .51
Q$_4$ +	Higher ergic tension	+ .44
Q$_2$ +	More self-sufficiency	+ .30
O +	More guilt proneness	+ .20

2. Objective Test Variables

Identifying Master Index Number		
211	More susceptibility to annoyance	+ .46
219	More willingness to admit common frailties	+ .22
108	Less confidence in skill in untried performance	+ .16

3. Physical and Physiological Variable

444	Higher systolic pulse pressure	+ .36
617	More plasma 17-OH in serum	+ .27
443	Lower absolute level of galvanic skin resistance	+ .26
77	Higher pH saliva (alkaline)	+ .23
	Higher hippuric acid in urine	+ .74*
	Higher tremor	+ .20

* In one study and indirect support in other studies.

mode of action of the given drug.   For example, what we call below
the unreactive or unexcited state (and indexed as PUI 1., i.e. P-technique universal index pattern No. 1; the pattern of largest variance)
apparently coincides with a fall of adrenalin in the blood.   It could
be that the excitant action of certain drugs is derived from their pos-
session of some part of a molecule similar to the missing adrenalin
component.   Or, again, in the anxiety state pattern it has been shown
that there is a fall of cholinesterase in the blood serum.   One might,
therefore, look for possible biochemical mechanisms in drugs opposing
anxiety in the form of some action with regard to the enzymes controlling cholinesterase.

However, from the psychologist's standpoint, in performing actual controlled experiments with drugs or other mood changers, and in using such designs as analysis of variance, the important thing is only to get the most valid unitary *psychological* measurement of the state, since this is usually the *dependent* variable. Indeed, it is desirable to dissociate the measurement as completely as possible from the *independent* variable, which is some kind of controlled physiological condition. Consequently, one ought to employ a purely psychological measurement of the factor and to use the psychological performance variables which have been shown to be the most valid measures of this unitary factor, i.e., the measures which over several factorizations have proved to have the highest *loading* on the factor.

Among the tests of an objective nature which proved to have substantial loadings of the factor, and which have been included in the regular battery constructed and standardized by Cattell and Scheier (1960), are: "willingness to admit common frailties," a test which draws its rationale from the tendency to self-depreciation present in the anxious person; "susceptibility to annoyance," which has consistently proved a high indicator of anxiety; "lack of confidence in untried performance," a test which probably is explicable on grounds of ego weakness; a device called "high emotionality of comment," in which the same misdirected emotionality as appears in the annoyability test is probably tapped, and "a tendency to agree," which is measured as a response set in any random set of opinion statements. All these tests are objective, not only in the sense of being behavioral, rather than self-evaluative, but also in the sense of being objectively scorable, i.e., they have selective rather than inventive answers, and are in other ways productive of a conspect reliability coefficient of unity (Cattell, 1957a).

It is noteworthy that defective perception, e.g., word reproduction, Bender figures, as hitherto used by several researchers (Basowitz, Persky, Korchin, and Grinker, 1955), as a measure of anxiety, though given plenty of opportunity to load in these experiments, never rose above a mean validity of about .15. Moreover, part of the variance in this performance decline seems to be accounted for by the effort stress factor defined below. Similarly, "faster rate of conditioning" loads the anxiety factor only moderately and is partially accounted for by other factors. In both these instances past experiments alleged to be about anxiety are undoubtedly at least equally concerned with measures of stress or adrenergic response and have quite low validity for measuring the definite unitary anxiety factor. Similarly, although muscle tension was investigated by several devices, it proves, except for the special case of muscle tension in the upper spinal region, namely in the trapezius muscle, to be unrelated to anxiety. Indeed, the writing pressure exerted in ordinary hand writing is actually significantly *reduced* in anxiety.

These studies on the anxiety pattern, covering some thousands of subjects and nearly nine hundred variables, thus lead, on the practical side, to the construction of what is known as the Objective Anxiety Factor Battery (Scheier and Cattell, 1959). Scheier has prepared this in five equivalent forms to facilitate the periodic testing of patients or experimental subjects. It takes about twenty minutes, as far as the group administrable subtests are concerned, and a little more than half an hour if one or two instrumental, only-individually-administrable-tests are included. At the same time, it has been possible to construct from the factors loading highly the second-order questionnaire factor in the 16 personality factor questionnaire a highly saturated questionnaire measure of the general anxiety factor (the IPAT Anxiety Scale, 1957). This takes only about seven or eight minutes to administer, covering forty items, and it has a validity, measured against the same essential factor as the objective battery is measured against, about equal to that of the objective test battery. Naturally, however, like all questionnaires, it is not suitable for use where answers might be faked; otherwise the objective test and the questionnaire are measures of one and the same anxiety factor.

More refined research should, in general, aim, in the choice of objective battery subtests, at a somewhat different emphasis in the battery for anxiety as a trait and anxiety as a state, but for the great majority of purposes a single battery will suffice for both. The measurements of anxiety as a state would be improved by putting somewhat more emphasis on individual, brass-instrument tests, notably the latency of the startle reaction pattern, and other tests which can be chosen from an inspection of the factor pattern set out above and elsewhere (Cattell and Scheier, 1960) for the state pattern. However, as far as can yet be ascertained, there is no great difference in the state and trait pattern as measured by questionnaire, providing, of course, the subjects are told to answer the questionnaire *as they view their behavior at the present moment.* Also, if retest is to be at a shorter period than, say, one week, it would be desirable to use a graphic response scale instead of the a, b, and c, three-response categories, the responses on which would have some danger of being remembered by the subject over a day or two.

The Nature of Anxiety

Having discovered a firm reference point in the tangle of alleged anxiety measurements, and having studied this factor and built up a just adequately valid battery for it, let us now consider its psychological nature more broadly, in the framework of possibly related, but, in the outcome, independent, conceptual dimensions. The chief concepts with which anxiety can be, and has been, confused, both theoretically and in setting up measurement devices, are neuroticism, stress response, fatigue, and adrenergic response. It has been shown, in studies determining the factors on which neurotics differ from normals, that characteristically there are differences on four or five factors, of which anxiety is only one. Thus, what Eysenck and his co-workers (1947) called the neuroticism factor, which we had independently located in normal personality dimensions as UI 23, undoubtedly distinguishes neurotics from normals more than anxiety does. So also do two other factors, into the nature of which we need not enter here (Cattell and Scheier, 1960). It is, therefore, disturbing to discover that quite a number of alleged anxiety scales have been "validated" in terms of their ability to distinguish neurotics from normals! Beyond a certain low level of correlation, the better the test is at doing this, the poorer it is as a measure of anxiety, because it becomes more and more systematically contaminated with the four or five other factors which distinguish neurotics from normals. Indeed, in some instances one would now make the judgment, from an inspection of the items, that such manifest anxiety scales are actually better measures of neuroticism than of anxiety. Although the several researches (Cattell and Scheier, 1960) now completed with the definite anxiety factor scale do show a positive correlation of anxiety with neuroticism, when the latter is defined clinically, by pointing to neurotic individuals, the correlation is still quite low. Moreover, the use of this same true anxiety factor measure shows that normal people, in certain life situations, can be decidedly higher on anxiety than most neurotics. Parenthetically, among the neurotics, the anxiety neurotics scored above other syndrome groups, and the psychosomatic patients scored below general neurotics, and even slightly below the normal average.

The separation of the anxiety response from the diurnal fatigue factor is easy (Cattell, 1957a), but its experimental separation from effort stress response would require far more technical discussion than its distinction above from the concept of neuroticism. However, it can be said that there are now several P-technique studies in which two distinct, well-characterized factors have appeared, one being the now easily recognized anxiety factor and the other being a somewhat related factor, in terms of physiological patterns of response, but quite unrelated in the psychological pattern. The physiological patterns of anxiety and this effort stress factor are similar in that there is raised 17-OH-corticosteroid excretion, raised serum glycine, raised systolic and diastolic blood pressure, but even here there is a different pattern of amino acid change. (The anxiety pattern shows higher hippuric acid excretion; the effort stress pattern shows more arginine excretion, and, in one experiment, an indication of *opposite* effects on glutamic acid level.) The effort stress reaction can be shown to be connected more immediately to environmental assaults, and, to run higher on its corticosteroid loading.

In *general*, "effort stress" is, thus, environmentally triggered, but, in accordance with our initial principle that the same reaction pattern may sometimes arise from distinctly different stimulus situations, there are experimental instances of the effort stress being aroused by three distinct classes of stimulus: (a) a sudden external threat, as here, (b) a determined attempt by the subject to control emotional expression of almost any kind, and (c) prolonged willed concentration on a high intellectual or motor performance. By reason of the last situation, although as stated above there is normally some tendency for the effort stress response pattern to produce some decline of performance, notably of perceptual performance, yet in particular cases it may be associated with psychological performance decidedly above average, this high performance being the source of the stress. No standardized battery has yet actually been worked out for the stress state response, but with attention to the published factor patterns and a little further work, it would be possible to develop a fairly satisfactory scale, though it would seem inevitable at present that certain individually measured and purely physiological variables would need to be included to get a sufficiently good measure. Parenthetically, the expression "effort stress" (or, in precise index, PUI 4) is used for this unitary dimension of change to distinguish it from the broader concept of generalized stress reaction or general adaptation syndrome developed by Selye (1952) and others.

We shall not digress too far into the family of nocive mood states having some generic relation to anxiety, for we are concerned here mainly with getting an adequate distinction from anxiety. It can be said that there are, besides effort stress, two other well-defined factors, namely, an adrenergic, sympathetic response and an unnamed factor involving a high serum cholesterol, rapid heart beat, and raised blood pressure. All three (stress and these two) fall, along with the anxiety factor, in a second-order factor which may well be taken as the psychometric concept equivalent to Selye's clinically deduced general stress pattern. That is to say, effort stress is only one of four factors in the general stress pattern which includes also the adrenergic response, anxiety, and the cholesterol-pulse factor. The actual second-order factor structure and loadings are shown in Figure 1, where this general stress versus anxiety is plotted against a second-order factor involving depression and high cholesterol-pulse primaries. An interesting and dynamically suggestive initial finding in this connection is that the anxiety factor is loaded in *one* direction on this massive second-order factor, while the other three stress factors are loaded in the *opposite* direction. The most likely explanation is that the indi-

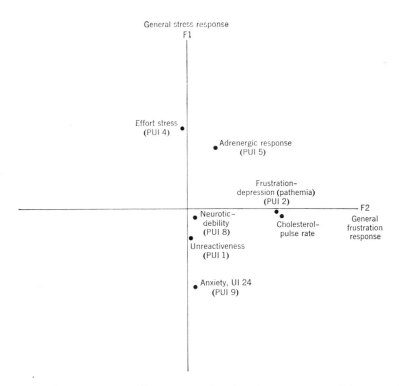

Figure 1. Primary response factors to nocive situations as structured in a second-order "general stress" factor. (General stress, F1, plotted against frustration response, F2.)

vidual may either positively react to a threat situation with action and stress ("general stress"), along the lines of the three stress factors, or, alternatively, for some reason, give up the external conflict and substitute an internal conflict, generating anxiety.

Incidentally, the three response dimensions other than anxiety in this broad stress adaptation pattern are comparatively "thin" in psychological content. They do not show up much in psychological report or in any psychological performance tests yet tried, though of course they will correlate substantially with measures of intensity of certain nocive stimulus situations. They can also be differentiated, up to a point, by being comparatively short-term, or, at least, immediate, responses to a situation, whereas anxiety typically lasts a long time, and, moreover, is generated by inner symbolic reference to remote situations, being thus, relative to the stress responses, uncorrelated with *immediate* situations. Setting aside these stress reactions, therefore, as something which the factor analyst and the physiologist can with relative ease distinguish from anxiety, let us look at other dimensions of change which are more important in *psychological* content, though perhaps needing less discussion in terms of danger of confusion with anxiety.

If one wishes to search for state response factors in terms of a truly comprehensive survey, it can be shown that state factors exist corresponding to about two-thirds of the twenty or more known personality trait dimensions (Cattell, 1957a). That is to say, on quite a number of dimensions which stably distinguish one person from another, any one person is *also* liable to some extent to fluctuation. Consequently, an exhaustive psychology of states and moods, such as that being undertaken by Green and Nowlis (1957), would need to take into account at least a dozen independent dimensions in which an individual's mood, performance and, probably, physiological state will be found to vary. On some of the more important dimensions of individual difference, such as general intelligence (UI 1), extraversion-introversion (UI 32), the variation has been so slight as so far to defy experimental demonstration, but on others, such as surgency-desurgency, corticalertia (UI 22), and ability to mobilize (UI 23), the daily variation with situation and internal physiological condition seems to be considerable. Our remaining discussion of anxiety and of dimensions needing separation from anxiety, will be confined, however, to only the three most important of these—important in the sense of being mood dimensions that have received the best cumulative experimental demonstration, and which appear to have the largest variance.

In the indexed series of observed P-technique and Incremental R-technique factors, being of largest variance, they naturally fall near the beginning and have been numbered PUI 1, excitability versus torpidness; PUI 2, elation versus frustration-depression (pathemia); PUI 3, diurnal fatigue; and PUI 8, high capacity to mobilize versus debility and overwroughtness. (The general diurnal fatigue factor is mentioned because of the importance of distinguishing it from the last of the factors just named, which also has the general character of fatigue, but not of a kind remedied immediately by sleep, and is one of the factors most strongly distinguishing the neurotic individual from the normal.)

The PUI 1 factor, excitability versus unreactiveness (Cattell, 1957a) seems to be virtually what the physiologist has thought of as the vagotonic or parasympathetic predominance pattern. It loads high skin resistance (at the torpidness pole), low blood sugar, raised serum cholinesterase, and, psychologically, various test performances indicating unreactiveness, inhibition, or disinclination to become involved, which *could* be mistaken for fatigue. It is conceivable also that the excitability pole of this state factor could be confused with anxiety. In theoretical development it has been natural for investigators, e.g., Wenger (1948), to make a strong case for this factor as parasympathetic predominance, and to develop a satisfactorily complete picture of its mechanism and nature in terms of its parasympathetic action. While we see no objection to this conceptualization in terms of any known facts of existing research, it would be desirable to investigate further before finally settling on this interpretation and label, and meanwhile we have, therefore, simply labeled it pattern PUI 1, indicating that it is one of the biggest dimensions of variation in the persons we have so far studied.

The PUI 2 pattern might at a glance fit the clinical stereotype of elation-depression, but the actual facts of the loading pattern give it a slightly, systematically, different slant from this popular conception, for the psychological variables in the "elation" at the positive pole tend rather to a state of calm—a serene and successful quality. This is also associated with a tendency to handle problems speedily, with effective cognitive skill, and in a rational and objective manner. Some of this does not normally belong in the concept of "elation," indeed, the latter, in manic behavior, often has poor judgment and impulsiveness combined in it. The depressive pole is associated with some tendency to *general* emotionality, with situations of frustration, and with a tendency to handle problems crudely, as if physiological activity were high at a "hypothalamic" level. In other words, there is general affectivity as well as depression, and this is supported on the physiological side by the finding of some loading on raised corticosteroids (at the depressive end), as well as a decidedly high cholinesterase serum level. Nevertheless, some of these physiological changes, which the physiologist might think of as associated with stress reaction, and which situationally are sometimes associated with frustrating stimuli, are in this pattern actually linked to a general slowing down of all psychological tempo and output measures, and sometimes of physiological measures. This "retardation" has long been noted in clinical observations of depression and is, as the figures show (Cattell, 1957a), one of the outstanding and characteristic features of the loading pattern defining this factor.

Nevertheless, as stated, one cannot, appropriately, simply call the mood axis "pure" elation-depression. On the elation side there is much that Lindsley (1951) would call "high activation," and this agrees with what we find on the loading pattern of this factor when it appears as a trait. Its best correspondence is with UI 22, a trait which we have called corticalertia, by reason of the facilitation of cortical activity which seems to characterize it (Cattell, 1955). Possibly further research will separate out another factor here and reinstate additionally the popular conception of euphoria versus depression, but on the present available evidence the euphoria is more of a serenity, with efficient cortical functioning, and the depression is more of a turgid, frustrated state with general retardation of cortical activity.

The chief importance of this state for studies on anxiety is that the depressive pole seems to have been confused a number of times with anxiety, because there is apparently a statistical tendency for anxiety and depression to go together. Both are *possible* consequences of a relatively total frustration, and it is not surprising, therefore, that a single clinical syndrome group has long been noted combining anxiety and depression. However, in terms of functionally unitary dimensions discoverable by P-technique and Incremental R-technique, these two dimensions can be separated; this means that individuals *can* move along one quite independently of movement along the other. A recognition of this difference is important because these dimensions have different psychological and physiological associations. The psychometrist does well to set up distinct batteries for these independent axes of mood swing and to treat them as conceptually distinct and, therefore, as potentially reacting to distinct drug influences.

Our third "nocive response" factor, indexed as PUI 8, and labeled descriptively "capacity to mobilize versus debility and overwroughtness," corresponds in individual differences to the trait factor UI 23, which, as stated, Eysenck in 1947 labeled the "general neuroticism factor," and which we independently find to be one of the factors most powerfully distinguishing neurotics from normals. The debility pole is characterized by high rigidity on classical motor-perceptual rigidity tests (Spearman), high taxic sway suggestibility, rapid increase of errors when speeded up on a performance, and generally poor co-ordination both at the motor level and at the level of ideation. Curiously enough, none of the areas of physiological association so far explored, e.g., autonomic responses, metabolic rate, amino acid metabolism, cardiovascular change, and corticosteroid enzymes has been found to have significant association with it, though some recent work of Grinker (Korchin, Schwartz, and Heath, 1959) suggests a possible association with ceruloplasm. Some theoretical explanation of this factor has recently been attempted (Cattell and Scheier, 1960) along the lines of considering that it corresponds to the psychoanalytic concept of instinctual regression, in the sense of incapacity to maintain fully developed relations to external objects of interest. It is hypothesized that the measured evidences, in our factor UI 23 ($-$), of inability to mobilize intellectual and motor resources (which resources of adaptation the patient can experimentally be shown fully to possess on other occasions) are an indication of this instinctual withdrawal of interest from objective attachments, in the general direction of narcissistic regression. One reason for attempting a theory along these lines is that normals and neurotics who are low on this factor show a significant rise in the direction of mobilization when subjected to challenging or even threatening environmental situations (Cattell and Scheier, 1960). This suggests that it is not so much a lack of cognitive resources, or of energy, that is causing the poor mobilization, but a lack of instinctual interest, which can be provoked, at least momentarily, by a rude challenge (Cattell and Scheier, 1959).

The possibilities of confusing this factor with anxiety have already been mentioned in connection with the conceptually inadequate practice of validating anxiety tests against neurotic-normal differences. Actual inspection of the objective test behavior pattern in this factor will readily show (Cattell, 1955), in any case, that it is totally different from that in anxiety, UI 24. Some attempts have nevertheless been made to justify the consideration of UI 23 as anxiety by arguing that it represents a "bound" anxiety, the high rigidity loading here being taken as one justification for this conclusion. Against this it must be pointed out that we have had psychiatrists rate some ninety clinically analyzed cases for free anxiety and for bound anxiety, and the bound anxiety showed little relation to this factor measurement (Cattell and Scheier, 1960). Even if *all* neurosis is considered "bound anxiety," this would not lead to an identification of UI 23 as bound anxiety, for, besides UI 23 and 24, there are, as stated above, at least three other personality dimensions distinguishing neurotics from normals (Cattell and Scheier, 1960).

The last paragraph raises the whole question of whether there is any advantage, theoretical or practical, to be gained by using the concept of bound anxiety. In the first place, it has proved difficult to define. In the researches on anxiety described above, repeated attempts were made to get from leading clinical psychologists some statements of behavior, or any objective and experimentally measurable manifestations, that could be considered a manifestation of bound anxiety as they defined it. There was considerable disagreement, and the problem was finally tackled, in the way indicated, by getting psychiatrists to make a rating of bound anxiety along with a rating of free anxiety and total anxiety. By this approach, the bound anxiety spreads itself demonstrably over at least three components notably over UI 17 (Cattell, 1957a), which has been defined as general inhibition, and UI 20, which has been defined as tendency to repress (Cattell, 1957a). Several of the manifestations commonly alleged to appear in bound anxiety actually loaded the general anxiety factor, UI 24, as defined above.

The best resolution of findings at the present moment seems to be to conclude that there is a single general anxiety factor, UI 24, which shows itself predominantly in introspectible and observer-ratable anxiety, but also in performance and physiological manifestations and in several forms that would be considered bound anxiety, e.g., certain rigidities and avoidances. The "boundness" of anxiety, by this analysis, is then accounted for by the new personality factors, especially UI 17 and UI 20, which, statistically, account for some of the variance of the behavior which has been said to indicate bound anxiety, but which are *not* themselves bound anxiety. Rather, these factors are to be considered instruments—binding influences—or secondary personality forces, which cause some of the expression of UI 24 to be tied down in bound forms. Since the operation of these factors and our interpretations of their nature are relatively new and need much more confirmation, this bound aspect of the expression of anxiety must be considered, for the time being, hypothetical. Meanwhile, the evidence is overwhelming that we can proceed with the measurement of the UI 24 factor with confidence that we are accounting for most of the variance of most of the things that most psychologists call anxiety.

The demonstration of the UI 24 pattern as a unitary factor, among some twenty other objective test factors, in seven successive studies, has occurred in the last five years, while the demonstration that this same factor also expresses itself as a second-order pattern in the primary questionnaire (16 PF Test) personality factors is only a couple of years old. Consequently, there has been little time for any experimental use of the new batteries to yield sequential, stimulus-response, or ecological, findings compared with the older arbitrary—and, indeed, premature—"anxiety" scales. However, a quite remarkable impetus has been given to anxiety research in the last two years by the availability of these scientifically meaningful measuring instruments, though naturally this is too recent for the greater part of it to have reached publication. Nevertheless, some experiments in real situations have been carried out, such as Sells's work (1957) showing that Air Force crews on dangerous flight missions scored significantly higher on tests from the objective anxiety battery than on ordinary flights. In another criterion field there is Tsushima's (1950) experiment showing that students tested and retested on the questionnaire measure of the anxiety factor showed significant rise when informed of failure in examinations. Scheier (Cattell and Scheier, 1960) has confirmatory findings, but also certain results which indicate that there may be a significant *fall* in anxiety when an individual actually meets a stress situation which he has long contemplated. For example, individuals who have long faced an important examination appear actually to drop in anxiety at the time of the examination. Some stress interview experiments by Basowitz, Persky, Korchin, and Grinker (1955) likewise showed only a slight change in anxiety at the time of the stress interview itself, though the effort stress and frustration-depression responses which we have defined experimentally above showed reaction to the stress in the expected direction and of considerable and statistically significant magnitude. This difference in the behavior of anxiety, so measured, is not at variance with what we should expect from insightful clinical theory, which has long recognized anxiety as something tied to remote, symbolic reference, unlike fear, which is tied to the immediate stress situation. One may recall that Grenfell's famous poem on anxiety before battle culminates in: "And when the burning moment breaks, and all things else are out of mind," and there are countless other observations by clinical and literary men instancing the dispersion of anxiety when the real situation breaks. This is one more reminder of the reasons for our initial model, which first discovers and recognizes a definite unitary response pattern, but leaves to further experiment the decision whether a particular stimulus is itself an anxiety stimulus.

Anxiety Scales and Psychoactive Drug Research

At present, then, the research need is for still greater definition and stabilization, in a highly loaded test battery, of the UI 24 anxiety measurement, and for the prosecution of "applied" researches with such batteries (Scheier and Cattell, 1959; I.P.A.T., 1957) in relation to a variety of psychoactive drugs, life situations, and therapeutic techniques. It may well prove, when such experiment is done, that existing conceptions about the rise and fall of anxiety with particular external situations will be proved quite erroneous. Furthermore, the effect of psychoactive drugs believed to operate on anxiety (UI 24 as a trait, or PUI 9 as a state) may prove in certain cases to be greater upon stress (PUI 4), upon depression (PUI 2), upon inhibition (PUI 1), upon the adrenergic response (PUI 5), upon fatigue (PUI 3), and so on. As far as anxiety and each one of these human "nocive" responses are concerned, it would be desirable to accumulate lists of the stimulus situations that are most highly provocative of this definite pattern, in our own culture, for the average man, so that we may gain a "quantitative taxonomy of situations" to aid the clinician in his calculations and prognostications.

Granting, then, that the measurement of anxiety in relation to psychoactive drugs is to be based on a definite objective or (equivalent) questionnaire test battery for UI 24, rather than upon any assumption that a particular arbitrary stimulus is causing a rise or fall of anxiety, the procedures in the application of such measurement to psychoactive drug experiments becomes relatively clear. Probably it would be desirable in general to measure the anxiety level simultaneously by the objective batteries, which now exist in a form suitable for repetitions up to five times (Scheier and Cattell, 1959), and by the questionnaire which, with a graphic scale, can be safely readministered to the same person providing the intervening period is not very brief (I.P.A.T., 1957).

Additionally, this analysis into five or six distinct directions of response to nocive stimulus situations indicates the need for a radical change in procedure, namely, taking account of dimensions other than anxiety, even when the experimenter's hunch is that the drug is affecting anxiety only. We have seen—and much more evidence could be presented if space permitted—that stimuli which are *supposed* to provoke anxiety frequently cause quite considerable and significant changes along other dimensions, even though the expected change along the dimension of increased anxiety also occurs. Experience in related experiments, e.g., on the effect of psychotherapeutic measures, has repeatedly shown that changes occur in dimensions never anticipated by the experimenter. The 16 PF changes of patients under therapy include not only rise of ego strength (C factor) and fall of anxiety, but also a rise in dominance (E factor). In this area there are indeed "more things in heaven and earth, Horatio" than are dreamt of in our philosophy.

In the field of study of individual differences and general personality change it has for several years been the writer's habit to advise the researcher pioneering in a particular field first to make a general exploration of the spectrum with the 16 Personality Factor Questionnaire, sweeping through all dimensions of personality so far known, instead of putting all his eggs in one basket by trusting to his all-too-confident conceptual predilection that some particular scale will be the one affected by the situation he applies. This recommendation has often been justified by the discovery of still bigger changes on some unsuspected dimension than on the favorite concept of the experimenter. By this principle, applied to the present situation, the writer would argue for entering any experiment on a presumed mood change, through a particular drug application, if possible by covering *initially at least* the six most clearly recognized dimensions of change. Even though the experimenter is himself concerned only to know whether there is or is not, say, a significant change on anxiety as a result of application of the psychoactive drug, he may start still more significant researches by his secondary findings on other dimensions, or may link up with the results of some other researcher who has been working on some other dimension. The wholistic approach has time and again proved to be the best one in anything having to do with the total personality in the present state of our ignorance. The particular dimensions which would seem to be practicable and most comprehensive at the present time for investigating the action of any drug are:

1. Anxiety.   Defined by the batteries for UI 24 or PUI 9 (Cattell, 1957a).

2. The effort stress response.   Defined as PUI 4.

3. The excitability versus "unreactiveness" or torpidness dimension. Defined by variables in factor PUI 1.

4. The elation versus frustration-depression axis.   Defined by the factor PUI 2.

5. The mobilization versus debility (regression) axis.   Defined by the battery for UI 23, PUI 8.

6. The adrenergic response pattern, defined by variables in PUI 5. Additionally, one would wish to avoid possible confusions with the diurnal fatigue pattern, PUI 3, in certain experimental designs.

Many workers with psychoactive drugs are beginning to say that we are badly in need of some frame of reference by which accurately to describe the action of each drug.   A mere resort to verbal refinement of all kinds of popular terms such as tranquilizing, exciting, or depressing is not enough.   Unless the proliferation of increasingly subtle expressions can be tied down, as one can tie down the artist's reference to subtle color in the psychologist's dimensions of hue or brightness, no real gain has occurred, and a Tower of Babel is being built.   Instead, scientific precision demands some way of psychologically quantifying the action of the drug, just as the chemist working in dyes can quantify the effects of various chemical groups upon color by reference to known physical properties of the spectrum.   The six dimensional scheme provides just such a basis, though one which may need to be expanded to further dimensions as research consolidates the other suspected dimensions of personality change.   If the effect of a given quantity of a given drug is measured simultaneously among these six axes in terms of the change produced in the average mental hospital patient (of defined syndrome) measured in the standard score distribution of these mood states for the general population, it should be possible to assign to any drug six scores.   The uniqueness of the drug would then be represented by a uniqueness of position in six-dimensional space, and the resemblance of one drug to another would be exactly representable by a pattern similarity coefficient, r_p, showing the distance apart of two such points (Cattell, 1949).   It may well be that certain drugs will be found which specifically influence only one dimension of change, but it is surely more likely that most will have a predominant action upon one dimension but appreciable subsidiary actions on others.   A rational pharmacology could then be worked out in terms of combining drugs, according to their indices, in ways required to produce a predefined vector of return to normality for a given patient or type of patient.

If this goal is to be insightfully achieved, the research of the next few years will need to concentrate on increasing precision of factorial definition of the dimensions already visible. There will need to be a much greater coordination of research at different centers in terms of careful attention to inclusion of identical "marker variables" (Cattell, 1952) for the chief factors so far isolated, so that results will have general conceptual negotiability. Fortunately, in regard to anxiety itself, there are available measures of substantial concept validity (Scheier and Cattell, 1959; I.P.A.T., 1957) which can be used to give a measure either of the unitary factor, UI 24, or, in the questionnaire form (I.P.A.T., 1957) can be broken down into certain primaries, (e.g., ego weakness, ergic tension, temperamental timidity) contributing to the anxiety level defined by the second-order factor. At present, these tests are standardized in the usual way, giving a percentile or standard score in relation to the distribution of scores in the total population, and it must be left to the individual experimenter to work out ipsative standardizations (Cattell, 1957b; Guilford, 1954) upon them if he wishes to give serial scores to single individuals repeatedly measured in an experimental sequence.

R E F E R E N C E S

Basowitz, H., Persky, H., Korchin, S. J., and Grinker, R. R. *Anxiety and stress.* New York: McGraw-Hill, 1955.

Cattell, R. B. r_p and other coefficients of pattern similarity. *Psychometrika,* 1949, 14, 279–298.

Cattell, R. B. *Factor Analysis: an introduction and manual for the psychologist and social scientist.* New York: Harper, 1952.

Cattell, R. B. The principal replicated factors discovered in objective personality tests. *J. abnorm. soc. Psychol.,* 1955, 50, 291–314.

Cattell, R. B. Second order factors in the questionnaire realm. *J. consult. Psychol.,* 1956, 20, 411–418.

Cattell, R. B. *Personality and motivation structure and measurement.* New York: World Book Co., 1957. (a)

Cattell, R. B. A universal index for psychological factors. *Psychologia,* 1957, 1, 74–85. (b)

Cattell, R. B. Anxiety, extraversion and other second order personality factors in childhood. *J. Pers.,* 1959, 2, 143–152.

Cattell, R. B., et al. The objective-analytic personality factor test battery. Institute Personal. and Abil. Testing, 1604 Coronado Drive, Champaign, Ill., 1959.

Cattell, R. B., and Scheier, I. H. *The meaning and measurement of neuroticism and anxiety.* New York: Ronald Press, 1960.

Cattell, R. B., and Stice, G. *The sixteen personality factor questionnaire.* (2nd ed.) I.P.A.T., 1604 Coronado Drive, Champaign, Ill., 1957.

Cattell, R. B., Stice, G., and Kristy, N. F. A first approximation to nature-nurture ratios for eleven primary personality factors in objective tests. *J. abnorm. soc. Psychol.*, 1957, 54, 143–159.

Eysenck, H. J. *Dimensions of personality.* London: Methuen, 1947.

Green, R. G., aand Nowlis, H. H. On the use of drugs in the analysis of complex human behavior, with emphasis on the study of mood. *Conf. on current trends in psychology.* Pittsburgh: Univer. of Pittsburgh Press, 1957.

Grinker, R. R., Korchin, S. J., Schwartz, N., and Heath, H. Personal communication in advance of publication, 1959.

Guilford, J. P. *Psychometric methods.* New York: McGraw-Hill, 1954.

I.P.A.T. The IPAT Anxiety Scale. 1604 Coronado Drive, Champaign, Ill., 1957.

Karson, S., and Pool, K. B. Second order factors in personality measurement. *J. consult. Psychol.*, 1958, 22, 299–303.

Lindsley, D. B. Emotion. In S. S. Stevens (Ed.), *Handbook of experimental psychology.* New York: Wiley, 1951, 453–516.

Rosenthal, F. A factor analysis of anxiety variables. Unpublished doctoral dissertation, Univer. of Illinois, 1955.

Scheier, I. H., and Cattell, R. B. Clinical validities by analyzing the psychiatrist exemplified in relation to anxiety diagnoses. *Amer. J. Orthopsychiat.*, 1958, 28, 699–713. (a)

Scheier, I. H., and Cattell, R. B. The nature of anxiety; a review of thirteen multivariate analyses composing 814 variables. *Psychol. Rep. Monogr. Suppl.*, 1958, 5, 351–388. (b)

Scheier, I. H. and Cattell, R. B. The IPAT O-A (Objective) Anxiety Battery. IPAT, 1604 Coronado Drive, Champaign, Ill., 1959.

Sells, S. B., Trites, D. K., and Parish, H. S. Correlates of manifest anxiety in beginning pilot trainees. *J. aviat. Med.*, 1957, 28, 583–588.

Selye, H. *The story of the adaptation syndrome.* Montreal: Acta Inc., 1952.

Taylor, J. A. A personality scale of manifest anxiety. *J. abnorm. soc. Psychol.*, 1953, 48, 285–290.

Tsushima, Y. Failure stress in examinations related to anxiety inventory scores. Master's thesis. Univer. of Illinois, 1950.

Wenger, M. A. Studies of autonomic balance in Air Force personnel. *Comp. Psychol. Monogr.*, 1948, 101–111.

Wolf, S. Cardiovascular reactions to symbolic stimuli. *Circulation*, 1958, 18, 287–297.

Behavioral methods for
assessing neuroses and psychoses

This chapter is devoted to a discussion of methods for the diagnosis of the neuroses and psychoses. Possibly the most important benefits to be gained from the use of psychoactive drugs will be in the treatment of the neurotic and psychotic patient. Tests that identify these patients should help us to clarify both our diagnoses and our understanding of the different components of behavior that are affected by the disease. The study of changes in these components, or factors, of behavior as a result of treatment with psychoactive drugs should increase our understanding of both the action of the drug and the dynamics of the disease.

It should be kept in mind that the best instrument for distinguishing a neurotic patient from a psychotic one is not necessarily the best instrument for the measurement of therapeutic changes in either type of patient. Once the diagnosis is securely established, the observation over time of an aspect of the personality which is most likely to show changes will be more useful than would be the repetition of the initial diagnostic measurements, which were perhaps based on entirely different aspects of the personality.

The chapter is divided into three sections. First there is a discussion of various views, based on experimental work, regarding the dis-

The literature search on which this chapter is based was supported by the Schizophrenia and Psychopharmacology Study, a joint research project of the Ypsilanti State Hospital and the University of Michigan (Ralph W. Gerard, Principal Investigator), United States Public Health Service Grant MY1972C. The assistance of Mrs. Eira I. Mattsson, M. Ph., is gratefully acknowledged.

tinction between the neuroses and the psychoses. In the second section multidimensional views of personality are presented.

The third section discusses a number of separate tests which have been used in the diagnosis of neuroses or psychoses. For each of these some of the more important statistical studies are considered briefly. Most of the papers reviewed were published between 1948 and 1958, but occasionally a relevant older report is mentioned. There is a heavy emphasis on schizophrenia throughout.

Neurosis and Psychosis: One Continuum or Two?

Are neuroses and psychoses fundamentally similar forms of mental illness, differing in degree of severity only, or are they quite separate, qualitatively different disease processes? A search of the psychiatric literature would reveal that there are many supporters for both theories.

If neuroses and psychoses are basically similar forms of illness, the situation depicted in Fig. 1 would obtain. The performance of neurotics on various psychological tests would generally place them in a position intermediate between normal subjects and psychotics.

The second theory suggests that neurotics and psychotics differ from normals, but not necessarily on the same variables. Figure 2 illustrates this alternative. The ideas of those who believe that the same individual may display both neurotic and psychotic behavior may perhaps be regarded as a variant of the second theory.

Eysenck has become the most explicit proponent of the second theory. He holds that two independent factors, which he calls neuroticism and psychoticism, form two continua on which every individual may be located by suitable psychological measurements. Figure 3 illustrates this theory schematically.

Eysenck reports to have found (1952, p. 217), in a continuing series of studies, that . . . psychotics are less fluent, perform poorly in continuous addition, perform poorly in mirror drawing, show slower oscillation on the reversal of perspective test, are slower in tracing with a stylus, are more undecided with respect to social attitudes, show poorer concentration,

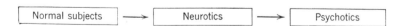

Figure 1. The "One Continuum" theory.

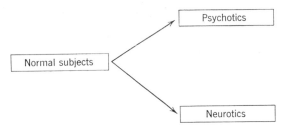

Figure 2. The "Separate Continua" theory.

have a poorer memory, tend to make larger movements and to over-estimate distances and scores, tend to read more slowly, to tap more slowly and to show levels of aspiration much less readily adapted. Those who would argue that of course psychotics are poorer in all tasks than are normals, and that consequently these results are hardly surprising, will have to explain why no such differences were observed with respect to the tests enumerated . . . above.

In the last sentence Eysenck refers to the tests which, he has found, discriminate well between normals and neurotics, such as tests of suggestibility, static ataxia, leg-lifting persistence, the Word-Connection List as well as an inventory of worries, annoyances, and interests. In the study to which Eysenck is referring, the group of psychotics was made up of schizophrenics and manic depressives. Table 1 presents the values of the *t*-test of the significance of the difference between: (1) normals and schizophrenics; (2) depressives and schizophrenics; and (3) normals and depressives.

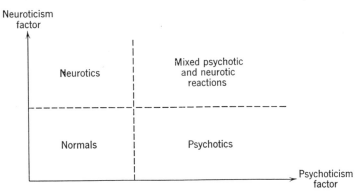

Figure 3. The bifactor theory of Eysenck.

TABLE 1. STATISTICAL SIGNIFICANCE OF THE DIFFERENCES BETWEEN
THE MEANS OF 50 SCHIZOPHRENICS, 50 DEPRESSIVES, AND 100 NORMALS
ON 20 PSYCHOLOGICAL VARIABLES AND IN AGE
(Data reworked from Eysenck, 1952)

Type of Test	Controls vs. Schizo.	Depressed vs. Schizo.	Controls vs. Depressed
Largest diameter of coin drawn (size estimation)	−3.74*	−1.05	−2.98†
Speed of reading prose passage	3.54*	−.31	3.95*
Minimum number of reversals of Necker cube	3.50*	−2.09	4.08*
Natural number of reversals of Necker cube	3.35*	.16	2.47
Number of taps in 15 seconds	3.35*	.81	2.27
Overestimation of short distances	−3.24†	−1.60	−1.60
Fewest additions in 15 half-minute periods	3.19†	−1.06	4.83*
Repeating backwards last 6 digits of series	3.16†	.37	3.42*
Largest diagonal of 3 squares drawn	−2.90†	1.53	−4.17*
Word fluency—animals	2.80†	−1.90	5.08*
Neutral responses on social attitude questions	−2.80†	−.07	−2.10
Speed in drawing 3 circles	2.72†	−1.40	3.12†
Time estimate for track tracing test	−2.69†	−.16	−2.90†
Average amplitude of waves drawn with eyes closed	−2.69†	3.57*	−7.16*
Average length of waves drawn with eyes closed	−2.44	2.88†	−5.40*
Estimate of time to trace diamond in mirror drawing	−2.43	2.33	−3.45*
Number of letters on card remembered	2.37	−2.09	4.96*
Length of the word "year" written slowly	−2.29	.96	−3.74*
Length of space used in writing numbers 1 to 20	−0.64	2.20	−2.91†
Amount of forward sway during suggestion	−0.33	−.24	−0.01
Age	−5.78*	−14.48*	9.18*

A minus sign in front of the value of t indicates that the second mean was higher.

* $p < .001$.

† $p < .01$.

In a later monograph Eysenck (1957) reports the results of a large-scale study of the diagnostic value of a new battery of tests, most of which consist of measures of simple and complex perceptual processes. Three groups of subjects were used: 106 normals, 20 neurotics, and 20 psychotics. Highly significant F-ratios were found for so many of the 91 measures that space does not permit a list of all them here. We have (Vandenberg, 1959) reanalyzed these data to obtain separate t-tests of the significance of the differences for these three comparisons. Table 2 summarizes the results of this analysis. In view of the pos-

TABLE 2

	Number of Variables Significant	
Groups Compared	$.01 < p < .05$	$p < .01$
Psychotics-normals	17	27
Neurotics-normals	13	21
Psychotics-neurotics	4	3

sibility that some patients may belong on both the neurotic and the psychotic continuum, it would be wise to include at least a few measures considered to be diagnostic of neuroticism in any larger test battery aimed at the description and measurement of psychotics, and vice versa.

In designing a comprehensive battery, measures should perhaps also be included which are not related to concepts of mental illness, but which are developed for the analyses of the personality of normal individuals. Bowman (1934), Bowman and Raymond (1929), Bowlby (1942), and even earlier Kraepelin (1925), were interested in seeing whether patients in certain diagnostic categories had particular traits in common in their prepsychotic personalities.

Multidimensional Theories

Some of the most fruitful ideas about the description of the normal personality have come from psychopathology. Conversely, many of the more recent ideas about the description and classification of the mentally ill derive from concepts gained from the study of the normal personality.

Encouraged by the success of refined measurement techniques and complex methods of multivariate analysis in the field of intelligence, many psychologists have been eager to apply similar factor analytic methods to the description and measurement of personality. Their rationale, which is shared by this author, is that one may expect to find at least as many independent factors in the personality as in the intellectual domain.

The success of such an undertaking depends on many conditions, a few of which are mentioned here. It is necessary to study a set of variables which are not a random collection, but which are meaningfully related to one another and which "cover" the problem area well. Fortunately there are mathematical techniques for "automatically" finding such groupings of variables if they exist. They are variously labeled factor analysis, principal components analysis, or simply multivariate analysis.

While there have been many multivariate analyses of personality variables, some of mental patients, many of normal subjects, and some of groups composed of both, the complexity of the problem is such that no reasonably clear and convincing picture has emerged as yet from the totality of these studies. Frequently this is due to failure to select a well-planned set of related variables. At other times the number of subjects is too small. Finally there is a lack of replication of studies. Several excellent books and monographs are available in which the constantly growing mass of such studies is reviewed and more or less successfully integrated (Wolfle, 1940; French, 1953; Cattell, 1946, 1950, 1957b; Eysenck, 1947, 1952, 1953; Diamond, 1957). Cattell (who details some of his work in Chapter 39) has made a single-handed attack—with a succession of able associates—on all fronts, studying abnormal and normal groups, and adults as well as children. He uses three types of variables: (1) subjective *ratings* of the person's personality and behavior by other individuals who are familiar with the person studied; (2) subjective self-reports from *questionnaires* especially designed by Cattell; (3) "objective" measures of *performance* on a large number of short experimental tests, many of which have been designed by Cattell.

Cattell has found 15 factors in personality ratings. He claims to have found the same 15 factors in questionnaire data, plus 8 additional ones which appear only in the questionnaires. Sells (1959) has insisted on the need for a thorough follow-up study of Cattell's work by a well-staffed and well-equipped research team.

Guilford is best known for his continuing studies of the dimensions of intelligence, with particular emphasis on reasoning, abstraction, and other higher-level cognitive abilities. He has also devoted considerable attention to the experimental study of personality. He has written a lucid review of the whole field (1959) and has constructed questionnaires designed to measure the following 13 independent traits:

S, sociability versus shyness.
T, preference for thought versus preference for action.
D, depression, pessimism.
C, emotional stability versus cycloid disposition.
R, freedom from worry, rhathymia.
G, general drive, alertness, energy.
A, ascendance versus submission.
M, masculinity of emotions and interest.
I, self-confidence versus inferiority feelings.
N, nervousness, jumpiness versus composure.
O, objective attitude versus hypersensitivity.
Ag, agreeableness versus quarrelsomeness.
Co, cooperativeness versus fault finding.

A study by Lovell (1945) indicates that the 13 traits measured by Guilford are in part correlated with one another. Factor analysis of the correlated factors led to a few superfactors. One of these looks like Eysenck's neuroticism factor: it contrasts emotional stability, objectivity, cooperativeness, agreeableness, self-confidence and masculine dominance with depression and nervousness. The other factor contrasts general drive, freedom from worry, social ascendance, and sociability and seems to be a surgency factor describing the direction in which a subject's energy is invested (cf. Jung's original extraversion-introversion dichotomy). Guilford and Zimmerman subsequently published one questionnaire (1949) which measures all these personality traits. While collecting data for his study of the relationship between hypnotic suggestibility and masculinity-femininity (which was found to be nil) Weitzenhoffer (1956) found rather high correlations between some of the traits measured by Guilford and Zimmerman and some of the 16 PF (1949) personality traits of Cattell.

Allen Edwards (1954a, b) has constructed a questionnaire for the measurement of some normal personality variables in which the influence of the social desirability of the responses has been carefully minimized by the selection of suitable statements. In addition, the questionnaire is somewhat disguised as a preference inventory. The personality variables measured by the Edwards Personal Preference Schedule, derived from Murray's need system, are: achievement, deference, order, exhibition, autonomy, affiliation, intraception, succorance, dominance, abasement, nurturance, change, endurance, heterosexuality, aggression, and, in addition, test consistency and profile stability. This questionnaire is a fairly new one and not much is known yet about its usefulness with mental patients, but the language of the questions appears to be simple and clear enough for individuals of average intelligence.

The Minnesota Multiphasic Personality Inventory was especially designed for the diagnosis of mental diseases by contrasting the responses of normals and patients in various diagnostic groups (Hathaway and McKinley, 1951). Single scales or profiles based on the scales have not been useful for the diagnosis of individuals (Benton, 1953). This may in part result from the fact that each scale is not really measuring one single factor. Comrey has performed a series of factor analyses of the individual items in each of the scales and found that none of the scales can properly be regarded as measuring a single

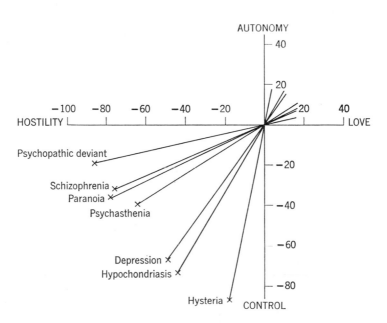

Figure 4. A circumplex analysis by Schaefer of the MMPI scales from data published by Williams and Lawrence (1954).

variable. Similar factors were found in several of the scales (Comrey, 1957a–c; 1958a–f, Comrey and Marggraff 1958).

There is some interesting evidence in a paper by Schaefer (1958) that the scales of the MMPI may be placed in a space defined by two axes, which appear to be somewhat similar to Eysenck's neuroticism and psychoticism factors. Schaefer claims that several published intercorrelation matrices of the Minnesota Multiphasic Personality Test fit the model shown in Fig. 4, which is based on the results from a study by Williams and Lawrence (1954).

Yet another personality inventory has been constructed by Gough (1957). He selected some items from the MMPI and added many new items. The 18 scales are labeled dominance, capacity for status, sociability, social presence, self-acceptance, sense of well-being, responsibility, socialization, self-control, tolerance, good impression, communality, achievement via conformance, achievement via independence, intellectual efficiency, psychological mindedness, flexibility, and femininity. The scale is designed primarily for use with normal subjects. Nevertheless the test manual reports sizable correlations between various MMPI scales and scales of the CPI.

It remains to be seen whether the personality inventories of Guilford, Cattell, Edwards, or Gough can contribute to differential diagnosis with more success than the MMPI can. It is quite possible that normal personality traits, or their extremes, can be measured better and will be more prognostic than traits of contrasted groups of patients.

Single Variables—
Measures of Neurosis and Psychosis

Now we shall turn our attention to a large number of psychological measures developed from a variety of theoretical positions. The schema adopted for the organization of the many unrelated studies into a connected account is the traditional psychiatric mental status report, as presented, for instance, by Menninger (1952) and Thorne (1955).

The psychological functions which will be briefly reviewed are the following: thinking (formal aspects); thinking (content); emotional life and anxiety; social behavior; self-evaluation; attention and motivation; perception; and psychomotor activity. Because such a division into separate functions is rather arbitrary, there will necessarily be considerable overlap among the sections devoted to them.

THINKING (FORMAL ASPECTS). This function is not impaired in neuroses but is much disturbed in psychoses. The formal aspects of this disturbed thinking have been easily demonstrated by suitable psychological tests, but attempts to do the same for the content in a systematic way have been less fruitful.

The most successful way of demonstrating and measuring the disturbance of thought processes has been through various sorting or concept formation tasks. The subject is asked repeatedly to sort real objects, or pictures, or words, into categories. Although such tests, which were originally developed by Ach (1935) of Göttingen, became first known as tests of brain damage because of the work of Goldstein and Scheerer (1941), similar methods were used by the Russians Vigotsky (1934, 1939) and Luria (1932) in the study of schizophrenia. Kasanin and Hanfmann (1938) adapted their methods and presented a quantitative evaluation. Schizophrenics were found to use fewer abstract concepts, staying at more concrete levels. Others have reported similar results (Rashkis, 1950; White, 1949). Vinacke (1951) reviewed many studies of concept formation. There is a continuing interest in the use of sorting tests in schizophrenia, and more detailed analyses have been presented of the nature of the deficits in abstraction in organics and schizophrenics. One of the newer measures is the Visual Verbal Test of Drasgow and Feldman (1957), reported to be quite successful in the differential diagnosis of organics and schizophrenics.

McGaughan and Moran (1956) made a searching analysis of these tasks and pointed out that at least four variables underlie the abstract-concrete distinction: amount of social agreement or communality; order or degree of conceptual classification; relative essentiality or saliency; presence or absence of generic terms. They also demonstrated the usefulness of these finer distinctions in several studies. It is interesting to compare these distinctions with the more descriptive characteristics of the abstract attitude listed by Goldstein (1946): To him the abstract attitude is basic for these abilities: to assume a mental set voluntarily; to shift voluntarily from one aspect of the situation to another; to keep in mind simultaneously various aspects; to grasp the essential of a given whole, to break a given whole up into parts, and to isolate them voluntarily; to generalize, to abstract common properties, to plan ahead ideationally, to assume an attitude toward the "mere possible," to think or perform symbolically; and to detach our ego from the outer world.

An interesting variant has been to present sentences with artificial words for which subjects have to furnish meanings (Werner and Kaplan, 1950; Heim, 1956). In some of this work it was found that material with social implications fared worse than did more neutral material if the subjects were schizophrenic patients.

Kahn has designed a symbol arrangement test which attempts to broaden the usefulness of the concept-formation sorting task (1957a, b). Fifteen objects are to be named and placed in various orders. Many of the objects have many common associations and seem to lend themselves particularly well to disordered thinking. Murphy, Bolinger, and Ferriman (1958) reviewed a number of studies of the Kahn test and concluded that the test has been amazingly successful in screening patients with chronic brain syndrome from matched groups without brain damage. The test manual reviews evidence indicating its power to distinguish between such various clinical groups as neurotics, patients with behavior disorders, borderline schizophrenics, and normals. Other new tests of concept formation which use blocks include the Grassi test (1953), the Shaw test presented by Bromley (1958), the test of Hetherington (1958), the Conceptual Reasoning Test of Maag (1957), and the Yacorzynski blocks (Altrocchi and Rosenberg, 1958; Rosenberg and Altrocchi, 1958).

Guilford and his co-workers have spent ten years doing large-scale analyses of what they called "high-level abilities" such as creativity, planning, and decision making. Among the tests developed by them are a number measuring types of abstract thinking. A recent paper by Guilford (1956) presents a summary of his findings and gives references. Because of their greater variety and interesting format, some of these tests might prove extremely useful in the study of the thought processes of mental patients.

The PSI (Problem Solving using Information) apparatus, developed by John, Rimoldi, Miller, and Molner (John and Miller, 1957), measures step-by-step performance on logical tasks. Problem solving can be observed and measured in action rather than as deduced from the finished solution only. Proverbs have been used for years in mental status examinations. Special attention was called to their value for the study of thought processes by Benjamin (1946), but it remained for Gorham to develop a standardized proverbs test. First results with schizophrenics have been promising (Elmore and Gorham, 1957; Gorham, 1956a, b).

Language is frequently disturbed in a striking way in schizophrenia. There have been interesting attempts to develop objective methods of analyzing schizophrenic language, but their usefulness is limited by the fact that little is known about language patterns of the average normal individual (R. Kahn and Fink, 1957; W. Johnson, 1944; Goodstein, 1951; White, 1949; Staats, 1957). In an interesting theoretical paper Goldman-Eisler (1958) demonstrated how much information can be obtained about the mental state of a speaker from a detailed analysis of fluctuations in the rate of speech. Luria has published (1958) interesting evidence on the influences of various cortical lesions on speech production.

Attempts to detect intellectual changes characteristic of various types of mental patients with the Wechsler Bellevue Intelligence Scale have been consistently unsuccessful. In fact, the excellent reviews of research with the Wechsler scale by Rabin (1945) and by Guertin, Frank, and Rabin (1956) leave little doubt about the hopelessness of attempts to identify any kind of psychopathology from the pattern of the Wechsler subtests. Similar conclusions were reached by Watson (1946), Marks (1953), and L. C. Johnson (1949). Since the eleven subtests which form the test were designed to give one overall estimate of intelligence rather than to measure various independent cognitive factors, this finding is not surprising. Nevertheless, attempts continue to develop from the Wechsler scale indices specific to various diagnostic categories (Olch, 1948; Levine, 1949; Schlosser and Kantor, 1949; Hunt and French, 1949; Garfield, 1948, 1949; Rogers, 1951; Harper, 1950).

Yates (1954, 1956) has reviewed the use of vocabulary in the measurement of intellectual deterioration and concluded that the experimental work supports the idea that vocabulary declines quantitatively and qualitatively in patients with brain damage, but that there is only a small possibility that qualitative changes of vocabulary are characteristic of schizophrenia.

THINKING (CONTENT). While the content of thought in individual psychotics differs, of course, from patient to patient, certain types of material seem frequently to be present. Among these are ideas of reference, delusions, or hallucinations in schizophrenia. Since various dynamic processes such as projection and repression shape the thought content, some discussion of experimental studies of these processes is pertinent here.

The most direct attempt to elicit the content of thought is made in the psychiatric interview. As a clinical technique, it is doubtful whether purely routine technical devices will ever be able to take its place. There have been a number of proposals to supplement or even supplant the interview by a standardized rating scale. When such a procedure is followed, it becomes possible to compute correlations between the items of the scale. Given enough cases, one can try to find clusters of items and personality profiles. These steps have been taken by Lorr, O'Connor, and Stafford (1957), Lorr, Rubenstein, and Jenkins (1953), Guertin and Jenkins (1956), Wittenborn (1950, 1955), Degan (1952), Moore (1933), and Guertin, (1955a, c; 1956). There remains one more step: to see whether these statistical syndromes are more useful than the clinical ones. Both types should be correlated with a variety of laboratory measures, psychological as well as biochemical and physiological. Similarly, the relative prognostic value of both approaches should be investigated.

It was mentioned earlier that the psychiatric interview makes the most direct assessment of the thought content. However, the development of the various projective tests was motivated by the hope that material could be elicited which would be amenable to more systematic analysis. No matter how one judges the present success, it must be pointed out that these methods are trying to do something which is not duplicated by any objective tests.

PROJECTIVE TECHNIQUES. The best-known projective test is Hermann Rorschach's *Psychodiagnostik*, published in 1921. After a slow start, the method has had a fantastically wide use. The number of articles and books published concerned with the Rorschach technique is well into the third thousand. Yet many scientists feel that it should be used with extreme caution (Thurstone, 1948; Vernon, 1935; Cronbach, 1949; Guilford, 1959; Eysenck, 1953; Knopf, 1956; Zubin, 1954). The problems encountered in an evaluation of the predictive usefulness of the Rorschach Test can be seen in a review of Rorschach studies of schizophrenics, as a sample of Rorschach studies in general.

By far the largest number of clinical studies with the Rorschach Test have been made during the last ten years. However, there have been only a few large-scale investigations. The remainder, which deal only with single aspects of the Rorschach, must be considered of minor importance. Consequently we shall review only that part of the literature which is most pertinent to larger correlative studies.

The total group of 288 mental patients on the performance of whom Rorschach's conclusions were based included 188 schizophrenics (105 males, 83 females). A control group included 117 normals (55 males, 62 females). Skalweit (1934) in Germany published findings based on 23 acute schizophrenia cases.

Since then, most Rorschach research in schizophrenia has been done in the United States. The earliest and rather full studies of the Rorschach records of schizophrenics were by Rickers-Ovsiankina (1938) and Beck (1938). In 1939 Kelley and Klopfer published a paper entitled "The Application of the Rorschach Method to Research in Schizophrenia."

In 1946 Rapaport, Schaefer, and Gill reported the results of their statistical investigation of diagnostic Rorschach indications in 271 cases, among them 120 schizophrenia patients and 54 normal controls. Two years later C. E. Johnson and Sherman (1948) published their report on the results obtained from 3000 Rorschach protocols. Beck (1954) published the results of new and rather original research in schizophrenia. We shall return to Beck's studies in a moment.

TABLE 3. SIGNIFICANT DIFFERENCES FOUND BY VARIOUS AUTHORS
BETWEEN SCHIZOPHRENICS AND NORMALS IN RORSCHACH
SCORING CATEGORIES

Author	Increases in Schizophrenia	Decreases in Schizophrenia
Rorschach (1921) Skalweit (1934)	No quantitative data given in a form which can be evaluated statistically.	
Rickers-Ovsiankina (1938)	W% (poor quality), D%, O%	F+, O+
Beck (1938)		W
Rapaport and Schaefer (1946)	Many differences reported as significant, but the authors' procedure has been criticized strongly by Cronbach (1959).	
Kelley and Klopfer (1939)	No specific criteria reported.	
Thiessen (1952)	Anatomy, Sex DW	Z, P, FC+, M, A%
Beck (1954)	λ index, DW, Sex, restricted responses	M, shading, F+, P

There are two other studies of the Rorschach in schizophrenia: one, dealing with a total of 518 subjects, among them 49 schizophrenics, was published in 1948 by Charlotte Bühler and her co-workers; the other, dealing with 60 schizophrenic adults and 157 normal controls, was done by Thiessen (1952).

The highlights of these studies are summarized in Table 3. Other signs which may occur from time to time in schizophrenic records are: confused order (e.g., W-Dd-D instead of normal W-D-Dd); greater variability: poor F response next to F+, poor original response next to O+, sudden changes in the speed and fluency at which responses have been given, and so forth; perseveration or monotypical production; mere description of a card; short reaction time, especially in paranoids; self-references; and unintelligible language. Since these signs appear only occasionally, it is difficult to use them in a statistical comparison of groups.

The same differences as are reported for the schizophrenics have been reported for organic patients. Furthermore, there has usually been no adequate matching of controls on intelligence—a possible explanation of some of the reported differences. In addition to single scores, patterns of scores have been tried. Thiessen suggested five patterns, which were checked by Rubin and Lonstein (1954), who failed to confirm any of them. Taulbee and Sisson (1954) found some evidence that three of these five were helpful in discriminating schizophrenics.

Bühler, Bühler, and Lefevre (1948) developed one basic Rorschach score and claimed that schizophrenics are lowest on this, with organics next, then depressives, then psychopaths, then neurotics, and finally normals, who are highest. Eysenck (1953) examined their work and found that the positions of neurotics and normals should be reversed. Finney (1955) used the basic Rorschach score and found that it was not adequate for the diagnosis of individual patients, although group means were significantly different between schizophrenics and normals ($p < .01$) and between schizophrenics and neurotics ($p < .05$).

In summary, we may say that investigators fail to agree about single Rorschach determinants as diagnostic indicators. Part of this lack of agreement may result from the fact that, even when fairly large collections of schizophrenic records are analyzed, there is so much idiosyncrasy in them that statistical techniques cannot cope with it.

Aside from these validity studies, several researches have been concerned with the nature of interrelationships among Rorschach signs (Sen, 1950; Stotsky, 1957; Wittenborn, 1950; Williams and Lawrence, 1954; Hsü, 1947; Hughes, 1950; Cox, 1951; Coan, 1956; Adcock, 1951; Consalvi and Canter, 1957). The main factors reported about which there is agreement are intelligence, fluency, and perhaps "neuroticism"—factors which may be measured more accurately by separate tests. Better techniques have to be developed to tease out the meaningful information that appears to be there.

"Objective" forms of the Rorschach (Munroe, 1944; Stone, 1957;

O'Reilly, 1956), which limit the responses to a choice between pre-selected alternatives, to a large extent defeat the purpose of the "projective" techniques, which is to elicit idiosyncratic responses in their full individual richness. A more promising idea is the Holtzman Inkblot Test (1958), in which the response is limited to one per card. To permit the collection of enough responses there are 50 cards in each of the two alternative forms.

But perhaps it is not so much the test that needs changing as the method of analyzing the results. Zubin (1956) and Zubin, Eron, and Sultan (1956) advocated more systematic content analysis, while Beck (1954) and Molish (1955) made the examiner part of the diagnostic instrument by having him rate the Rorschach protocol on a number of personality traits. Such a method, which demands that the examiner go far beyond the interpretation of single Rorschach determinants, is dependent on the examiner as part of the technique, and is only partly accessible to scientific study. In their studies Beck, Molish, and others analyzed the co-occurrence of traits and concluded that different personality constellations exist in schizophrenia. The constellations found in Beck's original study of children were in part replicated by Molish, in a study of 25 state hospital patients (1955); four out of six types were the same, and two of these four were also present in a naval hospital population (1956). Wertheimer (1957) compared methods and attitudes of the clinician who uses the Rorschach and the experimental psychologist studying perception.

In another attempt to improve the usefulness of the Rorschach, a set of rating scales for the systematic evaluation of various ego functions was developed by Klopfer, Crumpton, and Grayson (1958). These scales were intended for use with a battery of tests including the Wechsler-Bellevue, the Rorschach, the Shipley-Hartford, and thematic material, and the scales are restricted to test-derived concepts. A factor analysis of the 25 scales led to 14 orthogonal factors, of which the majority are characterized by only one or two loadings above .40.

Still another direction in current research on the use of the Rorschach for the diagnosis of mental patients is influenced by the distinction between "process" and "reactive" schizophrenia first proposed by Langfeldt (1937). In an interesting symposium on this topic Becker (1958), Kantor and Winder (1958), and Fine and Zimet (1958) each reported a significant correlation between the process-reactive dichotomy and a level-of-thinking organization based on the Rorschach.

The second most popular projective technique is Murray's Thematic Apperception Test (TAT), which consists of 20 pictures with one or more persons in settings which are only vaguely defined. The subject is asked to tell a story about each card. There are a number of scoring systems for the TAT. All are time-consuming and far from objective, and many of the scoring categories are not applicable in a great number of instances.

There are many other projective techniques. For excellent summaries see Bell (1948). Similar difficulties are present in the quantitative analysis of all of them.

Although there have been many clinical reports on the fantasies of patients, there seem to have been no direct attempts to differentiate psychotics from normals or subtypes from one another by objective analysis of habitual thought content, i.e., content not elicited by specific tests. A systematic exploration guided by questions about the future or about the past might be extremely useful. It should be possible to apply modern information theory to the analysis of schizophrenic language by measuring the redundancy and the degree of continuity of spoken material. One difficulty in such an approach would be that no comparison data exist on the speech of normals. That a careful analysis would be needed is indicated in a paper by Balken and Masserman (1940), who studied the language of fantasies of patients with conversion hysterias, anxiety states, and obsessive neuroses.

EMOTIONS AND ANXIETY. While the emotions of the manic depressive patient are readily understood as exaggerations of normal emotions, the emotional life of the schizophrenic is somewhat paradoxical. His emotions are believed to be shallow, because of the strength of deep-seated anxiety. Therefore measurements of emotions in the schizophrenic may be expected to be inconsistent. As long as the patient sees no personal threat, his reactions will be below normal strength; however, one may see a sudden increase when a task is perceived as threatening.

Richman (1957) asked schizophrenics to define words which were neutral and words which were affectively loaded. He found that the use of synonyms went up and the use of explanations went down when the emotional words were compared with the neutral ones. This was found in a more deteriorated group of patients also.

Attempts have been made to assess the presence of anxiety and its degree through questionnaires. The evidence is somewhat conflicting, especially regarding the usefulness of this method with psychotics. The most promising of these questionnaires are the Taylor Manifest Anxiety Scale (TMAS) derived from the Minnesota Multiphasic Personality Inventory (1953), and Cattell's anxiety scale (1957a).

In 1956 Glad and Shearn published a preliminary manual on their Emotional Projection Test which consists of 30 photographs of facial expressions. The subject has to indicate which feeling is expressed. The basic assumption is that responses are as much determined by the subject's own emotional condition as they are by the photograph. A few small unpublished studies give support to this view.

Spence and Taylor (1953) found a relation between the strength of a *conditioned* eyeblink and the TMAS, but not at a statistically significant level.

Blum (1950) devised an interesting technique, the *Blacky pictures*, which might be described as a semistructured projective test. A little dog named Blacky is shown in cartoon-like drawings in a number of situations chosen in such a way that they parallel important stages in human psychosexual development as described in psychoanalytic theory. Aronson (1953) found the test of some use in differentiating 30 paranoids from 30 other psychotics. Recently Blum has been working on intraindividual patterns of objective aspects of the responses, such as reaction time for each card and alterations in galvanic skin responses (1959). Because almost everyone is somewhat embarrassed in describing situations involving toilet training, masturbation, or breast feeding, these cards may provide suitable psychological stressors. Blum's method of comparing within the individual the relative strength of the disturbance caused by each card is promising because of the feasibility of using this technique to test Freudian psychodynamic concepts directly and objectively.

There have been several studies which showed that there is a relationship between personality type, mood, and preferences for paintings (Pickford, 1948; Harris, Bettelheim, and Diedrich, 1942; Eysenck, 1941; Cardinet, 1952, 1958; Morris, 1956; and at the California Institute of Personality Assessment Research). By selecting suitable reproductions one could perhaps construct a test of mood preference which would be more interesting to mental patients than other tasks such as the adjective check lists presently used. Something like this has been done in the Music Preference Test developed by Cattell. In a paper by Cattell and Anderson (1953) statistically significant differences are reported for this test among various kinds of patients as well as between patients and controls.

Finally, there are some indications that the reactions to a record with familiar sounds such as a typewriter, a dog barking, a glass breaking may give useful indications of the subject's emotional condition (Friedman, 1956; Bean, 1957).

SOCIAL BEHAVIOR. As with thought disturbance, abnormalities in social behavior are practically part of the definition of psychosis. Whether miniature situations will reflect the deficits in a psychotic's behavior in social situations in real life depends to some extent on the nature of the miniature situations.

Rating scales, discussed at length in Chapter 43, have been developed for the systematic evaluation of behavior on the ward or in such situations as occupational therapy. The success of such ventures is dependent on the carefulness and skill of the rater.

In a study by Shipman (1957), sociometric choices of mental patients revealed that paranoids had a statistically very significant preference for one another while the other schizophrenics chose each other only to a degree expected by chance. On the assumption that impairment of social relations leads to a decrease in understanding and predicting the behavior of others, Jackson and Carr (1955) used Fiedler's method (1953) and asked 20 female student nurses and 20 female schizophrenics to predict the questionnaire responses of an associate and of a normal and a psychotic individual. As expected, the schizophrenics did significantly more poorly.

Whiteman (1954) found more significant differences in favor of normal controls over schizophrenics in scores on a social concepts test than on two concept-formation tests which contained material of a more formal and non-social nature. Social understanding also has been assessed through the appreciation of humor. Roberts and Johnson (1957) of Michigan State University found a significant correlation between the degree of reality contact of 28 patients and their understanding of the point of 12 cartoons. Attempts to relate cartoon preferences to specific defense mechanisms in individuals have not been successful (Frankel, 1953; Weiss, 1954), although some psychological correlates of humor preferences were found by Grziwok and Scodel (1956), while More and Roberts (1957) were able to show social variations in humor responses to cartoons. H. D. Miller (1956) found more discrepancy between the observed expression of affect and the reported subjective experience for schizophrenics than for normal controls.

Diamond (1956) found that the convergence of judgments was less for pairs of schizophrenic patients than for pairs of drug addicts used as controls, when the subjects had to estimate the autokinetic phenomenon, e.g., amount of apparent movement of a stationary light in a darkened room, first alone and then in pairs.

Few experiments have been done which can be considered directly relevant to the social behavior of schizophrenics. This is strange since impaired social behavior is so close to the core of schizophrenia. It is true, of course, that therapy may be regarded as experimentation on the social behavior of the schizophrenic. This is especially true of therapy which does not rely on drugs or other somatic treatments and is most completely realized in group therapy. It falls outside the proper scope of this chapter to evaluate the vast literature on this topic, but one study in progress in the Perry Point Hospital and the Philadelphia State Hospital is of especial interest because it involves manipulation of the total social environment of small groups of patients as well as specific social situation tests consisting of real social problems (Sanders, 1957).

It would be profitable to use some of the methods for the analysis of small-group behavior developed by social psychologists in the study of ward behavior. The combination of such methods with a group therapy program seems particularly appropriate.

SELF-EVALUATION. Alterations in the psychotic's self-percept are generally regarded as a major component of the clinical picture. In the schizophrenic these alterations may be in the form of loss of self-esteem and increased sensitivity to failure with resultant withdrawal, or they may take the form of distortions of the body image, including confusions about sex identification or feelings of sexual inadequacy.

Because of lowered ability to tolerate frustration, the executive side of the ego may be expected to be weakened. Thus schizophrenics should have difficulty in making decisions and in planning. Distortion may affect time estimation.

Brownfain (1952) has developed a concept-of-self test, while Osgood's Semantic Differential (Osgood, Suci, and Tannenbaum, 1957) includes a dimension of self-evaluation. There is insufficient evidence about the usefulness of these techniques with schizophrenics, but what little there is shows promise.

Garmezy (1952) found that under threat of punishment the behavior of schizophrenics was dominated by avoidance responses. Under reward conditions there was no change in their performance. The performance of normals, on the other hand, improved under punishment as well as under reward conditions. The reward consisted of the word "Right" lighting up on a scoreboard; the punishment was the word "Wrong." Webb (1957) told schizophrenics and controls that they had done poorly and obtained significant improvement for the controls only. Bleke (1955) did a similar experiment but separated the schizophrenics on the basis of their premorbid personalities into two groups. The results for the group with the better premorbid personality were more like the results for the normals.

A promising use of conditioning was made in a study by Salsinger and Pisoni (1958). They found that affect statements can be conditioned in schizophrenics, and that the extinction curve may be a discriminating measure.

Epstein (1955) had 30 chronic schizophrenics and 30 matched normals evaluate their own expressive movements as well as those of others. He found the schizophrenics' self-evaluations to be higher than those of normals. Jost (1955) found that the level of aspiration measured by the Rotter technique was not consistently higher or lower in schizophrenics than in normals, but more variable.

Efforts to evaluate the body image from Draw a Man test designs have been unsuccessful. The idea that omissions or distortions in the drawing of a human figure would be due to changes in the body image has not been substantiated.

Since we may expect planning to be affected, the study of Singer, Wilensky, and McCraven (1956) is of interest. In a factor analysis of the scores of 100 schizophrenic males on a variety of tests measuring various aspects of delaying capacity, fantasy, and planning ability, they found four factors. These they interpreted as motor inhibition or planfulness; ambitiousness or need achievement; emotional surgency; and introspectiveness or introversion.

ATTENTION AND MOTIVATION. Attention and motivation are generally held to be altered or impaired in psychotics, the degree of impairment being partly dependent on the nature of the task. In schizophrenics this lack of attention and motivation is perhaps a learned pattern related to a fear of failure which had its beginning a long time before the illness became manifest (Mednick, 1958). In fact, Kendig and Richmond (1940) and Rappaport and Webb (1950) found that even in high school schizophrenics tend to be characterized by lack of attention and concentration, negativism, preoccupation, and apathy. The schizophrenic performance on interesting tasks tends to be better than on those devoid of interest, while tasks perceived as affectively neutral at times have been found to fare better than tasks seen as threatening to the ego. Narrowed attention may also result from neurophysiological changes (Callaway and Dembo, 1958) such as may be produceed by drugs like methamphetamine.

Attention and motivation have generally not been measured directly, but observations are frequently made about them which are incidental to the measurement of some other function (Rodnick and Garmezy, 1957).

To arrive at an estimate of attention and motivation for each subject, rather than to rely on one measure only, the performance of a few simple tasks should be averaged. (The early work of Ach [1935] or the factor analysis of Süllwold [1954] and Wittenborn [1943] may be consulted for such tasks.) The assumption will have to be made that the motivational level on these tasks is representative of motivation throughout the battery of tests rather than being specific for each test, although a review by Brengelmann (1954), as well as a factor analysis of tests of attention, show that it is to a considerable extent task-specific.

For many years Pauli demonstrated the value of work curves for diagnostic work (Pauli and Arnold, 1951). Such curves, based on continued simple arithmetic calculations, were first suggested by Kraepelin (1925). They are indices of fluctuations in both attention and motivation.

Mierke (1957) has underlined reduced ability to concentrate as an important clinical symptom, after a thorough review of the experimental literature in German.

An interesting report by Rosenbaum, MacKavey, and Grisell (1957) suggests a way in which the motivational factor in various tasks can be estimated. They found that an electrical shock to the hand produced greater decrease of reaction time in some male schizophrenics than in controls, but not in female schizophrenics.

PERCEPTION. An improvement over normals in size constancy (the tendency to attribute the same size to an object even though its distance from the observer changes) has been postulated, and observed, in schizophrenics by Raush (1952, 1956) on the basis of a reduction in what Thoules (1932) called "phenomenal regression towards the real object" (Ardis and Frazer, 1957). It has also been predicted—and found—that there is a *poorer* performance on size constancy tests because of the impaired ability to abstract, an ability considered essential in the maintenance of perceptual constancy

(Weckowicz, 1957; Chambers, 1956). Detailed discussions of some of the issues involved can be found in reviews by Taylor and Papert (1956), Jenkin (1957), and Zuckerman and Rock (1957). Without expressing a preference for either hypothesis here, we may note that the recent monograph by Eysenck, Granger, and Brengelmann (1957) furnishes abundant proof that impaired perceptual behavior is a rather general phenomenon in mental illness. Granger (1957a) reported some of the details of this work and reviewed the experimental literature (1957b, c; Granger and Franks, 1957).

While significant differences in critical flicker fusion (CFF) between schizophrenics and normals have been reported by several authors (for reviews see Irvine, 1954; Riccuiti, 1949; Zubin, Windle, and Hamwi, 1953), the many variables known to influence CFF have never been adequately controlled. (Landis, 1953, 1954; Roehrig, 1957; Gallup, 1957; Hylkema, 1942; Weekers and Roussel, 1948; Simonson and Brozek, 1953). New methods provide control of dimensions of CFF not studied before (de Lange, 1954).

No statistical difference was found between schizophrenics and organics in the perception of apparent motion (Saucer and Deabler, 1956), but both differed from the controls. This is one of the few studies in which both organics and schizophrenics were compared with controls and with one another. Gallese (1956) was unable to differentiate normals and schizophrenics before and after lobotomies with the spiral after-effect test, although Price and Deabler (1955) had earlier found this test to be highly effective in detecting organics. (See Stilson, Gynther, and Gertz, 1957, for a critical discussion.)

The ability to place a rod in the true upright position in spite of a tilt of the body or the room has been found to be a personality trait rather than an intellectual one; individual differences in this trait have been recognized for 30 years (Elderton, Moul, and Page, 1928). This test, developed by Witkin, forms part of the factual basis of the Wapner-Witkin sensory-tonic theory. It has been used with contradictory findings in a few studies of psychotics. Witkin's work was recently reviewed by Gruen (1957). Smaller figural after-effects for schizophrenics than for normals have been found by Wertheimer in three separate studies (1954a, b; 1957) and interpreted as related to a lower metabolic efficiency (Wertheimer and Wertheimer, 1954).

A considerable amount of work was done by Thurstone (1951) and some of his students on the development of perceptual tests as measures of personality variables. Because of Thurstone's death these tests have been published only in Reports from the Psychometric

Laboratory (1951, 1952, 1953a, b), and further development seems
to have come to a standstill. The most promising measures appear
to be the Color Form Movie (Thurstone, 1952; Bowles, 1955), the
homonym tests, and several closure tests (Pemberton, 1952a, b).
Mooney (1954, 1957) has developed two new closure tests which have
not yet received wide use.

Time estimation has been studied mostly in children (Smythe and
Goldstone, 1957) or normal adults (Cohen, 1954). Bindra and Waksberg (1956) reviewed methods and terminology. Differences have
been reported between controls and schizophrenics for estimation of
one-second durations (Lhamon and Goldstone, 1956), time orientation
concepts (de la Garza and Worchel, 1956), future time perspective
(Wallace, 1956), and the effects of various anchors on short interval
judgments (Weinstein, 1956).

So far there have been few major attempts to apply the concept of
stress in a systematic way to the study of schizophrenia. Miller's idea
of using an information input overload situation as a paradigm of
stress (J. G. Miller, 1959), seems promising. In addition to getting
a quantitative score of the subject's performance, it is possible to
categorize his reaction to overload stress into rubrics corresponding
to various defense mechanisms or adjustment processes. It would be
especially valuable to have at least two different degrees of threat
to the ego represented in the materials presented. Perhaps one set
of stimuli might be rather neutral, administered in a permissive
atmosphere by a technician, while the other might be more personal
(perhaps dealing with hospital adjustment or treatment), administered
by an authority figure. Stimuli related to social situations could
perhaps provide an intermediate degree of stress.

The technique of projecting photographs or drawings tachistoscopically or out of focus has been used to study fantasy life (Brigden,
1933; Canestrari and Bosinelli, 1953). In the first procedure the
number of presentations and the exposure times give quantitative information about the amount of stimulation required before the subject gives his first report. If presentations are continued after an
initial response, we can observe whether there are changes toward a
more correct response and, if so, how long it takes before such a shift
occurs. If the second procedure is used, the initial response time is
dependent on the exposure time and the sharpness of the focus. Shifts
or changes in the subject's response may also occur when this experimental procedure is used, and they can be scored in a similar manner.

Several investigators (Cullen, 1958; Merrell, 1954) have introduced a change in the stimulus to force a shift in the interpretation. Merrell's results are only moderately different for schizophrenics and for normals.

PSYCHOMOTOR ACTIVITY. Psychomotor activity is intimately related to the emotional level in the manic-depressive condition; the activity increases as the mood gets high or decreases as the mood goes down. In schizophrenia, psychomotor activity is generally believed to be slower, with decreased coordination and occasional blocking.

There is almost unanimous support for the idea that psychomotor behavior is altered in schizophrenia, in the experimental work of Shakow (1946), Rodnick and Shakow (1940), King (1954), and many others. Reaction time is generally found to be slower, particularly in multiple-choice reaction experiments. Decreases have also been reported for tapping speed and dexterity on the Purdue Pegboard (King, 1954). A question frequently raised—whether this reflects a true slowing or a lack of attention and motivation—may be a matter of definition. This issue is not easily settled. In view of the marked correlation between reaction time and age reported, for instance, by Bellis (1933), Goldfarb (1941), and Forbes (1945), age would have to be carefully controlled. It should also be kept in mind that older persons are less motivated to be fast, but that they may be more accurate. Although performance on pencil-and-paper mazes has been used mainly with juvenile delinquents and neurotics, Peters (1952) found a significant correlation between performance in a circular pencil maze and the hospital adjustment of 39 schizophrenics.

Among other measures of psychomotor activity used in studying schizophrenia, without success so far, may be listed scores based on various expressive movements such as gestures, posture, and gait, as well as handwriting and drawing. Suttell and Pascal (1952) devised a detailed scoring system for the Bender-Gestalt test, composed of geometric designs to be copied, and found that only four out of a list of twelve qualitative aspects of the designs discriminated between patients and normals, while no differences were found between schizophrenics and neurotics. They also concluded that "regression" as measured by this test is not peculiar to schizophrenia. Robinson's results (1953) were similar, showing overlap between schizophrenics and paretics on Bender results scored according to the Pascal-Suttell technique (Suttell and Pascal, 1952), but Bowland and Deabler (1956) claimed they could be differentiated. Scott (1956) analyzed Rorschach and Bender-Gestalt records of 37 schizophrenics and concluded that schizophrenia is more disintegrative than regressive. The value of the Bender-Gestalt Test is still uncertain in the diagnosis of schizophrenia, but Guertin (1954a, b; 1955b) has run three factor analyses of the distortions in the Bender drawing of schizophrenic patients.

The failure of handwriting and drawing analyses to distinguish schizophrenics from normals may in part result from failure to use scoring methods which are simultaneously sensitive and practicable. New instruments for recording speed, pressure, and other aspects of handwriting promise to produce more objective data (Steinwachs, 1952; Lüthe, 1953; Smith and Bloom, 1956; Tripp, Fluckiger, and Weinberg, 1957).

The few psychomotor tasks used most often might well be supplemented or replaced by tasks found to be representative of the various dimensions of motor skills found in factor analyses by Seashore (1940), Fleishman (1953), and others. (See Chapter 17.) Some tasks reported by Eysenck (1952, 1953) and by Cattell (1957a, b) to be useful in differentiating neurotics and normals deserve further study. (See Chapters 24 and 39.) The analysis by Takala (1953) of the relations in 82 college students between performance on the Luria techniques (1932), and Mira test (1940), and some new techniques should also be consulted. Takala found separate components for speed and smoothness of motor response, as well as for "jumpiness" and inner tension. That "disorders of skills" (Davis, 1950) should be of value in the diagnosis of neurosis seems not too surprising if one remembers that physical and social awkwardness or clumsiness may reinforce one another (Koch, 1955). It remains to be studied whether the impairment of motor skills in psychotics can be differentiated by a distinctive pattern from the impairment in neurotics.

Rimoldi's factor analysis (1951) of tests of personal tempo showed that there is no single variable which adequately measures such a characteristic, but Skinner's technique (1955) as applied by Lindsley (1956) may provide new data on this.

Concluding Remarks

As we have seen, there are few psychological tests which consistently discriminate between various types of mental patients, although hope springs eternal in this field. This lack of success arises partly from the poor criterion formed by the diagnostic categories, the inadequacies of which are often aggravated in studies of psychotics or neurotics by the lumping together of various clinical sub-groups. But, even if perfect criteria were available, it seems unlikely that single measures unequivocally related to such complex mental conditions as schizophrenia or obsessive compulsive neurosis will ever be found.

It seems more likely that multivariate analyses on large numbers of cases will eventually succeed in isolating various disease entities caused by distinct processes, be they biochemical or social-psychological, which have as a final common outcome the behavioral characteristics we recognize today as psychosis or neurosis. The probability that such multivariate studies will be fruitful will be increased by using many and varied experimental methods, advice which dates at least back to Gregor (1910).

REFERENCES

Ach, N. *Analyse des Willens.* Abt. 6. *Handb. d. biol. Arbeitsmeth. v. Abder-halden.* Berlin: Urban und Schwarzenberg, 1935.

Adcock, C. J. A factorial approach to Rorschach interpretations. *J. gen. Psychol.*, 1951, 77, 261–272.

Altrocchi, J., and Rosenberg, B. G. A new sorting technique for diagnosing brain damage. *J. clin. Psychol.*, 1958, 14, No. 1, 36–40.

Ardis, J. A., and Frazer, E. Personality and perception: the constancy effect and introversion. *Brit. J. Psychol.*, 1957, 48, 48–54.

Aronson, M. L. A study of the Freudian theory of paranoia by means of the Blacky pictures. *J. proj. Tech.*, 1953, 17, 3–19.

Balken, E. R., and Masserman, J. H. The language of phantasy: III. The language of the phantasies of patients with conversion hysteria, anxiety state, and obsessive compulsion neuroses. *J. Psychol.*, 1940, 10, 75–86.

Bean, K. L. Development of a sound apperception test. *Amer. Psychol.*, 1957, 12, 390.

Beck, S. J. Personality structure in schizophrenia: a Rorschach investigation on 81 patients and 64 controls. *Ner. ment. Dis. Monogr.*, 1938, No. 63.

Beck, S. J. *The six schizophrenias.* New York: Amer. Orthopsychiat. Ass., Res. Monogr. No. 6, 1954.

Becker, W. C. Process-reactive schizophrenia as levels of personality organization. *Amer. Psychol.*, 1958, 13, 370.

Bell, J. E. *Projective techniques: a dynamic approach to the study of the personality.* New York: Longmans, Green, 1948.

Bellis, C. J. Reaction time and chronological age. *Proc. soc. exp. Biol. Med.*, 1933, 30, 801–803.

Benjamin, J. D. A method for distinguishing and evaluating formal thinking disorders in schizophrenia. In J. S. Kasanin (Ed.), *Language and thought in schizophrenia.* Berkeley, Calif.: Univer. of California Press, 1946.

Benton, A. L.   A review of the MMPI.   In O. K. Baros (Ed.), *The fourth mental Measurements Yearb.*, Highland Park, N. J., 1953.

Bindra, D., and Waksberg, H.   Methods and terminology in studies of time estimation.   *Psychol. Bull.*, 1956, 53, 155–159.

Bleke, R.   Reward and punishment as determiners of reminiscence effects in schizophrenic and normal subjects.   *J. Pers.*, 1955, 23, 479–498.

Blum, G. S.   *The Blacky pictures: a technique for the exploration of personality dynamics.*   New York: Psychol. Corp., 1950.

Blum, G. S.   Psychoanalytic behavior theory.   In H. P. David and J. C. Brengelmann (Eds.), *Perspectives in personality research.*   New York: Basic Books, 1959.

Bowland, J. A., and Deabler, H. L.   A Bender Gestalt diagnostic validity study.   *J. clin. Psychol.*, 1956, 12, 82–84.

Bowlby, J.   *Personality and mental illness.*   New York: Emerson Books, 1942.

Bowles, J. W.   Preliminary analysis of the Thurstone Color Form dominance test.   *Tech. Rep.*, Air Force Personnel and Training Research Center, Lackland AF Base, San Antonio, Texas, 1955.

Bowman, K. M.   A study of the prepsychotic personality in certain psychoses.   *Amer. J. Orthopsychiat.*, 1934, 4, 473–498.

Bowman, K. M., and Raymond, Alice F.   A statistical study of a personality in schizophrenic patients.   *Proc. Ass. Res. nerv. ment. Dis.*, 1929, 10, 48–74.

Brengelmann, J. C.   Spaltungsfähigkeit als Persönlichkeitsmerkmal.   *Z. exp. u. angew. Psychol.*, 1954, 2, 455–494.

Brigden, R. R.   A tachistoscopic study of the differentiation of perception.   *Psychol. Monogr.*, 1933, 44, 197.

Bromley, D. B.   The Shaw test.   Paper read at the Birmingham Convention of the British Psychological Society, 1958.   (Abstract)

Brownfain, J. J.   Stability of the self concept as a dimension of personality.   *J. abnorm. soc. Psychol.*, 1952, 47, 597–606.

Bühler, C., Bühler, K., and Lefever, D. W.   *Rorschach standardization Study I: Development of the basic Rorschach score with manual of directions.*   Los Angeles, Calif.: Mimeogr., 1948.

Bühler, C., Bühler, K., and Lefever, D. W.   *Rorschach diagnostic sign list and record of the Rorschach standardization studies for the determination and evaluation of the basis Rorschach score.*   Los Angeles, Calif.: Western Psychological Service, 1954.

Callaway, E., and Dembo, D.   Narrowed attention.   *Arch. Neurol. Psychiat.*, 1958, 79, 74–90.

Canestrari, R., and Bosinelli, M.   L'inversione figura-sfondo nei soggetti normali e negli epilettici.   *Arch. Psi. Neurol. Psichiat.*, 1953, 14, 191–193.

Cardinet, J. M.   *Aesthetic preferences and personality.*   Doctoral dissertation, Univer. of Chicago, 1952.

Cardinet, J. M.   Préférences esthétiques et personalité.   *L'Année psychol.*, 1958, 58, 45–69.

Cattell, R. B.   *The description and measurement of personality.*   Yonkers, N. Y.: World Book Co., 1946.

Cattell, R. B.   *The sixteen personality factor questionnaire.*   Champaign, Ill.: Inst. for Pers. and Abil. Testing, 1949.

Cattell, R. B.   *Personality.*   New York: McGraw-Hill, 1950.

Cattell, R. B. *Handbook for the IPAT Anxiety Scale.* Champaign, Ill.: Inst. for Pers. and Abil. Testing, 1957. (a)

Cattell, R. B. *Personality and motivation structure and measurement.* Yonkers, N. Y.: World Book Co., 1957. (b)

Cattell, R. B., and Anderson, J. C. The measurement of personality and behavior disorders by the IPAT music test. *J. appl. Psychol.*, 1953, 37, 446–454.

Chambers, J. L. Perceptual judgment and associative learning ability of schizophrenics and nonpsychotics. *J. consult. Psychol.*, 1956, 20, 211–214.

Coan, R. A factor analysis of Rorschach determinants. *J. proj. Tech.*, 1956, 20, 280–287.

Cohen, J. Experience of time. *Acta psychologica*, 1954, 10, 207–219.

Comrey, A. L. A factor analysis of items on the MMPI Hypochondriasis Scale. *Educ. psychol. Measmt.*, 1957, 17, 568–577. (a)

Comrey, A. L. A factor analysis of items on the MMPI Depression Scale. *Educ. psychol. Measmt.*, 1957, 17, 578–585. (b)

Comrey, A. L. A factor analysis of items on the MMPI Hysteria Scale. *Educ. psychol. Measmt.*, 1957, 17, 586–592. (c)

Comrey, A. L. A factor analysis of items on the MMPI Psychopathic Deviate Scale. *Educ. psychol. Measmt.*, 1958, 18, 91–98. (a)

Comrey, A. A. A factor analysis of the items on the MMPI Paranoia Scale. *Educ. psychol. Measmt.*, 1958, 18, 99–109. (b)

Comrey, A. L. A factor analysis of the items on the MMPI Psychosthenia Scale. *Educ. psychol. Measmt.*, 1958, 18, 293–300. (c)

Comrey, A. L. A factor analysis of the items on the MMPI Hypomania Scale. *Educ. psychol. Measmt.*, 1958, 18, 313–324. (d)

Comrey, A. L. A factor analysis of the items on the MMPI F Scale. *Educ. psychol. Measmt.*, 1958, 18, 621–632. (e)

Comrey, A. L. A factor analysis of the items on the MMPI K scale. *Educ. psychol. Measmt.*, 1958, 18, 633–640. (f)

Comrey, A. L., and Marggraff, W. M. A factor analysis of the items on the MMPI Schizophrenia Scale. *Educ. psychol. Measmt.*, 1958, 18, 301–312.

Consalvi, C., and Canter, A. Rorschach scores as a function of four factors. *J. consult. Psychol.*, 1957, 21, 47–51.

Cox, S. M. A factorial study of the Rorschach responses of normal and maladjusted boys. *J. genet. Psychol.*, 1951, 79, 95–115.

Cronbach, L. J. Statistical methods applied to Rorschach scores: a review *Psychol. Bull.*, 1959, 76, 393–727.

Cullen, J. Personal communication, 1958.

Davis, D. R. Disorders of skill: an experimental approach to some problems of neurosis. *Motor Skills Res. Exch.*, 1950, 2, 56.

Degan, J. W. Dimensions of functional psychosis. *Psychometric Monogr.*, 1952, 6.

de la Garza, C. O., and Worchel, P. Time and space orientation in schizophrenia. *J. abnorm. soc. Psychol.*, 1956, 52, 191–194.

de Lange, H. Relationship between CFF and a set of low frequency characteristics of the eye. *J. opt. Soc. Amer.*, 1954, 44, 380–389.

Diamond, M. D. The ability of schizophrenics to modify responses in an interpersonal situation. *J. consult. Psychol.*, 1956, 20, 441–444.

Diamond, S. *Personality and temperament.* New York: Harper, 1957.

Drasgow, J., and Feldman, M. Conceptual processes in schizophrenia revealed by the Visual Verbal Test. *Percept. mot. Skills,* 1957, 7, 251–264.

Edwards, A. *Edwards Personal Preference Schedule.* New York: The Psychol. Corp., 1954. (a)

Edwards, A. *Manual for the Personal Preference Schedule.* New York: The Psychol. Corp., 1954. (b)

Elderton, E. M., Moul, M., and Page, E. M. On the growth curves of certain characters in women and the interrelationship of these characters. *Ann. Eugen.,* 1928, 3, 277–336.

Elmore, C. M., and Gorham, D. R. Measuring the impairment of the abstracting function with the Proverbs Test. *J. clin. Psychol.,* 1957, 13, 263–266.

Epstein, S. Unconscious self-evaluation in a normal and schizophrenic group. *J. abnorm. soc. Psychol.,* 1955, 50, 65–70.

Eysenck, H. J. Type-factors in aesthetic judgments. *Brit. J. Psychol.,* 1941, 31, 262–270.

Eysenck, H. J. *Dimensions of personality.* London: Routledge & Kegan Paul, 1947.

Eysenck, H. J. *The scientific study of personality.* London: Routledge & Kegan Paul, 1952.

Eysenck, H. J. *The structure of human personality.* London: Methuen, 1953.

Eysenck, H. J. *The dynamics of anxiety.* London: Routledge & Kegan Paul, 1957.

Eysenck, H. J., Granger, G. W., and Brengelmann, J. C. *Perceptual processes and mental illness.* Maudsley Monogr. Series. London: Chapman & Hall, 1957.

Fiedler, F. E. The psychological distance dimension in interpersonal relations. *J. Pers.,* 1953, 22, 142–150.

Fine, H. J., and Zimet, C. N. Process-reactive schizophrenia and genetic levels of perception. *Amer. Psychol.,* 1958, 13, 370.

Finney, B. C. The diagnostic discrimination of the "Basic Rorschach Score." *J. consult. Psychol.,* 1955, 19, 2, 96.

Fleishman, E. A. Testing for psychomotor abilities by means of apparatus tests. *Psychol. Bull.,* 1953, 50, 241–262.

Forbes, G. *J. exp. Psychol.,* 1945, 135, 153–162.

Frankel, Esther B. *An experimental study of psychoanalytic theories of humor.* Doctoral dissertation, Univer. of Michigan, 1953.

French, J. W. *The description of personality measurements in terms of rotated factors.* Princeton, N. J.: Educational Testing Service, 1953.

Friedman, H. The structural aspects of schizophrenic responses to auditory stimuli. *J. gen. Psychol.,* 1956, 89, 221–230.

Gallese, A. J. Spiral aftereffect as a test of organic brain damage. *J. clin. Psychol.,* 1956, 12, 254–258.

Gallup, H. F. Receptor contribution to the critical flicker frequency curve. *Diss. Abstr.,* 1957, 17, 1132–1133.

Garfield, S. L. Wechsler-Bellevue patterns in schizophrenia. *J. consult. Psychol.,* 1948, 12, 32–36.

Garfield, S. L. Wechsler-Bellevue patterns in schizophrenia. *J. consult. Psychol.,* 1949, 13, 279–287.

Garmezy, N. Stimulus differentiation by schizophrenics and normal subjects under conditions of reward and punishment. *J. Pers.,* 1952, 20, 253–276.

Glad, D. D., and Shearn, C. R.   An emotional projection test.   *Percept. mot. Skills Monogr.*, Suppl. 1, 1956.

Goldfarb, W.   *Teach. Coll. Contrib. Educ.*, 1941, No. 831, 1–76.

Goldman-Eisler, Frieda.   Speech analysis and mental processes.   *Lang. Speech*, 1958, 1, 59–75.

Goldstein, K.   Methodological approach to the study of schizophrenic thought disorder.   In J. S. Kasanin (Ed.), *Language and thought in schizophrenia*. Berkeley, Calif.: Univer. of California Press, 1946, 17–40.

Goldstein, K., and Scheerer, M.   Abstract and concrete behavior.   *Psychol. Monogr.*, 1941, 53.

Goodstein, L. D.   The language of schizophrenia.   *J. gen. Psychol.*, 1951, 75, 95–107.

Gorham, D. R.   A proverbs test for clinical and experimental use.   *Psychol. Rep. Monogr. Suppl.*, 1956, 1.   (a)

Gorham, D. R.   Use of the proverbs test for differentiating schizophrenics from normals.   *J. consult. Psychol.*, 1956, 20, 435–440.   (b)

Gough, H. G.   *Manual for the California Psychological Inventory.*   Palo Alto, Calif.: Consulting Psychologists Press, 1957.

Granger, G. W.   Effect of psychiatric disorder on visual thresholds.   *Science*, 1957, 125, 500–501.   (a)

Granger, G. W.   Eysenck's theory of anxiety and hysteria and the results of visual adaptation experiments.   *Acta Psychologica*, 1957, 13, 98–126.   (b)

Granger, G. W.   Night vision and psychiatric disorders: a review of experimental studies.   *J. ment. Sci.*, 1957, 103, 48–79.   (c)

Granger, G. W., and Franks, C. M.   Dark-adaptation and conditioning: some observed correlations.   *Amer. J. Psychol.*, 1957, 70, 462–464.

Grassi, J. R.   *The Grassi block substitution test for measuring organic brain pathology.*   Springfield, Ill.: Charles C Thomas, 1953.

Gregor, A.   *Leitfaden der experimentellen Psychopathologie.*   Berlin: S. Karger, 1910.

Gruen, A.   A critique and re-evaluation of Witkin's perception and perception-personality work.   *J. gen. Psychol.*, 1957, 56, 73–97.

Grziwok, R., and Scodel, A.   Some psychological correlates of humor preferences.   *J. consult. Psychol.*, 1956, 20, 42.

Guertin, W. H.   A transposed factor analysis of schizophrenic performance on the Bender-Gestalt.   *J. clin. Psychol.*, 1954, 10, 225.   (a)

Guertin, W. H.   A factor analysis of curvilinear distortions on the Bender-Gestalt.   *J. clin. Psychol.*, 1954, 10, 12–17.   (b)

Guertin, W. H.   A factor analysis of schizophrenic ratings on the hospital adjustment scale.   *J. clin. Psychol.*, 1955, 11, 70–73.   (a)

Guertin, W. H.   A transposed analysis of the Bender-Gestalt of paranoid schizophrenics.   *J. clin. Psychol.*, 1955, 11, 73–76.   (b)

Guertin, W. H.   A factor analytic study of the adjustment of chronic schizophrenics.   *J. Clin. Psychol.*, 1955, 11, 174–177.   (c)

Guertin, W. H.   A factor analysis of schizophrenics rated on the activity rating scale.   *J. clin. Psychol.*, 1956, 12, 163–166.

Guertin, W. H., Frank, G. H., and Rabin, A. I.   Research with the Wechsler-Bellevue Intelligence Scale: 1950–1955.   *Psychol. Bull.*, 1956, 53, 235–257.

Guertin, W. H., and Jenkins, R. L.   A transposed factor analysis of a group of schizophrenic patients.   *J. clin. Psychol.*, 1956, 12, 64–68.

Guilford, J. P. The structure of intellect. *Psychol. Bull.*, 1956, 53, 267–293.

Guilford, J. P. *Personality.* New York: McGraw Hill, 1959.

Guilford, J. P., and Zimmerman, W. S. *The Guilford-Zimmerman temperament survey.* Beverly Hills, Calif.: Sheridan Supply Co., 1949.

Harper, A. E. Discrimination of the types of schizophrenia by the Wechsler-Bellevue scale. *J. consult. Psychol.*, 1950, 14, 290–296.

Harris, C. W., Bettelheim, B., and Diedrich, P. D. Aspects of art appreciation. In *Appraising and recording student progress.* New York: Harper, 1942.

Hathaway, S. R., and McKinley, J. C. *Minnesota Multiphasic Personality Inventory.* (Rev. ed.) New York: Psychol. Corp., 1951.

Heim, Alice W. *Some preliminary experiments on a test of concept-formation, 1956.* Cambridge Univer., Cambridge, England. Dittoed Report.

Hetherington, R. *The Crichton sorting test.* Paper read at Birmingham Convention of the British Psychological Society, 1958. (Abstract)

Holtzman, W. H. The Inkblot Test, a provisional manual for research purposes only. Univer. of Texas, 1958.

Hsü, E. H. The Rorschach response and factor analysis. *J. gen. Psychol.*, 1947, 37, 129–238.

Hughes, R. M. A factor analysis of Rorschach diagnostic signs. *J. gen. Psychol.*, 1950, 43, 85–103.

Hunt, W. A., and French, E. G. Abbreviated scales containing non-verbal items. *J. consult. Psychol.*, 1949, 13, 119–126.

Hylkema, B. S. *De versmeltingsfrequentie bij intermitterend licht.* Assen, Netherlands: van Gorkum and Co., 1942.

Irvine, R. B. Critical flicker frequency for paretics and schizophrenics. *J. abnorm. soc. Psychol.*, 1954, 49, 87–88.

Jackson, W., and Carr, A. C. Emphatic ability in normals and schizophrenics. *J. abnorm. soc. Psychol.*, 1955, 51, 79–82.

Jenkin, N. Affective processes in perception. *Psychol. Bull.*, 1957, 54, 100–127.

John, E. R., and Miller, J. G. The acquisition and application of information in the problem-solving process. *Behav. Sci.*, 1957, 2, 291–300.

Johnson, C. E., Jr., and Sherman, J. E. The clinical significance of the Rorschach test. *Amer. J. Psychiat.*, 1948, 104, 730–737.

Johnson, L. C. Wechsler-Bellevue pattern analysis in schizophrenia. *J. consult. Psychol.*, 1949, 13, 32–33.

Johnson, W. Studies in language behavior. *Psychol. Monogr.*, 1944, 56, 2, No. 255.

Jost, K. C. The level of aspiration of schizophrenic and normal subjects. *J. abnorm. soc. Psychol.*, 1955, 50, 315–320.

Kahn, R., and Fink, M. Changes in language during electroshock therapy. In P. Hoch and L. Zubin (Eds.), *Psychopathology of communication.* New York: Grune & Stratton, 1957.

Kahn, T. C. *Clinical manual of administration, Kahn Test of Symbol Arrangement.* Grand Forks, N. D.: Southern Universities Press, 1957. (a)

Kahn, T. C. *Clinical manual of interpretation, Kahn Test of Symbol Arrangement.* Grand Forks, N. D.: Southern Universities Press, 1957. (b)

Kantor, R. E., and Winder, C. L. Process reactive schizophrenia. *Amer. Psychol.*, 1958, 13, 370.

Kasanin, J., and Hanfmann, E. An experimental study of concept formation in schizophrenia. I. Quantitative analysis of the results. *Amer. J. Psychiat.,* 1938, 95, 35–52.

Kelley, D. M., and Klopfer, B. Application of the Rorschach method to research in schizophrenia. *Rorschach Res. Exch.,* 1939, 3, 55–65.

Kendig, Isabelle, and Richmond, W. V. *Psychological studies in dementia praecox.* Ann Arbor, Mich.: Edwards Bros., 1940.

King, H. E. *Psychomotor aspects of mental disease.* Harvard University Press: Commonwealth Fund, 1954.

Klopfer, B., Crumpton, Evelyn, and Grayson, H. M. *Manual for rating scales for ego functioning applicable to diagnostic testing.* U.C.L.A. Students Store, Mimeogr. draft, 1958.

Knopf, I. J. Rorschach summary scores in differential diagnosis. *J. consult. Psychol.,* 1956, 20, 99–104.

Koch, Louise W. *Zur Phänomenologie der motorischen Ungeschicklichkeit (A contribution to the phenomenology of physical clumsiness).* Wageningen, Holland: H. Veenman, 1955.

Kraepelin, E. *Dementia praecox and paraphrenia.* Edinburgh: Livingston, 1925.

Landis, C. *An annotated bibliography of flicker fusion phenomena.* Ann Arbor, Mich.: Univer. of Michigan, NRC Vision Committee, 1953.

Landis, C. Crozier and Wolf on flicker fusion 1933–1944. *J. Psychol.,* 1954, 37, 3–18.

Langfeldt, G. Prognosis in schizophrenia and factors influencing course of disease. *Acta psychiat. neurol.,* 1937, Suppl. 13, 1–228.

Levine, L. S. Wechsler's patterns in the diagnosis of schizophrenia. *J. consult. Psychol.,* 1949, 13, 28–31.

Lhamon, W. T., and Goldstone, S. The time sense, estimation of one second duration by schizophrenic patients. *Arch. Neurol. Psychiat.,* 1956, 76, 625–629.

Lindsley, O. R. Operant conditioning methods applied to research in chronic schizophrenia. *Psychiat. Res. Rep.,* 1956, No. 5, 118–139.

Lorr, M., O'Connor, J. P., and Stafford, J. W. Confirmation of nine psychotic symptom patterns. *J. clin. Psychol.,* 1957, 13, 252–257.

Lorr, M., Rubinstein, E. A., and Jenkins, R. L. A factor analysis of personality ratings of outpatients in psychotherapy. *J. Abnorm. soc. Psychol.,* 1953, 48, 511–514.

Lovell, C. A study of the factor structure of 13 personality variables. *Educ. psychol. Measmt.,* 1945, 5, 335–350.

Luria, A. R. *The nature of human conflicts.* New York: Liveright, 1932.

Luria, A. R. Brain disorders and language analysis. *Lang. Speech,* 1958, 1, 14–34.

Lüthe, W. Die Elektroskriptograph. *Psychol. Forsch.,* 1955, 24, 2.

Maag, Clinton H. Development and evaluation of a conceptual reasoning test. *Educ. psychol. Measmt.,* 1957, 17, 230–239.

McGaughran, L. S., and Moran, L. J. "Conceptual level" vs. "conceptual area": analysis of object-sorting behavior of schizophrenic and non-psychiatric groups. *J. abnorm. soc. Psychol.,* 1956, 52, 43–50.

Marks, M. R. A criticism of the use of the Wechsler-Bellevue scale as a diagnostic instrument. *J. gen. Psychol.,* 1953, 49, 143–152.

Mednick, S. A. A learning theory approach to research in schizophrenia. *Psychol. Bull.*, 1958, No. 1, 55, 316–327.

Menninger, K. A. *A manual for psychiatric case study.* New York: Grune & Stratton, 1952.

Merrell, D. W. *A perceptual study of deviant cognitive processes in schizophrenia.* Doctoral dissertation, Michigan State Univer., 1954.

Mierke, K. *Konzentrationsfähigkeit und Konzentrationsschwäche.* Stuttgart: Huber, Bern/Klett, 1957.

Mira, E. The MPD. A new device for detecting the conative trends of personality. *Proc. roy. Soc. Med.*, 1940, 33.

Miller, H. D. *The relative appropriateness of responses to humor in schizophrenics.* Doctoral dissertation, Louisiana State Univer., 1956.

Miller, J. G. Information input overload and psychopathology. *Amer. J. Psychiat.*, 1960, 116, 695–704.

Molish, H. B. *Schizophrenic reaction types as evaluated from the Rorschach Test.* Doctoral dissertation, Univer. of Chicago, 1955.

Molish, H. B. *Schizophrenic reaction types in a naval hospital population.* Washington, D. C.: Bureau of Medicine and Surgery, Navy Department, 1956.

Mooney, C. M. A factorial study of closure. *Canad. J. Psychol.*, 1954, 8, 51–60.

Mooney, C. M. Age in the development of closure ability in children. *Canad. J. Psychol.*, 1957, 11, 219–226.

Moore, T. V. The essential psychoses and their fundamental syndromes. *Stud. Psychol. Psychiat.*, 1933, 3, 1–128.

More, D. M., and Roberts, A. F. Societal variations in human responses to cartoons. *J. soc. Psychol.*, 1957, 75, 233–275.

Morris, C. *Varieties of human value.* Chicago: Univer. of Chicago Press, 1956.

Munroe, R. L. The inspection technique: a method for rapid evaluation of the Rorschach protocol. *Rorschach Res. Exch.*, 1944, 8, 46–70.

Murphy, P. D., Bolinger, R. W., and Ferriman, M. R. Screening neuropsychiatric patients by means of the Kahn test of symbol arrangement. *Behav. Sci.*, 1958, 3, 344–346.

Olch, Doris R. Psychometric pattern of schizophrenics on the Wechsler-Bellevue test. *J. consult. Psychol.*, 1948, 12, 127–236.

O'Reilly, P. O. The objective Rorschach: a suggested modification of Rorschach technique. *J. clin. Psychol.*, 1956, 12, 27–31.

Osgood, C. E., Suci, G. J., and Tannenbaum, P. H. *The measurement of meaning.* Univer. of Illinois Press, 1957.

Pauli, R., and Arnold, W. *Der Pauli-Test.* München: Barth, 1951.

Pemberton, Carol. The closure factors related to temperament. *J. Pers.*, 1952, 21, 159–175. (a)

Pemberton, Carol. The closure factors related to other cognitive processes. *Psychometrika*, 1952, 17, 267–288. (b)

Peters, Henry N. Circular pencil maze performance in chronic schizophrenics. *J. clin. Psychol.*, 1952, 12, 170–173.

Pickford, R. W. "Aesthetic" and "technical" factors in artistic appreciation. *Brit. J. Psychol.*, 1948, 38, 135–141.

Price, A. C., and Deabler, H. L. Diagnosis of organicity by means of spiral aftereffect. *J. consult. Psychol.*, 1955, 19, 299–302.

Rabin, A. I. The use of Wechsler-Bellevue scales with normal and abnormal persons. *Psychol. Bull.*, 1945, 42, 410–422.

Rapaport, D., Gill, M., and Schafer, R. *Diagnostic psychological testing.* Vol. II. Chicago: Year Book Pubs., 1946.

Rapaport, D., Schaefer, R., and Gill, M. *Manual of diagnostic psychological testing, II: Testing of personality and ideational content.* New York: Josiah Macy, Jr. Foundation, 1946.

Rappaport, S. R., and Webb, W. B. An attempt to study intellectual deterioration by premorbid and psychotic testing. *J. consult. Psychol.*, 1950, 14, 95–99.

Rashkis, H. Two factors in disordered thinking. *J. nerv. ment. Dis.*, 1950, 3, 424–429.

Raush, H. L. Perceptual constancy in schizophrenics: I. Size constancy. *J. Pers.*, 1952, 21, 176–187.

Raush, H. L. Object constancy in schizophrenics: The enhancement of symbolic objects and conceptual stability. *J. abnorm. soc. Psychol.*, 1956, 52, 231–234.

Ricciuti, H. N. *A comparison of critical flicker frequency in psychotics, psychoneurotics and normals.* Unpubl. doctoral dissertation, Fordham Univer., 1949.

Richman, J. The effect of the emotional tone of words upon the vocabulary responses of schizophrenics. *J. gen. Psychol.*, 1957, 56, 95–120.

Rickers-Ovsiankina, M. The Rorschach test as applied to normal and schizophrenic subjects. *Brit. J. Psychol.*, 1938, 17, 227–257.

Rimoldi, H. J. A. Personal tempo. *J. abnorm. soc. Psychol.*, 1951, 45, 1–4.

Roberts, A. F., and Johnson, D. M. Some factors related to the perception of funniness in human stimuli. *J. soc. Psychol.*, 1957, 46, 57–63.

Robinson, Nancy M. Bender-Gestalt performances of schizophrenics and paretics. *J. clin. Psychol.*, 1953, 9, 291–293.

Rodnick, E. H., and Garmezy, N. An experimental approach to the investigation of motivation in schizophrenia. In *1957 Nebraska Symposium on Motivation, Vol. V.* Univer. of Nebraska Press.

Rodnick, E. H., and Shakow, D. Set in the schizophrenic as measured by a composite reaction time index. *Amer. J. Psychiat.*, 1940, 97, 214–225.

Roehrig, W. C. The influence of area and portion of the retina stimulated on the critical flicker fusion threshold. *Diss. Abstr.*, 1957, 17, 1820.

Rogers, L. S. Differences between neurotics and schizophrenics on the Wechsler-Bellevue scale. *J. consult. Psychol.*, 1951, 15, 151–153.

Rosenbaum, G., MacKavey, W. R., and Grisell, J. L. Effects of biological and social motivation on schizophrenic reaction time. *J. abnorm. soc. Psychol.*, 1957, 54, 364–368.

Rosenberg, B. G., and Altrocchi, J. The Yacorzynski Block technique: a cross-validation study. *J. consult. Psychol.*, 1958, 22, 122.

Rubin, H., and Lonstein, M. A cross-validation of suggested Rorschach patterns associated with schizophrenia. *J. consult. Psychol.*, 1954, 17, 371–372.

Salzinger, K., and Pisoni, Stephanie. Reinforcement of affect responses of schizophrenics during the clinical interview. *J. abnorm. soc. Psychol.*, 1958, 57, 84–90.

Sanders, R. Personal communication, Dep. of Welf., Philadelphia State Hosp., 1957.

Saucer, R. T., and Deabler, H. L. Perception of apparent motion in organics and schizophrenics. *J. consult. Psychol.*, 1956, 20, 385–389.

Schaefer, E. S. A circumplex model for personality development. *Amer. Psychol.*, 1958, 13, 327–328.

Schlosser, J. R., and Kantor, R. S. Wechsler's deterioration ratio in psychoneurosis and schizophrenia. *J. consult. Psychol.*, 1949, 13, 108–110.

Scott, E. M. Regression or disintegration in schizophrenia. *J. clin Psychol.*, 1956, 12, 298–300.

Seashore, R. H. An experimental and theoretical analysis of fine motor skills. *Amer. J. Psychol.*, 1940, 53, 86–98.

Sells, S. B. Structured measurement of personality and motivation: a review of contributions of Raymond B. Cattell. *J. clin. Psychol.*, 1959, 15, 3–21.

Sen, A. A statistical study of the Rorschach test. *Brit. J. Psychol.*, 1950, 5, 21–59.

Shakow, D. The nature of deterioration in schizophrenic conditions. *Nerv. ment. Dis. Monogr.*, 1946, No. 70.

Shipman, W. G. Similarity of personality in the sociometric preferences of mental patients. *J. clin. Psychol.*, 1957, 13, 292–294.

Simonson, E., and Brozek, J. *Flicker fusion frequency: background and applications.* USAF Sch. Aviat. Med. Rep. 2, Project 21-32-004, 1953.

Singer, J. L., Wilensky, H., and McCraven, V. G. Delaying capacity, fantasy and planning ability: a factorial study of some basic ego functions. *J. consult. Psychol.*, 1956, 20, 375–383.

Skalweit, W. *Konstitution und Progress in der Schizophrenie.* Leipzig: Georg Thieme, 1934.

Skinner, B. F. What is psychotic behavior? In *Theory and treatment of the psychoses.* Papers presented at the dedication of the Renard Hospital, St. Louis, Oct. 1955.

Smith, K. U., and Bloom, R. The electronic handwriting analyzer and motion study of writing. *J. appl. Psychol.*, 1956, 40, 302–306.

Smythe, E. J., and Goldstone, S. The time sense: a normative, genetic study of the development of time perception. *Percept. mot. Skills*, 1957, 7, 49–59.

Spence, K. W., and Taylor, Janet A. The relation of conditioned response strength to anxiety in normal, neurotic and psychotic subjects. *J. exp. Psychol.*, 1953, 45, 265–272.

Staats, A. W. Learning theory and "opposite speech." *J. abnorm. soc. Psychol.*, 1957, 55, 268–269.

Steinwachs, F. Die verfeinerte mechanische Schreibwaage. *Arch. Psychiat. u. Z. Neurol.*, 1952, 187.

Stilson, D. W., Gynther, M.D., and Gertz, B. Base rate and the Archimedes spiral illusion. *J. consult. Psychol.*, 1957, 21, 435–437.

Stone, J. B. *The industrial Rorschach test.* California Test Bureau, 1957, dittoed report.

Stotsky, B. A. Factor analysis of Rorschach scores of schizophrenics. *J. clin. Psychol.*, 1957, 13, 275–278.

Süllwold, F. Ein Beitrag zur Analyse der Aufmerksamkeit. *Z. exp. u. angew. Psychol.*, 1954, 2, 495–513.

Suttell, Barbara J., and Pascal, G. B. "Regression" in schizophrenia as determined by performance on the Bender-Gestalt test. *J. abnorm. soc. psychol.*, 1952, 47, 653–657.

Takala, Martti. Studies of psychomotor personality tests. I. *Ann. Acad. Sci. Tenn.*, 1953, Ser. B tom. 81, 2.

Taulbee, E. S., and Sisson, B. D. Rorchach pattern analysis in schizophrenia: a cross-validation study. *J. clin. Psychol.*, 1954, 10, 80–82.

Taylor, J. A. A personality scale of manifest anxiety. *J. abnorm. soc. Psychol.*, 1953, 48, 285–590.

Taylor, J. G., and Papert, S. A theory of perceptual constancy. *Brit. J. Psychol.*, 1956, 47, 216–224.

Thiessen, J. W. A pattern analysis of structural characteristics of the Rorschach test in schizophrenia. *J. consult. Psychol.*, 1952, 16, 365–370.

Thorne, F. C. *Principles of psychological examining.* Brandon, Vt.: J. of clin. Psychol., 1955.

Thoules, R. H. Individual differences in phenomenal regression. *Brit. J. Psychol.*, 1932, 22, 216–241.

Thurstone, L. L. The Rorschach in psychological science. *J. abnorm. soc. Psychol.*, 1948, 43, 471–475.

Thurstone, L. L. Experimental tests of temperament. *Rep. psychomet. Lab.*, *Univer. of Chicago*, No. 67, 1951.

Thurstone, L. L. Progress report on a color-form test. *Rep. psychomet. Lab.*, *Univer. of Chicago*, No. 80, 1952.

Thurstone, L. L. *The development of objective measures of temperament.* *Rep. psychomet. Lab.*, No. 71, 1953. (a)

Thurstone, L. L. Objective tests of temperament: tests of verbal associations. *Rep. psychomet. Lab.*, No. 72, 1953. (b)

Tripp, C. A., Fluckiger, F. A., and Weinberg, W. H. Measurement of handwriting variables. *Percept. mot. Skills*, 1957, 7, 279–294.

Vandenberg, S. G. Differences between neurotics, psychotics and normals on perceptual tests. *J. clin. Psychol.*, 1959, 15, 373–376.

Vernon, P. E. Recent work on the Rorschach test. *J. ment. Sci.*, 1935, 81, 894–917.

Vigotsky, L. S. Thought in schizophrenia. *Arch. Neurol. Psychiat.*, 1934, 31, 1063–1077.

Vigotsky, L. S. Thought and speech psychiatry. *J. Biol. Pathol. impers. Relations*, 1939, 2 (1).

Vinacke, W. E. The investigation of concept formation. *Psychol. Bull.*, 1951, 48, 1–31.

Wallace, M. Future time perspective in schizophrenia. *J. abnorm. soc. Psychol.*, 1956, 52, 240–245.

Watson, R. J. The use of the Wechsler-Bellevue scale: a supplement. *Psychol. Bull.*, 1946, 43 (1).

Webb, W. W. Conceptual ability of schizophrenics as a function of threat of failure. *J. abnorm. soc. Psychol.*, 1955, 50, 221–224.

Weckowicz, T. E. Size constancy in schizophrenic patients. *J. ment. Sci.*, 1957, 103, 475–486.

Weekers, R., and Roussel, F. La mésure de la fréquence de fusion en clinique. *Doc. ophthalmol.*, 1948, 2, 132–190.

Weinstein, A. D. The differential effects of anchors and anchor sequences on the temporal judgments of short intervals by schizophrenic and normal subjects. *Diss. Abst.*, 1956, 16, 2216–2217. (Abstract, doctoral dissertation, Univer. of Houston.)

Weiss, J. L. *An experimental study of the psychodynamics of humor.* Doctoral dissertation, Univer. of Michigan, 1954.

Weitzenhoffer, A. M. *Hypnotic susceptibility as related to masculinity-femininity.* Doctoral dissertation, Univer. of Michigan, 1956.

Werner, H., and Kaplan, Edith. Development of word meaning through verbal context: an experimental study. *J. Psychol.*, 1950, 29, 251–257.

Wertheimer, M. Figural aftereffects in schizophrenic and normal subjects. *Amer. Psychol.*, 1954, 9, 492. (a)

Wertheimer, M. The differential satiability of schizophrenic and normal subjects: a test of deduction from the theory of figural aftereffects. *J. gen. Psychol.*, 1954, 51, 291–299. (b)

Wertheimer, M. Perception and the Rorschach. *J. proj. Tech.*, 1957, 21, 209–216.

Wertheimer, M., and Jackson, C. W. Figural aftereffects, "brain modifiability" and schizophrenia: a further study. *J. gen. Psychol.*, 1957, 57, 45–54.

Wertheimer, M., and Wertheimer, Nancy. A metabolic interpretation of individual differences in figural aftereffects. *Psychol. Rev.*, 1954, 61, 279–280.

White, Mary A. A study of schizophrenic language. *J. abnorm. soc. Psychol.*, 1949, 44, 61–74.

Whiteman, M. The performance of schizophrenics in social concepts. *J. abnorm. soc. Psychol.*, 1954, 49, 266–271.

Williams, H. L., and Lawrence, J. F. Comparison of the Rorschach and MMPI by means of factor analysis. *J. consult. Psychol.*, 1954, 18, 193–197.

Wittenborn, J. R. Factorial equations for tests of attention. *Psychometrika*, 1943, 8, 19–35.

Wittenborn, J. R. A factor analysis of Rorshach scoring categories. *J. consult. Psychol.*, 1950, 14, 261–267.

Wittenborn, J. R. *Psychiatric rating scales.* New York: Psychol. Corp., 1955.

Wolfle, D. *Factor analysis to 1940.* Chicago: Univer. of Chicago Press, 1940.

Yates, A. J. The validity of some psychological tests of brain damage. *Psychol. Bull.*, 1954, 51, 359–379.

Yates, A. J. The use of vocabulary in the measurement of intellectual deterioration—a review. *J. ment. Sci.*, 1956, 102, 409–440.

Zubin, J. Failures of the Rorschach technique. *J. proj. Tech.*, 1954, 18, 303–315.

Zubin, J. The non-projective aspects of the Rorschach experiment: I. Introduction. *J. soc. Psychol.*, 1956, 44, 179–192.

Zubin, J., Eron, L. D., and Sultan, Florence. A psychometric evaluation of the Rorschach technique. *Amer. J. Orthopsychiat.*, 1956, 26, 773–782.

Zubin, J., Windle, C., and Hamwi, V. Retrospective evaluation of psychological tests on prognostic instruments in mental disorder. *J. Pers.*, 1953, 21, 342–355.

Zuckerman, C. B., and Rock, I. A reappraisal of the roles of past experience and innate organizing processes in visual perception. *Psychol. Bull.*, 1957, 54, 269–296.

Projective techniques and drug research

Projective techniques have their historical roots in experimental psychology but have found their greatest utility in clinical exploration and personality research. The methodological problems present when these instruments were first conceived of as psychological tests are, for the most part, still with us. To put these techniques to profitable use in drug research, the methodological issue must first be considered within the context of problems concerning personality processes which have been raised as a consequence of drug investigations. Interesting findings pertinent to the relationship of drugs and personality have appeared, and the questions central to the following discussion will have to do primarily with the usefulness of projective instruments at different stages of investigation in this area. Their advantages and disadvantages as clinical instruments in exploratory research and as objective tests in more definitive types of research will be explored, with the principal objective in mind of combining the advantages of these techniques with the potential value of drugs as instruments for the study of personality processes.

Drug Effects and Personality Variables

In the literature dealing with the effects of tranquilizers and stimulants on human behavior, the behavior primarily in focus has been the clinical symptom or diagnostic pattern. Interest in these classes of drugs derived from their beneficial effects on clinical conditions, and it is only natural that research in this area has moved in

501

the direction of attempts to specify effects of a given drug on mentally disturbed behavior. Although psychotomimetic agents have also, in scattered instances, been put to therapeutic use, research emphasis with these drugs has been on very different kinds of behavior. Their effects, for example, on intellectual performance, perception, and fantasy have been more intensively studied. There has also been less tendency to attribute their effects solely to hypothetical physiological and biochemical causes. Because of the more immediate and dramatic impact that lysergic acid diethylamide (LSD) has on the subject (e.g., the release of "repressed materials"), the psychodynamicists have not been reluctant to discuss the implications of such behavior for understanding disturbed functioning and the nature of neurotic processes. This has not been true with the more therapeutically potent drugs. Research with the tranquilizers has usually been of the more applied or practical type, and where theory has been permitted to develop it has been almost exclusively within a biological framework. It may simply be that personality theorists lack interest in or fail to be convinced of the potency of these drugs, but the fact is that there has been relatively little concern with the psychodynamic aspects of drug effects. There are now classes of drugs of varying effects and potency that are capable of producing profound effects on behavior. These effects are not confined to "calming," "exciting," and "disorganizing" but can produce states that border on euphoria, radical shifts in the manner in which a given situation and people are reacted to, temporary release from guilt and anxiety, and even closer touch with reality. The effects can be temporary, but the questions which they raise are as pertinent to our understanding of personality processes in general as they are to our specific need to modify disturbed behavior.

As noted, the literature in which psychodynamically oriented explanations are offered for drug effects is practically non-existent. This lack may come about for several reasons, some of which require some scrutiny. The assumption that patterns of adjustment developed over a life's span are not likely to be modified easily has made suspect the idea that short-term or even chronic administration of psychoactive drugs promotes any radical change in the personality structure. Even where drugs have been shown to effect real change in the symptom picture, the tendency has been to avoid, in as cautious a manner as possible, concluding that these changes are other than superficial. It is, however, important to note that these studies have not, by and large, been concerned with the measurement of effects at other than the surface level of personality. The point is not that changes more profound than symptom reversal really happen under drugs, but rather that there has been little information about the possible occurrence of such change. Within the psychoanalytical frame of reference, Kubie (1958) has raised the question of the stage in the neurotic process at which the drug exercises its influence. Because symptoms fluctuate during the course of psychotherapy, he cannot accept symptom reduction as a sufficient criterion of core personality change. Yet he is willing to accept the idea that easing the more uncomfortable consequences of a neurosis can in itself sometimes upset the direction of the process. If a drug can stop compulsive repetitive behavior, for example, what are the implications of this symptom loss for other aspects of behavior? The question arises whether even this example is entirely hypothetical or whether evidence exists that drugs can be markedly upsetting to ongoing patterns of behavior. Let us look at several examples in the literature which are highly suggestive of radical change in personality as a consequence of drug action.

Savage and Day (1958) describe dramatic changes in three of four chronic schizophrenics who prior to reserpine therapy had resisted all other types of intensive treatment procedures introduced during a one- to two-year period of hospitalization. These changes were obviously not a mere reduction of symptoms; relatively uncommunicative hostile patients became reasonably social and approachable human beings. The change was described as remarkable, but apparently it lasted only so long as the older reality problems could be avoided. Once outside the hospital, these patients could not maintain the improvement, and the relationship with the therapist, although different and more cordial than before the drug, did not result in any enhancement of psychotherapeutic progress. LSD administration, which has marked effects on perception and mood of the normal subject, has also been reported to produce the same kind of radical, if not entirely consistent, effects when used as therapy for the mentally disturbed. Busch and Johnson (1950) report on disturbances in repressive mechanisms in several of a group of psychotics, and Sandison and Whitelaw (1957) describe similar kinds of experiences with obsessional neurotics. Savage's description (1957) of the breakdown in resistance of patients in psychoanalysis after LSD is equally impressive, but here again disruption of defensive patterns did not in itself result in improvement. On the contrary, these patients became worse. The difference, as implied by Savage, was that, having disrupted defenses, having done away with some areas of resistance, the therapists were somewhat at a loss to know how to make beneficial use of these situations. These instances are mentioned merely to indicate that a great deal of change can be expected to occur with drugs, but our lack of understanding of the underlying mechanism of these changes retards our making adequate use of their effects.

The disruption of defensive patterns as witnessed in LSD reactions represents one of the problems which seem to require integration of physiological and psychodynamic viewpoints. Several earlier studies of LSD effects have indicated that autonomic effects (such as mydriasis, sweating, or flushing) precede behavioral effects (such as perceptional distortions or mood changes) (Wikler, 1957). There has been a tendency to assume that the behavioral effects can be traced directly to physical causes, but there is also sufficient reason to hypothesize that individual variations are based on the subject's idiosyncratic reaction to the autonomic imbalance provoked by this drug. There is at present no way of predicting whether an individual subject will react with euphoria, anxiety, apathy, or all of these.

The problems of personality theory, disruption of defense patterns, the effects of anxiety reduction on other aspects of behavior, of different reactions to similar compounds, of therapeutic utility have all been raised in drug investigations. These are problems of some interest to psychodynamic and psychoanalytic theorists and practitioners. Although an adequate approach to objectifying drug effects on mood and behavior ratings appears to be well under way in this field, there are still these other aspects of psychological functioning that really have not begun to be tapped. There has been increased interest, for example, in the factors within the individual (von Felsinger, Lasagna, and Beecher, 1955) and the situation that affect a given subject's response to a drug (Nowlis and Nowlis, 1956). This interest has grown out of the relatively consistent findings (especially in regard to LSD) of variability among subjects' reactions to a specific drug. Although there is good reason to believe that personality factors are related to differential reactions, we have been slow to test hypotheses in this area. There have been some such attempts, but the range of psychological instruments available in this area is limited in comparison with tools available to study the intellectual and psychomotor aspects of psychological functioning. It would appear that projective techniques could make a contribution in this realm. These instruments have historically been the tools of the psychodynamic practitioners and theorists. They have found their greatest utility in the clinic. However, their productivity as research tools has been seriously questioned, and their value in this respect continues to be controversial. Before specifying situations in which they appear to be promising as research instruments, it might help to comment on some of the methodological problems involved in the use of these techniques.

Projective Techniques as Research Tools

The concept of projective techniques is broad. Theoretically, these instruments should be characterized by qualities which permit the subject to project certain aspects of his personality and problems onto some relatively unstructured ambiguous stimulus. The amount of stimulus structure can vary from a blank sheet of paper and the instructions "draw something" to the request to describe the relatively structured situations represented in the Thematic Apperception Test pictures. The subject's performance can involve a combination of perceptual and verbal activities (Rorschach Test), problem solving, or creative drawing. There are any number of variations that have been and can be developed on this theme, but what seems to underlie most of them is adherence to the rule of limited ambiguous structure, the implication that there are no right or wrong answers, and sufficient freedom for the open-ended response.

There is no question that these instruments have always been intriguing both to experimenters and to clinicians. At the same time their research history, as noted, has been marked by controversy, on the one hand, because of their questionable quantifiability and, on the other, because of their obvious clinical utility. As tests, the projective instruments have always had difficulty in meeting basic reliability and validity requirements. Since they are not simple instruments, the task of evaluating their reliability and validity has been extremely difficult. There is the question, for example, whether all aspects of a projective test should be reliable. The basic personality structure is hypothesized to be relatively stable; therefore, those aspects of the projective test designed to measure personality structure should be reliable. On the other hand, there are characteristics associated with personality which are expected to vary from day to day or from situation to situation. Elements in the instruments expected to reflect this variability cannot be reliable in the same sense. The question is then raised as to what in a given projective test is measuring the stable, and what is measuring the variable, elements of the personality. Projective instruments have always had the fortunate or unfortunate quality of seeming to encompass all these aspects of personality. No one would argue the fact that some elements of personality are reflected on these tests; the questions have always centered on *which* elements. For example, there is a lack of certainty even today as to what the Rorschach Test measures validly and what it does not measure. As a test, there is evidence that some aspects are reliable, others are not. Zubin, Eron, and Sultan (1956) have strongly suggested that those elements expected to be most stable (the distribution of location and determinant scores) turn out to be less reliable than the theoretically superficial response aspects (the content of the response). The point is that the Rorschach test and other projective techniques are still difficult to deal with objectively, despite much effort at validational research. As a test, then, the clinician knows that the Rorschach reveals something about the subject's approach in difficult situations—whether he is likely to be outgoing, the extent to which he relies on fantasy for problem solution, his level of self-respect, and the nature of his expectations of other people—but it has never really been demonstrated that the Rorschach is valid in these areas. Consequently, the extent to which it is useful in revealing these qualities seems to hinge more on the quality of the clinician than on the test itself. It is this peculiar usefulness that will require some analysis in line with the aims of this chapter.

The value of the Rorschach Test in the clinic seems to reside, at least partly, in the unusual nature of the situation it presents to the subject and the examiner. Simply stated, the projective instrument provides a vehicle whereby a patient seeking help can communicate to a potential therapist the substance of problems he either cannot, or would not want to, express directly. In so doing he reveals personality characteristics related to other aspects of his approach to difficulties. This definition of the projective situation assumes several things, all of which have relevance to problems in personality research. It assumes, first, that because of his discomfort the patient or subject is motivated to communicate certain aspects of his particular state of mind and emotions to the examiner. The instrument further provides, through the ambiguity of its stimulus and the open-ended nature of its response requirements, a good deal of freedom for the subject as to the manner and the content of the response. Finally, it requires of the interpreter a certain amount of ingenuity and understanding of personality process in order to deal in a meaningful way with the information. The last requirement places a heavy burden on the clinician. If we take the position that a great deal about personality processes is still far from completely understood, then the clinician, even with a great deal of experience and ingenuity, cannot do a completely adequate job in this area. But, in general, these are precisely the characteristics which have made the projective techniques valuable in personality research. If the first assumption is met—that the subject desires to communicate—then it is an asset that the response is a free one. The major handicap lies in the clinician's ability to understand or interpret the response.

The freedom of response that these techniques provide results in data which can lead to greater understanding of personality processes. The use of the ambiguous stimulus in personality research has been productive in this sense. Rorschach, for example, is associated primarily with the test, but his major contribution is probably his stimulation of the broad perceptual approach to the study of personality which has led to a significant increase in our information in this area. To cite a supporting example of the productivity of the ambiguous stimuli in this respect, one has only to review some of Bartlett's early work (1932) with ink blots and other such stimuli to find original and fruitful ideas about personality and memory processes.

There is sufficient evidence to indicate that personality variables play some part in drug effects. The role of projective techniques in determining the nature and extent of this relationship at two different stages of drug investigation is discussed below.

EXPLORATORY DRUG RESEARCH. The psychological information of prime interest in the early investigation of a new drug with human subjects usually concerns overt behavioral changes and effects on mental state. Overt behavior of interest to the investigators can be categorized and rated, and within certain limits the subject can provide responses to standard psychometric instruments designed to record any felt mood, psychomotor, or thought changes. These are relatively straightforward objective approaches to classifying the effects of a given drug, but they do not usually represent the first approach. The initial stage is more likely to be carried out with few subjects and with detailed free description of behavior by knowledgeable observers. The subject is also asked simply to describe the experience he is undergoing, and when his free associations fall off he is encouraged by questions to continue to introspect. The questions cannot avoid being leading, and consequently no great argument can be made for the complete objectivity of this procedure. But objectivity, although desirable at this stage, is probably less important than the need to draw the subject out on the nature of his experience.

The objective here is simply to get some leads, ideas about the nature of this drug's action, directly or indirectly, on the psychological functioning and behavioral activity of the subject. Hopefully, the more promising of these ideas will be tested in a more definitive manner in a subsequent experiment. From the observer's standpoint, these situations require a background of experience with other drugs and, equally, if not more, important, they also require an understanding of human behavior in normal as well as unusual circumstances. The search, then, at this stage is for ideas about drug effects, but the effects under investigation are not or should not be confined to overt behavior. If the interest is in mood change, fantasy, the manner in which unstructured situations are dealt with, then projective techniques can be productive again, given some background on how the subject deals with the instrument under normal conditions. Projective instruments can be applicable in situations where other more structured tests would not be: First, the impact of the drug may be such that the administration of a structured test is not feasible; second, the methods of administering projective tests are consistent with the permissive nature of the conditions of exploratory investigation; and, third, when the interest is in changes in affect, defense patterns, or fantasy content, then these tests have potentially more to offer than the standard psychometric instrument.

As described here, the exploratory approach is more an idea-seeking stage than it is definitive research. The subjects are few, their reactions are studied intensively, and the observers attempt to arrange the situation so that a great deal of freedom in response is permitted the subject. The observers describe, question, and interpret. The search is for changes in the subjects' behavior from the predrug to the drug period. In citing the requirement that the investigator be experienced in observing and interpreting behavior under drugs, I am only reaffirming the obvious—an astute clinician who has been experimenting with new drugs for mental patients over a number of years is more likely to know when he has a "different" drug than is either the inexperienced or the less astute observer. A similar situation prevails for the clinician who relies on response to projective techniques, rather than on clinicial behavior alone, as his source of information about individual patients. He would in a sense be simply deriving his conclusions from a different source of data.

If it were granted that promising hypotheses could result from this approach, then one real difference between the exploratory and clinical approaches still requires some comment. Though the investigator in exploratory research attempts to maintain as neutral and objective a pose as possible, the clinician is more likely to look for changes which represent improvement rather than changes *per se*. The chances that the clinician will overlook other important changes are, of course, increased. "Improvement" is an important and useful concept in clinical research, but it is an interpretation, a value judgment, and it would appear to be more important in early trials with a new drug to establish that something has changed before offering an interpretation of the change. Again, it is obvious that more is known about describing behavior than is known about interpreting it. There can, for example, be much disagreement about what represents improvement or therapeutic efficacy, even though the agreement and hence the reliability of judgments of change from passive to aggressive behavior can be high from observer to observer. The sharp differences between the objectivist and the clinician stem more from the former's difficulty in understanding the clinician's *interpretation* of the data (his use of "improvement") rather than from his *report* of the data.

There is an example in the clinical research literature (Azima, Durost, and Azima, 1958) in which the critical variable under study was change rather than improvement, and the results were promising. Ten patients were tested under four conditions (reserpine, phenobarbital, and two without drug) and were identified on the Rorschach Test as demonstrating the most marked change under reserpine. The judge sorted the protocols without awareness of the treatment procedures. Although other Rorschach indices differentiated significantly among the treatments, the results should be cross-checked because the group was small and there were some weaknesses in the research design. The order of treatments did, however, protect against invalidating the finding that reserpine provoked more change in the patients' responsivity to stimulus characteristics on the Rorschach than did the other conditions. That significant change does occur under this drug having been established, it becomes more reasonable to investigate the nature of these changes. There are two other studies that demonstrate the value of this approach, if somewhat indirectly. Levine, Abramson, Kaufman, Markham, and Kornetsky (1955), using Rorschach scores, found a number of significant differences between LSD and no-drug conditions, but the meaning of this potentially important set of findings is buried under a maze of interpretations, which at times are extremely idiosyncratic. In a study by Castner, Covington, and Nichols (1958), there were again indications of significant change on the Rorschach Test as a function of chlorpromazine, but in this case the changes were not predicted and there was little attempt at interpretation. The first of these studies found significant "global" change; the other two resulted in changes in the standard Rorschach scores. Because of the difficulties in interpreting scores, none of the three can provide reliable information on what it is that actually changed in the subject, but the studies encouraged further exploration of the meaning of these changes.

The importance of projective instruments in the early stages of new drug investigation resides, first, in their sensitivity and potentiality for establishing that change has or has not taken place in the responsivity of the subject and, second, in their capacity for provoking ideas about how these changes take place. Azima, Durost, and Azima (1958) in referring, for example, to shifts in defensive patterns, indicate what they consider to be the bases for the Rorschach changes under reserpine, but the thesis here is that too few astute clinicians have applied themselves to either task—establishing change or interpreting projective data—to give us any real basis for evaluating the utility of these instruments in the exploratory stages of drug research.

DEFINITIVE DRUG RESEARCH. The role of projective techniques in definitive research must be characterized somewhat differently from that described in the previous section. In the discussion of exploratory research, these instruments are seen as valuable as an extension of the clinician's skills and as a source of ideas about psychological changes that occur under drugs. As a tool in definitive research, the interest must shift from their more global use to evaluating their utility in testing hypotheses as to specific relationships between personality variables and drug effects. The question central to this set of problems is whether these techniques can be relied on to measure aspects of personality and affect change consistent with our interest in characterizing and generalizing the effects of specific drugs.

In a review of the literature dealing with the effects of LSD on psychological functioning (Katz, 1958), it was noted that failures to confirm with standard psychometric instruments some of the earlier exploratory work were much more frequent than the successes in these studies. This represents somewhat of a puzzle where LSD is concerned because its marked effects on psychomotor functioning, perception, and thought processes have been reported many times over in earlier investigations. Several factors are probably responsible for this discrepancy, but some suggest themselves more strongly than others.

Forcing the subject to respond to a concrete task, such as that represented in the standard psychometric instrument, in combination with the more obvious individual differences in response to LSD, will tend to obscure the more general effects of the drug. We have also been made aware in more than one instance of the importance of situational effects on drug response (Nowlis and Nowlis, 1956; Cahn, 1953). The factors underlying drug response are, then, obviously complex, and they again emphasize two different but related sets of problems in drug research. There is the problem of determining specific effects of various drugs that can be generalized, and there is also the problem of determining which internal and external factors interact with drug effects to produce individuality in response. In seeking effects which can be generalized, there is less inclination to be concerned with individual differences. In studying the factors that influence drug response, predictions are made, for example, as to the personality characteristics associated with a given drug reaction. The applicability of projective techniques to either of these two problems depends in great part on the hypotheses to be tested. Objective methods have been developed for dealing with aspects of projective data, but again it is a matter of the specific behavior to be investigated, the experimenter's interests, and his judgment of the reliability and appropriateness of any of the available methods. Rather than focus on specific hypotheses and methods, I shall describe two methods which exemplify common approaches to the objectification of projective data. Both seem to have promise for drug research, although neither has been used for this purpose as far as I know.

Two Methods for Objectifying Projective Data in Drug Research

The effects of a given drug on the affective state of the subject are of prime interest in drug research. That is, aside from measurable changes in overt behavior there are concerns about whether the subject has become more hostile, anxious, depressed, or elated as a result of the drug. This kind of affect change is sometimes apparent in his verbal report of the experience or in his responses to a questionnaire. The introspective report is informative but difficult to objectify, and the inventory may place more restrictions on the subject's response freedom than the investigator wants.

DeVos (1952) describes in detail an approach to dealing with affect on the Rorschach Test through the categorization of response content.

The system provides for score estimates of levels of hostility, anxiety, dependency, and positive affect derived from a classification of fantasy content. The reliability coefficients for the scores of five of the seven affect categories range from .85 to .99 (based on average correlation of the author's ratings and the independent ratings of each of four judges). Although not in itself evidence of the validity of each of the categories, of 15 statistical comparisons of the five category scores among groups of normals, neurotics, and schizophrenics, 13 of the differences were significant at the .05 level or better, in the expected direction. Where the interest, then, is in determining the level in fantasy of such affect as anxiety, bodily preoccupation, generally unpleasant or pleasant feeling, the method described is workable. The high reliability speaks for agreement among raters as to the content of the response. It may not permit conclusions about the overt behavior to be expected, but within the limits described it looks like a worthwhile approach.

Thaler, Weiner, and Reiser (1957) have used the method in a comparative study of hypertensive and peptic ulcer patients and found some interesting and significant differences between the groups. This system should have more appeal for experimental work than the standard Rorschach scoring approach, because it requires less interpretation and fewer assumptions about the meaning of scores. Whereas the content of a response in the DeVos system can be judged reliably and has obvious face validity, the standard Rorschach scores have to be interpreted on the basis of assumptions that have, for the most part, never been satisfactorily justified. Although DeVos sees his system as complementary to the scoring of location and determinants, it would seem to represent a significant departure and a promising one, useful independently.

The second method to be described is also primarily concerned with content analysis, but from a different viewpoint. This system has its roots in the interpersonal theory of Sullivan (1947). Leary (1957) and associates have developed objective rating methods for measuring interpersonal behavior consistent with the general tenets of this theory. The prime instrument is a rating scale comprised of some 100 descriptive items which can be categorized into eight major classes of interpersonal characteristics. The inventory can be used to rate self and others, and it has been more recently put to use in rating fantasy material (Leary, 1956). The last-mentioned interest is in line with this group's attempt to compare behavior at the overt and the covert levels by applying the same measuring instrument to different sources of information. In the rating of fantasy material, Leary makes use of the Thematic Apperception Test (TAT). The method essentially consists in having several judges independently rate the "hero" figures in the subjects' TAT stories with the Interpersonal Checklist. The investigator is primarily concerned with the discrepancies between the subject's self-rating and the rating of the characters in the TAT stories, and whether these discrepancies can predict the direction and amount of change the subject will undergo over the course of psychotherapy. The method was only partially successful as a predictive device, but it exemplifies a fairly common approach to objectifying projective data: that is, the use of reliable objective rating scales in the ordering of projective material. The technique has been applied to the testing of hypotheses relative to psychotherapy and personality dynamics, but it should also be possible to apply it to testing of fantasy change under drugs.

In summary, this approach makes use of key responses to projective instruments, those involving the subject's interpretations of human interaction; it provides a theoretically consistent framework for the classification of such responses and a reliable rating approach to objectifying the content of these responses.

Whereas the first approach is more applicable where changes in affect are the major concern, the second may provide opportunities for testing hypotheses as to the effects of drugs on interpersonal perception and fantasy. These are, of course, only two of several possible techniques for objectifying projective data.

R E F E R E N C E S

Azima, H., Durost, H., and Azima, Fern J. Alterations of schizophrenic psychodynamic structure concomitant with reserpine administration. Unpublished manuscript, Dep. of Psychiatry, McGill University, Montreal, 1958.

Bartlett, F. *Remembering: a study in experimental and social psychology.* Cambridge: Cambridge Univer. Press, 1932.

Busch, A. K., and Johnson, W. C. LSD-25 as an aid in psychotherapy. Preliminary report of a new drug. *Dis. nerv. Sys.,* 1950, 11, 241–243.

Cahn, C. H. The effect of drugs on group therapy: an experiment. *J. nerv. ment. Dis.,* 1953, 118, 516–526.

Castner, C. W., Covington, C. M., and Nichols, J. E., Jr. The effects of a Thorazine-centered treatment program with psychological evaluations. *Tex. Rep. Biol. Med.,* 1958, 16, 21–30.

DeVos, G. A quantitative approach of affective symbolism in Rorschach responses. *J. proj. Tech.,* 1952, 16, 133–150.

Katz, M. M. The psychological effects of psychochemical compounds. Paper read at Symposium IX, U.S. Army Chemical Warfare Laboratories, Army Chemical Center, Maryland, June 25, 1958.

Kubie, L. The investigation of the pharmacology of psychological processes: Some methodologic considerations from the point of view of clinical psychoanalysis. In H. H. Pennes (Ed.), *Psychopharmacology.* New York: Hoeber-Harper, 1958, 302–315.

Leary, T. F. A theory and methodology for measuring fantasy and imaginative expression. *J. Pers.,* 1956, 25, 159–175.

Leary, T. F. *Interpersonal diagnosis of personality; a functional theory and methodology for personality evaluation.* New York: Ronald, 1957.

Levine, A., Abramson, H. A., Kaufman, M. R., Markham, S., and Kornetsky, C. Lysergic acid diethylamide (LSD-25): XIV. Effect on personality as observed in psychological tests. *J. Psychol.* 1955, 40, 351–366.

Nowlis, V., and Nowlis, H. H. The description and analysis of mood. *Ann. N.Y. Acad. Sci.,* 1956, 65, 345–355.

Sandison, R. A., and Whitelaw, J. D. A. Further studies in the therapeutic value of lysergic acid diethylamide in mental illness. *J. ment. Sci.,* 1957, 103, 332–343.

Savage, C. The resolution and subsequent remobilization of resistance by LSD in psychotherapy. *J. nerv. ment. Dis.,* 1957, 125, 434–437.

Savage, C., and Day, Juliana. Effects of a tranquilizer (reserpine) on psychodynamic and social processes. *Arch. Neurol. Psychiat.,* 1958, 79, 590–596.

Sullivan, H. S. *Conceptions of modern psychiatry.* Washington, D.C.: The William Alanson White Psychiatric Foundation, 1947.

Thaler, Margaret, Weiner, H., and Reiser, M. F. Exploration of the doctor-patient relationship through projection techniques; their use in psychosomatic illness. *Psychosom. Med.,* 1957, 19, 228–239.

von Felsinger, J. M., Lasagna, L., and Beecher, H. K. Drug-induced mood changes in man. 2. Personality and reactions to drugs. *J. Amer. med. Ass.,* 1955, 157, 1113–1119.

Wikler, A. *The relation of psychiatry to pharmacology.* Baltimore: Williams & Wilkins, 1957.

Zubin, J., Eron, L. D., and Sultan, Florence. Current status of the Rorschach test. Symposium, 1955. 1. A psychometric evaluation of the Rorschach experiment. *Amer. J. Orthopsychiat.,* 1956, 26, 773–782.

The use of drugs
in information-seeking interviews

In the physician's customary role as a helping-person and as a healer, it is generally contrary to his method of operation to employ any coercion, overt or subtle, to induce a patient to behave in a way that may be detrimental to himself or his social or national group of origin.   Coercion may be used, however, if the patient is considered to be behaving in a manner that is destructive to himself (e.g., a diabetic refusing to take insulin or an alcoholic refusing to stop drinking) or to his social group.   Furthermore, the code of ethics, particularly of the psychiatrist, ordinarily binds the physician to keep confidential the secrets that his patients impart to him, whether or not the patient has been aware or unaware of their nature.

The use of drugs in obtaining a confession from a criminal, or in obtaining information that a source may consciously wish to keep confidential for fear of repercussion on himself or his group, is fraught with ethical conflicts for the physician.   This explains in part why there is a relative paucity of systematized published scientific investigation by physicians on this matter.   The general feeling in western countries regarding the employment of chemical agents to "make people do things against their will" has precluded serious systematic study, at least in openly published materials, of the potentialities of drugs for interrogation.   It has not precluded considerable speculation on the subject; however, some of it rather unrealistic.   The following is a

This chapter is based upon work done by the author as a consultant to the Bureau of Social Science Research, Inc., Washington 8, D.C.   The work was supported in part by the U.S. Air Force under contract AF 17(600)1797 monitored by the Rome Air Development Center of the Air Research and Development Command.

brief summary of conclusions reached in an extended survey of this problem (Gottschalk, 1961).

An examination of the literature to find experimental and clinical studies that bear directly on the use of drugs in interrogation procedures reveals that there are relatively few. Studies and reports dealing with the validity of material extracted from reluctant informants, whether criminal suspects or experimental subjects, indicate that there is no "truth serum" which can force every informant to report all the information he has. Experimental and clinical evidence indicates that not only may the inveterate criminal psychopath lie or distort under the influence of a drug, but also that the relatively normal and well-adjusted individual may, with some drugs, successfully disguise factual data. Less well-adjusted individuals, plagued by guilt and depression, or suggestible individuals, who are compliant and easily awed, are more likely to reveal withheld information; but they may, at times, unconsciously distort this information and present fantasies as facts. The anesthetic action of the drug, as in narcosis with barbiturates, can interfere with cerebral functioning and promote the presentation of fantasy material as fact, or otherwise alter the form of verbalizations so that they are relatively unintelligible. It would be very difficult under these circumstances for an interrogator to distinguish when the verbal content was turning from fact to fantasy, when the informant was simulating deep narcosis but actually falsifying, which of contrary stories told under narcosis was true, and when a lack of crucial information coming from a subject under a drug meant the informant had none to offer.

Barbiturates tend to increase contact and communication, decrease attention, decrease anxiety, decrease psychotic manifestations, and make mood more appropriate and warmer. Combined with interview techniques that aim at arousing emotions, strong emotional reactions may be catalyzed for psychotherapeutic abreaction. Barbiturates have been found helpful in detecting whether an individual is feigning ignorance of the English language and in getting mute catatonic schizophrenics and hysterical aphasics to talk. They are of no avail in remedying the speech defects of true aphasics, even transiently. Barbiturates have helped to get more reliable estimates of intelligence and personality through psychological tests, particularly in emotionally upset individuals.

The use of various stimulant and antidepressive drugs has been explored for diagnostic and therapeutic purposes in psychiatric practice but not to any extent for interrogation. Amphetamine, pipradrol, methylphenidate have in common the capacity to produce an outpouring of ideas, emotions, and memories. An injection of amphetamine following an intravenous barbiturate is said to provoke a striking on-rush of talking and emoting from psychiatric patients. Without adequately controlling his study, one author claims that methamphetamine produces such a strong urge to talk that the criminal who feigns amnesia or withholds vital information cannot control himself and gives himself away. Iproniazid, a new antidepressive drug, which is relatively slow to show a therapeutic effect but which rather frequently is dramatic, should be considered for experimentation. This drug (and similar but less toxic analogs which are being developed now) might be considered for use in special instances. For example, informants suffering from a chronic severe depression, whether due primarily to emotional factors or physical debilitation, might become very responsive after being on a medicament of this type for a while. As a class, the stimulants probably present the most obvious exploitative potential for an interrogator.

The psychotomimetic and hallucinogenic drugs, mescaline and LSD-25, have been used largely to study the etiogenesis of psychotic states and, in a minor way, as an adjuvant in psychotherapy. The use of such drugs by an interrogator would tend to produce a state of anxiety or terror in most subjects and to promote perceptual distortions and psychotic disorientation. Their use could constitute a definite threat to most medically unsophisticated subjects, i.e., threat of making the subject crazy. When the subject is not under the influence of such drugs, vital information might be extracted, as a price for ceasing further medication. An enlightened informant would not have to feel threatened, however, for the effect of these hallucinogenic agents is transient in normal individuals. The information given during the psychotic drug state would be difficult to assess, for it may be unrealistic and bizarre.

There is a possibility that tranquilizers might be of use in selected informants who are highly agitated and disturbed, and who might give information they prefer to withhold in return for the tranquility they experience with such a sedative. Under the influence of such a drug, the less emotionally upset informant might find that he can better master his anxieties and keep his resolve to remain silent. These are speculations and require testing and experimentation.

Addiction is an added vulnerability to influence. The ability of the subject to give information is not notably affected by a maintenance dosage. The motivational effects, while extreme, are not of a different order for most subjects than those which the interrogator could produce by other more rapid means, however. The exploitation of addiction probably constitutes a threat to persons previously addicted, or to those who become addicted in the captivity situation as a sequel to other aspects of their treatment, rather than through the deliberate creation of addiction for the exploitative purpose.

Another use to which interrogators might put drugs and placebos would involve their ability to absolve the subject of responsibility for his acts. The popular meaning of being "drugged" or "doped" implies that an individual in this state has lost control over his actions and that society will not hold him responsible for them. When the transmittal of information is likely to induce guilt in the source, the interviewer can forestall some of this reaction by the administration of a placebo or drug. In some cases this will be all that is required to remove the barrier to information transmittal. In the avoidance-avoidance conflict between the source's guilt over yielding information and his anxieties over the possible consequences of non-cooperation, the "inescapable" power of the drug or placebo serves to justify any of the source's actions to himself and to the world.

What are the overall conclusions that can be drawn from this review and critical analysis of the use of pharmacologic agents in obtaining information?

Are pharmacologic agents of any value to the interrogator in eliciting vital information? The answer is that drugs can operate as positive catalysts to productive interrogation. Combined with the many other stresses in captivity that an individual may be obliged to undergo, drugs can add to the factors aimed at weakening the resistance of the potential informant. But, for many reasons, the use of drugs by an interrogator is not sure to produce valid results. The effects of drugs depend to a large extent on the personality makeup and physical status of the informant and the kind of rapport that the interrogator is able to establish with him. Knowing the predominating pharmacologic actions of a number of psychoactive drugs, an interrogating team might choose that chemical agent which is most likely to be effective in view of the informant's personality, physical status, and the various stressful experiences he has already undergone. Even under the most favorable circumstances the information obtained could be contaminated by fantasy, distortion, and untruth, especially when hallucinogenic or sedative drugs are employed.

REFERENCE

Gottschalk, L. A. The use of drugs in interrogation. In A. D. Biderman and H. Zimmer (Eds.), *The manipulation of human behavior.* New York: Wiley 1961, in press.

Rating scales, behavior inventories, and drugs

Rating scales and behavior inventories have grown in popularity as measuring devices and as instruments for the development of psychological theory. Literally dozens of scales and behavior checklists have been constructed for use in hospitals and clinics to record patient behavior and to evaluate the effects of treatment on mental patients. The history of their use goes back at least a half century. The Phipps Psychiatric Clinic Behavior Chart developed about fifty years ago (Kempf, 1915) was one of the earliest reported in the literature and is still in use. Plant (1922) described a scheme for rating patient ward conduct. Moore (1933) constructed a schedule of rating scales which were then employed to evolve factor analytically defined psychotic syndromes.

Before presenting a description and an evaluation of some of the better-developed, more widely known and more promising instruments, a set of evaluative criteria will be outlined. Some of the problems of developing and constructing measuring devices will also be discussed.

Problems of Observation

Perhaps the first question to be asked in designing or selecting a scale concerns the class of patients to be observed. Is the scale, for example, applicable to mute, inaccessible, or disturbed patients, or is it intended for the psychotic patient in relatively good contact? The range of application should be clearly stated and reflected in the normative data reported. Next, what behavior and interpersonal interaction patterns are to be observed or measured? Presumably item or scale construction has been guided by hypotheses concerning the manifestation of traits or symptom syndromes. A correlative requirement is to know under what standard stimulus conditions observations and inferences are to be made. Is the patient to be observed in isolation, in a diadic relationship, or while interacting with others on the ward or in group psychotherapy? How and to what degree is the stimulus situation to be structured? The scale should specify the physical environment, the role of the interviewer or therapist, the number and types of patients present in the group, and the period of observation. In other words, controlled objective observations call for a clear definition of the behaviors to be observed and definite specification of the conditions for eliciting behavior.

The degree of structure or control imposed can, of course, vary enormously. Practically none of the rating schedules specifies the questions to be asked or the order in which they are to be asked. Yet the importance of the question, its context, and its position have been clearly shown in interview surveys of public opinion. Saslow and Matarazzo (1955) are among the few who have attempted to examine the behavior of patients when the interviewer's behavior is controlled. At present, rating scale and checklist observations are naturalistic or semistructured. They do not represent the result of controlled observations. Some fail even to specify the period of observation or the place of observation.

Problems of Reliability

There are three distinct facets to the problem of estimating the reliability of behavior inventories or rating schedules. Consider a set of ratings made by m observers on N patients over n rating scales. The degree of internal consistency among scales provides a measure of scale homogeneity. Typically it is estimated by the Kuder-Richardson formula (Guilford, 1954). The extent of agreement among raters across scales represents observer consistency. The intraclass correlation coefficient is often used to estimate this level of agreement. Finally, if the ratings are repeated by the same observers after a suitable time interval, a measure of construct stability may be obtained by correlating the two sets of average ratings received by patients.

All three indices are of interest and should be available to the user of a scale. If patients are to be rated singly rather than multiply, agreement among observers is probably most important because it

then becomes possible to consider behavior consistency. The rate-re-
rate coefficient, on the other hand, provides a measure of the trait's
stability and contributes to the user's understanding of the underlying
trait itself. However, it is possible for two or more raters to be consistent over time but not be in high agreement among themselves.
Each rater may be reporting a unique aspect of the behavior observed.

The intraclass Pearson r correlation for average ratings increases
with the number of (equivalent) judges, just as test consistency increases with the number of parallel units added. Whether it is better
to estimate the reliability of individual ratings or the reliability of
average ratings depends upon the uses and decisions to be made of the
ratings. In research and experimental work the average rating is
likely to be the more useful base for estimating reliability. However,
if the patient is not likely to be rated by more than one rater, then the
reliability of individual ratings is the appropriate index. Either index
may be obtained if one is known (Ebel, 1951).

Evidence of Validity

A measure of behavioral deviation or psychopathology has construct
validity to the extent that it measures some existent functional unity.
Its construct validity is established on the basis of three distinct but
convergent types of evidence (Loevinger, 1957). The content of the
items or scales should be consistent with the proposed interpretation of
the measure. In other words, an unbiased examination of the items
should lead to an explanation of the underlying variable that is in
harmony with the one hypothesized. Second, the structural relations
of the items, such as their intercorrelations, should be consistent with
the nonscale structural evidence of the trait or syndrome. If, for example, a cumulative or additive model is postulated, then the number
of manifestations will be directly related to the amount of the trait.
This relation should be maintained when non-test information is obtained. On the other hand, a class model implies that a trait is either
present or absent. All but possibly one or two signs must be present
before it can be said that the syndrome is present. Each structural
model implies the presence of certain distinctive relations among the
items constituting the scale. Third, the correlations of the scale measure with other variables should not all be zero and should be consistent with expectations based on the psychological interpretation of the
trait or syndrome. Thus there should be evidence of predictive and
discriminative validity for the measure. For example, a measure of

severity of illness derived by ward observations should distinguish open from closed ward patients and might be expected to correlate significantly with other evidence such as, for instance, elevated MMPI scores.

The point of view taken here is that the most fruitful direction for the development of scales and behavioral inventories is toward the measurement of attributes and reactions which can advance psychological theory. All instruments to record mental status examinations or global measures of hospital adjustment are administrative tools, useful no doubt, but of little or no scientific interest. Rather, there is need for measures based on theory that possess some level of generality beyond the specific uses of the moment.

Problems of Scale Construction

It is not our intent to outline in any detail the theory and methods of psychological scaling. Torgerson (1958) provides a comprehensive survey of traditional procedures and recent developments in scaling. Edwards (1956) and Guilford (1954) present more elementary descriptions. However, it seems appropriate to indicate briefly the psychometric characteristics of rating scales and behavioral inventories.

The raw data of scaling consist of responses to each of a number of stimuli. The systematic variations in the reactions of the judges to the stimuli may be attributed (a) to differences in the subjects, (b) to differences in the stimuli, and (c) to variations both in the judges and in the stimuli. When the immediate purpose of the study is to scale the judges who are assigned scores (as with the Likert method), we are in the field of mental testing. If the purpose is to scale the stimuli, whether these be patients, words, or colors, the procedure is stimulus-centered and may be called the judgment approach. It is this procedure that is involved in developing rating scales and behavioral inventories. Finally, in the response approach, variations of reactions to stimuli are ascribed to variations in both judges and stimuli. The Guttman scaling method illustrates the last approach.

Torgerson (1958) groups the judgment methods into the quantitative-judgment and the variability of judgment approaches. In the first the unit of measurement is directly obtained from the quantitative judgments of the stimuli with respect to the attribute scaled. The observer must rate, sort, or arrange stimuli in a series such that the ratios among the numbers assigned to stimuli are equal to the ratios of the distances separating the stimuli on the psychological continuum. For the second group the variability of judgment with respect to each stimulus is used to derive a unit of measurement.

Most current rating scales may be categorized into the subjective estimate procedures of the quantitative judgment approach. The essential procedure is to present a series of stimuli, such as adjectives, to an observer or judge who is instructed to give a quantitative judgment of the amount of a specified attribute possessed by each of the stimuli. The judgment follows the presentation of a single stimulus in the single-stimulus or rating-scale methods. In the multiple-stimuli methods an entire series of stimuli are presented. Both the single-stimulus and the multiple-stimuli methods may involve a limited number of discrete intervals or steps, or an unlimited number of steps. The graphic rating scales may be classified as a single-stimulus procedure involving an indefinite number of steps. Implicitly or explicitly, the judge makes his rating on an equal-interval scale, or it is assumed that he will do this.

Thurstone's judgment scaling model represents one of the variability of judgment approaches. The law of categorical judgment applies to the case where the stimuli are allocated to categories which are ordered with respect to the trait or attribute investigated. In the method of successive intervals the observer's task is to sort the stimuli into successive piles so that the first pile includes the stimuli most extreme with respect to the attribute; the second pile, the stimuli next most extreme; and so on. The only requirement is that the piles be in rank order. In rating procedures the observer rates each stimulus separately with respect to the attribute on a numerical, adjectival, or graphic scale arbitrarily divided into a number of categories. Rank-order procedures require the judge to rank the stimuli. Each rank may be taken as a category.

The test model most frequently used, especially by the factor analysts, is the quantitative cumulative model. It is assumed that, the greater the number of manifestations, the greater is the intensity or degree of the syndrome or trait. Or, phrased alternatively, the greater the amount of the trait, the greater is the probability that the trait will manifest itself to the observer in behavior. A group of scales or a cluster of statements about behavior may be identified by their positive intercorrelations. A score then becomes the sum of the items in a cluster that the observer checks as present. Separate clusters or groups can be identified either through the usual methods of multiple-group factoring or by the Loevinger, Gleser, DuBois (1953) procedure for constructing homogeneous subtests.

The normal-ogive model developed by Tucker (1955) could be

TABLE 1. CHARACTERISTICS

Type of Patients Observed	Behavior Observed or Judged	Observer and Observation Period	Number and Types of Scale Items
			Psychiatric Rating Scales
Mental patients	Currently observable behavior and symptoms	Observation period not specified Psychiatrist, psychologist, or competent observer	52 symptom-rating scales each with three or four statements
			Multidimensional Scale for Rating Psychiatric
Hospitalized psychiatric patients	Interview and current ward behavior	One-hour interview by psychologist or psychiatrist for Interview Section One to two weeks' observation by aide or nurse for Ward Section	40 graphic scales with four or five cues in Interview Section and 22 scales in the Ward Section
			Symptom Rating Scale (Jenkins,
Hospitalized psychotic patients	Interview behavior and symptoms	Psychiatrist or psychologist 30–60 minute interview	20 four-interval scales and 46 checklist items
			MACC Behavioral Adjustment
Hospitalized psychiatric patients	Motility, affect, cooperation, and communication on ward	Any observer familiar with the patient Period of observation not specified	14 scales with five cues each
			Activity Rating Scale for Psychiatric
Hospitalized male psychiatric patients	Any hospital activity	Ancillary Service personnel who have known patient for about one year	50 questions each rated on a five-point scale of frequency, and 26 questions rated as to degree
			Weyburn Assessment Scale
Chronic hospitalized schizophrenic patients	Psychiatric examination by interview	Psychiatrist Length of interview not reported	36 scales each defined by five cues

Derived Scores	Scale Reliability	Predictive or Discriminatory Validity	Norm Data
(Wittenborn, 1955)			
Nine cluster scores established by factor analysis	Odd-even reliability median .82 ($N = 100$) for nine clusters	No data presented in manual	Median standard cluster scores for 1000 consecutive admissions to Connecticut State Hospital
Patients (Lorr, Jenkins, and Holsopple, 1953)			
11 "factor" scores established by factor analysis and a Morbidity Score	Intraclass r of .89 for morbidity score ($N = 545$; two raters) Median intraclass r of .71 for factor scores	(1) Differentiates open from closed ward patients (2) Reflects change resulting from tranquilizers and lobotomy	Centile ranks for morbidity score and for factor scores based on 417 patients from five hospitals
Stauffacher, and Hester, 1959)			
Psychotic symptoms	Median inter-rater $r = .75$ ($N = 20$) for 20 scales	None reported	None reported
Scale (Ellsworth, 1957)			
Total behavioral adjustment Four behavioral adjustment areas	Rank order r of .86 ($N = 20$) for two raters on total score Median rerating r, one-week interval, is .91	(1) Differentiates open from closed ward patients (2) Time spent on pass predicted by amount of improvement on MACC	Total adjustment centiles for 335 patients from two hospitals Distributions of four cluster scores
Patients (Guertin and Krugman, 1959)			
Six factors established by factor analysis	None reported	None reported	None reported
(Blewett and Stefaniuk, 1958)			
Separate scores on Behavior, Appearance, Thought, Memory, and Mood	Inter-rater r .70 to .80	None reported	None reported

TABLE 1.

Type of Patients Observed	Behavior Observed or Judged	Observer and Observation Period	Number and Types of Scale Items
		L-M Fergus Falls Behavior Rating	
Hospitalized psychiatric patients	Hospital and ward behavior	Psychiatric aide or nurse Observation period not specified	11 rating scales each defined by five descriptive statements
		SELH Behavior Rating Scale (Hine, Bass,	
Hospitalized psychiatric patients	Symptomatic behavior	Ward attendants and nurses Observation indefinite	32 scales, each four point
		Institute of Living Clinical Rating	
Hospitalized schizophrenics	Interview and ward behavior	Separate scales for nursing personnel and attendants Observation period not specified	Two forms of 12 rating scales; four scales common; the five steps of each scale defined
		Q-Rating Scale of Ward	
Hospitalized psychiatric patients	Ward behavior	Psychiatric aides Two weeks of observation or more	Two forms of 54 statements; each *Q*-sorted into forced distributions of 11 piles
		Northampton Activity Rating	
Hospitalized psychiatric patients	Behavior shown in rehabilitation and activity therapies	Rehabilitation therapists One week of observation	46 scales defined by three or four descriptive statements
		Gardner Behavior Chart	
Continued-care psychiatric patients	Ward and hospital behavior	Nurse or aide Observation period one day to six months	15 scales each in four steps defined by brief phrases

CONTINUED

Derived Scores	Scale Reliability	Predictive or Discriminatory Validity	Norm Data
Sheet (Lucero and Meyer, 1951)			
Total score and subscales on response to work, other patients, nurses, doctors, and therapy Measures one factor	Inter-rater r of .84 for total score Subscale median r of .65	(1) Differentiates nurses from patients (2) Discriminates between open and closed wards	Total and subscale scores for total state hospital ($N = 1925$) Data on age, sex, diagnosis, education, etc.
Dawson, Wurster, and Dobbins, 1957)			
Mental status, general behavior, speech, emotional behavior, content of thought	Average reliability .71 to .08; median .42	None reported	None reported
Scales (Reznikoff and Zeller, 1957)			
Mental status judgments; insight and judgment, phantasy life, social behavior, etc.	Pairs of nurse raters agree completely on 69% of ratings; reratings by doctors yield 68% total agreements	None reported	None reported
Behavior (Darbes, 1954)			
Measures of psychological structure, psychosexual development, interpersonal relations, and libidinal vector a la Freudian theory	Rate-rerate mean r of .65 ($N = 20$)	None reported	None reported
Scale (Scherer, 1951)			
Ratings on work, interpersonal relations, and ideation	Inter-rater correlation median of .74 for 44 items ($N = 27$)	None reported	None reported
(Wilcox, 1942)			
Ratings on control, work, and appearance	None reported	None reported	None reported

TABLE 1.

Type of Patients Observed	Behavior Observed or Judged	Observer and Observation Period	Number and Types of Scale Items
			Elgin Behavior Rating Scale (Rev.)
Hospitalized psychiatric patients	Ward and interview behavior	Professional (?) Period of observation not reported	26 rating scales in six areas; steps defined by descriptive phrases
			Psychiatric Rating Scale
Hospitalized psychiatric patients	Ward and interview behavior	Nurses and trained interviewers Observation over 24 hours on ward	19 bipolar scales; each step defined by a psychiatric term
			Social Adjustment Scale (Barrabee,
Patients in social case work treatment and psychotherapy	Not specified (Interview?)	Social worker and psychotherapist Observation period not specified	39 scales in four areas
			Multidimensional Scale for Rating Psychiatric Patients,
Patients seen in psychotherapy	Interview behavior and report	Professional interviewer or therapist One to three interviews required	50 rating scales; each defined and with four to six cues
			Rating Scale for Evaluation
Patients seen in psychotherapy	Interview behavior and reports	Therapist who has seen in treatment at least several times	37 scales each defined by four descriptive statements

CONTINUED

Derived Scores	Scale Reliability	Predictive or Discriminatory Validity	Norm Data
(Wittman, 1948)			
Scores on behavior labeled Somatic, Social, Mental, Psychotic, Neurotic, and Antisocial	None reported	None reported	None reported
(Malamud and Sands, 1947)			
Total score and measures of 19 psychological functions	Inter-rater r of .92 on total score ($N = 26$)	Reflects change resulting from electroshock and lobotomy	None reported
Barrabee, and Finesinger, 1955)			
Scores on Employment, Economic Adjustment, Family Life Adjustment, and Community Adjustment	None reported	None reported	None reported
Outpatient Form (Lorr, Rubinstein, and Jenkins, 1953)			
10 personality and symptom "factors" derived by factor analysis	Median rate-rerate for 10 factors is .60 ($N = 74$) over six months Intraclass r median is .80	(1) Differentiates severely ill from mildly ill patients (2) Differentiates patients from professional workers	Centiles on 10 factors for 325 male outpatients
of Psychotherapy (Morse, 1953)			
Ratings in six areas: Symptoms, Vocational or School Adjustment, Social Adjustment, Sexual Adjustment, Family Adjustment, and Accessibility to Psychotherapy	None reported	Reflects change following psychotherapy	None reported

TABLE 1.

Type of Patients Observed	Behavior Observed or Judged	Observer and Observation Period	Number and Types of Scale Items
			Q.P.S.S. Rating Sheet
Hospitalized psychotic patients	Overt psychotic symptoms and behavior	Psychiatrist conducts mental status interview and secures reports of ward behavior	35 scales of severity each with four steps; also checklists
			Clyde Mood Scale
Primarily outpatients and inpatients in good rapport	Aspects of mood and behavior influenced by drugs	Observers with at least 8 grades of education Observation period depends on purpose	133 descriptive adjectives to be sorted into four piles of degree

applied to scale such categorical data. The model assumes that the correlation between items can be accounted for by a single trait or factor. Furthermore it is postulated that no two items have a relation to each other beyond that which can be accounted for by their separate relations to the underlying variable. The "trace" line or curve for an item gives the probability that a behavior will be manifested by patients located at any given position on the underlying variable. The curve is assumed to be a normal ogive. The relation between a patient's total score and his score on any given item is thus probabilistic. As yet, none of the scales published has been so scaled.

Table 1 presents data on some 19 rating scales currently available for research use or for clinical practice. No effort has been made to list all published scales. Only the better developed and the more promising devices reported in the literature are described. Of those included less than half provide manuals for scoring and interpretation. A fair proportion fail to provide evidence of discriminatory or predictive validity, and a few even fail to report reliability information.

Nine behavioral inventories are listed in Table 2. All except the Post Hospital Adjustment Scales (HAS) are for use in hospitals and clinics to assess diagnostic interview, individual or group psychotherapy, and ward behavior. Since the appearance of the HAS, behavioral inventories have grown rapidly in popularity. They are reported to be easier to complete, less demanding, and less likely to

CONTINUED

Derived Scores	Scale Reliability	Predictive or Discriminatory Validity	Norm Data
(Goodrich, 1953)			
An overall mean symptom severity score	None reported	None reported	None reported
(Clyde, 1958)			
7 mood factors: Earnest, Adventurous, Contented, Energetic, Friendly, Desperate, Fearful	None reported	None reported	None reported

arouse choice anxiety in the uncertain rater than rating scales. The item structure is appealing to the psychologist accustomed to self-report questionnaires. The behavior to be checked concerns specific, concrete observable acts. Rating scales, on the other hand, are not uncommonly written in ambiguous abstract language. Judgments are likely to involve inference or to be based on broad characteristic behavior cutting across many situations.

It is generally believed that rating scales are more sensitive to change and more discriminating than behavior inventories. The typical scale has available four or five graded steps that may be checked. The graphic scale provides for an indefinite number of steps. Whether a group of rating scales defining a trait are collectively more discriminating than a group of statements is a moot question much in need of investigation. In theory it would seem that behavioral inventory measures can be constructed to be as sensitive and as differentially discriminating as a group of rating scales.

The rating scales described in Table 1 may be differentiated on the basis of method of development employed. The Wittenborn PRS, the Multidimensional Scale, the MACC, and indirectly the Symptom Rating Scale (Jenkins, Stauffacher, and Hester, 1959) and the Clyde Mood Scale attempt to measure relatively independent dimensions of behavior deviation derived by factor analysis or cluster techniques.

TABLE 2.   CHARACTERISTICS

Type of Patients Observed	Behavior Observed or Judged	Observer and Observation Period	Number and Types of Scale Items

Hospital Adjustment Scale (McReynolds,

| Hospitalized psychiatric patients | Most hospital behavior (self care, communication and interpersonal relations, work activities and recreation) | Two weeks to three months
Psychiatric aide or nurse | 90 statements marked True, Not True, or Doesn't Apply |

Albany Behavioral Rating Scale

| Hospitalized psychotic or long-term mental patients | Ward and social adjustment | Two weeks to three months
Nurses and rehabilitation personnel | 100 statements to be marked Yes or No |

Mental Status Scale (Bostian, Smith,

| Psychiatric patients | Psychiatric examination by interview | Psychiatrist or psychologist
Length of interview not reported | 55-item checklist |

Psychotic Reaction Profile (Lorr,

| Hospitalized psychotic patients | Ward and general hospital behavior | Nurse or psychiatric aide
Observation period of three days to one week | 85 descriptive statements marked True, Not True, Doesn't Apply |

Post Hospital Adjustment

| Discharged hospital patients on home care placements | Behavior in the home | Relatively naive raters report observations during past three weeks to three months | 80 descriptive statements marked True or Not True |

OF 9 BEHAVIORAL INVENTORIES

Derived Scores	Scale Reliability	Predictive or Discriminatory Validity	Norm Data
Ballachey, and Ferguson, 1952)			
Measures of level of hospital adjustment; also measures of "expansion" and "contraction"	Test-retest: .79 Two aides rating same patients: .84	(1) Differentiates open from closed ward patients (2) Differentiates schizophrenics in remission from those who are not	Percentile ranks for 353 males and 165 females from four hospitals
(Shatin and Freed, 1955)			
A total score as a measure of behavioral adjustment	Two nurses rating same patients .79 ($N = 31$), .84 ($N = 25$); a K-R coefficient of .97 ($N = 56$)	(1) Differentiates open from closed ward patients (2) Scores correlate with adjustment ratings	None reported
Lasky, Hover, Ging, 1958)			
"Mental status" of patient	None reported	None reported	None reported
O'Connor, and Stafford, 1959)			
Independent measures of Thinking Disorganization, Withdrawal, Paranoid Belligerence, and Anxious Depression	Reliability coefficient (alpha) of .90, .93, .90, and .75	Differentiates open from closed ward patients	Centile ranks by sex from 40 hospitals on four measures (500 males and 250 females)
Scale (Hamister, 1956)			
Measure of Expansion-Contraction; also Self-esteem, Upsetness, Conformity, and Dependency	Odd-even reliability .90 for total score ($N = 95$); mean of .87 for four subscales	Differentiates between successful and unsuccessful home care patients	Scores for 95 cases in home care program

TABLE 2.

Type of Patients Observed	Behavior Observed or Judged	Observer and Observation Period	Number and Types of Scale Items
			Critical Behavior Record
Hospitalized psychiatric patients	Specific incidents of improvement or need for further hospital help	Nurses and nurse assistants Observation period not stated	14 behavior categories
			Palo Alto Group Psychotherapy
Inpatients or outpatients with psychiatric problems	Interpersonal behavior in group therapy setting	Group leaders and nurses Observation period not stated	88 descriptive statements marked True, False, or Doesn't Apply
			Social Adjustment Scale
Hospitalized psychiatric patients	Hospital and ward behavior	Nurse and aide Observation period not stated	100 descriptive statements marked True, Not True, and Doesn't Apply
			Interpersonal Checklist
Outpatients in group psychotherapy	Behavior during group psychotherapy	Therapists and trained observers Observation period not specified	128 descriptive phrases and adjectives, 8 for each of 16 interpersonal scale variables

Except for the HAS and Darbes *Q*-Scale, the schedules represent efforts simply to quantify observable interview and ward behavior. The Hospital Adjustment Scale items were validated against a concept of contraction and expansion. The behavior statements compiled by Darbes are based on a Freudian theory of components.

The behavioral inventories may also be categorized on the basis of mode and theory of construction. The Psychotic Reaction Profile (PRP), the Mental Status Scale (Bostian, Smith, Lasky, Hover, and Ging, 1958), and the Interpersonal Checklist (ICL) are based on correlational analyses and homogenous keying techniques. The PRP

Derived Scores	Scale Reliability	Predictive or Discriminatory Validity	Norm Data
(Flanagan and Schmid, 1958)			
Three major areas: Aggressive vs. Considerate, Immature vs. Mature, Irrational vs. Rational Behavior	Coding agreement of 77% for five students on 14 areas	None reported	Incident frequency on 324 patients in three mental hospitals
Scale (Finney, 1954)			
Total score of adequacy of interpersonal relations	Inter-rater reliability for total scores is .90	Discriminates between groups differentiated as to interpersonal adjustment ($N = 26$)	Total scores on outpatient sample ($N = 82$) and inpatient sample ($N = 128$)
(Aumack, 1957)			
Scores on Socialization Level and Work Level	Not reported	Discriminates between high and low patients on a ward	None reported
(LaForge and Suczek, 1955)			
16 interpersonal variable scores in two dimensions	Test-retest mean r is .73 for 16 scales	None reported	None reported

was constructed on the basis of a set of hypothesized dimensions of behavior deviation. The ICL was in part formulated on the basis of Murray's need system. Most but not all the remaining devices represent efforts to measure currently observable behavior deviations and symptoms quite independently of any theory. The Post Hospital Adjustment Scale and the Palo Alto Group Psychotherapy Scale are efforts to measure in terms of certain clinical theories of behavior.

It seems likely that devices developed in the near future will be in the form of behavioral inventories and checklists. With careful construction, a reliability of .90 can be achieved with as few as 12 statements. Rater and response bias can be controlled more easily by including positive and negative statements and by randomizing the order of item presentation. Greater use of controlled observation and the development of structured interviews may also be anticipated.

Use of Rating Devices in Evaluating Drugs

Even a hasty reading of a few of the hundreds of papers concerned with the effects of the tranquilizer drugs on psychiatric patients is a sobering experience. The range in scientific merit of the criteria of change utilized is very considerable. At one end of the scale is the criterion that simply refers to "symptomatic improvement" without further elaboration, as though such matters were obvious. Further along the continuum are those criteria that measure three or more degrees of an undefined global improvement, i.e., slight, mild, moderate, or marked improvement. At a somewhat more sophisticated level the criterion is likely to be defined in specific terms and the various degrees of improvement are spelled out. However, the criterion is still unidimensional and ordinarily stated in broad general terms.

In the middle of our scale of merit are a much smaller number of criteria designed to measure specific aspects of ward behavior or response to nursing care. Sometimes reliabilities are reported, but more typically little or no reference is made to the concept. Also typical is the failure to test or try out the devices constructed to ascertain their sensitivity to change or their validity as reflected in the ability to discriminate between such patient groups as open and locked ward patients.

Finally, there is that increasing number of studies that utilize standardized, well-designed checklists and behavior-rating schedules. Some of the rating schedules most frequently used are the Fergus Falls Behavior Rating Scale, the Hospital Adjustment Scale, the Multidimensional Scale for Rating Psychiatric Patients, the Wittenborn Psychiatric Rating Scale, and the Jenkins Symptom Rating Scale.

Virtually all the controlled clinical studies supported by the National Institute of Mental Health grants and by the Veterans Administration, and those obtaining state support, include rating schedules or checklists as primary tools for assessing change. They are used to measure such aspects as psychiatric status, change in specific syndromes such as depression, post-hospital adjustment, and home adjustment. Until objective psychological and psychomotor tests are further developed and demonstrated to reflect changes of importance, behavioral inventories and rating scales will play a valuable role in drug research.

R E F E R E N C E S

Aumack, L. *Social Adjustment Rating Scale.* Roseburg, Ore.: Veterans Administration Hospital, 1957.

Barrabee, P., Barrabee, Edna L., and Finesinger, J. E. A normative social adjustment scale. *Amer. J. Psychiat.*, 1955, 112, 252–259.

Blewett, D. B., and Stefaniuk, W. B. Weyburn Assessment Scale. *J. ment. Sci.*, 1958, 104, 359–371.

Bostian, D. W., Smith, P. A., Lasky, J. J., Hover, G. L., and Ging, R. J. Some empirical observations on mental status examination. *Amer. Psychol.*, 1958, 13, 334. (Abstract)

Burdock, E. I., Sutton, D., and Zubin, J. Personality and psychopathology. *J. abnorm. soc. Psychol.*, 1958, 56, 18–30.

Clyde, D. J., *Clyde Mood Scale.* Bethesda, Md.: National Institute of Mental Health, 1958.

Cohen, L. H., Malmo, R. B. and Thale, T. Measurement of chronic psychotic overactivity by the Norwich Rating Scale. *J. gen. Psychol.*, 1944, 30, 65–74.

Darbes, A. Development of a Q-rating scale of ward behavior of hospitalized psychiatric patients. *Amer. Psychol.*, 1954, 9, 354. (Abstract)

Ebel, R. L. Estimation of the reliability of ratings. *Psychometrika*, 1951, 16, 407–424.

Edwards, A. *Techniques of attitude scale construction.* New York: Appleton-Century-Crofts, 1956.

Ellsworth, R. B. *Manual for the MACC Behavioral Adjustment Scale.* Los Angeles, Calif.: Western Psychological Services, 1957.

Finney, B. C. *A scale to measure interpersonal relationships in group therapy.* Palo Alto, Calif.: Veterans Administration Hospital, 1954.

Flanagan, J. C., and Schmid, F. W. The critical incident approach to the study of psychopathology. *Amer. Psychol.*, 1958, 13, 330. (Abstract)

Gertz, B., Stilson, D. W., and Gynther, M. D. Reliability of the HAS as a function of length of observation and level of adjustment. *J. clin. Psychol.*, 1959, 15, 36–39.

Goodrich, B. W. Quantifications of the severity of overt psychiatric symptoms. *Amer. J. Psychiat.*, 1953, 110, 334–341.

Guertin, W. H., and Krugman, A. D. A factor analytically derived scale for rating activities of psychiatric patients. *J. clin. Psychol.*, 1959, 15, 32–35.

Guilford, J. P. *Psychometric methods.* New York: McGraw-Hill, 1954.

Hamister, R. C. *The Post Hospital Adjustment Scale.* Palo Alto, Calif.: Veterans Administration Hospital, 1956.

Hine, J. R., Bass, B. M., Dawson, J. G., Wurster, C. R., and Dobbins, D. A. Measurement of symptomatic changes in hospitalized psychiatric patients. *Dis. nerv. Sys.*, 1957, 18, 3–7.

Jenkins, R. L., Stauffacher, W., and Hester, R. A symptom rating sheet for use with psychiatric patients. *Arch. gen. Psychiat.*, 1959, 1, 197–204.

Kempf, E. J. The behavior chart in mental disease. *Amer. J. Insanity*, 1914–15, 71, 761–772.

LaForge, R., and Suczek, R. F. The interpersonal dimension of personality. III. An interpersonal checklist. *J. Pers.*, 1955, 24, 94–112.

Leary, T. F., and Coffey, H. S. Interpersonal diagnosis: some problems of methodology and validation. *J. abnorm. soc. Psychol.*, 1955, 50, 110–125.

Loevinger, Jane. Objective tests as instruments of psychological theory. *Psychol. Rep.*, 1957, 3, 635–694.

Loevinger, Jane, Gleser, G. D., and DuBois, P. H. Maximizing the discriminating power of a multiple-score test. *Psychometrika*, 1953, 18, 309–317.

Lorr, M. Rating scales and checklists for the evaluation of psychopathology. *Psychol. Bull.*, 1954, 51, 119–127.

Lorr, M., Jenkins, R. L., and Holsopple, J. Q. Multidimensional Scale for Rating Psychiatric Patients, Hospital Form. *U. S. Vet. Admin. tech. Bull.*, TB 10-507, 1953. Washington, D. C.: Veterans Administration.

Lorr, M., Jenkins, R. L., and O'Connor, J. P. Factors descriptive of psychopathology and behavior of hospitalized psychotics. *J. abnorm. soc. Psychol.*, 1955, 50, 78–86.

Lorr, M., O'Connor, J. P., and Stafford, J. W. A psychotic reaction profile. *J. clin. Psychol.*, 1960, in press.

Lorr, M., and Rubinstein, E. A. Personality patterns of neurotic adults in psychotherapy. *J. consult. Psychol.* 1956, 20, 257–263.

Lorr, M., Rubinstein, E. A., and Jenkins, R. L. A factor analysis of personality ratings of outpatients in psychotherapy. *J. abnorm. soc. Psychol.*, 1953, 48, 511–514.

Lucero, R. J., and Meyer, B. T. A behavior rating scale suitable for use in mental hospitals. *J. clin. Psychol.*, 1951, 7, 250–254.

McReynolds, P., Ballachey, E. L., and Ferguson, J. T. Development and evaluation of a behavior scale for appraising the adjustment of hospitalized patients. *Amer. Psychol.*, 1952, 7, 340. (Abstract)

Malamud, W., and Sands, S. L. A revision of the Psychiatric Rating Scale. *Amer. J. Psychiat.*, 1947, 104, 231–237.

Matarazzo, J. D., Saslow, G., and Matarazzo, Ruth G. The interaction chronograph as an instrument for objective measurement of interaction patterns during interviews. *J. Psychol.*, 1956, 41, 347–367.

Meyer, B. T., and Lucero, R. J. A validation study of the L-M Fergus Falls Behavior Rating Scale. *J. clin. Psychol.*, 1953, 9, 192–195.

Moore, T. V., The essential psychoses and their fundamental syndromes. *Studies in psychology and psychiatry*, 1933, 3, No. 3. Baltimore: Williams & Wilkins Co.

Morse, P. W. Proposed technique for the evaluation of psychotherapy. *Amer. J. Orthopsychiat.*, 1953, 23, 716–731.

Plant, J. S. Rating scheme for conduct. *Amer. J. Psychiat.*, 1922, 1, 547–572.

Rashkis, H. A., and Smarr, E. A. Psychopharmacotherapeutic research. *Arch. Neurol. Psychiat.*, 1957, 27, 202–209.

Reznikoff, M., and Zeller, W. W. A procedure for evaluating the status of schizophrenic patients using combined physician and nurse judgments. *J. clin. exp. Psychopath.*, 1957, 18, 367–371.

Rowell, J. T.   An objective method of evaluating mental status.   *J. clin. Psychol.*, 1951, 7, 255–259.

Saslow, G., and Matarazzo, J. D.   The stability of interaction chronograph patterns in psychiatric interviews.   *J. consult Psychol.*, 1955, 19, 417–430.

Scherer, I. W.   *Northamptom Activity Rating Scale, Form D.*   Springfield, Mass.: Meed Scientific Apparatus Co., 1951.

Shatin, L., and Freed, E. X.   A behavioral rating scale for mental patients.   *J. ment. Sci.*, 1955, 101, 644–653.

Sines, L. K.   A note on the reliability of the L-M Fergus Falls Behavior Rating Scale.   *J. clin. Psychol.*, 1958, 14, 95–98.

Smith, J. A.   An observation chart for ward personnel.   *J. nerv. ment. Dis.*, 1956, 124, 417–420.

Stilson, D. W., Mason, D. J., Gynther, M. D., and Gertz, B.   An evaluation of the comparability and reliabilities of two behavior rating scales for patients.   *J. consult. Psychol.*, 1958, 22, 213–216.

Torgerson, W. S.   *Theory and methods of scaling.*   New York: Wiley, 1958.

Tucker, L. R.   Some experiments in developing a behaviorally determined scale of vocabulary.   Paper read at Amer. Psychol. Assn. San Francisco, September, 1955.

Wilcox, P. H.   The Gardner Behavior Chart.   *Amer. J. Psychiat.*, 1942, 98, 874–880.

Wittenborn, J. R.   *Psychiatric Rating Scales.*   New York: Psychological Corp., 1955.

Wittenborn, J. R., and Holzberg, J. D.   The generality of psychiatric syndromes.   *J. consult. Psychol.*, 1951, 15, 372–380.

Wittman, P. M.   The Elgin checklist of fundamental psychiatric behavior reactions.   *Amer. Psychol.*, 1948, 3, 280.   (Abstract)

Chapter 44 *Julian J. Lasky*

Veterans Administration cooperative chemotherapy projects and related studies

The first published report in English on the therapeutic effectiveness of chlorpromazine appeared in 1952 (Delay, Deniker, and Harl). Numerous studies, both in this country and abroad, soon followed. However, when Bennett (1957) reviewed 962 articles on chlorpromazine which were published between 1952 and 1956, he found that only 10 described controlled studies. Typically, a single investigator administered a drug to a small series of patients and reported his observations in terms of clinical course, side effects, and percentage of patients who, in his judgment, had improved. Although this type of study undoubtedly contributed useful and important clinical information, many readers were understandably skeptical. Hopes had been raised too often by early, glowing reports of the success of other somatic treatments, only to crumble slowly in the face of hard experience or rigorous investigation. The discerning reader could rarely be certain whether the clinical changes reported were attributable to the drug under study, to chance fluctuation, or to some other source such as staff enthusiasm. Control groups, objective measures, statistical tests of probability, and methods for evaluating bias, error, and other sources of variation were used only occasionally.

In an attempt to promote systematic investigation of chemotherapy as it related to mental illness, the Veterans Administration organized a cooperative research program in 1956. This program now consists

The author wishes to express his appreciation to the following for their constructive review of the manuscript: Drs. C. James Klett and Josephine Ball of the CNPRU staff, and Dr. Eugene M. Caffey of the Veterans Administration Hospital, Perry Point, Maryland.

540

of two divisions: *projects* in which all participating hospitals and clinics use the same, commonly agreed upon, procedure and methodology and contribute data to a central point for analysis, and *related studies* which are conceived, designed, conducted, and analyzed by investigators working independently on problems which are related to the projects.

The organizational structure for the overall program consists of an Executive Committee, the Central Neuropsychiatric Research Unit, the Washington Neuropsychiatric Research Laboratory, and participating hospitals and mental hygiene clinics. The Executive Committee, maintaining close communication with the participants, selects problem areas for study, recommends major features to be incorporated into new projects, reviews and revises reports prior to publication, and formulates general policy. The executive committee is assisted by committees on: new drugs and toxicity, evaluation of patient change, physiological studies, follow-up, and publications. The Central NP Research Unit and the NP Research Laboratory are responsible for developing design and methodology, processing and analyzing data, and reporting findings to the executive committee. Each participating hospital or mental hygiene clinic appoints a Principal Investigator from its own staff to manage the program locally.

Veterans Administration Program of Chemotherapy in Psychiatry

A wide range of individual and group researches on drugs and behavior are under way in the Veterans Administration, but we must here limit consideration to four projects, detailing the experimental designs, the statistical models, and selected findings as the basis for some methodological comments and suggestions for further investigation.

EXPERIMENTAL DESIGN. PROJECT 1. In Project 1 the relative therapeutic effectiveness of chlorpromazine, promazine, phenobarbital, and lactose on schizophrenic patients was investigated. Phenobarbital, with its sedative effect, represented an active control substance which could mimic some of the effects of the tranquilizer drugs.

The four preparations were randomly assigned to 692 male schizophrenic patients, ranging in age from 18 to 51 years with an average of 36 years 5 months, at 37 VA neuropsychiatric hospitals. Using two or more years of hospitalization as a definition of chronicity, 81 per

cent of the patients were chronic. As judged by psychiatrists, 73 per
cent were non-disturbed and the remainder were disturbed.

Daily dosage was fixed at 3 grains of phenobarbital and 400 mg. of
the phenothiazines. The four substances were administered orally
in a double-blind manner for 12 weeks. Identical capsules were used
for all preparations and the contents were all of the same color and
taste. Patients were taken off all tranquilizers for a period of two
months before being introduced to the study. During the study,
certain treatment activities, such as transfer from one ward to another
and psychotherapy, were restricted.

Four sets of measures and over 600 staff raters were used to evaluate
the patients at the beginning, middle, and end of the 12-week study.
The measures were the Multidimensional Scale for Rating Psychiatric
Patients (MSRPP) (Lorr, 1953; see also Chapter 43), Manifest Anxiety
Scale (MAS) (Taylor, 1953), Clinical Estimate of Psychiatric Status
(Veterans Administration, 1958), and body weight. The MSRPP
is divided into two parts the first of which is based on impressions
gained by a team of psychiatrists and psychologists during an evaluative interview. The second part is based on observations of ward
behavior by a team of nurses and attendants. Eleven factor scores
representing various areas of psychopathology and a total morbidity
score are derived from the MSRPP. The MAS was completed by the
patient, and the Clinical Estimate of Psychiatric Status schedule was
completed by the psychiatrist. The four sets of measures contributed
25 criteria in all.

Previous investigators (e.g., Zubin, 1959) had emphasized that patient characteristics such as social background factors, premorbid personality traits, vital statistics and physical characteristics, course of illness, feelings and emotions, and thought processes might all be related
to prognosis. Since the influence of these factors might confound the
interpretation of changes resulting from drug effects, data were
gathered on seven "prognostic" or control variables: age, chronicity,
length of current hospitalization, degree of disturbance, duration of
illness, weight, and MSRPP morbidity at the beginning of the study.

Toward the end of Project 1 it was decided that extending the time
period of the project would yield valuable data as well as providing
an opportunity to investigate the effects of alternating tranquilizers
and control substances in various combinations. Accordingly, an additional 12-week study, using a crossover design, was planned and was
designated Project 2.

PROJECT 2. Of the 692 patients who were studied in Project 1, 489 continued without interruption into Project 2. Project 2 patients were assigned to 12 groups and were evaluated at the beginning, middle, and end of the second 12 weeks of study. In four groups, the four treatments of the first 12 weeks were continued through the second 12 weeks. In the remaining eight groups, the study medications used during the first 12 weeks were replaced during the second 12 weeks— each of the two tranquilizers by each of the two control substances in four groups and the converse in four other groups. The same study medications and criteria used in Project 1 were used in Project 2.

PROJECT 3. This is a 12 weeks double-blind study, now being analyzed, of the relative therapeutic effectiveness, side effects, and toxic reactions of six drugs: phenobarbital and the following five phenothiazines, chlorpromazine, mepazine, perphenazine, prochlorperazine, and trifluopromazine. These six drugs were randomly assigned to 635 male schizophrenics who were newly admitted to 34 neuropsychiatric, and general medical and surgical hospitals.

The therapeutic effects of the drugs will be evaluated somewhat more extensively than in the first two projects. Information was collected on the following 13 control variables: age, number of previous hospitalizations, nature of onset of first illness, nature of onset of current illness, marital status, occupational level, chronicity, educational level, body weight, MSRPP premorbidity score, type of hospital, history of previous tranquilizer chemotherapy, and concomitant psychotherapy. A study of possible toxic effects of the drugs will be based on the incidence of side effects, weekly white blood cell count and differential count, and liver function (serum alkaline phosphatase) data. Patients were evaluated with the MSRPP and a revision of the Clinical Estimate of Psychiatric Status schedule immediately before drug administration, after four weeks on a specified dosage schedule, and again after eight additional weeks on an individualized, flexible dosage schedule. Dosage patterns and reasons for changing dosages during the flexible dosage period will also be studied.

Related Studies. Nineteen investigators from 14 hospitals are conducting 46 individual and collaborative studies related to Project 3. Data are being collected on perceptual, cognitive, personality, psychomotor, and central and autonomic nervous system functions. Perceptual functions are sampled and measured by: Archimedes Spiral after-image, autokinetic movement, critical flicker fusion, flutter fusion, kinesthetic figural after-effect, phantom sound, size constancy, tachistoscopically presented stimuli, various types of reaction times, and a visual field test. Cognitive measures include the Benton Visual Retention Test, Gorham Proverbs Test, Wechsler Adult Intelligence Scale, and the Wechsler Memory Test. Personality measures are represented by an attitude scale, Gorham's AAMI Scale, Holtzman's Ink Blot Test, McReynold's Concept Evaluation Technique, Moran's Repetitive Measures, and estimation of time. The following psychomotor measures are being used: dotting, General Aptitude Test Battery, Purdue Pegboard, pursuit rotor, and tapping. Central and autonomic nervous system functions are being measured by cerebral synaptic action potential, electroencephalogram, galvanic skin response, and the mecholyl chloride autonomic reactivity test.

STUDY OF ADJUNCT CHEMOTHERAPY WITH PSYCHIATRIC OUTPATIENTS. The Neuropsychiatric Research Laboratory of the Veterans Benefits Office in Washington, D. C., under the direction of Maurice Lorr, and 24 VA Mental Hygiene Clinics are currently conducting a 12-week double-blind study of the relative effectiveness of five treatment combinations. Approximately 250 male psychiatric outpatients were randomly assigned to five treatment groups and will receive individual psychotherapy throughout the study period. In addition, patients in four of the groups will receive either chlorpromazine, meprobamate, phenobarbital, or placebo. After eight weeks, the study substances will be discontinued to assess any carryover or withdrawal effects during the last four weeks of the study.

The aims and hypotheses of this project are as follows:

1. The project will compare the influence of the five treatments on anxiety and hostility. The hypotheses to be tested are that psychotherapy with either tranquilizer will be more effective treatment in reducing anxiety and hostility than psychotherapy alone, psychotherapy with phenobarbital, or psychotherapy with a placebo.

2. The combined influence of education, occupational level, and annual earnings on the effects of the five treatments will be studied. The hypothesis is that patients with little education, small earnings, and holding unskilled jobs will show the greatest reduction in anxiety and hostility as a result of the addition of tranquilizer drugs to psychotherapy.

3. The project will endeavor to identify some of the attitudinal characteristics of patients predictive of favorable response to the tranquilizing drugs.

4. An effort will be made to identify some of the attitudinal characteristics associated with differential response to placebos.

Analysis of Data

Analysis of multiple covariance of a simple randomized design (Snedecor, 1955) was the statistical procedure used in the first three projects. This method, as applied to these projects, is described in detail by Gordon (1958). The success of random assignment of patients was confirmed by testing for homogeneity of means and variances for all criteria and control variables at the start of the first two projects. Control variables were selected because they were believed to be related to prognosis. Changes in a patient's subsequent status which were associated with these prognostic variables could confound possible changes due to drug effects. Even if these control variables were not related to differential treatment effect, they would still decrease the sensitivity of the analysis by increasing individual subject variability if they were correlated with the criterion to any appreciable degree. The analysis of multiple covariance which was adopted permitted linear adjustments of criterion differences to be made, at each evaluation period, to remove the effect of the control variables, and to adjust for earlier status on the criterion measure. That is, a criterion score at a later period was adjusted, not only for the score on each of the control variables but also for criterion score at an earlier period or periods. The significance (5 per cent level) of the net differences for all treatment contrasts was determined. There were 6 contrasts for Project 1 and 66 for Project 2, on each of 25 criteria for 3 evaluation periods in Project 1 and 9 in Project 2.

In addition to this main analysis of the criteria of therapeutic change, a number of supplementary analyses will be carried out for Project 3 data. The multiple covariance approach, although it adjusts or compensates for the variance attributable to the control variables, does not permit evaluation of the joint effects of treatment and control variables acting together. The use of a factorial design (treatment by levels of control variable), with earlier status on the criterion serving as a covariate, provides not only a test of the main treatment effects and an evaluation of the effect of each control variable, one at a time, but also of their interaction (Hazel, 1946). In the event of significant interactions, the data will be further analyzed to determine whether (a) there is a significant difference among treatments at any single level of control variable and whether (b) there is a significant difference among levels of the control variable within any treatment. Unfortunately, this type of analysis for 26 criteria over three time periods becomes so detailed (858 analyses without analysis of significant interactions) that the cost of computation is prohibitive, even if carried out on an electronic computer. Therefore this supplementary analysis of covariance based on a factorial design will be carried out only for the major criterion, MSRPP total morbidity.

Another supplementary analysis based on a sequential probability ratio test (Wald, 1947) was used in Project 3 for two reasons: to evaluate differential treatment effects quickly, and in terms that might have more clinical significance than mean differences. Even with the aid of a high-speed computer, six months had elapsed after the data for Projects 1 and 2 were gathered before findings became available. Since projects overlap, it was not possible to take advantage of the experience gained from the analysis of the first two projects before starting the third project. The method of sequential analysis enables the investigator to become aware of trends and findings as quickly as consecutively collected data are sufficiently accumulated on channeled graphs.

Of more importance than the need for speedily learning the results in a protracted, large-scale project is the need to consider the clinical significance and meaning of the obtained findings in addition to their statistical significance. The sequential analytic method was selected because it incorporates the concept of clinical significance within a statistical procedure. In Project 3 a clinical decision was made that, if random pairs of patients receiving different drugs were compared, one drug would be designated superior to another only if, in 65 per cent or more of the pairs, greater therapeutic change had occurred for the member of the pair receiving that drug. The percentage actually chosen was a matter of clinical judgment and could vary according to the weight given such considerations as therapeutic effectiveness, toxic and side reactions, speed of patient response, and cost. Although sequential analysis can provide decisions about differential treatments in terms of percentage of patients, it is not offered as the complete or only answer to the problem of clinical significance. This particular method merely serves to remind us that this kind of problem exists and needs to be considered, even in the quantitative analysis of data.

Selected Findings

PROJECTS 1 AND 2. At the end of 12 weeks of treatment in Project 1, on the MSRPP, the most comprehensive of the 25 criteria (a re-

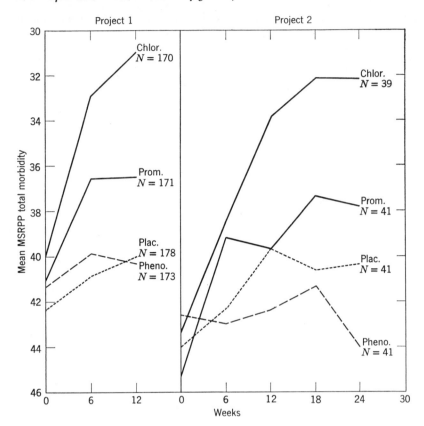

Figure 1. Mean MSRPP total morbidity scores, adjusted for background variables, against time.

duction in the total number and severity of all symptoms) chlorpromazine was more effective than promazine, and both were more effective than either of the control substances. There was no significant difference between phenobarbital and placebo (see Fig. 1).

After 12 and 24 weeks of treatment in Project 2 and with reference to the same criterion, chlorpromazine was again more effective than the other three preparations (see Fig. 1). Again, there was no difference between the control substances. In contrast to Project 1, however, the difference between promazine and placebo was not significant at any point in Project 2. There was no difference be-

tween promazine and phenobarbital at 12 weeks, but promazine was
more effective than phenobarbital at 24 weeks.

The discussion which follows is based on the brief findings presented
above and will deal with population, dosage, criteria measures, and
controls. A complete account of the findings from the two projects
will be found elsewhere (Casey, Bennett, Lindley, Hollister, Gordon,
and Springer, 1960).

Population Sample

An effort was made, in Project 1, to select a restricted, but representative, sample of male schizophrenic patients under treatment in
VA neuropsychiatric hospitals. The sample excluded patients: over
50 years of age; not cooperative enough to take oral medication; with
ground privileges; receiving psychotherapy; with a history of lobotomy,
seizures, or central nervous system disease; or with any active illness
or disease that might have been aggravated by the study medications.
Each hospital was instructed to follow a procedure for randomly
selecting a sample of patients from patients eligible for the project.
Some selective factors and practical considerations may have biased
the sample. For example, only those hospitals participated in the
projects who elected to do so. Hospitals were not selected at random,
since voluntary participation is one of the necessary features of this
cooperative research program. Whether there is a relationship between voluntary participation in a research program and type of
patient hospitalized is not known. This possibly selective factor cannot be eliminated, nor can it be evaluated readily. Even though the
nature of the population from which the sample for Project 1 was
drawn cannot be exactly specified, assignment to treatment groups
was random. This prevented any systematic error in evaluating
treatments.

The population in Project 2 was a nonrandom sample of the population in Project 1, since Project 2 was, in some ways, an extension of
Project 1. The percentage of chronic patients in Project 2, 96.5 per
cent, was significantly greater than the percentage of chronic patients
in Project 1, 81 per cent.

No differences, other than in chronicity, were found with respect to
the control variables at the beginning of treatment, although there
might be a number of other ways in which the two project populations
differed. In examining the effect of chronicity, however, it was noted
that even though patients in both projects were chronic, the dif-

ferences between the promazine group and the two control groups were significant in the less chronic Project 1 population but were not significant in the more chronic Project 2 population. This suggests that chronicity may be a parameter related to drug effects and, as such, it warrants further study.

Dosage

The standard, fixed daily dose of 400 mg. of chlorpromazine or promazine was selected for the two projects to represent an effective therapeutic dose. However, if there had been an absence of significant findings, the explanation might have been offered, from among many possible explanations, that an effective dose had not, in fact, been chosen. It may also be argued that the superiority of chlorpromazine over promazine in these projects is a function of a less-than-effective dose set for promazine. Another difficulty with a single level dose is that it might be effective for many, even for most, but not for all patients. For some patients the standard dose might be too small to produce an observable behavioral response. In other cases the standard dose might be too large, causing an excessive number of patients to develop undesirable side reactions. Even for patients for whom it is effective, the standard dose may not be optimally effective. Still another difficulty with the standard dose is that the needs of the patient may change over the course of a long study, and a fixed dose cannot be adjusted to meet these changes.

Because of dissatisfaction with the standard, fixed, equivalent dosage schedule used in Projects 1 and 2, an attempt was made to devise a dosage schedule for Project 3 which would more nearly supply an optimal therapeutic dose to each patient. During the first month of this three-month study, all patients were given a fixed, standard dose. This was done to ensure that all patients would receive an average therapeutic dose over a reasonable period of time, to get them started. During the second and third months of the study, however, each psychiatrist was asked to make individual adjustments in dosage to elicit the maximum therapeutic response from each patient. A record of the amount of drug used each week and the reason for every change in dosage was kept for each patient.

As an indication of how this fixed-flexible dosage schedule works in practice, information gained from Project 3 will be cited. Preliminary results based on a sequential analysis of MSRPP total morbidity scores indicated that, after one month of treatment, one of the five phenothiazines, drug X, was significantly less effective than the other four. There was no important difference between this drug and phenobarbital. At this point a dilemma existed because drug X, itself, might have been an ineffective preparation or the equivalent dose of this drug might have been inadequate. At the end of three months of treatment, drug X is still significantly less effective than the other four phenothiazines and, again, drug X cannot be differentiated from phenobarbital. Dosage curves based on individualized drug administration during the second and third months help to resolve the dilemma. The curves for the other four phenothiazines remain relatively flat and at essentially the same level as during the first month of fixed dose administration. This is taken to mean that the psychiatrists were apparently satisfied with patient response at this dosage. The dosage curves for drug X and phenobarbital climbed steadily until the end of the study. Apparently, physicians kept increasing the amounts of drug X and phenobarbital in an effort to elicit a maximum therapeutic response. Since drug X was used over a considerable range during the second and third months of the study, the contention is strengthened that drug X, itself, is less effective than the other four phenothiazines studied.

One of the more provocative findings of Project 2 was the inability to differentiate statistically between the mean change of a group treated by chlorpromazine for 24 weeks and the mean changes of eight other groups treated by *any* combination of 12 weeks on either of the two phenothiazines and 12 weeks on either of the two control substances. Each of these eight "combination" groups improved more than a group which received phenobarbital for 24 weeks. A similar finding based on a comparable, independent study of chlorpromazine and placebo has been reported by Good, Sterling, and Holtzman (1958). Although failure to obtain reliable differences in these comparisons cannot, in the logic of statistics, lead to the conclusion that the treatments are equally effective, these findings raise the possibility that intermittent courses of tranquilizers may be as effective as continuous, extended courses with hospitalized, chronic schizophrenic patients.

These findings may be related to a psychological phenomenon in which the individual patient, having been helped to bind his anxiety with chemical assistance, can continue, for a time at least, with his more adequate ego resources without the support of the medication. They may also reflect a social psychological phenomenon in which the staff, being more relaxed, tolerant, and understanding because of the calming effect of tranquilizers on patients, can provide a more therapeutic milieu which in turn supports chronic patients, even during periods when they are off medication. Or, it may be a purely physiological phenomenon in which physiological imbalances have been corrected and systems stay in balance, for a time at least, without chemical support.

Criteria Measures

Product-moment correlations were computed for total MSRPP morbidity and for 11 MSRPP factors on 179 schizophrenic males in Project 1 before and after six weeks' inclusion in a lactose placebo group. The correlation coefficient for total morbidity was .74, which compares favorably with .80 reported by Stilson, Mason, Gynther, and Gertz (1958) for total morbidity using chronic schizophrenic females when three weeks intervened between ratings.

The Manifest Anxiety Scale (Taylor, 1953) was selected so that patients could report their own anxiety levels. However, this paper-and-pencil inventory was apparently too formidable a task for half or more of the patients in the first two projects. When the MAS data were analyzed, there were no significant differences between the treatment groups in the two projects.

Controls

All four projects have been conducted in a double-blind manner (Modell and Houde, 1958). At the conclusion of Project 1, physicians who had known the patients throughout the course of the study were asked to guess which of the four preparations each patient had received. They were able to identify correctly patients who had received chlorpromazine or placebo significantly more often than chance expectation. It is recognized that this was far from an adequate study of the double-blind procedure. Physicians might have been asked weekly to make their predictions and to state the bases for their predictions as, for example, side effects, therapeutic response, unique drug characteristics, patient report, and pure guessing. Nevertheless, it seems likely that the double-blind procedure reduces, rather than prevents, one kind of rater bias.

Studies in Progress

Three more projects are in various stages of data collection and analysis.

Faced with a growing number of chronic schizophrenic patients who have responded in a very limited manner to conventional tranquilizers, VA investigators in Project 4 selected a combination treatment approach which would, we hoped, bind the patient's anxiety while stimulating him to higher levels of activity, alertness, and interest. Pilot studies suggested that long-hospitalized, withdrawn anergic schizophrenics who were being maintained on a phenothiazine derivative might respond more favorably to a combination of dibenzazepine or hydrazide derivatives added to the phenothiazine derivative. This treatment approach was then studied for 20 weeks by treating 540 chronic male schizophrenics hospitalized currently for an average of 8¼ years in 27 NP hospitals with chlorpromazine in combination with one of the following: imipramine, isocarboxazid, trifluoperazine, and an inert substance. The therapeutic efficacy and toxicity of these drug combinations are being analyzed. Marked changes in body weight accompanying treatment and relationships between prognostic variables, patient-staff attitudes toward chemotherapy, and response to treatment are also being studied.

Project 5, a 52 weeks study, will evaluate the response of 420 newly admitted male and female primarily depressed patients from 35 NP and general medical and surgical hospitals to amobarbital-dextroamphetamine, isocarboxazid, imipramine, and an inert substance. The study will investigate the relative therapeutic effectiveness, speed of clinical response, incidence and severity of clinically observed and laboratory determined side effects, spontaneous remission rate, and the relevance of prognostic variables. After 12 weeks of chemotherapy or less, patients will be followed for 40 weeks to study the use of further treatment and their hospital and/or community adjustment. Relationships between patient response, dosage, and various conventional and operationally derived classification categories of depressive reactions and types will be examined. Various parameters of depression will be explored in the search for an objective definition of depression which is related to clinical response and short-term prognosis. Data collection was started in January, 1960, and it will probably take all of 1960 to build up the sample.

Project 6, which was started in September, 1960, is a 24 weeks double-blind, controlled study of the effects of six drugs, randomly assigned to newly admitted schizophrenic male patients. The drugs include chlorpromazine, fluphenazine, reserpine, thioridazine, chlorprothixene, and triflupromazine. Dosage will follow a 4 weeks fixed–20 weeks ad libitum schedule. Therapeutic effects are being evaluated by means of independent interview and ward behavior rating scales to be completed before, and after, 8 and 24 (or less) weeks of treatment. Side effects and untoward behavior are reported weekly. Each patient's ability to function responsibly and effectively as a total, integrated, social person is being evaluated monthly, immediately before and during the study period, by a scale designed to measure the patient's progress through the hospital treatment program. In order to study the relationship between treatment and the ability to think concretely and abstractly, a proverbs test will be administered before and after treatment. Selected items of background information (personal history and illness characteristics related to the process-reactive schizophrenia dimension) are being collected in an attempt to determine which patients do and do not respond to treatment. Significant predictors of patient change from these prognostic variables will also be used for control purposes; i.e., to equate treatment groups for initial differences.

Final Comments

As mentioned in the beginning of this chapter, many clinically oriented investigators, after having administered a tranquilizing drug to a small series of patients in an uncontrolled manner, erred on the side of being overly enthusiastic, extravagant, and premature when they interpreted and reported their findings. On the other hand, methodologically oriented investigators sometimes err on the side of setting up artificial conditions or may be so conservative in their interpretation of results as to be sterile. The practitioner is often exasperated, after laboriously reading through a carefully controlled study which has been analyzed statistically, to learn only that the null hypothesis has or has not been rejected. A statement regarding the likelihood that the findings did not occur as a result of chance is certainly a highly necessary, but not a sufficient statement. Before the practitioner can act intelligently on the basis of findings from controlled studies, he must know whether the statistically significant findings which were obtained were of sufficient magnitude to be of *practical importance in a treatment setting.* A treatment method, such as tranquilizing drug therapy, should be evaluated broadly; on all levels of behavior, in the context of the total treatment process, in comparison to other treatment methods, and in relation to the natural course of deep-seated, long-lasting disease processes.

REFERENCES

Bennett, I. F.   Chemotherapy in psychiatric hospitals: critical review of the literature and research trends.   In V.A. Dep. of Med. and Surg.   *Trans. first Res. Conf. Chemother. in Psychiat.*   Washington, D. C.: 1957, 1, 15–20.

Casey, J. F., Bennett, I. F., Lindley, C. J., Hollister, L. E., Gordon, M. H., and Springer, N. N.   Drug therapy in schizophrenia: A controlled study of the relative effectiveness of chlorpromazine, promazine, phenobarbital, and placebo.   *Amer. Med. Ass. Arch. gen. Psychiat.*, 1960, 2, 210–220.

Delay, J., Deniker, P., and Harl, J. M.   The treatment of excitation and agitation states by a method of medication derived from hibernotherapy.   *Ann. Med. Psychol.*, 1952, 110, 267.

Good, W. W., Sterling, M., and Holtzman, W. H.   Termination of chlorpromazine with schizophrenic patients.   *Amer. J. Psychiat.*, 1958, 115, 443–448.

Gordon, M. H.   Analysis of research data.   In V.A. Dep. Med. Surg., *Trans. Second Res. Conf. Chemother. in Psychiat.*   Washington, D. C.: 1958, 2, 19–22.

Hazel, L. N.   The covariance analysis of multiple classification tables with unequal subclass numbers.   *Biometrics*, 1946, 2, 21–25.

Lorr, M.   Multidimensional scale for rating psychiatric patients, hospital form.   *U.S. Vet. Adm. tech. Bull.*, TB-10-507, Nov. 16, 1953.

Modell, W., and Houde, R. W.   Factors influencing clinical evaluation of drugs with special reference to the double blind technique.   *J. Amer. med. Ass.*, 1958, 167, 2190–2199.

Snedecor, G. W.   *Statistical methods.*   (5th ed.)   Ames, Iowa: Iowa State College Press, 1955, 420–424.

Stilson, D. W., Mason, D. J., Gynther, M. D., and Gertz, B.   An evaluation of the comparability and reliabilities of two behavior rating scales for mental patients.   *J. consult. Psychol.*, 1958, 22, 213–216.

Taylor, Janet A.   A personality scale of manifest anxiety.   *J. abnorm. soc. Psychol.*, 1953, 48, 285–290.

Veterans Administration.   Clinical estimate of psychiatric status.   In V.A. Dep. Med. and Surg., *Trans. Second Res. Conf. Chemother. in Psychiat.*   Washington, D.C.: 1958, 2, 183–185.

Veterans Administration Dept. of Med. and Surgery.   *Trans. first Res. Conf. Chemother. in Psychiat.*   Washington, D.C.: 1957, 1.

Veterans Administration Dept. of Med. and Surgery.   *Trans. second Res. Conf. Chemother. in Psychiat.*   Washington, D.C.: 1958, 2.

Veterans Administration Dept. of Med. and Surgery.   *Trans. third Res. Conf. Chemother. in Psychiat.*   Washington, D.C.: 1959, 3.

Wald, A.   *Sequential analysis.*   New York: Wiley, 1947.

Zubin, J.   Role of prognostic indicators in the evaluation of therapy.   In J. O. Cole and R. W. Gerard (Eds.), *Psychopharmacology: Problems in Evaluation.*   Washington, D.C.: Nat. Acad. Sci., 1959.

Use of behavioral adjustment techniques in evaluating tranquilizers, and the value of drugs in social rehabilitation

The drug evaluation studies described in this chapter are presented in sequence, to enable the reader to share the step-by-step development of the method employed. Behavioral adjustment (rather than change in psychopathological symptoms) was used as the criterion of improvement in all our studies. A cluster-analyzed behavioral adjustment scale, measuring motility, affect, cooperation, and communication was devised from the behavioral data of our first study on reserpine. This MACC Behavioral Adjustment Scale (Ellsworth, 1957) proved useful in studying the *differential* behavioral effects of various drugs in our second study. The scale was so designed that it could be used reliably by any rater in any observational area. A later study (Ellsworth and Clayton, 1959) revealed that behavioral adjustment was significantly related to severity of illness (as measured by length of hospital stay) and adequacy of post-hospital adjustment, while extent of psychopathology was not. Thus the use of behavioral adjustment as the criterion of improvement in mental illness appeared to be more valid and meaningful than the traditional estimate of symptom change.

The Studies

RESERPINE. Twenty-seven chronic schizophrenics, randomly assigned to a drug (13 patients) and a placebo (14 patients) group

The summarized drug research studies were conducted at the Veterans Administration Hospital, Salt Lake City, Utah, between 1953 and 1958.

were chosen to test the effects of reserpine on the behavior of these patients (McDonald, Ellsworth, and Enniss, 1956). Three milligrams of reserpine or a like amount of placebo powder was mixed with the coffee or orange juice of the 13 drug and 14 placebo patients each morning, unknown to the patients. The nurse, the only one who knew which patients received which medication, did not participate in the ratings of these patients. The study extended over a 73-day period.

Predrug behavioral ratings were obtained. The Hospital Adjustment Scale (Ferguson, McReynolds, and Ballachey, 1953) was completed by the aides to describe the patient's ward behavior, and special rating scales were completed by the activity therapists covering his behavior in Occupational Therapy (OT) and Correctional Therapy (CT). At the end of 73 days the behavioral ratings were again completed, and significant changes were recorded for the ward, OT, and CT behavior of the patients. Five experimental patients improved significantly in two of three activity areas; none of the control patients improved significantly in two of three areas. This difference was significant at the .03 level of confidence and reflected a positive change in 38 per cent of the experimental group.

None of the raters was able to identify significantly better than chance patients who had received reserpine. At the end of the study the identity of the drug and placebo patients was divulged. Thirty days later the raters were again asked to rate the patients, all of whom were still receiving either reserpine or placebo. As compared with the baseline, predrug ratings, 100 per cent of the experimental patients "improved" significantly on one of the scales. From this study we obtained evidence that the chronic schizophrenic patient could serve as his own control, and that the "control group" was useful primarily as a guard against rater bias. We also discovered that the best estimate of drug effectiveness occurred when the patient was rated independently by multiple observers who observed the patient's ward and clinic behavior. A patient who showed significant improvement in his OT behavior, for instance, may have done so because of circumstances peculiar to that particular area. Unless this improvement was also observed independently in his CT or ward behavior or both, it was regarded as a change stimulated by local circumstances.

RESERPINE, CHLORPROMAZINE, AND RESERPINE-CHLORPROMAZINE COMBINATION. A ward of 32 regressed chronic schizophrenics were divided randomly into three groups of 10 each: one to receive reserpine, one chlorpromazine, and one a combination of reserpine and chlorpromazine in a ratio of 1:100 mg. (Barrett, Ellsworth, Clark, and Enniss, 1957). Because of the limited number of subjects available for this study, we could not afford the luxury of a control group; we successfully utilized the raters' belief in the existence of the control group to guard against rater bias. A double-blind design was maintained by giving all patients capsules of similar appearance, some of which were inert. Each patient served as his own control, since all patients had been stabilized at their low level of adjustment for several months. The physician adjusted the dosage for each patient until, in his opinion, the maximum benefit had been obtained for each patient. The average amount of reserpine given was 5.9 mg. per day, and the average amount of chlorpromazine was 520 mg. per day.

The belief that there was a control group was instilled in the thinking of the raters by frequent referral to the "control group." This deception proved successful, and the rater bias was well controlled. Actually the reserpine group served as a modified "control" group, since it was already known from the first study what percentage of these chronic patients would be likely to show significant improvement in response to the reserpine alone.[1]

The MACC Behavioral Adjustment Scale (Ellsworth, 1957; see also Chapter 43) was rated by ward aides and by occupational and correctional therapists. The amount of score change necessary to reach the .01 level of significance was calculated by combining rated-rerated baseline scores of the three raters (aide, OT, and CT). Each behavioral adjustment score (motility, affect, cooperation, and communication) and the total adjustment scores were handled in this manner.

Three of ten patients in the reserpine group improved significantly on total adjustment scores. This was slightly below the percentage who improved significantly in the first reserpine study, demonstrating that rater enthusiasm and bias were well controlled with the rater's belief of the existence of a control group. Five of 10 patients on chlorpromazine improved significantly, and seven of ten on reserpine-chlorpromazine improved significantly in total adjustment scores after three months of medication.

An analysis of covariance revealed that reserpine increased motility significantly as compared with chlorpromazine; and that the reserpine-

[1] The use of another tranquilizing drug the effects of which are known actually results in a better "control group" than use of a placebo. If a placebo control group is used, the double-blind method may be rendered ineffective, since raters are often able to identify which patients are on the "real stuff."

chlorpromazine combination significantly improved the communication scores as compared with reserpine alone.

PREDICTION OF RESPONSE TO DRUG THERAPY. An extension of the second study (Ellsworth and Clark, 1957) included an analysis of predrug palmar sweat patterns (Mowrer, 1953) and later response to medication. The variability of successive palmar sweat print readings was found to be highly correlated with the amount of behavioral improvement, as measured by the MACC Behavioral Adjustment Scores (Ellsworth and Clark, 1957) for both the chlorpromazine and reserpine groups. The "variably anxious" schizophrenic (high variability score) showed much more improvement in response to reserpine and chlorpromazine alone (more improvement on chlorpromazine than on reserpine) than did the non-variable schizophrenic. The combination of reserpine and chlorpromazine was more effective than either drug alone with the non-variable schizophrenic. Chlorpromazine alone thus appeared to be most effective with the variably anxious schizophrenic, reserpine-chlorpromazine combination with the non-variable (flattened?) schizophrenic.

TREATMENT OF DRUG-RESISTANT CHRONIC SCHIZOPHRENICS. At the time the studies on reserpine and chlorpromazine were completed, the supply of chronic schizophrenics not treated by drugs had been exhausted (Mead, Ellsworth and Grimmett, 1958). A group of patients who had shown no response to the previous medication trials was left, however. These 32 patients were gathered and stabilized without drug, in a separate ward.

Since there was some evidence in the last study that the "anxious" (sweat-variable) schizophrenic responded best to chlorpromazine, a search was undertaken for an agent to induce anxiety and sweat variability. It was hypothesized that the effect of chlorpromazine could be enhanced if such an agent was used before chlorpromazine treatment. Ephedrine was selected, after a series of clinical trials, as the agent best suited to produce the desired effect.

In a double-blind study (all capsules identical in appearance, raters unaware of the identity of the various groups) patients were matched on palmar sweat data in groups of three, and randomly assigned to one of three groups. One group received chlorpromazine (400 mg. per day); one group received ephedrine alone for three weeks, followed by a chlorpromazine-ephedrine combination (400:300 mg. per day) for 12 weeks; and the third group received ephedrine

(200 mg. per day) alone for 15 weeks, and then chlorpromazine (400 mg. per day) alone for 12 weeks.[2]

Each patient was rated on the MACC Behavioral Adjustment Scale before, during, and at the end of the study and received a composite score from the ratings of an aide, the OT therapist, and the CT therapist. The behavioral rating data revealed that both groups treated with ephedrine prior to chlorpromazine improved significantly in MACC Scale total adjustment scores while the group treated with chlorpromazine alone did not. In a post-experimental study the chlorpromazine patients received the combination of ephedrine and chlorpromazine. It was determined that the combination had little effect, and that the prior use of ephedrine alone appeared to give the best results.

It would appear that the induction of "tension" prior to chlorpromazine treatment in the drug-resistive chronic schizophrenic may result in increased response to chlorpromazine. Not all patients responded to the ephedrine in the expected manner, and it was felt that, if a more effective tension-producing agent could be found, the treatment of these patients with chlorpromazine would be considerably improved.

Two additional drug studies, one on methylphenidate (Clark, Ellsworth, Barrett, Thurman, and Holland, 1956) and an unpublished one on azacyclonol were completed. Both studies failed to confirm the premature claims made for these drugs and demonstrated the danger of uncontrolled clinical studies so common during the introductory phases of most psychoactive drugs.

Tranquilizers and Social Rehabilitation

New tranquilizers, at first heralded by poorly controlled clinical studies and premature enthusiasm, are later generally subjected to some carefully designed and controlled studies. Some of these drugs do prove to be potent in modifying the behavior and symptoms of the psychotic hospitalized patient to a "statistically" significant degree. The question remains, however, whether the widespread introduction of these drugs has resulted in any changes in practical aspects of the hospitalized psychiatric patient's adjustment, namely, his chances to

[2] In this study the chlorpromazine group served as the "control group" since it was already known that these patients would not improve significantly on chlorpromazine alone.

leave the hospital sooner or his ability to remain in the community after discharge.

In many poorly staffed state hospitals, a drop of census after the introduction of tranquilizers, in spite of increased admissions, suggests strongly that these drugs are indeed responsible, either directly or indirectly (because of such factors as increased staff interest) for these changes. Some well-staffed hospitals were reporting excellent discharge rates before the advent of tranquilizers. In the Veterans Administration Hospital at Salt Lake City, Utah, for instance, we found that, prior to the use of tranquilizers, 82 per cent of psychotic admissions had been discharged within one year from the time of admission, 94 per cent within two years, and only 1 per cent remained at the end of four years (these data are based on 200 successive psychotic admissions, 1953–1954). The return rate to that hospital was 26.3 per cent within one year after discharge.

During 1955 the tranquilizers, primarily chlorpromazine, began to be used with the psychotic patients. By late 1956, 89 per cent of all psychotics were receiving tranquilizers from the time of admission to the time of discharge. Did this widespread use of drugs result in increased discharge rates and, more important, decreased return rate? A study was undertaken to determine this (Ellsworth and Clayton, 1960).

Two hundred successive psychotic patients admitted between July 1, 1953, and July 1, 1954 (in the predrug era), and 200 successive psychotic patients admitted between July 1, 1956, and April 29, 1957 (drug era), were studied. The first question which had to be answered was whether we were dealing with identical populations; and, if not, were the variables by which they differed related to length of hospitalization, rate of return, or both. An examination of the data on all 400 psychotics revealed that two variables (marital status and state of residence) were related to length of hospital stay. No variable (including length of illness) was found, however, which was related to the return of the patient to the hospital. When the patients were matched on marital status and state of residence for both the predrug (134 patients) and drug (134 patients) eras, it was found that there were no statistically significant differences in either the length of hospitalization or the return rate of the two groups.

The directions of these non-significant differences were interesting; the psychotic patients treated in the drug era left the hospital slightly sooner than those treated in the predrug era (median difference between 6 and 20 days) but tended to return more rapidly than the predrug patients (31.3 per cent of the drug patients and 25.3 per cent of the predrug patients returned within one year). This suggests strongly that the heavy utilization of tranquilizers in this well-staffed hospital was without significance in the overall adjustment of the newly admitted psychotic patient.

Why were these drugs relied on so heavily in the hospital? The answer, of course, is that the physicians were convinced of their usefulness. Electroshock was used less and the wards were quieter. Aside from these superficial results, however, the conviction remained that medication was largely responsible for the change in a newly admitted patient's behavior. The physicians, on ward rounds, would often observe a marked reduction in the patient's confusion, agitation, or other symptoms a few days after starting him on medication. Aside from the patient's receiving medication, many other concomitant events were also taking place: the patient's removal from the outside stress, his forming new interpersonal relationships with activity therapists, aides, and other patients; and his meeting with a different understanding and expectation regarding his condition than that which he met with outside the hospital. Which of these factors was responsible for the change which the ward physician observed on ward rounds? Any or all might be, but often only the drug gets credit.

At first blush, the results of this study may seem to indicate that the conclusions of many carefully controlled drug studies are invalid with respect to the therapeutic effect of tranquilizers. It must be remembered that statistically significant improvement is not necessarily synonymous with a marked clinically improved state in which the patient is ready for discharge. Our experience with the effects of tranquilizers on chronic schizophrenics suggests that these drugs do modify behavior to a statistically significant degree. Few of these chronic patients, however, were ready for discharge at the end of any drug study. The stimulus effect of the drug in modifying patient behavior also stimulated the personnel to take an active interest in the improved patient after the drug study was over. Discharge usually came about after several weeks or months of interaction between patient and staff. Although our discharge rate of the chronic schizophrenic patient increased after the introduction of tranquilizers (Ellsworth, Mead, and Clayton, 1958), this increased discharge rate was not found to result from the effects of the drug alone. The drugs appeared to stimulate the beginning of a long and complex cycle of retraining for the chronic patient in social skills, responsibility, work habits, and subsequent discharge. The drugs themselves, then, are definitely limited in their effects on patient rehabilitation. The vast majority of acute patients in a well-staffed hospital get better without them. The chronic patient gets out only after additional extensive social rehabilitation.

The evaluation of the overall effects of these tranquilizers, then, relies on carefully designed comprehensive research, preferably at the early stages of the introduction of a new compound. We are too sophisticated in experimental design to foster the invalid overenthusiasm which is generated by, and always follows, poorly designed drug research. The evaluation of a particular drug must be based on a design which includes objective measurement of important criteria of improvement, double-blind techniques, and the use of control groups, especially in studies with acute psychotics. It should also attempt to explore the part these drugs play in the patient's overall rehabilitation, discharge, and adjustment after discharge.

R E F E R E N C E S

Barrett, W. W., Ellsworth, R. B., Clark, L. D., and Ennis, June. Study of the differential behavioral effects of Reserpine, Chlorpromazine, and a combination of these drugs in chronic schizophrenic patients. *Dis. nerv. Sys.*, 1957, 18, 1–7.

Clark, L. D., Ellsworth, R. B., Barrett, W. W., Thurman, A. C., and Holland, W. Study of the Behavioral effects of Ritalin. *Dis. nerv. Sys.*, 1956, 17, 3–7.

Ellsworth, R. B. MACC Behavioral Adjustment Scale. Los Angeles, Calif.: Western Psychological Services, 1957.

Ellsworth, R. B., and Clark, L. D. Prediction of the response of chronic schizophrenics to drug therapy: a preliminary report on the relationship between palmar sweat and the behavioral effects of tranquilizing drugs. *J. clin. Psychol.*, 1957, 13, 59–61.

Ellsworth, R. B., and Clayton, W. H. Measurement of improvement in mental illness. *J. consult. Psychol.*, 1959, 23, 15–20.

Ellsworth, R. B., and Clayton, W. H. The effects of chemotherapy on length of stay and rate of return for psychiatrically hospitalized patients. *J. consult. Psychol.*, 1960, 24, 50–53.

Ellsworth, R. B., Mead, B. T., and Clayton, W. H. The rehabilitation and disposition of chronically hospitalized schizophrenic patients. *Ment. Hyg.*, 1958, 42, 343–348.

Ferguson, J. T., McReynolds, P., and Ballachey, E. *Hospital Adjustment Scale*. Palo Alto, Calif.: Stanford Univer. Press.

McDonald, R. E., Ellsworth, R. B., and Enniss, June. Behavioral changes of chronic schizophrenics in response to Reserpine. *Arch. Neurol. Psychiat.*, 1956, 75, 575–578.

Mead, B. T., Ellsworth, R. B., and Grimmett, J. O. The treatment of drug-resistive chronic schizophrenics. *J. nerv. ment. Dis.*, 1958, 127, 351–358.

Mowrer, O. H. *Psychotherapy, theory and research*. New York: Ronald, 1953.

Methods for the objective study
of drug effects on group functioning

This chapter is addressed to the reader who has been concerned with the effects of drugs on relatively isolated individuals and is now interested in the feasibility and potential outcome of drug research on subjects in small, face-to-face groups. Because little of such research has been done as yet, significant though the field may be, we must deal chiefly with potential methods rather than with completed drug studies. The first section reviews traditional methods for study of social behavior in group settings, methods which have had some aspects of their reliability and validity demonstrated in a variety of research studies. In the second section empirical relations in the domain of individual social behavior are considered, and in the last section relations based on group characteristics are discussed.

Studies of Social Behavior
in Groups

To ask whether a specific drug influences the observable social behavior of an individual in a social situation is a reasonable question which, nevertheless, often yields unsatisfactory answers. Fiske, in his discussion of situational tests in Chapter 19, explains such failures by the fact that the drug may have lesser influence than at least ten other sources of variance, which may be unmeasured, uncontrolled, uncon-

Decision to prepare this chapter was based, in part, on its relevance to the author's research project on mood and attitude change, which is supported by ONR under Contract Nonr-668(12), Project No. NR 171-342, between the University of Rochester and the Office of Naval Research.

trollable, and/or interactive.   Similar reasons severely restrict the usefulness of observations of changes in social behavior following medication in academic, custodial, familial, therapeutic, work, and other situations, whether studied inside or outside the laboratory.   Such justifiable strictures can be fatal to one's interest in assessing the overall social-behavioral effects of mild drugs.   Perhaps such effects can be more efficiently studied by methods to be described later.   But there are and will be powerful new drugs, like lysergic acid diethylamide (LSD), which have such profound effects that thorough and prompt exploratory study of their effects on a wide spectrum of social behavior is justified.

Reliable, if time-consuming and difficult, methods for investigating a wide range of social behavior are readily available: (a) some based on direct controlled observation with immediate coding or rating by the observer, (b) some on retrospective or somewhat delayed rating of longer sequences of behavior by the observer or subject, and (c) others based on analysis of permanent sound, photographic, or transcribed records.

DIRECT CONTROLLED OBSERVATION.   In the 1920's child psychologists at Minnesota, Iowa, Columbia, and Toronto developed a method called time-sampling (Arrington, 1943) for obtaining through observation of the child (or adult) in his natural environment a quantitative estimate of different aspects or categories of his behavior.   Meticulous attempts were made, particularly by Thomas (1929; Thomas, Loomis, and Arrington, 1933), to establish reliable procedures for such observations, but experimentally oriented workers like Goodenough (1936), who had published one of the earliest papers in the area (1928), soon decreased their interest because of the degree to which the method permitted and perhaps even encouraged absence of manipulative control over the situation in which the behavior occurred.   The history of later observational studies of individual social behavior indicates that significant control of the situation is sometimes possible (Sears, 1942; Bishop, 1951), while the Barker-Wright (1951) study of the ecology of behavior is a fairly recent and important example of observation of behavior in a social situation almost devoid of experimental intervention.

In the meantime Chapple (1940), Lewin, Lippitt, and White (1939), Bales (1951), Nowlis (1941a, b), and others were studying *interaction,* which is action and reaction in a sequence involving at least two individuals, i.e., a group.   Observation now had to focus on two or more individuals simultaneously or in quick succession, and recording had to permit subsequent analysis of the influence of each member's behavior on that of others. Familiar problems of experimental control again arose, for, as in Gold and Hoyle's theory of continual creation of the universe, there is a sense in which the interaction of the group is continually created by a series of individual acts, each with its own unique remote and multiple determination, leaving the researcher almost helpless with respect to many of the controls he would like to establish over the moment-to-moment input into the social system. But, as will be shown in the last section of this chapter, some of the major sources of variance can be controlled. Furthermore, the subjects themselves have been confronted throughout life with these spontaneities of social interaction and have, as Chapple, for example, finds, learned patterns of reaction which tend to override inconsistencies in a partner.

Another difficulty which the method of controlled observation has partially solved resides in the making of a judgment of congruence with respect to social behavior. The basic datum in science involves a judgment of agreement, consistency, or correspondence. Instrumentation frequently involves setting up situations in which a physical attribute of a phenomenon can be judged as to how congruent it is with physical points on a contiguous scale, or dial. In social psychology such instrumental convenience is often impossible, and the observer is required to make a judgment of congruence between (a) observed social behavior and (b) a carefully defined category which he has trained himself to understand and to apply to the perceptual data available to him as he observes the subject. When he judges that congruence exists between the observed behavior and one of the remembered categories he records the judgment. By this method the human observer is a scanning and recording instrument as well as the judge of congruence. Such a scheme does not necessarily violate the rules of scientific evidence, but it does make the task of the observer and of the coordinator of observers unusually difficult. Nevertheless, despite the rapidity, intangibility, and complexity of social interaction, there can be little doubt that useful levels of observer reliability may be attained through careful definition of selected categories and through training in perceptual and recording skills. "Controlled" observation refers to the use of trained observers, carefully defined categories, and standardized techniques of scanning, timing, and recording.

Reviews and discussions of observational methods are abundant (Heyns and Zander, 1953; Peak, 1953). Heyns and Lippitt (1954) contribute an excellent review of 13 different observational systems which, although many are already over ten years old, can still be used for a variety of purposes. The abecedarian can study these for guidance in the essential preliminary practice in definition of categories, observation of subjects, recording of judgments, and statistical analysis of observational data. The 13 systems differ not only in the technical details of observing and recording but also in the aspects of social interaction selected for study.

As example, the sparsest method is that of Chapple (1949), which simply requires the observer to record on a chronograph tape the beginning and termination of each unit action of each subject observed. In a dyadic conversation or interview, chiefly involving verbal communication, the observer's task is as simple as any now available and the data can later be combined with some confidence into a variety of significant composite measures. Saslow and his colleagues (Matarazzo, Saslow, and Guze, 1956) have found the interaction chronograph useful in the study of interaction in therapeutic and other interviews, as has Goldman-Eisler (1956), who has gone on to refine her recordings to the point of getting respiration rate and output of speech per breath, with additional measures of content.

By contrast, another widely used method, Bales' category system, is intriguingly complex. The categories were worked out not only on the basis of extensive observations of small groups in various kinds of interaction but also on the basis of a theory about the major dimensions of interaction which can be identified when a group forms and attempts to select and solve a problem. A popular introductory manual was published by Bales in 1951 and a description of the requirements of a group laboratory was presented later (Bales and Flanders, 1954). With the use of comparable facilities, trained observers can be expected to yield reliable records for all the individuals in groups ranging in size from two to at least ten.

Of the inclusive systems appearing since the Heyns-Lippitt review, one of the most interesting is that of Ruesch (1957). Although the investigator will have to work out his own practical applications of what is essentially a heuristic scheme, Ruesch provides an abundance of new discriminations and suggestions which may be essential for drug research on groups. Birdwhistell (1952b) provides a manual (1952a) for those who would study non-verbal communication, expressive behavior, or kinesics—"an annotation system for analysis of body motion and gesture." While it is the most difficult system of all to learn to use, it is also the one which might prove most sensitive in detecting a variety of drug effects.

Interviewing is a special kind of interaction between investigator and subject. Hyman (1954), Kahn and Cannell (1957), Kinsey, Pomeroy, and Martin (1948, Ch. 2), and Maccoby and Maccoby (1954) are standard sources.

RATINGS. While methods of controlled observation often yield frequency data based on recorded judgments of presence or absence of specified behavior within specified temporal intervals, they may also yield ratings based on impressions of intensity or amplitude or persistence of specific behavior. Such ratings may be made not only simultaneously with the observations of the behavior but also retrospectively and thus, in contrast to frequency data, may be made not only by the observer but also by the subjects themselves. The chief advantage of ratings compared with frequency recordings for the observer is that the former may permit him to contemplate larger and longer units of behavior and also to record his impressions of the relative significance of a dramatic act which occurred infrequently as compared with seemingly inconsequential acts which occurred repeatedly. Carter, Haythorn, Meirowitz, and Lanzetta (1951) have compared the results of categorizations and ratings in the observation of small groups.

A review of the kinds of social behavior that have been rated is provided by way of the index entry "Ratings, impressions and judgments" in the useful volume by Hare, Borgatta, and Bales (1955), listing over 200 relevant studies. Technical problems of design of rating scales are discussed by Newman and Jones (1946), Cronbach (1949), and Guilford (1954).

The ratings and rankings of acquaintances on the basis of interpersonal attraction by means of sociometric techniques are reviewed by Lindzey and Borgatta (Lindzey, 1954). Gardiner and Thompson (1956) have recently developed a sociometric rating method which can be used even by individuals with limited capacities (Davol, 1957). Tagiuri and Bruner (Tagiuri and Petrullo, 1958) have added an important component to sociometric ratings by requiring the subject not only to judge his partners but also to judge his partners' judgments of him and of others, a method called relational analysis.

ANALYSIS OF PERMANENT RECORDS. With increase in funds for research and greater availability of efficient cinema cameras and sound recorders, tape and film are sometimes used for permanent recording of social interaction. This does not eliminate the human observer, since sooner or later the permanent record has to be translated selectively into quantified data by means essentially similar to those used in direct observation. The risk of missing events which may eventually prove of significance is reduced, but the normal tedium and encumbrances of observation and judgment usually are not reduced through delayed transfer to an artificial situation and may indeed be increased to overwhelming and impractical levels when the records have been ground out indiscriminately.

The one somewhat unique general method applicable to transcribed records is that of content analysis, described fully by Berelson (1952) and by Auld and Murray (1955). Some of the solutions available for categorizing and cross-indexing paragraphs of typed material and rating them according to carefully defined scales are discussed by Nowlis (1952), Sears, Whiting, Nowlis, and Sears (1953), and Whiting and Child (1953).

Studies of the Psychological Antecedents of Social Behavior of the Individual

The methods in the preceding section should help the reader in exploratory tests of the *general* effects of a powerful drug on observable social behavior. Now we ask whether the drug influences the relation between two variables one of which is a variable in the social behavior of an individual. We enter the realm of multivariate analysis, discussed in its full complexity by Cattell in his recent book (1957), and selectively in Chapter 39 of this volume. For present purposes, let us look at the simplest model, involving a system of relations among only three variables, such that there is a relationship between variables a and s when variable d is absent, but a different relationship or no relationship when d is present. As Lazarsfeld (1959) points out in a lucid discussion of this model, the relation between a and s is here conditional on a third factor, d. Let variable a be an antecedent factor, variable s a social-behavioral factor, and variable d a drug factor. The stage is thus set for an interesting search of the social psychological literature for relations which might be modified by drugs. But first we must note that in the domain of non-social animal behavior the rapid adoption of Skinnerian operant behavior procedures for drug research is based on the usefulness of such a model (Dews, 1956). Through reinforcement schedules, the behavior of the animal is put under the control of known antecedents. Drugs are then found to influence these relations, with consequent increase in understanding of both the drug and the psychological relation.

In the domain of individual behavior that is both human and social, antecedent-consequent relationships that have been identified as a result of experimental studies can be classified according to areas of theoretical interest, theory being most often focused on the characteristics of the psychological process intervening between antecedent and consequent. Drug researchers who wish to do more than go on fishing expeditions with the methods described in the preceding section will therefore have to become acquainted with psychological theories about individual social behavior. Current statements of such theories, together with relevant empirical work, can be found in the following studies and reviews: expectancy (Stogdill, 1959); comparison level (Thibaut and Kelley, 1959); set (Christie, Havel, and Seidenberg, 1958, Jones and Thibaut, 1958); frame-of-reference (Sherif and Sherif, 1956); adaption level (Helson, 1959); interpersonal attraction (Newcomb, 1956); cognitive balance (Heider, 1958); cognitive structure (Peak, 1958; Rosenberg, 1956); cognitive dissonance (Festinger, 1957); Lewinian theory (Cartwright, 1959); personal construct (Kelly, 1955); connotative meaning (Osgood, Suci, and Tannenbaum, 1957); person perception (Tagiuri and Petrullo, 1958); mood (Nowlis, 1958); trust and suspicion (Deutsch, 1957); approach-avoidance gradient (Janis, 1958); reaction potential (Cervin, 1957); hypothetical mediating process (Cofer, 1958); liberalized S-R theory (Miller, 1959); reinforcement (Verplanck, 1956; Estes, 1957; Lanzetta and Kanareff, 1959); purposive behavior (Tolman, 1959); choice behavior (Luce, 1959).

In an excellent article on the interaction between model and method in contemporary social psychology, Guetzkow (1958) points out that in this area, at least, model has had more influence on method than method has had on model. In the area of social influence processes, for example, neither the clear and direct methods of Hovland and others (1953, 1957) nor the elaborate and subtle methods of Festinger (1957) are fully comprehensible without knowledge of the theoretical analyses that instigated their studies.

A knowledge of psychological theories about social behavior and of the empirical relationships on which these theories are based is necessary for two reasons: first, to suggest relationships which may be conditional on drug effects; second, to provide an understanding of the special methods which may have been developed just to test a specific theory.

Studies of Group
Functional Characteristics

In the domain of group functioning we find a substantial and rapidly growing body of empirical relations many of which might be conditional with respect to drug action.   Furthermore, whereas many of the recent reports referred to in the preceding section have yet to be harvested by reviewers in integrating reports, there are excellent and up-to-date reviews of the main findings from the study of groups (Bales, Hare, and Borgatta, 1957; Cartright and Zander, 1953; Lindzey, 1954).   Fairly specific suggestions for promising problems involving drugs are readily formulated.

Before undertaking such formulation, it may be helpful to point to a major difference between contemporary models of the individual and those of the group.   The reader is familiar with a general behavioral model of the individual, used by psychologists of diverse interests, which presents a system with objectively observable inputs and outputs and an intervening black box which cannot be opened for full inspection before some future neurophysiological Christmas Day. Most experimental psychologists accept the thesis that it must be possible, in principle, to predict future behavior (output) on the basis of sufficient information about objectively defined environmental (input), physiological, and behavioral variables (Bergmann, 1956).   Insufficient knowledge about the physiological variables has thus far prevented their extensive use in such lawful predictions.   Unobservable mediating constructs, such as intervening variables and hypothetical constructs, have been used instead, with debatable success.   An analogous general model of a small group as a social system has received study.   One of its forms, based on the input-output systems used by economists (Leontief, 1953; March and Simon, 1958) in analyzing firms and industries, presents a system with input variables, mediating and transactional processes, and output variables.   One advantage of this model, in comparison with the individual "black box" model, is that it permits a larger degree of *direct inspection* of its mediating processes, i.e., of the social interactions and the modifications in the characteristics of individual members which accompany or determine a change in the social system from one state to another.   To its disadvantage, however, there is little agreement on which variables in the model are to be classified as input, output, or mediating, because, once the social interaction begins, mediating processes and outcomes provide new input for the system by way of many feedback mechanisms. Usually classed as input variables are such factors as: (a) group size, (b) communication network, (c) nature of task, (d) personal and social characteristics of the members, (e) initial expectancies of the members with respect to each other, the group, the group task, and the goals of the group, and (f) the setting in which the group is observed (Bales, Hare, and Borgatta, 1957). Output variables include such group characteristics as (a) cohesiveness, (b) productivity, (c) morale, and (d) integration (Stogdill, 1959). Mediating factors include the social interaction and the observable or measurable changes in the perceptions, expectancies, statuses, dispositions and satisfactions of the individual members. The best discussions of the interrelations of these variables that I have encountered are, in order of appearance, those of Kelley and Thibaut (1954), Bales, Hare, and Borgatta (1957), Roby and Lanzetta (1958), Stogdill (1959), Bales (1959), and Thibaut and Kelley (1959).

In the literature are many limited relations between input and output factors, between input and mediating factors, and between mediating and output factors. In accordance with the model developed in the last section, let us see whether there are any relations which might be expected to be modified by, or conditional with respect to drugs. Following the example of Bales, Hare, and Borgatta (1957) and utilizing their discussion as well as those of Kelley-Thibaut and Stogdill, let us review the empirical evidence relating four input variables (group size, communication network, nature of task, personality of members) to mediating and/or output variables.

GROUP SIZE. As Bales, Hare, and Borgatta (1957) point out, this variable has three interdependent aspects: the simple quantitative one related to number of members, a dichotomous one based on whether the group is odd- or even-numbered, and a complex quantitative one based on the number of possible relationships in the group by pairs and larger subgroups, a quantity which increases faster than does number of persons. Increase in number of persons in a small face-to-face group affects each member by (a) decreasing the relative time he has for expressing himself to the group and, more particularly, to each member in the group; (b) increasing the difficulty of attending to, comprehending, remembering, and exploring the viewpoint of every other member. (These two consequences make for an increase in feelings of threat and frustration.) Increase in group size also (c) increases the difficulty in coordinating the activities and contributions of members and subgroups and (d) increases the amount and range of potentially available information, judgments, values, experience, skills, abilities, and power.

These direct consequences of increase in group size have many effects on group process and structure, such as: overall average decrease in effectiveness of individual performance, increased readiness to perceive others as members of subgroups rather than as persons, probable emergence of a leader and greater tolerance of leader-centered direction of activities, emergence of spokesmen for minority subgroups, changes in requirements for selection, a more formal procedure and more mechanical way of introducing information, more direct attempts at social control but greater tolerance of unresolved differences, less involvement in the group task and more frequent joking and laughter. Greater success at some tasks results from the additive nature of resources each member brings to the group, but these increments are accompanied by the constricting phenomena listed above. On the other hand, groups of less than five may produce other kinds of frustration due partly to the odd-even dichotomy in group size. There are strong strains toward superficial agreement in the dyad, with problems involving 2-to-1 coalitions in the triad, and problems of deadlocked dyads in the four-man groups. Optimal satisfaction may be reported when the work-oriented group includes five members.

In face-to-face groups a significant portion of the known mediating and output variables which vary with change in group size can be described in quantitative form by means of the twelve categories of the Bales method of interaction process analysis, with specification of the source and target of each act. Supplemental ratings of selected characteristics of the group and its members can be obtained from subjects and observers at the end of each session. Guetzkow and Bowes (1954) and Kennedy (1955) have been exploring the problems of describing and analyzing social interaction in large groups and subgroups over many hours, in simulated "quasi-companies" with sales and production subgroups, and in simulated information-processing organizations.

Certainly some of the basic studies in this area should be replicated with drugs as additional input variables. A good basic study on size of group is that of Bales and Borgatta (1955), requiring a group laboratory, 108 subjects in 24 groups, each group observed in four 40-minute sessions by at least two investigators trained in the Bales observation system, using discussion tasks and statistical procedures readily available from the authors. A replicative study on group size would disclose a variety of effects for further investigation with drugs. For example, the increase in feelings of threat and frustration with increase in group size would certainly be affected in a variety of ways by different drugs. The decrease in relative time for self-expression with increase in group size would have one kind of consequence with a drug which instigated simultaneous talking by several subjects and other consequences with a drug which greatly decreased verbal output. The relation between group size and relative forcefulness of an emergent leader might be drastically modified by tranquilizers, on the one hand, and stimulants on the other.

THE COMMUNICATION NETWORK. This complex variable refers to the network of links among individual members of a group when communication is limited to such channels as telephone circuits or written messages relayed by the experimenter. By metaphoric extension, the variable also refers to the behaviorally restricted patterns of communication which develop in groups, not limited to telephone or written messages, on the basis of such factors as interpersonal attraction, propinquity, and degree of deviation from group norms (Riley and Riley, 1959). Similarly, the formal structure of a large organization can be analyzed in terms of the channels along which information flows. Only physically restricted networks will be discussed here.

Whereas with increase in group size the mediation processes which affect output occur more or less spontaneously, some of these processes can be controlled by the experimenter in the design of networks. Quality of the message can be varied by means of variations in signal-to-noise ratio. Another aspect of interaction can be controlled by making a circuit one-way or two-way, i.e., with or without feedback for the sender from the receiver, and with or without reciprocity of sending and receiving roles. A great range of differences among networks and among the individual positions in a network can be produced by altering the number and distribution of the links in the patterned network. Topographical description of these patterns sometimes refers to such terms as the "chain," "wheel," "star," "circle," "slash," and "concom." Quantification of the patterns is possible by means of a transmittance matrix (Roby and Lanzetta, 1958), linear graph analysis (Cartright and Harary, 1956), or by measures of the centrality (Leavitt, 1959) or independence (Shaw, 1954) of each of the stations. The latter measures are based on the total number of stations an individual has to depend on to communicate to all other individuals, on the number of channels directly available to him, and on the number of stations for which he is a relayer of information, taking into account the total number of links in the network. As with variation in group size, variation of the network produces measurable changes in the opportunities the individual has for expressing himself and for being perceived by others, in the difficulty he has in understanding and relating to all other members, and in the pooling of resources, with measurable consequences for individual and group satisfaction, efficiency, leadership, perception of role, and adaptability to new problems.

Experiments varying restricted communication networks have also tended to restrict arbitrarily the possible content of communication, thus making a Bales-type recording system inappropriate. But all the usual ratings with respect to group, self, and fellow-member characteristics can be made at the end of the session. A good deal of attention has been given to the development of tasks suitable for such networks and to the identification of task dimensions. An excellent example is the Leavitt symbol task (1951), one form of which presents to each of a variable number of members in the network a variable number of different sets of symbols, the task being to identify that one symbol presented to all members.

Selection of a reference experiment for replication will again depend on the substantive research problem the researcher has selected. If group performance is the interest, the Heise-Miller study (1951) is simple and precise and involves a procedure and method which could easily be adapted to drug research. If measures of individual and group satisfaction and of recognition as leader are the interest, the work of Shaw (1954) is relevant. Three possible patterns of drug distribution would be of interest: (a) the same dosage of the same drug to all members, with tests for interaction between network characteristics and drug; (b) the same drug to members at selected levels of an input variable like centrality in the same network, with tests for interaction between station characteristic and drug; and (c) different drugs to different stations (which is intriguing but would be difficult to evaluate).

TYPE OF TASK. Type of task is important to the drug researcher in at least a cautionary way since three decades of social psychological studies on different tasks yield little generalization from task to task. One solution to this embarrassing block on the road to a general experimental social science is to use only tasks that are carefully designed to help test a specific theory, as Festinger (1957) does. Another possible solution is to develop a model to isolate and define important characteristics of certain tasks. Roby and Lanzetta (1958), like Glazer (1958), have developed such a model for military group tasks. Their paradigm yields a four-stage cycle of task events: (a) task input variables, such as instructions, information, and demands coming from the surrounding environment; (b) group input activities, such as responses to incoming information and distribution of this information; (c) group output activities, such as decisions and implementations; and (d) task output variables, such as performances and the intended and unintended consequences of performance on the surrounding environment. Each of these classes of variables is then described according to three types of objective property: their descriptive aspects, distribution, and functional behavior. Similarly, Lorge, Fox, Davitz, and Brenner (1958) discuss the relation of nature of task to indices of judgment, learning, social facilitation, problem solving, memory, and productivity. Other reviews of the area are found in Ray (1955) and in Duncan (1959).

PERSONALITY CHARACTERISTICS OF THE MEMBERS. Personality assessment of an individual which is carried out by studying him in various social situations is discussed by Fiske in Chapter 19. In this section we are concerned with preassessed personality characteristics as input for the social interaction of the group. Bales, Hare, and Borgatta (1957) find three different approaches: preassessment on the basis of a personality test, of individual interaction characteristics in other groups, and of a composite index based on a range of information about the subject. Their model suggests that the immediate consequence of personality characteristics is in terms of the quality and amount of interaction, and their own research demonstrates many such effects as measured by interaction process analysis.

Cattell, who with Saunders and Stice (1953), did the earliest major work in this area, thoroughly discusses his method (1957). Personality traits are assessed by means of the Cattell 16 PF test. Group characteristics are independently identified through observational and rating data obtained from observers and subjects. In the early study Cattell and his associates found certain personality traits in which average of scores for group members was associated with specific group characteristics, but, for other traits, variance of scores was associated with group characteristics, suggesting a compatibility principle.   A recent book by Schutz (1958) is the latest important contribution to the problem of combining members according to optimal compatibility.   Starting with the compound postulate that "every individual has three interpersonal needs: inclusion, control, and affection" and that these three needs "contribute a sufficient set of areas of interpersonal behavior for the prediction and explanation of interpersonal phenomena," Schutz develops a questionnaire, "FIRO-B," with six scales for measuring the expressed or wanted behavior related to each of these needs.   By means of selection of group members with carefully and operationally specified degrees of interpersonal compatibility on these three needs, Schutz empirically demonstrates that predetermined compatibility affects group production, cohesiveness, and interpersonal attraction.   The work of Janis (1954, 1958) also provides important hypotheses on the relation of personality systems, modifiable by drugs, to social interaction.   A very extensive and helpful review of this area has just been published by Mann (1959).

Summary

Social psychologists, both in psychology and sociology, have developed reliable and valid techniques for observing, recording, categorizing, and quantifying social behavior and social interaction. These methods, used independently of the various theoretical contexts in which they grew, have some limited usefulness in the exploratory study of gross effects of powerful experimental treatments, such as some drugs, on social behavior.   The study of more subtle effects requires the specification and control of the non-drug factors which influence social behavior.   Interest in and dependable knowledge about such antecedent-consequent relations are largely confined to social psychologists, extremely few of whom have as yet investigated the usefulness of drugs as research instruments in their field.   The future development of better methods for the objective study of drug effects on group functioning will probably represent a by-product of activities by social psychologists in solving their own research problems rather than a direct result of drug research, which is aimed at the description and prediction of drug effects.   As for another major goal of science—the elimination of ignorance and avoidance of error—social psychologists can importantly and immediately serve the cause of drug research with extensive support of Crisswell's Rule (Crisswell, 1958): *Identify and constantly attend to all of the expectations of the subject and the experimenter with respect to all aspects of the research enterprise.*

REFERENCES

Allen, R. G. D. *Mathematical economics*. London: Macmillan, 1957.

Arrington, Ruth. Time sampling in studies of social behavior, *Psychol. Bull.*, 1943, 40, 81–124.

Auld, F., Jr., and Murray, E. J. Content analysis studies of psychotherapy. *Psychol. Bull.*, 1955, 52, 377–395.

Bales, R. F. *Interaction process analysis*. Cambridge, Mass.: Addison-Wesley, 1951.

Bales, R. F. Small group theory and research. In R. K. Merton, L. Broom, and L. S. Cottrell, Jr. (Eds.), *Sociology today*. New York: Basic Books, 1959, 293–308.

Bales, R. F., and Borgatta, E. F. A study of group size: size of group as a factor in the interaction profile. In A. P. Hare, E. F. Borgatta, and R. F. Bales, *Small groups: studies in social interaction*. New York: Knopf, 1955.

Bales, R. F., and Flanders, N. A. Planning a laboratory. *Amer. soc. Rev.*, 1954, 19, 771–781.

Bales, R. F., Hare, A. P., and Borgatta, E. F. Structure and dynamics of small groups: a review of four variables. In J. B. Gittler (Ed.), *Review of sociology*. New York: Wiley, 1957.

Barker, R. G., and Wright, H. F. *One boy's day*. New York: Harper, 1951.

Berelson, B. *Content analysis in communications research*. Glencoe, Ill.: Free Press, 1952.

Bergmann, G. The contribution of John B. Watson. *Psychol. Rev.*, 1956, 63, 265–276.

Birdwhistell, R. L. *Introduction to kinesics*. Louisville, Ky.: Univer. of Louisville Press, 1952. (a)

Birdwhistell, R. L. Body motion research and interviewing. *Human Organ*, 1952, 11, 37–38. (b)

Bishop, B. M. Mother-child interaction and the social behavior of children. *Psych. Monogr.*, 1951, 65, No. 11.

Carter, L. F., Haythorn, W., Meirowitz, B., and Lanzetta, J. The relation of categorizations and ratings in the observation of group behavior. *Human Relations*, 1951, 4, 239–254.

Cartright, D. Lewinian theory. In S. Koch (Ed.), *Psychology, a study of a science, Study 1*. Vol. 2. New York: McGraw-Hill, 1959.

Cartright, D., and Harary, F. Structural balance: an extension of Heider's theory. *Psychol. Rev.*, 1956, 63, 277–293.

Cartright, D., and Zander, A. F. (Eds.) *Group dynamics: research and theory*. Evanston, Ill.: Row, Peterson, 1953.

Cattell, R. B. *Personality and motivation structure and measurement*. Yonkers, N. Y.: World Book Co., 1957.

Cattell, R. B., Saunders, D. R., and Stice, G. F. The dimensions of syntality in small groups. *Human Relations*, 1953, 6, 331–356.

Cervin, V. Relationship of accendant-submissive behavior in dyadic groups of human subjects to their emotional responsiveness. *J. abnorm. soc. Psychol.*, 1957, 54, 241–249.

Chapple, E. D. Measuring human relations: an introduction to the study of interaction of individuals. *Genet. Psychol. Monogr.*, 1940, 22, 1–247.

Chapple, E. D.   The interaction chronograph: its evolution and present application.   *Personnel,* 1949, 25, 295–307.

Christie, R., Havel, J., and Seidenberg, B.   Is the F scale irreversible?   *J. abnorm. soc. Psychol.,* 1958, 56, 143–159.

Cofer, C. N.   The mediation hypothesis in the analysis and description of behavior.   In R. Glazer et al., *Current trends in the description and analysis of behavior.*   Pittsburgh: Univer. of Pittsburgh Press, 1958.

Crisswell, J.   The psychologist as perceiver.   In R. Tagiuri and L. Petrullo (Eds.), *Person perception and interpersonal behavior.*   Palo Alto, Calif.: Stanford Univer. Press, 1958.

Cronbach, L.   *Essentials of psychological testing.*   New York: Harper, 1949.

Davol, S. H.   Some determinants of sociometric relationships and group structure in a Veterans Administration Domicilliary.   Unpublished doctoral dissertation, Univer. of Rochester, 1957.

Deutsch, M.   Conditions affecting cooperation.   Final Tech. Rep. for O. N. R., Feb. 1957.

Dews, P. B.   (Ed.)   Techniques for the study of behavioral effects of drugs.   *Ann. N. Y. Acad. Sci.,* 1956, 65, art. 4, 247–356.

Duncan, C. P.   Recent research on human problem solving.   *Psychol. Bull.,* 1959, 56, 397–429.

Estes, W. K.   Of models and men.   *Am. Psychol.,* 1957, 12, 609–617.

Festinger, L.   *A theory of cognitive dissonance.*   Evanston, Ill.: Row, Peterson, 1957.

Gardiner, E. F., and Thompson, G. G.   *Social relations and morale in small groups.*   New York: Appleton-Century-Crofts, 1956.

Glazer, R.   Descriptive variables for the study of task-oriented groups.   In R. Glazer et al., *Current trends in the description and analysis of behavior.*   Pittsburgh, Pa.: Univer. of Pittsburgh Press, 1958.

Goldman-Eisler, F.   A contribution to the objective measurement of the cathartic process. I.   *J. ment. Sci.,* 1956, 102, 78–95.

Goodenough, F. L.   Measuring behavior traits by means of repeated short-samples.   *J. juv. Res.,* 1928, 12, 230–235.

Goodenough, F. L.   The observation of children's behaviors as a method in social psychology.   *Soc. Forces,* 1936, 15, 476–479.

Guetzkow, H.   Interaction between methods and models in social psychology.   In R. Glazer et. al., *Current trends in the description and analysis of behavior.*   Pittsburgh, Pa.: Univer. of Pittsburgh Press, 1958.

Guetzkow, H., and Bowes, A. E.   *Preliminary report on the development of organizations with a division of labor.*   Pittsburgh, Pa.: Carnegie Institute of Technology, 1954.

Guilford, J. P.   *Psychometric methods.*   (2nd ed.)   New York: McGraw-Hill, 1954.

Hare, A. P., Borgatta, E. F., and Bales, R. F.   *Small groups: studies in social interaction.*   New York: Knopf, 1955.

Heider, F.   *The psychology of interpersonal relations.*   New York: Wiley, 1958.

Heise, G. A., and Miller, G. A.   Problem solving by small groups using various communication nets.   *J. abnorm. soc. Psychol.,* 1951, 46, 327–336.

Helson, H.   Adaptation level theory.   In S. Koch (Ed.), *Psychology, a study of a science, Study 1.*   Vol. 1.   New York: McGraw-Hill, 1959.

Heyns, R. W., and Lippitt, R. Systematic observational techniques. In G. Lindzey (Ed.), *Handbook of social psychology.* Cambridge, Mass.: Addison-Wesley, 1954.

Heyns, R. W., and Zander, A. F. Observations of group behavior. In L. Festinger and D. Katz (Eds.), *Research methods in the behavioral sciences.* New York: Dryden, 1953.

Hovland, C. I., James, I. L., and Kelley, H. H. D. *Communication and persuasion.* New Haven, Conn.: Yale Univer. Press, 1953.

Hovland, C. I., (Ed.) *Order of presentation in persuasion.* New Haven, Conn.: Yale Univer. Press, 1957.

Hyman, H. *Interviewing in social research.* Chicago: Univer. of Chicago Press, 1954.

Janis, I. L. Personality correlates of susceptibility to persuasion. *J. Pers.,* 1954, 22, 504–518.

Janis, I. L. *Psychological stress.* New York: Wiley, 1958.

Janis, I. L. Decisional conflicts: a theoretical analysis. *J. Confl. Resol.,* 1959, 3, 6–27.

Jones, E. E., and Thibaut, J. W. Interaction goals as bases of inference in interpersonal perception. In R. Tagiuri and L. Petrullo (Eds.), *Person perception and interpersonal behavior.* Palo Alto, Calif.: Stanford Univer. Press, 1958.

Kahn, R. L., and Cannell, C. F. *The dynamics of interviewing.* New York: Wiley, 1957.

Kelley, H. H., and Thibaut, J. W. Experimental studies of group problem solving and process. In G. Lindzey (Ed.), *Handbook of social psychology.* Cambridge, Mass.: Addison-Wesley, 1954, 735–785.

Kelly, G. A. *The psychology of personal constructs.* New York: Norton, 1955. 2 vols.

Kennedy, J. L. The systems research laboratory and its program: description of experiments. Santa Monica, Calif.: The Rand Corporation, July 29, 1955.

Kinsey, A. C., Pomeroy, W., and Martin, C. *Sexual behavior in the human male.* Philadelphia: Saunders, 1948.

Lanzetta, J., and Kanareff, V. T. The effects of a monetary reward on the acquisition of an imitative response. *J. abnorm. soc. Psychol.,* 1959, 59, 120–127.

Lazarsfeld, P. F. Problems in methodology. In R. K. Merton, L. Brown, and L. S. Cottrell, Jr., *Sociology today.* New York: Basic Books, 1959.

Leavitt, H. J. Some effects of certain communications patterns on group performance. *J. abnorm. soc. Psychol.,* 1951, 16, 38–50.

Leontief, W. W. *Studies on the structure of the American economy: theoretical and empirical explorations in input-output analysis.* New York: Oxford Univer. Press, 1953.

Lewin, K., Lippitt, R., and White, R. K. Patterns of aggressive behavior in experimentally created "social climates." *J. soc. Psychol.,* 1939, 10, 271–279.

Lindzey, G. (Ed.) *Handbook of social psychology.* Cambridge, Mass.: Addison-Wesley, 1954.

Lorge, I., Fox, D., Davitz, J., and Brenner, N. A survey of studies contrasting the quality of group performance and individual performance, 1920–1957. *Psychol. Bull.,* 1958, 337–372.

Luce, R. D. *Individual choice behavior: a theoretical analysis.* New York: Wiley, 1959.

Maccoby, E. E., and Maccoby, N. The interview: a tool of social science. In G. Lindzey (Ed.), *Handbook of social psychology.* Cambridge, Mass.: Addison-Wesley, 1954.

Mann, R. D. A review of the relationships between personality and performance in small groups. *Psychol. Bull.,* 1959, 56, 241–280.

March, J. G., and Simon, H. A. *Organizations.* New York: Wiley, 1958.

Matarazzo, J. D., Saslow, G., and Guze, S. B. Stability of interaction patterns during interviews: a replication. *J. consult. Psychol.,* 1956, 20, 267–274.

Miller, N. E. Graphic communication and the crisis in education. *Audio-visual communication Rev.,* 1959, 7, 5, 1–120.

Newcomb, T. N. The prediction of interpersonal attraction, *Amer. Psychol.,* 1956, 11, 575–586.

Newman, F. B., and Jones, H. E. Adolescent in social groups. *Appl. Psychol. Monogr.,* 1946, No. 9, 1–94.

Nowlis, V. Companionship preference and dominance in the social interaction of young chimpanzees. *Comp. Psychol. Monogr.,* 1941, 17, No. 1, 1–57. (a)

Nowlis, V. The relation of degree of hunger to competitive interaction in chimpanzees. *J. comp. Psychol.,* 1941, 32, 91–115. (b)

Nowlis, V. The search for significant concepts in a study of parent-child relationships. *Amer. J. Orthopsychiat.,* 1952, 22, 286–299.

Nowlis, V. On the use of drugs in the analysis of complex human behavior with emphasis on the study of mood. In R. Glazer et al., *Current trends in the description and analysis of behavior.* Pittsburgh, Pa.: Univer. of Pittsburgh Press, 1958.

Nowlis, V., and Nowlis, H. H. The description and analysis of mood. *Ann. N.Y. Acad. Science,* 1956, 65, 345–355.

Osgood, C. E., Suci, G. J., and Tannenbaum, P. A. *The measurement of meaning.* Urbana, Ill.: Univer. of Illinois Press, 1957.

Peak, H. Problems of objective observation. In L. Festinger and D. Katz, (Eds.), *Research methods in the behavioral sciences.* New York: Dryden, 1953.

Peak, H. Psychological structure and psychological activity, *Psychol. Rev.,* 1958, 325–347.

Ray, W. S. Complex tasks for use in human problem solving research. *Psychol. Bull.,* 1955, 52, 134–149.

Riley, J. W., Jr., and Riley, M. W. Mass communications and the social system. In R. K. Merton, L. Brown, and L. S. Cottrell, Jr. (Eds.), *Sociology today.* New York: Basic Books, 1959.

Roby, T. B., and Lanzetta, J. T. Considerations in the analysis of group tasks. *Psychol. Bull.,* 1958, 55, 88–101, 1958.

Rosenberg, M. Cognitive structure and attitudinal affect. *J. abnorm. soc. Psychol.,* 1956, 53, 367–372.

Ruesch, J. *Disturbed communication.* New York: Norton, 1957.

Schutz, W. *FIRO: a three-dimensional theory of interpersonal behavior.* New York: Rinehart, 1958.

Sears, Robert R. Success and failure: a study of motility. In Q. McNemar and M. M. Tames (Eds.), *Studies in personality.* New York: McGraw-Hill, 1942.

Sears, R. R., Whiting, J. W. M., Nowlis, V., and Sears, P. S. Some child-rearing antecedents of aggression and dependency in young children. *Genet. Psychol. Monogr.*, 1953, 47, 135–234.

Shaw, M. E. Group structure and the behavior of individuals in small groups. *J. Psychol.*, 1954, 38, 139–149.

Sherif, M., and Sherif, C. W. *An outline of social psychology.* (Rev. ed.) New York: Harper, 1956.

Stogdill, R. *Individual behavior and group achievement.* New York: Oxford Univer. Press, 1959.

Tagiuri, R., and Petrullo, L. *Person perception and interpersonal behavior.* Palo Alto, Calif.: Stanford Univer. Press, 1958.

Thibaut, J. W., and Kelley, H. H. *The social psychology of groups.* New York: Wiley, 1959.

Thomas, Dorothy S. Some new techniques for studying social behavior. *Child Develpm. Monogr.*, 1929, No. 1.

Thomas, Dorothy S., Loomis, A. M., and Arrington, R. E. *Observational studies of social behavior.* New Haven: Institute of Human Relations, Yale University, 1933.

Tolman, E. C. Principles of purposive behavior. In S. Koch (Ed.), *Psychology: a study of a science, Study 1.* Vol. 2. New York: McGraw-Hill, 1959.

Verplanck, W. The operant conditioning of human motor behavior. *Psychol. Bull.*, 1956, 53, 70–83.

Whiting, J. W. M., and Child, I. L. *Child training and personality.* New Haven: Yale Univer. Press, 1953.

Controlled
Subjective
Measures

Self-ratings

When drugs are being evaluated for their usefulness in psychiatric treatment, it is almost mandatory that self-ratings be included among the measuring instruments. External criteria of adjustment are not enough. We all know people who outwardly are living well-adjusted lives—they are not in mental hospitals or jail, they have steady jobs, and they are raising families—but who inwardly feel miserable. As long as we are treating human beings, their inner feelings should be taken into account in measuring the effectiveness of drugs.

When a drug is being studied for some experimental purpose other than to determine its utility for psychiatric treatment, the case for self-ratings is not so strong. The measurements that are made depend upon the investigator's particular hypotheses and interests. The experiment may be focused upon some aspect of behavior for which introspective reports are irrelevant. However, in many investigations it seems wasteful to disregard a source of data that may clarify some of the subtle changes produced by drugs.

The field of psychopharmacology is so new that until recently there have been no standardized scales specifically designed for self-ratings of drug effects. If we wish to deal with experimental subjects who are naive with respect to psychology and psychiatry, we must avoid technical jargon in our rating scale and express the items in simple, everyday terms. Since we do not know exactly what drug effects to anticipate, the items should cover a wide range of social and emotional reactions.

Pioneer work along these lines has been done by Wendt and by Nowlis and Nowlis (1956). They utilized simple adjective checklists and learned that many subjects can make reliable and valid ratings of their reactions to drugs. Gough (1955) and LaForge and Suczek (1955) developed similar checklists and showed their feasibility for self-ratings, although these investigators have not reported their use in studying drug effects.

Certainly in the case of severely psychotic or mentally defective subjects, little would be gained by attempting to obtain self-ratings. However, we should not be so pessimistic about mild psychotics, neurotics, or people of average intelligence. Experience with questionnaires such as the Minnesota Multiphasic Personality Inventory clearly shows that very enlightening responses can be obtained from these groups, and there is every reason to believe that the same fruitful results might follow from self-ratings of drug effects.

We decided to construct a scale which would fill the need of investigators who wished to collect self-ratings in drug studies. We started with a list of adjectives from Wendt and Nowlis, discarded some which had not appeared useful in their studies, and added some suggested by clinical reports of the effects of tranquilizing and stimulant drugs. We ended up with a list of 133 adjectives. We printed each item on a prepunched IBM card. The subject is asked to sort these cards into four piles to show the degree to which they describe his feelings. The cards are then fed directly into an electronic computer for scoring and item analysis. This procedure permits rapid statistical treatment without the usual time-consuming steps of scoring or punching cards by hand.

The chief difficulty in validating most behavioral measures is the unreliability of the criterion. In psychopharmacology we have a chemical criterion against which to validate our behavioral rating scales. The scale which best differentiates two drugs or drug groups is the most valid for contrasting those pharmaceutical effects. The fact that we have reliable criteria in psychopharmacology opens up exciting possibilities for research and should enable us to forge ahead much more rapidly than our colleagues who are struggling with behavioral measurement in other fields. For one thing, we can determine objectively whether self-ratings are adding to our knowledge in a drug experiment. Suppose we have two groups of subjects, one given a psychoactive drug and the other a placebo. We can end up with two sets of ratings, one by the subjects themselves and another by a trained observer, and we also have a chemical criterion against which to validate them.

Let us say that we have devised a scoring system for our rating scale which yields a total score. We compute two scores for each subject, one from his self-rating and one from the observer's rating. We correlate these scores with the drug-placebo criterion and obtain the following hypothetical correlations:

Self-rating and criterion .48
Observer's rating and criterion .60

We also compute the correlation between the two sets of ratings and obtain the following coefficient:

Self-rating and observer's rating .18

This is all the information we need to determine whether the self-ratings add to our knowledge of drug effects in this experiment. The validity of the observer's ratings alone is .60 but when we add to them the self-ratings the multiple correlation is .73. Evidently we have gained some additional information by asking the subjects to sort the cards.

The interpretation of the results of this fictitious experiment would be that the subjects perceived certain drug effects and the observer perceived others, and that the most complete picture is obtained by considering both points of view.

Of course, actual drug experiments might not turn out the way our example did. For all we know at the present time, self-ratings might prove to be of considerable value by themselves, whereas under certain circumstances ratings by professional observers might be worthless. Since we have reliable chemical criteria, we are in a position to find out.

Warshaw (1959), utilizing our deck of IBM rating cards, discovered that neurotics could feel the difference between a placebo and 400 mg. of meprobamate, but that emotionally stable subjects could not. In evaluating the effectiveness of a drug for psychiatric treatment, we should study it in people who need psychiatric treatment.

Self-ratings have great potentialities for classifying the effects of new drugs and showing how they resemble the actions of previously known compounds. For example, with the collaboration of a number of investigators, we have gathered ratings contrasting the effects of meprobamate and placebo. These ratings have been item analyzed to determine which specific aspects of mood and behavior are affected by the drug. The significant items can be combined to form a scoring key for meprobamate. When this scoring key has been cross-validated by other investigators, we will have confidence that it shows in a reproducible way what meprobamate is doing to people. We can follow the same procedure with other drugs, and after a period of time we will accumulate scoring keys to describe the effects of a number of known compounds. Then, when we wish to find out what a new drug does, we can ascertain which old drug the new drug most nearly resembles. By such objective statistical means we can employ self-ratings to reveal the properties of new experimental compounds.

The question of individual differences in reactions to psychoactive drugs is elucidated by making use of self-ratings. In general, as a result of examining self-rating data collected so far from a variety of controlled studies, we are not convinced that many of our present-day drugs do produce individual differences in response. An exception to this statement is lysergic acid diethylamide (LSD). Ostfeld and Abood (1959) administered our rating cards to seven subjects before and after a 100-μg. dose of LSD. A score was computed from each deck of cards to show how contented the subject felt at the time. The variance of these scores increased markedly after administration of the drug, as shown by the following figures:

Variance of "contented" score before LSD	34.93
Variance of "contented" score after LSD	112.36

This means that different subjects were reacting quite differently to the drug.

Human beings show individual differences in mood and behavior before they take drugs, so it is to be expected that they will show differences afterwards as well. But, if a drug is accentuating these differences, the subjects would ordinarily show an even greater variability after the drug. Most of our self-rating data regarding psychoactive drugs do not show any increase in variability from predrug to postdrug rating. Ostfeld and Abood's findings with LSD are all the more significant because they are so different from those found with other psychoactive drugs.

R E F E R E N C E S

Gough, H. G. *Reference handbook for the Gough adjective check list.* Berkeley, Calif.: University of California Institute of Personality Assessment and Research, 1955.

LaForge, Rolfe, and Suczek, R. F. The interpersonal dimension of personality. III. An interpersonal check list. *J. Pers.*, 1955, 24, 94–112.

Nowlis, V., and Nowlis, Helen H. The description and analysis of mood. *Ann. N. Y. Acad. Sci.*, 1956, 65, 345–355.

Ostfeld, A. M., and Abood, L. G. Personal communication, 1959.

Warshaw, L. J. Personal communication, 1959.

48 *Louis A. Gottschalk*

Introspection and free association
as experimental approaches
to assessing subjective and behavioral
effects of psychoactive drugs

Introspection and self-observation of the subjective and behavioral effects of psychoactive drugs provide leads to specific psychopharmacologic effects, leads that may promote further investigation of drug effects using other experimental approaches.

In one systematic study a team of subjects (composed of psychiatrists, pharmacologists, and a psychologist) who were able to communicate their subjective experiences freely and lucidly took varying doses of an experimental drug (pipradrol) and kept notes of their subjective experiences. After two preliminary experimental periods of familiarizing themselves with the specific subjective reactions they had to the experimental drug, the subjects demonstrated in a third double-blind experiment a sound ability ($p < .001$) to discriminate between the psychologic effects of pipradrol and a placebo; 47 judgments out of 60 trials were correct. The findings of this study supported the viewpoint that the data of introspection and self-observation are reliable for the scientific investigation of psychopharmacologic relationships, provided proper research procedures and controls are used (Gottschalk, Kapp, Ross, Kaplan, Silver, MacLeod, Kahn, Van Maanen, and Acheson, 1958).

The free-associative technique has been used in a modified form by having our subjects speak for short periods in a situation simulating the psychoanalytic interview. The interviewer asks the subject to talk about any interesting or dramatic personal life experiences for a three- or five-minute period during which time the interviewer indicates that he will not reply to any questions until the period is over. The verbalizations are recorded on an electronic tape recorder. The typed transcript is the only material studied. The verbal analysis includes a treatment of the data at the level of word-types, according to a grammatical and a "psychologic" classification (for further details see Gleser, Gottschalk, and John, 1959; Gottschalk and Hambidge, 1955; Gottschalk, Gleser, and Hambidge, 1957; Gottschalk and Gleser, unpublished) and an analysis at the level of themes or psychodynamic trends (Gottschalk and Hambidge, 1955). The specific themes coded and counted have varied, depending on the particular purpose of a research project, whereas the word-types analyzed have remained essentially the same for several different projects.

The productive application of our method of "verbal behavior analysis" in the investigation of other psychiatric problems has afforded us hope that this approach might be one enlightening way to evaluate psychoactive drug effects. For example, our experimental method of microscopically analyzing small samples of speech has been found to provide reasonably precise indices of the relative intensity of a complex psychologic state (a masochistic solution to frustrated dependency) in a psychosomatic study (Kaplan, Gottschalk, and Fleming, 1957; Gottschalk and Kaplan, 1958); indices of the relative degree of social alienation and personal disorganization in a longitudinal study of schizophrenics (1958); and indices of value in differentiating genuine from false suicide notes (Gottschalk and Gleser, 1960).

The application of our method of verbal behavior analysis to psychopharmacologic relationships has just begun to get under way.

In one preliminary double-blind experiment (Gottschalk, Kapp, et al., 1956), using either a placebo or pipradrol (4 mg. by mouth), a subject was asked to associate freely about any topics for three-minute periods before and approximately 2, 6, and 24 hours after ten separate trial ingestions of the unknown substances. The mean number of words spoken in three minutes after pipradrol was 327 and after the placebo was 294. The significance of the difference between these means was $p < .03$. Since introspective observations suggested that pipradrol increased psychologic and motor activity, it was inferred that after ingestion of pipradrol there might be a relative increase in the number of verbal references to accomplishments and strivings for recognition. The relative number of such thematic items was compared in the verbal samples produced under pipradrol and the placebo; the average of such thematic references was significantly higher in the verbal samples given under pipradrol ($p < .025$).

In a preliminary study (1960), we collected a series of five-minute verbal samples on different subjects receiving either a placebo or perphenazine. The same subject was asked to give daily verbal samples, under one or the other treatment, in response to the same open-ended instructions and in the presence of the same investigator.

The subjects were patients with various skin diseases on the wards of the Dermatology Service, Cincinnati General Hospital. Half the patients were placed on a regimen of perphenazine, 4 mg. q.i.d. by mouth for 5 days, then no drug for 2 days, then placebos for 5 days; the other half were placed on the same regimen in the reverse order. In addition, three other subjects were given placebos solely for 2 to 3 weeks continuously. On each day on which the patients received medication, except on weekends, each gave five-minute verbal samples.

Analysis of our data indicate that, as a group, the experimental subjects made significantly fewer thematic references in their speech to hostile experiences and destructive events when taking perphenazine than when taking a placebo. There was suggestive evidence, which needs further checking, that those subjects who were exceptions to this significant trend were individuals who, from psychologic test data, showed evidence of tolerating poorly submission or dependence on other people. Other effects of perphenazine appeared to depend even more definitely on individual reaction types, and these relationships merit much more study. We are of the opinion that drug administration on a schedule such as we used in this experiment lends itself more to discriminating drug effects shared by a group of individuals rather than to clarifying individual effects. Since we are interested in studying individual as well as collective effects, we are planning to give the active principle or the placebo for short periods in a randomized order for ten or more trials.

In summary, our experiments to date on methods of assessing psychopharmacologic effects of drugs in men indicate that the tools of introspection and free association have the fine sensitivity and the broadness of selection of psychologic events that may well be required to evaluate adequately the possible subtle effects of psychoactive drugs on mental processes.

R E F E R E N C E S

Gleser, G. C., Gottschalk, L. A., and John, W. The relationship of sex and intelligence to choice of words: a normative study of verbal behavior. *J. clin. psychol.*, 1959, 15, 182–191.

Gottschalk, L. A., and Gleser, G. C.   An analysis of the verbal content of suicide notes.   *Brit. J. med. Psychol.*, 1960.   (In press.)

Gottschalk, L. A., Gleser, G. C., Daniels, R. S., and Block, S.   The speech patterns of schizophrenic patients: a method of assessing relative degree of personal disorganization and social alienation.   *J. nerv. ment. Dis.*, 1958, 127, 153–166.

Gottschalk, L. A., Gleser, G. C., and Hambidge, G., Jr.   Verbal behavior analysis: some content and form variables in speech relevant to personality adjustment. *Arch. Neurol. Psychiat.*, 1957, 77, 300–311.

Gottschalk, L. A., Gleser, G. C., Springer, K. J., Kaplan, S. M., Shanon, J., and Ross, W. D.   Effects of perphenazine on verbal behavior patterns: A contributions to the problem of measuring the psychologic effects of psychoactive drugs. *A. M. A. Arch. gen. Psychiat.*, 1960, 2, 632–639.

Gottschalk, L. A., and Hambidge, G., Jr.   Verbal behavior analysis: a systematic approach to the problem of quantifying psychologic processes.   *J. proj. Tech.*, 1955, 19, 387–409.

Gottschalk, L. A., and Kaplan, S. M.   A quantitative method of estimating variations in intensity of a psychologic conflict or state.   *Arch. Neurol. Psychiat.*, 1958, 79, 688–696.

Gottschalk, L. A., Kapp, F. T., Ross, W. D., Kaplan, S. M., Silver, H., MacLeod, J. A., Kahn, J. B., Van Maanen, E. F., and Acheson, G. H.   Explorations in testing drugs affecting physical and mental activity.   *J. Amer. med. Ass.*, 1956, 161, 1054–1058.

Kaplan, S. M., Gottschalk, L. A., and Fleming, D. E.   Modifications of the oropharyngeal bacteria with changes in the psychodynamic state.   *Arch. Neurol. Psychiat.*, 1957, 78, 656–664.

Chapter 49   *Roy M. Whitman, Chester M. Pierce,*

and James Maas

Drugs and dreams

In the past, investigators of dreams have been limited by the capriciousness or defensiveness of memory. Resistance to yielding up of dreams can be easily documented in the clinical course of any psychoanalysis. But, recently, a technique for recapturing dreams has been discovered by Aserinsky and Kleitman (1953) and elaborated by a number of other investigators (Dement, 1955; Dement and Kleitman, 1957a, b; Wolpert and Trosman, 1958). This technique seemed ideal for use in recovering exact dreams of individuals on tranquilizing drugs, and it bypassed some of the secondary elaboration and distortion found in the dream text as verbally recounted one or more days later.

Method

We have therefore set up an experiment utilizing encephalographic tracings from the parietal and occipital areas of sleeping subjects and electromyographic tracings from the muscles around the outer canthi of the eyes. The tracings are obtained from four leads of a Grass III model electroencephalograph (EEG), the scalp areas being recorded by monopolar reference to one of the ear lobes. The machine is permitted to run at 3 cm. per second for the duration of the experiment, being stopped only when the subject is awakened and interviewed.

Since the number of contributing variables is one of the ever-present problems in the evaluation of behavior, we attempted to minimize the "therapeutic" interaction between the subject and the experimenters by arriving after the patient was ready to go to sleep. The electrodes had already been affixed by the EEG technician. Verbal exchange between subject and experimenter was kept to a minimum, although the content of the dreams clearly indicated, as might have been guessed, that his primary orientation during the night was toward the experiment and experimenters.

Following a procedure described elsewhere (Dement, 1955; Dement and Kleitman, 1957a), when characteristic electro-ocular muscle motility and brain-wave formation indicated the likelihood that the patient was dreaming, he was awakened by one of the experimenters after five minutes of "dreaming" had passed. A structured interview was conducted consisting of the following questions: (1) Would you tell me your dreams, please? (2) What does the dream as a whole mean to you? (3) What are your specific associations to [different parts of the dream]? (4) Which part of the dream had the most emotional charge to you? An exact recording of this interview was made and typed the next day.

Our initial study with meprobamate,[1] enabled us to perfect our apparatus and technique. We had intended to conduct a double-blind study, but the patient was unable to remain in the hospital for a sufficient length of time and it was impossible to disguise the medication from the experimenters because of the characteristic changes that meprobamate produced in the EEG (Henry and Obrist, 1958).

For eight nights of observation, EEG, and EMG recording, the patient received no medication. For the last nine nights, he was on continuous clinical dosage of meprobamate, 400 mg. by mouth, four times a day.

The other major portion of the experiment required the scoring and interpretation of the dreams. We broke down the manifest content of the dream as reported spontaneously by the subject into phrases consisting of a circumscribed idea—grammatically, a subject and predicate with supporting words.

To score the manifest content of the dream, we used as a model the hostility scale of Saul and Sheppard (1956). Then we devised six more scales in the areas of anxiety, dependency, intimacy, motility, heterosexuality, and homosexuality. All these scales were constructed on a 0–6 continuum, and each phrase was scored on this scale by three judges. It is worth mentioning that, although we used the manifest content of the dream in our scoring technique, we also made free use of the associations, related manifest content, and the connotations, as

[1] Support for this study and supplies of meprobamate (Miltown) were received from the Wallace Laboratories, New Brunswick, N. J.

well as stated meanings, of various words. We decided that it was an injustice to the richness of the manifest dream if we did not treat it as a complex, symbol-laden, condensed psychological product. After independent scoring and tabulation, the data were treated by statistical analysis to determine if there were shifts in the dynamics of the various categories listed above after the subject was placed on the drug.

Results

Twenty-six dreams were reported in eight nights of observation with no medication. After the patient had been on a clinical dosage of meprobamate for one week, this dosage was continued and there were nine nights of observation, during which time eighteen dreams were reported. The results tend to confirm clinical observations as to decreased dreaming under meprobamate (Selling, 1955). The subject was awakened at six A.M., and consequently we were unable to obtain the most usual dream, the early morning preawakening dream. Our dreams per night, therefore, were less than reported in the literature by others using this technique.

In terms of gross description by both patient and experimenters, the dreams before medication could not be distinguished from those during medication. Such adjectives as "bizarre," "vivid," "colorful," and "frightening," as used in the literature (Prigot, Barnes, and Barnard, 1957) to describe changes in dreams of patients on tranquilizing drugs, did not seem adequate or clarifying for our purposes.

The scoring by the three judges was statistically reliable on all scales. In terms of the content analysis along the six-point scale of the seven areas examined, only two showed significant differences between the periods with and without meprobamate. These two were motility and dependency and were significantly different at the $p = .02$ level, in the direction of increased motility and dependency scores after meprobamate was given.

The fact that an increased amount of motility appears in the dreams after meprobamate suggests an inverse relationship between the fantasy life and the physiological state of the organism under this muscle relaxant which probably diminishes motility. We are quite accustomed to seeing this in other physiologically altered states, such as sexual or food deprivation, when the dream life compensates for missing satisfaction. A similar model seems reasonable as an explanation of the increased motor activity in the dreams under meprobamate.

The increased amount of dependency seen in the latter half of the experiment does not fall so neatly into this scheme. Here we have to invoke another of the diverse variables that make human drug experimentation so complex. We speculate that increased dependency fantasy is a consequence of being "given something." Whereas previously the experimenters had stayed their distance therapeutically from the patient, here they were supplying him something by mouth with therapeutic implications, thus increasing his hopes of being cared for further (French, 1958).

It would appear that, in this particular patient given this dosage in this setting, psychodynamic changes were minimal, as illustrated in his dreams. This was a patient with little anxiety, whose pathological patterns were bound up in his character defenses—a situation which meprobamate might well not affect.

Discussion

We are using this particular experiment on one patient to illustrate a methodological approach to the evaluation of psychoactive drugs.

Our approach rests on several assumptions: that the dream represents the most significant, condensed psychological product of the individual; that the psychoactive drugs may affect dreams; and that quantification of psychological forces in the dream is feasible. At present we are also operating under the assumption that study of traditional vectors of psychodynamic forces will yield results.

In our next study we intend to use a depressant drug of the phenothiazine group and compare it with an energizer in a larger group of patients, hoping to accentuate differential effects on the dream life.

R E F E R E N C E S

Aserinsky, E., and Kleitman, N. Eye movements during sleep. *Fed. Proc.*, 1953, 12, 6–7. (Abstract)

Dement, W. Dream recall and eye movements during sleep in schizophrenics and normals. *J. nerv. ment. Dis.*, 1955, 122, 263–269.

Dement, W., and Kleitman, N. Cyclic variations in EEG during sleep and their relation to eye movements, body motility and dreaming. *Electroencephalog. clin. Neurophysiol.*, 1957, 9, 673–690. (a)

Dement, W., and Kleitman, N. The relation of eye movements during sleep to dream activity: an objective method for the study of dreaming. *J. exper. Psychol.*, 1957, 53, 339–346. (b)

French, T. M. *The integration of behavior.* Chicago: Univer. of Chicago Press, 1952, 1954, 1958. 3 vols.

Henry, C. E., and Obrist, W. D.   The effect of meprobamate on the electroencephalogram.   *J. nerv. ment. Dis.*, 1958, 126, 268–271.

Prigot, A., Barnes, A. L., and Barnard, R. D.   Meprobamate therapy.   *Harlem Hosp. Bull.*, 1957, 10, 63–77.

Saul, L., and Sheppard, E.   An attempt to quantify emotional forces using manifest dreams: a preliminary study.   *J. Amer. Psychoanal. Ass.*, 1956, 4, 486–502.

Selling, L. S.   A clinical study of a new tranquilizing drug.   *J. Amer. med. Ass.*, 1955, 157, 1594–1596.

Wolpert, E. A., and Trosman, H.   Studies in psychophysiology of dreams.   *Arch. Neurol. Psychiat.*, 1958, 79, 603–606.

Chapter 50 *Chester C. Bennett*

The drugs and I

Psychopharmacology is enormously stimulated by discoveries emerging in steady procession from the biological laboratories. It becomes increasingly more evident that psychological concepts must be reconciled with more elaborate and subtle neurological and biochemical events than we had realized. In the process, psychology is challenged to re-examine its concepts and to reconsider its distinctive contribution to the concourse of behavioral sciences. As a psychologist, I believe this contribution extends beyond the assessment of reactive behaviors. When the reverberating circuits and the tryptophan metabolism are fully understood, there remains the problem of experience, the self, and the reactions, paradoxically, of the drugs to persons. Let me hasten to add that this chapter in no sense represents the definitive contribution of psychology to psychopharmacology. It is in the psychological tradition, however, to examine chemical events in personal, experimental terms.

A sabbatical year at the Worcester Foundation for Experimental Biology in 1957 provided an opportunity to exploit my curiosity about the psychoactive drugs. I had wondered about their inclusive effects on personality, mood, and self-regard, as distinct from specific behavioral reactions. I had wondered about the subjective effects that may not be fully communicated to a scientific observer, nor to a ministering physician. The obvious source of data on problems of this order was myself—so I took some drugs.

It will facilitate communication to give the reader a descriptive account of the project before considering its implications. The medication schedule was entrusted to Dr. Harry Freeman, then Director of

Research at the Worcester State Hospital. I was interested in sampling chlorpromazine, prochlorperazine, meprobamate, reserpine, iproniazid, and lysergic acid diethylamide (LSD). For comparative purposes we added phenobarbital, dextro-amphetamine, and interspersed placebos. Each drug was to be taken twice, but at different dosage levels, with a minimum 48-hour interval between sessions. On Mondays, Wednesdays, and Fridays, at 9:00 A.M., I took an unidentified capsule. Midway through the project, we decided to include alcohol also. This was not disguised.

There is reason to suspect that these several compounds produce a variety of effects. I wanted to tap a number of areas of response. I was also determined to objectify the approach as much as possible. I was fortunate in having the assistance of Dr. Donald Krus, of Clark University, both in planning the assessment program and in administering a battery of measures which could not readily be self-administered. We developed a standard regimen, making use of scorable tests when feasible, and resorting otherwise to improvised measures and recorded impressions. The choice of procedures was based on a mixture of theoretical, empirical, and practical considerations. In one way or another we tried to assess perceptual processes, motoric and cognitive efficiency, tempo of response, judgment, mood, affect, and certain components of self-regard.

The Investigative Procedure

At the risk of being tedious, I should like to describe the assessment schedule. At the time of medication, 9:00 A.M., I filled out an adjective check list, adapted from one of the University of Rochester lists, as a basal mood-of-the-day report. Some time was spent recording my impressions of the day and my physical and psychological condition. Sensations that might be drug induced were noted, and I kept a record of any early speculations about what I had taken. About 10:00 A.M. I read six abstracts from the American Psychological Association convention program. Preselected by a colleague, these abstracts of standard length provided roughly equivalent memory tasks from session to session. I tested my time estimation, counting 60 seconds against a stop watch, and indulged in further introspection.

Dr. Krus arrived at 10:30. He administered the Strupp Test. The critical card on this test contains the words *red, green,* and *blue,* each word printed in one of the other colors. The subject is instructed to name in succession the colors in which the words are printed. He

must suppress entrenched reading habits. Then he gave me a measure of spontaneous tapping rate and selected items from the Street
Gestalt and World Context tests. We tested my estimation of the size
of my head and the displacement of my estimates when pressure was
applied to one side. We then adjourned to a light-proof room where
readings were taken of visual acuity, critical flicker-fusion (CFF)
threshold, the apparent horizon, an autokinetic effect, and the apparent
vertical. This was followed by the Titchener Circles, a hand-steadi-
ness test, an audiometer measure of acuity, and gray threshold readings
on the color wheel. We developed a "danger distance" measure in
which I walked up to a barrier blindfolded to see how near I would
come without bumping my nose. I also walked a chalk line.

This battery kept us busy until noon, when I had a standard lunch
at the hospital canteen. After another period of recorded introspection, I tried solving a crossword puzzle. The daily *New York
Times* was considerate enough to supply this relatively high level
task in unlimited, but roughly equivalent, alternate forms. At this
point I filled out the adjective check list again and tried writing the
abbreviations of the 48 states against time. The 60-second time
estimation was repeated, and I estimated the passage of "filled" time
while guessing the populations of the countries of the world. I timed
myself while writing "The United States of America" ten times as
rapidly as I could. Next I performed a Q sort of self-referent statements adapted from the Rogers technique. I tried to recall the
six abstracts I had read in the morning, filled out the Walter V. Clarke
Placement Analysis, and wrote brief character sketches of three
students I had known. The assessment program ended around 3:00
P.M. with a final period of recorded introspection. I made a point of
noting my best guess about the drug I had taken, in consideration of
the possibility that some effects might correlate with this intuition
rather than the actual pharmacological condition.

The psychological assessment program was complemented by biological studies conducted at the Worcester Foundation. As a part of
my routine, I supplied them with urine samples for analysis. This
phase of the project has been reported by Feldstein, Hoagland, and
Freeman (1959).

The assessment regimen was followed, with some concessions to our
resources and to my condition, on 24 days. There were eighteen
sessions in the presence of a drug, three genuine placebo sessions,
one preliminary and two follow-up sessions under known no-drug
conditions.

Methodological Problems

The idea of examining drug effects through first-hand experience is not original. Wendt, Nowlis, and Nowlis (1956) tested numerous compounds on themselves. Osmond (1957) has discussed the effects of various psychotomimetic agents which have been taken, in the interest of understanding, by many scientific workers, including himself. Hofmann's accidental experience with LSD in 1943 has drawn attention to this compound which has now been studied at first hand by a number of researchers (Rubin, 1957). Reports of such experiences have been made public, as in Wasson's account (1957) of the hallucinogenic mushrooms, and Smith's introspections (1959) on taking mescaline. My only claim to distinction as a guinea pig rests on the comparison of several drugs and the attempt to objectify that comparison as much as possible. The setting and procedures were standardized. The drugs were taken "blind." Scorable devices were introduced to quantify a number of the observations. The total approach, however, made liberal use of introspection and intuitive judgment. My goal was understanding rather than data.

The scientific status of an investigation in which the observer himself supplies the data, and the subject becomes his own observer, is an interesting problem. The usual question is whether such findings can be objectified, quantified, communicated, and replicated. The issue is not unique to drug research, nor even to psychology. Oppenheimer (1956, p. 134) was referring to the data of physics when he spoke of "the inseparability of what we are studying and the means that are used to study it, the organic connection of the object with the observer . . . . If one looks at an atomic phenomenon between the beginning and the end, the end will not be there, it will be a different phenomenon."

Granting that science must take its chances with the observer as a source of variance, there remains the question of the validity of the data when the observer observes himself. Introspection, despite its historic importance in psychology, has fallen into disuse. As Boring (1953) points out, however, certain "modern equivalents" persist as psychology continues to struggle with consciousness as a conceptual problem. Bakan (1954) is more forthright in defending introspection, not merely as a game try, but as the method of choice in approaching certain data, especially when the phenomena of unconscious, as well as conscious, experience may be involved. Admittedly, the data of introspection are difficult to handle, but it is not the habit of science to discard data because they are difficult. As for myself, I can only report that some of the things I learned about drug effects might have been observed in other subjects; some of them could not.

A few years ago my approach might have been criticized for its dependence upon the single subject. As Stephenson (1953) pointed out, however, intrasubject process relationships, obscured by "census research," may be of more theoretical importance than intersubject comparisons. In paradoxical juxtaposition, it is probably Rogers (1951) and Skinner (1956), with their interests in sequential rather than average behaviors, who share the major credit for refocusing psychology on the individual. Today it is quite respectable to control for variables like drug effects through repeated measurement of the single subject. Of course, the number of observations should be sufficient to establish the variability of performance, with and without the drug.

Having defended certain aspects of my method in principle, I am quite prepared to recognize its limitations. The fundamental breach of scientific etiquette was that I hurried. With limited time at my disposal and an inclusive curiosity, I elected, quite deliberately, to sample many relationships rather than confirm a few. My data can be characterized as an array of forty or more performance scores across twenty-four drug conditions, with one observation in each cell. On this basis alone the investigation can be disqualified as a scientific contribution. It was search, rather than research; an attempt to generate, rather than test, hypotheses.

The project had other limitations. It should be noted that my observations were confined to single dose effects which may be qualitatively different from those of sustained medication. The timing of drug effects varies from compound to compound, and from one response modality to another. A fixed assessment schedule necessarily displaced the tests with respect to the peak effects of different drugs. It is quite possible that my six-hour program missed completely some effects of the slow-acting compounds, reserpine and iproniazid. It is also possible that traces of drugs in the system after 48 hours could confound the effects I was studying.

My orientation as a psychologist was probably both an asset and a liability. I was certainly a cooperative subject. My pattern of living was evenly paced, and I was a little surprised at the general stability of my placebo performance. It increased my confidence in moderate deviations. On the other hand, my well-schooled impulsion to do well on any psychological test may have operated to minimize drug, as well as placebo, variance. The posture of introspection, and a general disinclination to abdicate ego controls to the dictates of chemistry, probably made me less vulnerable to motivational caprice than a less determined subject.

There are certain tests which cannot meaningfully be administered to a psychologist. There are others which cannot meaningfully be administered to anyone 24 times. In planning the battery, Dr. Krus and I searched our experience for measures which are independent of sophistication and of learning, and we were somewhat surprised by the relative absence of data on assessment devices administered repeatedly to the same subject beyond one or two retests. Subjectively I discovered, after a few sessions, that specific previous performances were usually blurred and forgotten. Each task acquired a distinctive for-the-present quality. I should mention that all my notes and records were promptly filed and not re-examined until the investigation terminated. Objectively we noted the appearance of performance trends, some of them quite unexpected, as a function of repetition rather than of drugs. I found that I "learned to see" a visual stimulus with improved acuity over the first several sessions. There was an appreciable tendency, on several measures, for my responding to become more deliberate, perhaps more introspective, when increasing assurance and promptness might have been expected. We were also surprised by increased susceptibility to certain illusions, although other responses moved in the direction of veridicality. We anticipated some learning curves but were quite unprepared for dramatic improvement on a simple steadiness task. I would certainly have thought that I could hold a stylus in a small hole about as steadily on one occasion as another. Yet with 60 seconds of practice at intervals of at least two days, my error scores declined from 25 per cent on a time basis to less than 1 per cent, with no indication of an asymptote above zero.

The interpretation of drug effects is complicated by such performance trends. A given numerical score has different meaning early and late in the series. Each drug must be judged by score displacements relative to the performance level operating at the time. This procedure is open to question when the adjacent scores may be associated with a different drug and when the variability of placebo performance must be estimated on a sliding scale.

In the face of these problems of interpretation, it would be meaningless to burden the reader with data. Score values are arbitrary, and many of mine were based on unique techniques. Statistical tests are not applicable to most of these findings. With all their limitations, however, some of the observations may be worth reporting and deserve further study. As I comment upon the drugs in turn, it should be remembered that each was taken twice, but at different dosage levels. As might be expected, my more vivid impressions were usually associated with the higher dosages. In general, those I report were confirmed, or at least not infirmed, by the companion experience.

The Tranquilizers

Chlorpromazine, at 100 mg., gave me my least efficient day with the exception of alcohol and LSD. I was drowsy within an hour, experienced increasing lethargy, and actually dozed off while trying to work. This was not attributable to my morning mood, which was good. Perceptual acuity and thresholds were not much affected, but my responses were sluggish and indecisive. Tapping rate was slower than usual. My performance on cognitive tasks was consistently inferior. I abandoned the crossword puzzle unfinished after 35 minutes, though later I found the puzzle easy to complete. I also felt unmotivated and let myself omit the character sketches. The one bright moment of the day was a relatively superior performance on the steadiness test. This is particularly interesting in relation to Blough's report (1958) that pigeons improved with chlorpromazine when the criterion task was to hold their heads still. Since my overall impression was one of sedation, I concluded that I had taken a substantial dose of phenobarbital. By 3:00 P.M. the effect was largely dissipated. At that time I completed a second crossword puzzle in 16 minutes.

Prochlorperazine, at 50 mg., produced subjective effects quite similar to those of chlorpromazine, but without the loss of efficiency. I experienced some mild digestive tension, but the major reference in my notes was to drowsiness, lethargy, and deliberate, obsessive responding. Perceptual functions were normal except for depression of the apparent horizon, second only to reserpine. This interesting illusion provides a dimly lit bar in a darkened room which is raised or lowered to the subject's perception of eye level. It responds directly to the up-down quality of mood (Wapner, Werner, and Krus, 1957). I felt inefficient, and yet my scored performance on all the cognitive tasks compared well with placebo levels. I also sensed a loss of motivation, felt bored, and neglected to do the character sketches. I concluded that I had been tranquilized rather than merely sedated, and guessed I had taken chlorpromazine, assuming at the time that other tranquilizers were "less powerful."

The effects of meprobamate, at 800 mg., were intermediate. I felt inefficient, but less so than with either of the preceding drugs. The measured effects proved greater than those of prochlorperazine but less than those of chlorpromazine. I noted some drowsiness within an hour, but resisted it. My mood remained good, and companionable. I called myself "relaxed" and "lazy" rather than sedated. There was certainly some loss of efficiency; the more difficult crossword puzzle and abstract recall tasks were hard to "keep my mind on." I did, however, complete the character sketches. Perceptual acuity seemed unimpaired, but there were peculiar distortions of judgment—a sweeping overcorrection on the apparent vertical, variability in estimating time, and erroneous judgment of distance. This was the day I bumped my nose on the "danger distance" task. Again I concluded that I had been tranquilized, and attributed it to chlorpromazine.

Reserpine was taken at 1.0 mg. and 0.5 mg. On both days my mood was good in the morning and remained so. There were indications of variability in perceptual functioning—a visual decrement on 0.5 mg. and an auditory decrement on 1.0 mg. Cognitive efficiency seemed totally unaffected. On both days I decided I had taken a tranquilizer, the clues being a mild sense of drowsiness and a "passive lazy feeling." I could easily conclude that reserpine effects were not experienced within six hours, but for one striking observation—a consistent depression of the apparent horizon. Krus, Wapner, and Freeman (1958) have confirmed the sensitivity of this test to reserpine in mental patients. My lowest readings on the apparent horizon occurred with this drug.

Phenobarbital

My experience with 100 mg. of phenobarbital proved interesting. I knew I had been drugged. My notes refer to lethargy, a sense of inefficiency, and finding it hard to work. The scores confirm the fact that cognitive functioning was impaired. I felt "confused" by abstract relationships and did poorly on verbal tasks. The scores also suggest decrements in visual and auditory acuity and CFF threshold, and the apparent horizon was depressed. Throughout the day, however, I remained intellectually curious. My notes are extensive. Reaction times were prompt. There are references to an energetic start, followed by errors. I was tempted to view my condition as accident-prone. Feeling slightly bewildered at the time about what was happening to me, I concluded that the drug had been reserpine. In retrospect, I am inclined to say that phenobarbital interfered physiologically with my ability to function, without relaxing my aspiration and needs for mastery. The result was tension and some insult to the self-concept.

Stimulants

Now for the stimulant drugs. I took 50-mg. and 100-mg. doses of iproniazid. On both days I experienced fleeting digestive tension, as well as transient drowsiness—even an outright urge to go to sleep—which came and went abruptly. At other times I was alert and even restless, and caught myself tapping my feet in a meaningless way. On both days my mood was positive and my cognitive efficiency remained at placebo levels. On both days the records show an impairment of visual acuity and a suggestion of impairment in auditory acuity. The apparent horizon was somewhat depressed in contrast to Krus's finding (1958) of a non-significant displacement upward. In general, the effects of iproniazid were moderate and might be entirely discounted except for their consistency. I realized at the time that I had taken a drug. The episodes of drowsiness misled me to suspect a tranquilizer, without much idea which one.

My one distinctly euphoric day came early in the series with 10 mg. of dextro-amphetamine. In less than an hour I felt stimulated, alert, and somewhat restless. It was a good feeling. I thought I was functioning well, felt imaginative and sociable. My notes are extensive. Time seemed to pass quickly. Actually, I was not doing so well as I thought on scored measures of cognitive functioning. I was somewhat distractible. I recognized the stimulant quality of the drug and called it iproniazid. I specifically asked Dr. Freeman to repeat it. The next experience with dextro-amphetamine, at 5 mg., produced a similar, but more moderate, reaction. I had a fine day and this time maintained placebo levels of cognitive efficiency. Again I attributed the effects to iproniazid. Later the 10-mg. dose was repeated, but the euphoria failed to materialize. My impressions were ambiguous. I experienced some early drowsiness, mixed with autonomic tension and restlessness, and called the drug reserpine. Efficiency remained normal. Perhaps the most significant finding I have to report was a decrement in visual acuity on all three days with dextro-amphetamine. Auditory acuity was also inferior on two days. With parallel effects on iproniazid, this finding of perceptual impairment was general to the stimulants in my experience.

Alcohol

Many people have experienced the effects of alcohol, but they are not so often measured as experienced. Out of curiosity, we decided to subject this drug to our assessment program. My potion one morning was 70 cc. of 190 proof ethanol—roughly equivalent to three high-balls. No disguise was attempted; I knew the drug for what it was. The effects were prompt, emphatic, and short-lived. Within thirty minutes I was feeling mellow and uninhibited. In a sense, I could read abstracts of psychological research. The words registered, but their import did not. At the moment this seemed not to matter. In about two hours the expansive reaction had passed. Responding to the verticality test in a darkened room with the chair tilted 30 degrees to the side, I was primarily experiencing unpleasant sensations of nausea, apathy, and drowsiness. I was able to perform the perceptual tasks, though the scores suggest moderate decrements in auditory acuity, CFF threshold, and steadiness. Visual acuity was normal and so was walking the chalk line. Subjective time passed slowly. By 1:00 P.M., four hours after medication, the threat of illness had given way to marked sedation. I was sleepy and could not focus on intellectual tasks. I left the crossword puzzle unsolved and recalled nothing of the morning's abstracts. In another two hours I was completely sober, alert, and able to solve a second crossword puzzle efficiently. It should be noted that my experience was based upon medicinal administration of alcohol, taken at 9:00 A.M., without an olive. It may have little application to social drinking.

Lysergic Acid

The most dramatic of the drugs I took, of course, was LSD. The drama was heightened by the fact that inadvertently I was given a rather large dose—500 μg. Psychotics seem to have a remarkable tolerance for many drugs. According to Cline and Freeman (1956), some of them are little affected by LSD in doses ranging up to 600 μg. With normal subjects, the effects of 100 μg. are usually vivid. My experience was stressful. We had completed only a few of the assessment measures before I capitulated and was put to bed. In the light of this experience, we reduced the dosage to a conservative 25 μg. for my second day with LSD. At this level I was able to maintain the observer role and to complete the testing program.

Precautions to disguise the drug were meaningless with LSD. In

30 minutes I knew what I had taken.   The initial sensations were physiological—a feeling of lightheadedness much like the early response to alcohol.   There was a distinctive quality, however, of suspense and excitement.   It was like the actor's experience (or more like that of the audience) when he forgets his part.   My throat felt dry.   I inhaled deeply, as one does when shivering.   Other LSD subjects have reported tremors.   I did not experience them, although I can easily see how the tremulous breathing could produce them.   I took it to be a homeostatic oxygen need, and my hands remained steady.   The overall reaction was experienced as disruption of autonomic functions.   I felt as though the drug had induced a biological condition of anxiety without psychological content for it.   That came later.

Let me emphasize that there was no amnesia associated with LSD. I was quite aware of what took place.   The experience had a peculiar vividness, in fact, and is clear in memory.   I became distractible, or perhaps differentially preoccupied, and "things happened so fast" that I could not attend to everything.   But what registered, registered distinctly.   The sensorium remained clear.   Other subjects have reported perceptual distortions—walls that curved and moved, shifting perspectives, and hallucinatory colors.   I saw little of this, except a few fleeting color sensations.   When I tried to read the abstracts—a demanding task in terms of visual-motor precision—the lines of print appeared to undulate.   I was not interested in reading anyway.   In general, my perceptions seemed sharpened.   I have photographic recollections of the scene.   I find it noteworthy that, when measurements were taken on 25 μg. of LSD, I registered my best performance in both visual and auditory acuity.   This observation is compatible with Trehub's study (1954) of the relationship between the galvanic skin response and visual threshold.   If LSD produces anxiety, a moderate or early phase of the reaction may be accompanied by increased perceptual efficiency which shifts to decrement as the reaction is intensified.

One concomitant of LSD that I shared with other subjects was distortion of the time sense.   The subjective clock appeared to race. This was observed even at 25 μg. in counting 60 seconds.   My tapping rate was also speeded up.   On the larger dose, my time sense was displaced by hours.   I thought the afternoon was well spent when it was only 1:00 P.M.   I could look at my watch and realize the error, but I continued to be disoriented in time.   The time sense depends on the way time is "filled," and I was probably responding to the quickened tempo of experience.

This was, in fact, my overwhelming impression of LSD.   Beginning with the physiological sensations, I was shortly flooded by a montage of ideas, images, and feelings that seemed to thrust themselves upon me unbidden. I had glimpses of very bright thoughts, like a fleeting insight into the psychotic process, which I wanted to write down or report to Dr. Krus. But they pushed each other aside. Once gone, they could not be recaptured because the parade of new images could not be stopped. At this point I should have settled back to enjoy a dreamlike or perhaps hallucinatory fantasy. As an introspective clinical psychologist, however, I tried to think. I tried to think about the meaning of the experience, about the integrity of the self, and about the difference between sanity and insanity. These can be troublesome thoughts when one is lucid. When they become the content of an uncontrolled, free-wheeling flight of ideas, they become frightening. The issue of mastery over apperception became an issue of selfhood. I had lost the observer role. I could tell myself that people recover from the LSD reaction. At the same time, I was informed enough to realize that I was taking it harder than most people do. Perhaps I would be the historic exception who did not recover. As a dynamically oriented psychologist, I now became disturbed that I could entertain such a possibility. By this time, I had superimposed a real psychogenic anxiety on the effects of the drug itself—and Dr. Freeman took me in hand. It was not until I slept, and awoke the next morning, that I felt myself again.

The subsequent LSD session with 25 μg. was anticlimactic. It provided some measured confirmation of the first experience in the errors of time estimation and the sharpened perceptual acuity. I was a little distracted and not at my best, particularly on the Strupp Test. This measure of adaptive flexibility, with the colored words, may be especially sensitive to LSD. I also experienced again, on minimal dosage, some of the autonomic tensions, the dry throat, and the sense of impending excitement which I associated with anxiety.

In conclusion, I sampled a number of drugs which have come to have medical importance primarily for their effects on psychological processes. I attempted in various ways to measure their effects on myself, and at the same time to examine, introspectively, effects that could not be measured. It should be noted that interpretation of the measures is itself judgmental and introspective. My observations were limited to single doses of medication, and to single experiences with any one drug condition. I can only estimate, without statistical support, those variations of behavior and experience which appear to me significant and worth reporting. The project was designed to give me considerable information about my normal or placebo response patterns as a basis for differentiating drug effects. Yet the ultimate basis of comparison was my ongoing knowledge of myself and the kind of person I am. Any and all of the drugs might affect another person differently. I hope it is quite clear that my "findings" may have no firm application to anyone else, let alone to psychology in general. They are reported only to suggest hypotheses, some of which may be worthy of further study and confirmation.

Man continues his search for the jinni that will come out of a bottle and do his work for him. I did not find it. Each of the drugs I took, in one way or another, impaired what I conceive to be my optimal functioning. None of them gave me any substantial sense of betterment. The effects of meprobamate, reserpine, and iproniazid, at the dosage I took, might have been imperceptible had I not been looking for them. With any of these drugs, except alcohol and LSD, I could have done a normal day's work.

R E F E R E N C E S

Bakan, D. A reconsideration of the problem of introspection. *Psychol. Bull.,* 1954, 51, 105–118.
Blough, D. S. New test for tranquilizers. *Science,* 1958, 127, 586–587.
Boring, E. G. A history of introspection. *Psychol. Bull.* 1953, 50, 169–189.
Cline, H. S., and Freeman, H. Resistance to lysergic acid in schizophrenic patients. *Psychiat. Quart.,* 1956, 30, 676–683.
Feldstein, A., Hoagland, H., and Freeman, H. Blood and urinary serotonin and 5-hydroxyindoleacetic acid levels in schizophrenic patients and normal subjects. *J. nerv. ment. Dis.,* 1959, 129, 62–68.
Krus, D. M., Wapner, S., and Freeman, H. Effects of reserpine and iproniazid (Marsilid) on space localization. *Arch. Neurol. Psychiat.,* 1958, 80, 768–770.
Oppenheimer, R. Analogy in science. *Amer. Psychol.* 1956, 11, 127–135.
Osmond, H. A review of the clinical effects of psychotomimetic agents. *Ann. N. Y. Acad. Sci.,* 1957, 66, 418–434.
Rogers, C. R. Studies in client-centered psychotherapy III: the case of Mrs. Oak—a research analysis. *Psychol. Serv. Center J.,* 1951, 3, 47–165.
Rubin, L. S. The psychopharmacology of lysergic acid diethylamide (LSD-25). *Psychol. Bull.,* 1957, 54, 479–489.
Skinner, B. F. A case history in scientific method. *Amer. Psychol.,* 1956, 11, 221–233.
Smith, P. B. A Sunday with mescaline. *Bull. Menninger Clin.,* 1959, 23, 20–27.
Stephenson, W. *The study of behavior.* Chicago: Univer. of Chicago Press, 1953.
Trehub, A. A theory of sensory interaction: an experimental investigation of

the relationship between autonomic activity and visual sensitivity. Unpublished doctoral dissertation, Boston Univer., 1954.

Wapner, S., Werner, H., and Krus, D. M. The effect of success and failure on space localization. *J. Pers.* 1957, 25, 752–756.

Wasson, R. G. Seeking the magic mushroom. *Life*, May 13, 1957, 42, 100–120.

Wendt, G. R., Nowlis, Helen, and Nowlis, V. The effects of drugs on social and emotional behavior. Unpublished Progress Report, Univer. of Rochester, Project M-681(c), 1956.

Objectively measured behavioral effects of psychoactive drugs

Thousands of papers about psychoactive drugs have been published in the past few years, but scarcely a hundred have reported objective behavioral tests of their effects on human subjects. Yet these new drugs have their crucial effects on behavior, and the problems of experimental methodology still plague even the best clinical research into drug effects. These are precisely the problems that the experimental psychiatrist and psychologist have made the greatest steps toward solving. The good experimentalist's ingenuity, objectivity, firm control, and skepticism are increasingly evident from the continually improving methodology followed in the clinical evaluation of the new drugs. But imaginative extension of these methods has scarcely begun.

To the extent that psychology has developed as an experimental science, we should be able to introduce a new independent variable—the new drug—at any appropriate spot along the physiological network that controls behavior, and then determine the drug's effects. As a screening for a drug with behavioral effects, this seems essential. When the drug is prescribed, the physician would ordinarily like to know why, where, and how it is acting. When there are so many subtle questions about the behavioral toxicity of the drug, we should be certain of its lack of deleterious effects on all important functions, for all types of people. The typical clinical evaluation of a new drug too often gives a subjective, unspecified overall picture of its action,

The writing of this paper was supported in part by Grant M-1871 from the United States Public Health Service.

plus screening as to its physical side effects. An adequate objective evaluation should specify as clearly, at the level of "emotion" and "behavior," the specific drug effects, both beneficial and toxic, on human beings. The facts that we know about drugs are almost always chemical and physiological facts about their actions on lower animals. These have been gathered during the rough screening period that determines whether the drug may have any possible relevance for treatment of any particular human disease, and whether it is safe to take a chance on further trials with human beings. But, when the crucial questions as to what the drugs actually are doing to human beings are asked, we too often accept a vague generality with an unspecified quaver of uncertainty in the tone.

Of great importance for the science of behavior are the control, specificity, and power of manipulation that drugs offer. A variety of relatively safe changes in behavior can now be experimentally introduced, in controlled amounts, for controlled periods of time, with the absolute minimum of confusion from individual differences in reaction to stimuli, problems of objective versus subjective field, or questions as to the mechanisms upon which action is taking effect.

This chapter will review only experiments that test the effects on the objectively measured behavior of human beings of drugs that have come into widespread use, in the past few years, as either tranquilizers or energizers. There is probably no justification for limiting the drugs reviewed in this way, including pipradol and meprobamate but ignoring amphetamines and barbiturates, but limits had to be drawn.

There are probably two fundamental aspects to the concept "objective." First, the specificity of the measurement made: more "whatness" can be stated about the comparison between two measures than is implied by such general words as "better" or "more"—and, second, the minimization of the possibility of subjective bias great enough to contaminate the results. A good observer attempts to minimize bias. But we can never be sure that he does; we can never make an independent check of his data to eliminate the inevitable mistakes. And we know of too many experiments in which the good observer was not nearly so good as he thought.

The chapters in this book report studies of drug effects chosen as good examples of the types of researches that have been conducted to date, with the expectation that they will suggest new areas for study. This chapter will briefly review the body of objective behavioral experiments on the effects of the new psychoactive drugs on human behavior. Work that is covered in more detail elsewhere in this book will be referred to by chapter number as well as by reference; for example, Kornetsky and Humphries (1958) (18). This review will begin with experiments using normal subjects, followed by studies on patient populations. (Except as noted, the former employ acute, and the latter chronic, drug treatments.) Studies will be grouped together, to the extent possible, by the functions of behavior examined and by drugs tested. Most of the studies reported, except when qualified as showing tendencies or trends, employed double-blind and placebo controls and got findings significant at the 5 per cent level or higher.

Experiments with Normal Subjects

SIMPLE PSYCHOMOTOR AND PERCEPTUAL TESTS. Kornetsky, Humphries, and Evarts (1957) found increasing impairment under increasing amounts of chlorpromazine on simple psychomotor and cognitive tests, such as pursuit rotor and digit symbol (18). Kornetsky and Humphries (1958) tested the effects of single doses of chlorpromazine on normal subjects' performance on simple psychomotor tasks (18). In comparison to effects on schizophrenics (see 18), more pronounced deficits were obtained.

Lehmann and Csank (1957) found a number of drug effects on a battery of perceptual and psychomotor tasks yielding 11 measures. Reserpine affected after-images in a direction opposite that of chlorpromazine and prochlorperazine. Chlorpromazine affected flicker fusion and tapping speed in a direction opposite to dextro-amphetamine sulfate. Prochlorperazine improved steadiness, digit span and digit symbol, acting in a direction opposite that of secobarbital (4). Lehmann and Hanrahan (1954) report that Vincent (1955) found that small doses of chlorpromazine given normal subjects resulted in "an increase of certain signs assumed to be indicators of anxiety." Schneider and Costiloe (1959) found tendencies toward increased reaction times under chlorpromazine and decreased reaction times under phenidylate (35). Benjamin, Ikai, and Clare (1957b) found no significant effects from 10 mg. of prochlorperazine on 16 behavioral measures (chiefly on simple psychomotor tasks).

Burbridge (1958) determined the maximum amount of alcohol his subjects could take without any changes in behavior, and then gave them that amount in combination with a drug. Reserpine and chlorpromazine produced decrements in key tapping, flicker fusion threshold, "overt behavior and speech," finger-to-finger, and Rhomberg reaction. Meprobamate produced a change only in flicker fusion threshold. DiMascio, Klerman, Rinkel, Greenblatt, and Brown (1958) found, through analysis of "drug action profiles" that phenyltoloxamine was similar in CNS action to meprobamate and secobarbital in normal subjects, in contrast to reserpine (25).

Kornetsky (1958) found no effects on normal subjects from small (800 mg.) doses of meprobamate, but significant decrements from large (1600 mg.) doses, on learning and reaction times. Upton and Chambers (1959) found performance on pursuit and coordination tests to be impaired by meprobamate.

Payne and Moore (1955) found that pipradol delayed the typical fatigue-induced decrease in performance during a long (four-hour) time period of the SAM multidimensional pursuit test, but did not produce the early rise in proficiency found under amphetamine. Gutewa (1957) found increased mental achievement under phenidylate on simple tasks of persistence, intellectual productivity, and perception.

Hess and Jacobsen (1957b) found increases in reaction time and in errors on intensive tests of simple and complex reactions under benactyzine. Kehlet-Munro (1955) found significant impairments of memory-attentive processes and of assessment of time durations under benactyzine. Coady and Jewesbury (1956) and Hess and Jacobsen (1957a) report the effects of a large dose of benactyzine on one subject as general motor incoordination.

COMPLEX PSYCHOMOTOR TESTS. Marquis, Kelly, Miller, Gerard, and Rapoport (1957) found no significant effects, from either meprobamate or meprobamate plus alcohol, on 21 behavioral measures from tests of simulated driving, vision, and steadiness (20). Uhr and Miller (1960a), using the same battery plus additional tests, found some impairment in accuracy and braking reaction time under meprobamate (20). Emylcamate, in 800-mg. but not 400-mg. doses, slowed reaction time. Kristofferson and Cormack (1958) found no effects from oxanamide on simulated driving (21).

Melander (1957) reported no effects from meprobamate on simulated driving. Loomis and West (1958) found decrements in performance in very well-trained subjects on their simulated driving instrument under the effects of chlorpromazine, secobarbital, and meprobamate, but not phenaglycodol (22).

Kelly, Marquis, Miller, Gerard, and Uhr (1958a), in a test of effects of chronic administration of meprobamate and of prochlorperazine on their behavioral toxicity battery plus perceptual, cognitive, and psychomotor tests yielding 30 additional measures, found no effects from either drug (20).

TESTS OF SENSATION AND PERCEPTION. Holland and Treadwell, working with Eysenck (1959) found several significant effects from meprobamate (24). Light thresholds at the perimeter were reduced for ingoing stimuli but increased for outgoing stimuli, while light sensitivity was decreased. Tracking ability was also found to be impaired, as predicted.

Miller, Marquis, Platz, Clay, and Uhr (1960) found no consistent effects for all (16 normal) subjects under meprobamate, although there were indications of individual consistences in effects and of a slight statistically significant decrease in acuity whose practical significance, they conclude, cannot at present be evaluated. Subjects were tested, under systematically varied doses and time delays of the drug, for visual sensory threshold changes (23) and simple psychomotor, cognitive, and emotional effects.

Primac, Mirsky, and Rosvold (1957) found impairment on their continuous performance test under chlorpromazine, but not under secobarbital (29). Townsend (1957) found no impairment, on the same test, from either meprobamate or phenobarbital (29). Mirsky, Primac, and Bates (1959) confirmed their earlier findings as to chlorpromazine and secobarbital (29).

Most of these experiments appear consistent in their findings that ordinary doses of the stronger tranquilizers (chlorpromazine, reserpine) impair speeded, coordinated psychomotor and simple perceptual skills. Indications for the newer phenothiazine derivatives, and for meprobamate, are more equivocal. These drugs probably also occasionally lead to some behavioral toxic impairment. But the magnitude of this impairment seems variable. Proper assessment of its practical importance by the clinician, and proper observation and handling of the patient may be enough to combat this effect. The excitant drugs appear to improve some performances.

STRESS AND NEED AROUSAL TESTS. Holliday and Dillie (1958) used drugs to combat experimentally aroused stress effects on well-trained subjects performing a repetitive tracking task. Meprobamate improved performance during threat of stress periods, while chlorpromazine tended to depress performance. Neither drug was significantly different from placebo during interspersed physical stress periods (37). Uhr, Platz, and Miller (1960) found a similar improvement in performance with meprobamate on a simple attention test, under threat of stress conditions.

Schneider and Costiloe (1957) examined drug effects on spontaneous recovery and extinction of galvanic skin response to a previously conditioned signal (using shock as the unconditioned stimulus). Chlorpromazine inhibited reconditioning. Phenidylate facilitated reconditioning. Amytal inhibited spontaneous recovery and tended to inhibit reconditioning (35). Uhr, Clay, Platz, Miller, and Kelly (1960) attempted to repeat aspects of this experiment. Prochlorperazine was found not to inhibit reconditioning, as had chlorpromazine, although there was a tendency in the same direction. Meprobamate had no effects. A second parallel conditioning experiment was also run, in an attempt to examine drugs' effects on a positively reinforced response (with sexual arousal as the unconditioned stimulus). Prochlorperazine had no effects. Meprobamate increased both spontaneous recovery and reconditioning, as contrasted with placebo.

Traugott and Balonov (1958) tested the effects of chlorpromazine on unconditioned and conditioned reflexes and on tests of reactions and word associations. They found indications of lessened simple unconditioned reflexes, along with impaired conditioned activity. Their patients appeared less tense, more accessible, and better oriented.

Benjamin, Ikai and Clare (1957b) found baseline galvanic skin resistance and pain thresholds (both posited as indicators of emotional tension) to be reduced by prochlorperazine, as contrasted with no treatment. Kristofferson and Cormack (1959) found decreased responsivity to a "lie detector" test, as measured by galvanic skin response (GSR), after administration of 400 mg. of meprobamate (32). Laties (1957, 1959) found that meprobamate reduced sweating under both stress and non-stress conditions but did not appear to reduce stress-induced sweating (which has been considered by some a measure of anxiety). Meprobamate also reduced the number of unpleasant symptoms subjects reported but did not affect self-ratings of fear.

Uhr and Miller (1960b) found that meprobamate decreased baseline galvanic skin resistance throughout a period of experimentally aroused stress and lowered feeling of activity but did not affect performance on simple behavioral tests or other self-reported reactions (23).

Burnstein and Dorfman (1959) tested the effects of meprobamate on normal subjects' performance of anxiety-related learning tasks. Predictions were confirmed that the drug's effect on anxiety would lead to better learning of word lists on which anxiety normally impairs performance, but poorer learning on word lists on which anxiety normally facilitates performance. Brown, DiMascio, and Klerman (1958) found similar effects for meprobamate and for phenyltoloxamine (25). Pronko and Kenyon (1959) found no effects from meprobamate in counteracting delayed auditory feedback stress on behavior, autonomic measures, and mood (38). Meprobamate had no effect in counteracting the heightened visual-spatial stimulus generalization gradient produced by a shock stress (Knopf, Wolff, and Worell, 1958).

Sikorski (1958) found significant effects from meprobamate and from prochlorperazine in lowering anxiety-related needs, as measured on objectively scored responses to Thematic Apperception Test (TAT) cards. Results confirmed hypotheses that need for aggression and need for sex would find greater expression in the projective situation when mediating anxiety was allayed by the drug.

Several tranquilizers (especially meprobamate and chlorpromazine) rather consistently improve performance under stress and, apparently by lowering anxiety level, definitely affect motivation level. There is also some indication that this tranquilizing effect is felt subjectively and can be observed to have autonomic influences, but it does not lead to improved performance. This absence of facilitation of behavior could well be caused by counteracting behavioral toxic effects or the absence of disruptive anxiety in normal subjects who work at simple, straightforward tasks. But, when tests are chosen because they are sensitive to and disrupted by anxiety, or when high anxiety levels are induced by laboratory stressors, performance tends to be improved by tranquilizers.

Experiments with Patients

STANDARD DIAGNOSTIC INSTRUMENTS FOR INTELLECTUAL AND EMOTIONAL FUNCTIONING. Abrams (1958) tested the effects of four months of chlorpromazine on female chronic schizophrenics. Of 16 Wechsler-Bellevue and two Rorschach scores, only on the similarities subtest did chlorpromazine lead to significant improvement. (Of 12 Lorr Scale behavior ratings, six showed significantly greater improvement under chlorpromazine, in the direction of quieting.) Gardner, Hawkins, Judah, and Murphee (1955) found tentative indications of improvement in performance, under either chlorpromazine or reserpine, on Wechsler-Bellevue picture completion and on Porteus Mazes.

Gibbs, Wilkens, and Lauterbach (1956) found no effects from combined chlorpromazine and psychotherapy, in contrast to psychotherapy alone, on Wechsler-Bellevue IQ or on Minnesota Multiphasic Personality Inventory (MMPI) scales.

Gilgash (1957) found significant increases in Wechsler-Bellevue IQ in 44 catatonic schizophrenics after 30 days of chlorpromazine. Picture Arrangement, Block Design, and Verbal Comprehension were the subtests showing greatest improvement. Ayd (1956) reported a striking increase in IQ on the Wechsler-Bellevue under azacyclonol in a single patient in whom a toxic psychosis had been induced. Gilgash (1958) reported a similar striking improvement in a single psychotic patient after 30 days of treatment with chlorpromazine.

Nickols (1958) found no significant effects from chlorpromazine given female schizophrenics on the Wechsler-Bellevue and Arthur Point Stencil. Some favorable trends on individual performance scales, plus interesting Rorschach changes (e.g., increased spontaneity), were found. Ison (1957) found no increase in Wechsler-Bellevue IQ scores in mentally defective patients given chlorpromazine. Durling, Esen, and Mautner (1956) found a 10-point increase in IQ as compared with a 7.6 point increase after placebo treatment in retarded preadolescent non-psychotic boys, after eight weeks of chlorpromazine treatment.

Daston (1959) tested 26 male chronic schizophrenics with Wechsler Logical Memory and Paired Associate Memory subtests. Chlorpromazine improved paired associate performance; promazine had no effect. Kovitz, Carter, and Addison (1955) found a significant increase in Wechsler-Bellevue IQ after chlorpromazine, but not after reserpine, treatment.

Pallister and Stevens (1957) found no effects from reserpine on Stanford-Binet IQ in mental defectives. Behavior, as measured by demerits received, was improved. Timberlake, Belmont, and Ogonik (1957) found no improvement on Stanford-Binet IQ from reserpine treatment given to mentally retarded children.

Zimmerman and Burgemeister (1958) found some indications of improved performance IQ (on either the Stanford-Binet or the Wechsler-Bellevue) in ambulatory outpatients given phenidylate. Verbal intelligence was not improved. Treatment with reserpine had no effects.

Porteus (1956, 1957a, b; Porteus and Barclay, 1957) has found, in a series of studies, significant decrements in performance on the Porteus Maze in patients under chlorpromazine (28). Bloom (1960) discovered similar decrements on the Maze from other psychoactive drugs (28). Mason-Browne and Borthwick (1957) found that perphenazine improved tapping and dotting performance and ratings (Wittenborn), whereas chlorpromazine did not. No effects from either drug were found on digit symbol, digit span, and Porteus Mazes. Moss, Jensen, Morrow, and Freund (1958) found no significant changes from chlorpromazine on Peter's Circular Maze and Word Meaning Tests and the Moss Picture Frustration Test. There was a trend toward reduced anxiety on the Taylor, plus significant changes on the Lorr and Gardner rating scales. Grygier and Waters (1958) found significant improvement in behavior ratings in female schizophrenics treated with chlorpromazine. They did not find (nor had they expected) changes in performance on cognitive tests of vocabulary, information, orientation, and Porteus Mazes. Robin and Wiseberg (1958) found no effects from phenidylate on Porteus Maze performance or the MMPI.

Daston (1958) found no difference in stylus maze performance by chronic schizophrenics under 1200 mg. of chlorpromazine per day, as compared with placebo, when tested daily for 19 days. Phenidylate given along with the chlorpromazine produced no effect, but given along with placebo it improved performance. Lafon, Boyer, Duc, Minvielle, and Pouget (1956) found tentative indications of improvement in performance on simple matrices and digit span, along with greater release of aggression on the Szondi, under reserpine and under serotonin (27). A second study by Lafon and his co-workers (Lafon, Duc, Boyer, Abric, and Pouget, 1956) found possible indications of improved attention (inferred from the psychomotor Zazzo Test) and increased expression of aggression (Szondi) from reserpine, but no changes in digit span memory or intelligence on the Raven matrices. Acute doses to four patients gave similar tentative effects (27).

Petrie and LeBeau (1956) found nine days of chlorpromazine treatment similar in effects to those from a cingulectomy, but opposite those from a leukotomy. Eysenck's objective personality tests plus the Wechsler-Bellevue were used to obtain the profiles of treatment effects. The authors concluded that chlorpromazine, which improved verbal and performance IQ and led to decreases in rigidity, suggestibility, and tracking performance, produced a pattern of increased introversion and decreased psychosis. Tanck (1958) found significant improvement in a number of Wechsler-Bellevue subtests (especially vocabulary) from reserpine given to combative, hostile, excited patients. There was some improvement as measured by Lorr scales, but none on Klopfer's RPRS scoring method for the Rorschach. A curious finding was a general lack of drug effect (except for some of the Wechsler subtests) in those patients (serving as their own controls) to whom the placebo treatment was given before reserpine, as compared to those given reserpine first and then placebo. Azima, Sangodwicz, Spindler, and Azima (1959) found tentative indications of meprobamate-induced changes in 15 patients, including schizophrenics, depressives, and anxiety neurotics, on Wechsler-Bellevue, Rorschach and Figure Drawings, in the direction of emergence of aggression and of mood swings.

Kirk and Bauer (1956) reported no Stanford-Binet IQ changes from reserpine given to emotionally maladjusted, mentally retarded patients. There were no clear-cut Rorschach effects, but there were some indications of increased confusion and inner turmoil under reserpine. Nicolau and Kline (1955) found some indications of changes in disturbed adolescents after reserpine in Wechsler-Bellevue and Rorschach indices. They describe their patients as "less impulsive and less spontaneous, but more objective and detached." Rosenblum, Callahan, and Buoniconto (1958) found no significant results, on the Children's Manifest Anxiety Scale, Lie Scale, Stanford-Binet, and Anxiety Pictures, from reserpine treatment given to maladjusted, retarded children.

Winter and Frederickson (1956) found no significant effects from one week of chlorpromazine on Bender-Gestalt, MMPI, and ward ratings. Merry, Pargiter, and Munro (1957) found no significant effects from chlorpromazine on patients with chronic tension. Clinical assessments, patients' assessments, the projective Make-A-Picture Story, and an addition test were used. Kulcsar and Erdelyi (1957) found indications of improvement in emotional tension after chlorpromazine treatment, as measured by the Szondi. They found additional clinically reported effects in a few patients on the Rorschach and the Man-Tree-House tests.

Both MMPI and clinicians' ratings, by means of Q sorts, of 123 items describing behavior, were found by Fleeson, Glueck, Heistad, King, Lykken, Meehl, and Mena (1958) sensitive to improvement in outpatients under one phenothiazine derivative ("TP-21," Sandoz) as compared to a second ("KS-75," Sandoz) or to placebo.

Forster, Schlichter, and Henderson (1955) found no effects from reserpine on the Bender-Gestalt and Rorschach. Hauck, Philips, and Armstrong (1957) similarly found no effects from reserpine on Bender-Gestalts, Rorschachs, and Figure Drawings. Cowden, Zax, and Sproles (1955, 1956) found no effects, on the Bender-Gestalt, TAT, and other projective tests, from reserpine, or reserpine plus group psychotherapy, as compared with group psychotherapy plus placebo or usual hospital maintenance therapy. They found marked improvements or Lorr scale ratings and tallies of behavior incidents (greatest for reserpine plus psychotherapy). Meath, Feldberg, Rosenthal, and Frank (1956) reported significant improvements in two of 26 psychiatric outpatients treated with reserpine. Azima, Durost, and Azima (1958) and Savage and Day (1958) found tentative indications that Rorschachs were sensitive to changes in patients under the effects of reserpine. Dice, Bagchi, and Waggoner (1955) found tendencies toward improved integration and emotional control in patients given reserpine. Ferguson (1956) found no effects from reserpine on Sidney Crown's Word Connection List.

Coleman, Nelson, Olson, Roths, and Wiener (1958) found significantly more variability (i.e., changes in both directions), in patients given meprobamate for 30 days, on three MMPI scales—hypochondriasis, hysteria, and paranoia. Rosenthal and Imber (1955) reported no effects from mephenesin on the Bender-Gestalt, or on a psychiatric check list. Lauer, Inskip, Bernsohn, and Zeller (1958), although they found no consistent effects for all patients, got some indications of MMPI shifts in individuals after treatment with iproniazid plus tryptophane.

A number of other studies have also found some tentative indications of change from tranquilizers (often without sufficient controls) in chronically treated patients: Bair and Herold (1955), Carter (1956), Castner, Covington, and Nickols (1958), Dúbravec (1957), Finn, Nadolski, Guy and Gross (1955), Freed and Peifer (1957), Madgwick, McNeill, Driver, and Preston (1958), Motz (1955), Pisani, Micalizzi, and Motta (1955), Rambelli and Agostini (1955), Shatin, Rockmore, and Funk (1956), Simon, Wirt, Wirt, Halloran, Hinckley, Lund, and Hopkins (1958), Wright, Pakorny, and Foster (1956), Ware, Sleer, Motz, and Kinross-Wright (1957).

It seems difficult to generalize about these studies. The majority find improvement in intelligence after medication, but a sizable minority contradicts this finding. There are some indications that the patients who did not improve come from populations with organic rather than psychic disturbance. Thus it seems reasonable to hypothesize that the improvements in effective intelligence reflect a lessening of disruption rather than any direct effect of drug upon performance. But the results of the projective tests in many of these studies do not appear to support this suggestion. To some extent, we can be skeptical of their validity. And the findings from the MMPI, self-reports, and objectified ratings (including the Q sort) do, in fact, appear to give somewhat more clear-cut and positive results.

SIMPLE PSYCHOMOTOR AND PERCEPTUAL TESTS. Tourlentes, Hunsiker, and Hurd (1958) found no effects on 25 scores from chlorpromazine given chronic schizophrenic females. Tests used included Wechsler-Bellevue subtests, Kent-Rosanoff word associations, weight suggestion, tapping, hidden pictures, sociometric evaluations, and movie samples of behavior in groups.

Heilizer (1959) found a decrease in variability of reaction time under chlorpromazine, but no changes in mean reaction time, finger dexterity, or the Pascal-Suttell score of "goodness" of Bender-Gestalt drawings. Weight changes were also found to be related to decreased variability within the chlorpromazine group (Planansky and Heilizer, 1959). Kornetsky, Pettit, Wynne, and Evarts (1959) tested the effects of both acute and chronic doses of chlorpromazine on schizophrenic patients' performance on simple psychomotor tests. Two weeks of treatment did not impair performance, although a single 200-mg. dose did. The single dose gave less impairment than had been found in studies with normal subjects (18). Lehmann and Hanrahan (1954) and Reda, Ballardina, and Riccio (1955) found tentative indications of chlorpromazine's influence on simple psychomotor and cognitive tests. Five phenothiazine derivatives uniformly tended to lower patients' performance on 10 psychophysical tests (Newbrough and Beck, 1959). Whitehead and Thune (1958) found no effects from chlorpromazine given to chronic psychotics on serial verbal learning, pursuit rotor, and problem-solving performance. They did find significant effects on the number of patients who would cooperate in the tests, and on patients' choice of the correct social response on a verbalized social adaptation scale developed by them. Mead, Ellsworth, and Grimmett (1958) found some indications of improvement, both on rated behavior and on simple psychomotor tests, in patients treated first with ephedrine and then with chlorpromazine, as contrasted with chlorpromazine treatment alone (45).

LeGuillant and collaborators (1957) found indications of motor difficulties in patients treated with chlorpromazine and reserpine (36). Viviano (1956) found decreased reaction times from reserpine treatment. Abse, Curtis, Dahlstrom, Hawkins, and Toops (1956) found no improvement on the Purdue Pegboard after one week of reserpine.

Sibilio, Andrew, Dart, Moore, and Stehman (1958) found no effects on simple reaction time from promazine hydrochloride. Reitan (1957) found no effects from six days of phenaglycodol or of meprobamate on outpatients' performance on eight simple psychomotor tests. A large acute dose given normal subjects reduced performance, indicating that the tests were sensitive to the drugs used (26). Kleemeier, Rich, and Justiss (1956) examined the effects of one week of pipradol, given aged men, on 30 measures of psychomotor performance. Significant improvements in grip strength, judgments of time durations, and Draw A Person variables were found. Cohen (1956) found some indications of best results from combined pipradrol and reserpine treatment, as compared both with placebo and with reserpine alone, on psychomotor, fluency, projective, and ethnocentrism test performances after one week of administration to anxious and depressed patients.

COMPLEX PSYCHOMOTOR TESTS. Uhr, Pollard, and Miller (1959) tested for the chronic effects of meprobamate on anxiety neurotics, using behavioral tests, self-report ratings, peer ratings, and objectified assessments from psychiatric interviews. Subjects were slower in reaction under meprobamate, more accurate in estimating time under misleading clues, calmer, and judged improved by their friends and by the psychiatrist (20, 23). Smith, Uhr, Pollard, and Miller (1958) compared small numbers of patients in different diagnostic groups on a large battery of behavioral tests, including the driving battery (20) and PSI (23) under the influence of benactyzine. They reported trends toward improved performance, especially among obsessive-compulsive patients.

TESTS OF SENSATION AND PERCEPTION. Saucer (1959) found that chlorpromazine raised the threshold for perception of apparent motion in schizophrenics, in the direction of performance by normal subjects. Rosner, Levine, Hess, and Kay (1955), in tests of effects of chlorpromazine and of reserpine, found only a decrease in flicker fusion threshold under the latter. Ronco and Cacopardo (1957) found improvements in a figure-ground reversal test given to chronic alcoholics after treatment with either reserpine or chlorpromazine. Tedeschi and Vella (1957) found improvement in attention in neurotic patients under the effects of phenidylate, in contrast to no changes in normal control subjects. Krus, Wapner, and Freeman (1958) confirmed their prediction of a significant downward shift in apparent horizon after acute administration of reserpine to chronic schizophrenics. Iproniazid led to a non-significant upward shift.

MISCELLANEOUS TESTS. Carran (1959) found that tranquilizing drugs lowered activation level of patients as measured by the GSR (33). Mitchell and Zax (1958) discovered that patients given chlorpromazine could not be conditioned as readily as controls. Dickes, Flamm, Coltrera, and Tobin (1955) found increases in perceptual thresholds and decreases in muscular tension under mephenesin when either emotionally charged or neutral words were presented tachistoscopically. Maxwell and Paterson (1958) found beneficial effects from meprobamate given to severe stutterers. Holliday (1958) reported no significant effects from meprobamate on objective measures of the number of words stuttered and mean blocking time, but did find significant improvement in rated tension (37). Azima (1958) found an increase in the number, clarity, and vividness of dreams in two female anxiety neurotics given *Rauwolfia serpentina*. Gottschalk, Kapp, Ross, Kaplan, Silver, MacLeod, Kahn, Van Maanen, and Cheson (1956) found that experienced judges could differentiate, through introspection, between the effects of pipradrol and of placebo. They also found that verbal analyses from standardized free-association periods were sensitive to the effects of pipradrol (48).

Uhlenhuth, Canter, Neustadt, and Payson (1959) found no differences in effects between meprobamate, phenobarbital, and placebo, given to 52 neurotic outpatients. When the patients of one psychiatrist were compared to those treated by another, significantly superior effects from the active agents were found for one group but not for the other. These differences appeared to be related to differences in the psychiatrists' interests, as measured on the Strong inventory.

Eisen, Sabshin, and Heath (1959) found similar effects from the investigators' and therapists' attitudes on the evaluation of drug effects.

The relatively few studies of chronic drug effects on patients in which laboratory tests, rather than the more traditional diagnostic batteries, have been used give a picture of minimal behavioral toxic effects from the tranquilizers tested. There are indications that these are smaller for patients than for normal subjects, and that often the emotion- and anxiety-related effects are overriding factors.

More important for experimental design, several studies indicate the specificity of drug effect to symptom. Yet scarcely any studies have been conducted in which such variables as anxiety, drive, and structuring of the treatment program have been manipulated.

Prediction of Individual Personality
Differences in Drug Effects

Of objective drug experiments, the rarest type, strangely, is one of the simplest to conduct. It is directed toward answering the physician's perpetual question: Of all the treatments at my disposal, which would best suit this unique patient? And, for the personality theorist, it would have the greatest theoretical implications. This is the study of individual personality differences that explain differences in the subject's response to drug therapy. One method of posing this problem is not too uncommon (witness Hauck, Philips, and Armstrong [1957], who divided subjects into four groups bases on severity of pathology, and Smith, Uhr, Pollard, and Miller [1958], who separately studied groups of patients differing in neurotic syndromes). But the vast literature of researches on objective personality testing, which would have the advantages of minimizing human fallibility and bias and allow for more precise and more specific statements about subjects, has scarcely been started.

NORMAL SUBJECTS. Kornetsky and Humphries (1957) related scores on four MMPI subscales with the performance of subjects in their already reported experiment (18). The psychasthenia and the depression scale each predicted changes in subjective reports of the effect of 200 mg. of chlorpromazine. Although the other two scales and the four scales as predictors of *objective* effects did not attain statistical significance, the 6 correlations (rhos) were all positive, some closely approaching significance. Kornetsky and Humphries (1958) found further indications of differences between subjects in general drug responsivity (18).

Kaplan (1960) found that chlorpromazine increased the hypertensive reactions to the mecholyl test of initially hypertensive patients, whereas it tended to restore the autonomic balance as measured by an after-image test of differential sensitization (34). Kelly, Miller, Marquis, Gerard, and Uhr (1958b), using 68 objectively measured personality variables (from the Minnesota Multiphasic Personality Inventory, California Personality Inventory, Edwards' Personal Preference Schedule, Cattell's 16 Personality Factor Test, Miller Analogies Test, and Blacky Analogies) first determined their interrelations by means of a factor analysis, and then correlated 20 selected variables with drug effects on 40 of the behavioral measures used (Kelly, Miller, Marquis, Gerard, and Uhr, 1958a). They did not find many more significant correlations than might be expected by chance alone, and therefore they concluded that individual significant relations could not be asserted, but might fruitfully serve as hypotheses for further validation studies (23). Klerman, DiMascio, Rinkel, and Greenblatt (1958) determined that sedative drug action was ego-threatening to athletic, extrapunitive subjects but anxiety-reducing to passive, intra-punitive, anxious subjects (25).

PATIENTS. Ellsworth and Clark (1957) found that variability in palmar sweat significantly predicted subsequent improvement in behavioral scores of patients administered reserpine, chlorpromazine, or both (45). Heller, Walton, and Black (1957) found that division of subjects into two personality types—Eysenck's hysterics and dysthymics (anxious)—enabled them to predict which subjects would decrease in tension (as measured by items chosen from the MMPI) as a result of meprobamate. They found no effects from meprobamate on their entire group of subjects, and no effects within groups on Taylor Manifest Anxiety or on a headache scale.

A surprisingly large percentage of the studies that have tried to correlate the personality of the patient with his response to drug therapy has yielded positive results. Differences between subjects might well turn out to be crucial in the future untangling of apparently opposing results from different laboratories where, inevitably, different populations are treated and examined.

Further studies of this sort, along with basic researches on behavioral toxicity, stress reactions, and positive behavioral and emotional effects, under the large number of drugs for which data are incomplete, may well lead to a sharpening of our picture of differential drug effects. A more profound clinical understanding of the complex interrelated factors involved in psychopathology or, indeed, in any motivated behavior should help the experimenter become clearer about which factors at precisely what points in the causal chain he is manipulating when he administers a drug. It would seem quite likely that a psychoactive drug brings about more than one change in the subject, and that often these several changes work in opposing directions as far as the behavior being measured, the dependent variable, is concerned. Thus, in one experiment these effects might cancel out, in a second experiment one effect might predominate, while in a third a different effect. This would, of course, become even more likely as a result of individual differences between subjects.

Despite the occasional contradiction in findings, the differences among the three general classes of strong tranquilizers, mild tranquilizers, and excitants are becoming clear. But, as yet, only a few drugs have been subjected to any but the most basic tests. Only a beginning has been made toward the development of valid and theoretically and clinically meaningful batteries of drug screening tests. And scarcely any use has been made of the potentialities of these drugs as readily manipulable independent variables, or reversible "chemical lesions," in laboratory experimentation on human behavior.

REFERENCES

Abrams, J. Chlorpromazine in the treatment of chronic schizophrenia. *Dis. nerv. Sys.*, 1958, 19, 20–28.

Abse, D. W., Curtis, T. E., Dahlstrom, W. G., Hawkins, D. R., and Toops, T. C. The use of reserpine in the management of acute mental disturbance on an in-patient service: preliminary report. *J. nerv. ment. Dis.*, 1956, 123, 239–247.

Ayd, F. J., Jr. Physiologic and neurologic responses to chlorpromazine: their clinical significance and management. *Psychiat. Res. Rep.*, 1956, 4, 64–70.

Azima, H. The possible dream-inducing capacity of the whole root of rauwolfia serpentina. *Canad. Psychiat. Ass. J.*, 1958, 3, 47–51.

Azima, H., Durost, H., and Azima, Fern J. Alterations of schizophrenic psychodynamic structure concomitant with reserpine administration. Unpublished manscript, 1958.

Azima, H., Sangodwicz, J., Spindler, Joan, and Azima, Fern J. Psychodynamic alterations concomitant with intensive meprobamate administration. *Dis. nerv. Sys.* Monogr. Suppl., May 1959, 151–160.

Bair, H. V., and Herold, W. Efficacy of chlorpromazine in hyperactive mentally retarded children. *Arch. Neurol. Psychiat.*, 1955, 74, 363–364.

Benjamin, F. B., Ikai, K., and Clare, H. E. Effects of a tranquilizing agent on galvanic skin response. *J. appl. Physiol.*, 1957, 11, 216–218. (a)

Benjamin, F. B., Ikai, K., and Clare, H. E. Effect of proclorperazine on psychologic, psychomotor, and muscular performance. *U. S. Armed Forces med. J.*, 1957, 8, 1433–1440. (b)

Bloom, B. L. Ataractic drugs and psychosurgery: psychological test parallels. 1960, in press.

Brown, J., DiMascio, A., and Klerman, G. L. An exploratory study of the effects of tranquilizers on paired associate learning. *Psychol. Rep.*, 1958, 4, 583.

Burbridge, T. N. Personal communication reporting results of experimentation reported upon in the Alcoholic Rehabilitation Commission's Interim Report, 1958.

Burnstein, E., and Dorfman, D. Some effects of meprobamate on human learning. *J. Psychol.*, 1959, 47, 81–86.

Carran, A. B. Reliability of activation level during adaptation to stress. *Science*, 1959, 129, 784.

Carter, C. H. The effects of reserpine and methyl-phenidylacetate (Ritalin) in mental defectives, spastics, and epileptics. *Psychiat. Res. Rep.*, 1956, 4, 44–48.

Castner, C. W., Covington, C. M., and Nickols, J. E. The effects of a thorazine-centered treatment program with psychological evaluations. *Texas Rep. Biol. Med.*, 1958, 16, 21–30.

Coady, A. and Jewesbury, E. A clinical trial of benactyzine hydrochloride (Suavitil) as a physical relaxant. *Brit. Med. J.*, 1956, 1, 485–487.

Cohen, S. Clinical experience with pipradol and pipradol-reserpine combination. *Int. Rec. Med. and G. P. Clin.*, 1956, 169, 751–756.

Coleman, E. L., Nelson, S. E., Olson, F. P., Roths, O. N., Jr., and Wiener, D. N. A controlled study of the use of meprobamate in a mental hygiene clinic. *J. clin. exp. Psychopath.*, 1958, 19, 323–329.

Cowden, R. C., Zax, M., and Sproles, J. A. Reserpine; alone and as an adjunct to psychotherapy in the treatment of schizophrenia. *Arch. Neurol. Psychiat.*, 1955, 74, 518–522.

Cowden, R. C., Zax, M., and Sproles, J. A. Group psychotherapy in conjunction with a physical treatment. *J. clin. Psychol.*, 1956, 12, 53–56.

Daston, P. G. Stylus maze performance of chronic schizophrenics taking chlorpromazine. *J. consult. Psychol.*, 1958, 22, 384.

Daston, P. G. Effects of two phenothiazine drugs on concentrative attention span of chronic schizophrenics. *J. clin. Psychol.*, 1959, 15, 106–110.

Dice, N., Bagchi, B. K., and Waggoner, R. W. Investigation of effects of intravenous reserpine in disturbed psychiatric patients. Electroencephalographic correlation. *J. nerv. ment. Dis.*, 1955, 122, 472–478.

Dickes, R., Flamm, G. H., Coltrera, J., and Tobin, M. The effect of mephenesin on muscle tension. An experimental study. *Arch. Neurol. Psychiat.*, 1955, 74, 590–597.

DiMascio, A., Klerman, G. L., Rinkel, M., Greenblatt, M., and Brown, J. Psychophysiologic evaluation of phenyltoloxamine, a new phrenotropic agent. A comparative study with reserpine and placebo. *Amer. J. Psychiat.*, 1958, 115, 301–317.

Dúbravec, L. I. El meprobamata en la investigación y clínica psiquiátrica [meprobamate in experimental studies and in the psychiatric clinic]. *Medicina (Madrid)*, 1957, 25, 153–177.

Durling, D., Esen, Fatima, and Mautner, H. Central autonomic regulation and mental retardation. *Ann. Paediat.*, 1956, 187, 467–470.

Eisen, J. B., Sabshin, M., and Heath, Helen. A comparison of the effects of investigators' and therapists' attitudes in the evaluation of tranquilizers prescribed to hospital patients. *J. nerv. ment. Dis.*, 1959, 128, 256–261.

Ellsworth, R. B., and Clark, L. D. Prediction of the response of chronic schizophrenics to drug therapy: a preliminary report on the relationship between palmar sweat and the behavioral effects of tranquilizing drugs. *J. clin. Psychol.*, 1957, 13, 59–61.

Eysenck, H. J. *Experiments in personality.* London: Routledge & Kegan Paul, 1959.

Ferguson, R. S. A clinical trial of reserpine in the treatment of anxiety. *J. ment. Sci.*, 1956, 102, 30–42.

Finn, M. H. P., Nadolski, F., Guy, W., and Gross, M. Clinical, psychological and myoneural changes in psychotic patients under oral serposil medication. *J. nerv. ment. Dis.*, 1955, 122, 458–462.

Fleeson, W., Glueck, B. J., Heistad, G., King, Janet E., Lykken, D., Meehl, P., and Mena, A. The ataraxic effect of two phenothiazine drugs on an outpatient population. *Univer. Minn. med. Bull.*, 1958, 29, 274–286.

Forster, W., Schlichter, W., and Henderson, A. L. Reserpine in chronic psychosis. *Canad. med. Ass. J.*, 1955, 73, 951–955.

Freed, H., and Peifer, C. A. Treatment of hyperkinetic emotionally disturbed children with prolonged administration of chlorpromazine. *Amer. J. Psychiat.*, 1957, 113, 22–26.

Gardner, M. J., Hawkins, H. M., Judah, L. N., and Murphee, O. D. Objective measurement of psychiatric changes produced by chlorpromazine and reserpine in chronic schizophrenia. *Psychiat. Res. Rep.*, 1955, 1, 77–83.

Gibbs, J. J., Wilkens, B., and Lauterbach, C. G. A controlled clinical psychiatry study of the drug chlorpromazine. *Amer. J. Psychiat.*, 1956, 113, 254–255.

Gilgash, C. A. Effects of thorazine on Wechsler scores of adult catatonic schizophrenics. *Psychol. Rep.*, 1957, 3, 561–564.

Gilgash, C. A. Drug therapy with a pseudo–mentally retarded psychotic: a case study. *Psychol. Newsltr, N. Y. U.*, 1958, 9, 85–87.

Gottschalk, L. A., Kapp, F. T., Ross, W. D., Kaplan, S. M., Silver, H., MacLeod, J. A., Kahn, J. B., Jr., Van Maanen, E. F., and Cheson, G. H. Explorations in testing drugs affecting physical and mental activity. *J. Amer. med. Ass.*, 1956, 161, 1054–1058.

Grygier, Patricia, and Waters, M. A. Chlorpromazine used with an intensive occupational therapy program. *Arch. Neurol. Psychiat.*, 1958, 79, 697–705.

Gutewa, J. Der Wert des psychologischen Tests für die Untersuchung der Wirkung von Medikamenten auf psychische funktionen. *Psychiat. Neurol. (Basel)*, 1957, 134, 224–235.

Hauck, P., Philips, H., and Armstrong, R. The effects of reserpine on psychotic patients of varying degrees of illness: a pilot study. *J. clin. Psychol.*, 1957, 13, 188–190.

Heilizer, F. The effects of chlorpromazine upon psychomotor behavior of chronic schizophrenic patients. *J. nerv. ment. Dis.*, 1959, 128, 358–364.

Heller, G. C., Walton, D., and Black, D. A. Meprobamate in the treatment of tension states. *J. ment, Sci.*, 1957, 103, 581–588.

Hess, Grethe, and Jacobsen, E. The effect of benactyzine on the electro-encephalogram in man. *Acta Pharmacol. Toxicol.*, 1957, 13, 125–134. (a)

Hess, Grethe, and Jacobsen, E. The influence of benactyzine on reaction time. *Acta Pharmacol. Toxicol.*, 1957, 13, 135–141. (b)

Holliday, Audrey R. The effect of meprobamate on stuttering. *Northwest Med.*, 1958, 58, 837–841.

Holliday, Audrey R., and Dillie, J. The effects of meprobamate, chlorpromazine, pentobarbital, and a placebo on a behavioral task performed under stress conditions. *J. comp. Physiol. Psychol.*, 1958, 51, 811–815.

Ison, M. G. The effects of Thorazine on Wechsler scores. *Amer. J. ment. Def.*, 1957, 62, 543–547.

Kaplan, S. D.   Autonomic visual regulation.   II. Differential color sensitivity to autonomic drugs in mental disease.   *Psychiat. res. Rep.*, 1960, in press.

Kehlet-Munro, H.   On the effects of Sauvitil (benzilic acid diethylaminoethyl ester hydrochloride) in the higher mental functions of normal subjects.   *Acta Psychiat. Neurol. Scand.*, 1955, 30, 721–728.

Kelly, E. L., Miller, J. G., Marquis, D. G., Gerard R. W., and Uhr, L.   Effects of continued meprobamate and proclorperazine administration on the behavior of normal subjects.   *Arch. Neurol. Psychiat.*, 1958, 80, 247–252.   (a)

Kelly, E. L., Miller, J. G., Marquis, D. G., Gerard, R. W., and Uhr, L.   Personality differences and continued meprobamate and proclorperazine administration.   *Arch. Neurol. Psychiat.*, 1958, 80, 241–246.   (b)

Kirk, D. L., and Bauer, A. M.   Effects of reserpine (Serpasil) on emotionally maladjusted high grade mental retardates.   *Amer. J. ment. Def.*, 1956, 60, 779–784.

Kleemeier, R. W., Rich, T. A., and Justiss, W. A.   The effects of alpha-(2-piperidyl) benzhydrol hydrochloride (Meratran) on psychomotor performance in a group of aged males.   *J. Geront.*, 1956, 11, 165–170.

Klerman, G. L., DiMascio, A., Rinkel, M., and Greenblatt, M.   The influence of personality factors on the effects of phrenotropic agents.   (An experimental procedure to integrate physiologic and psychologic action.)   Paper read at meeting of Soc. Biolog. Psychiat., San Francisco, 1958.

Knopf, I. J., Wolff, H., and Worell, J.   The effects of an "anxiety reducing" drug on stimulus generalization under experimental stress.   *Amer. Psychol.*, 1958, 13, 343.   (Abstract)

Kornetsky, C.   Effects of meprobamate, phenobarbital and dextro-amphetamine on reaction time and learning in man.   *J. Pharmacol. exp. Therap.*, 1958, 123, 216–219.

Kornetsky, C., and Humphries, O.   Relationship between effects of a number of centrally acting drugs and personality.   *Arch. Neurol. Psychiat.*, 1957, 77, 325–327.

Kornetsky, C., Humphries, O., and Evarts, E. V.   Comparison of psychological effects of certain centrally acting drugs in man.   *Arch. Neurol. Psychiat.*, 1957, 77, 318–324.

Kornetsky, C., and Humphries, O.   Psychological effects of centrally acting drugs in man.   Effects of chlorpromazine and secobarbital on visual and motor behavior.   *J. ment. Sci.*, 1958, 104, 1093–1099.

Kornetsky, C., Pettit, M., Wynne, R., and Evarts, E. V.   A comparison of the psychological effects of acute and chronic administration of chlorpromazine and secobarbital (Quinalbarbitone) in schizophrenic patients.   *J. ment. Sci.*, 1959, 105, 190–199.

Kovitz, B., Carter, J. T., and Addison, W. P.   A comparison of chlorpromazine and reserpine in chronic psychosis.   *Arch. Neurol. Psychiat.*, 1955, 74, 467–471.

Kristofferson, A. B., and Cormack, R. H.   Some effects of Quiactin on normal behavior.   *Clin. Res.*, 1958, 6, 416.   (Abstract)

Kristofferson, A. B., and Cormack, R. H.   Meprobamate and electrical conductivity of the skin.   Mimeographed paper, 1959.

Krus, D. M., Wapner, S., and Freeman, H.   Effects of reserpine and iproniazid (marsilid) on space localization.   *Arch. Neurol. Psychiat.*, 1958, 80, 768–770.

Kulcsar, S., and Erdelyi, S.   Recherches sur le test de Szondi au cours du traitement par la chlorpromazine [research on the Szondi test during the course of treatment with chlorpromazine]. *L'Encéphale*, 1957, 46, 140–145.

Lafon, R., Boyer, Duc, N., Minvielle, J., and Pouget, R. Effets comparatifs de l'injection intraveineuse de sérotonine et de réserpine. Étude psycho-métrique neuro-végétative et électroencéphalographique. *Ann. méd. Psychol.*, 1956, 114, 463–466.

Lafon, R., Duc, N., Boyer, Abric, J., and Pouget, R. Exploration psychologique des malades traités par le 4560 RP (chlorpromazine) et la réserpine. *L'Encéphale*, 1956, 45, 996–999.

Laties, V. G. Effects of meprobamate on fear and palmar sweating. *Fed. Proc.*, 1957, 16, 315. (Abstract)

Laties, V. G. Effects of meprobamate on fear and palmar sweating. *J. abnorm. soc. Psychol.*, 1959, 59, 156–161.

Lauer, J. H., Inskip, Wilma M., Bernsohn, J., and Zeller, E. A. Observations on schizophrenic patients after iproniazid and tryptophan. *Arch. Neurol. Psychiat.*, 1958, 80, 122–130.

LeGuillant, L., and collaborators. Le syndrome neuroleptique: étude clinique et psychotechnique. *Ann. méd. Psychol.*, 1957, 115, 316–329. (From Abstract in *Dig. Neurol. Psychiat.*, 1957, 24, 270.)

Lehmann, H. E. A dynamic concept of the action of chlorpromazine at physiological and psychological levels. *L'Encéphale*, 1956, 45, 1113–1118.

Lehmann, H. E., and Csank, J. Differential screening of phrenotropic agents in man: psychophysiologic test data. *J. clin. exp. Psychopath.*, 1957, 222–235.

Lehmann, H. E., and Hanrahan, G. E. Chlorpromazine: new inhibiting agent for psychomotor excitement and manic states. *Arch. Neurol. Psychiat.*, 1954, 71, 227–236.

Loomis, T. A., and West, T. C. Comparative sedative effects of a barbiturate and some tranquilizer drugs on normal subjects. *J. Pharmacol. exp. Therap.*, 1958, 122, 525–531.

Madgwick, J. R. A., McNeill, D. C., Driver, Marie, and Preston, G. C. Stelazine (trifluoperazine). A preliminary report on a clinical trial. *J. ment. Sci.*, 1958, 104, 1195–1198.

Marquis, D. G., Kelly, E. L., Miller, J. G., Gerard, R. W., and Rapoport, A. Experimental studies of behavioral effects of meprobamate on normal subjects. *Ann. N. Y. Acad. Sci.*, 1957, 67, 701–712.

Mason-Browne, N. L., and Borthwick, J. W. Effect of perphenazine (Trilafon) on modification of crude consciousness. *Dis. nerv. Sys.*, 1957, 18, 300–306.

Maxwell, R. D. H., and Paterson, J. W. Meprobamate in the treatment of stuttering. *Brit. Med. J.*, 1958, 5075, 873–874.

Mead, Beverley T., Ellsworth, R. B., and Grimmitt, J. O. The treatment of drug-resistive chronic schizophrenics. *J. nerv. ment. Dis.*, 1958, 127, 351–358.

Meath, J. A., Feldberg, T. M., Rosenthal, D., and Frank, J. D. Comparison of reserpine and placebo in treatment of psychiatric outpatients. *Arch. Neurol. Psychiat.*, 1956, 76, 207–214.

Melander, B. Psychotechnological investigation of car drivers in model equipment. Translated by The Mental Health Research Institute, Ann Arbor, Mich., from the draft from the Research Division of A/B Kabi, Stockholm, 1957.

Merry, J., Pargiter, R. A., and Munro, H. Chlorpromazine and chronic neurotic tension. *Amer. J. Psychiat.*, 1957, 113, 988–992.

Miller, J. G., Marquis, D. G., Platz, A., Clay, M., and Uhr, L.   The effects of meprobamate on visual sensory threshold and behavior.   M. H. R. I.   Preprint, 1960.

Mirsky, A. F., Primac, D. W., and Bates, R.   The effects of chlorpromazine and secobarbital on the continuous performance test.   *J. nerv. ment. Dis.,* 1959, 128, 12–17.

Mitchell, L. E., and Zax, M.   The effects of ataractic therapy on conditioning rate of GSR in a group of psychiatric patients.   *Amer. Psychol.,* 1958, 13, 343. (Abstract)

Moss, C. S., Jensen, Ruth E., Morrow, W., and Freund, H. G.   Specific behavioral changes produced by chlorpromazine in chronic schizophrenics.   *Amer. J. Psychiat.,* 1958, 115, 449–451.

Motz, G. P.   Effects of chlorpromazine on overt behavior, intellectual efficiency, and figural aftereffects.   *Dissertation Abstr.,* 1955, 15, 1903.

Newbrough, J. R. and Beck, E. C.   Sensory changes with ataraxic medication in schizophrenic patients.   *Amer. Psychol.,* 1959, 14, 372.   (Abstract)

Nickols, J. E.   A controlled exploratory investigation into the effects of thorazine upon mental test scores of chronic hospitalized schizophrenics.   *Psychol. Rec.,* 1958, 8, 67–76.

Nicolau, G. T., and Kline, N. S.   Reserpine in the treatment of disturbed adolescents.   *Psychiat. Res. Rep.,* 1955, 1, 122–132.

Pallister, P. D., and Stevens, R. R.   Effects of serposil in small dosage on behavior, intelligence and physiology.   *Amer. J. ment. Def.,* 1957, 62, 267–274.

Payne, R. B. and Moore, E. W.   The effects of some analeptic and depressant drugs upon tracking behavior.   *J. Pharmacol. exp. Therap.,* 1955, 115, 480–484.

Petrie, A. and LeBeau, J. Psychologic changes in man after chlorpromazine and certain types of brain surgery.   *J. clin. exp. Psychopath.,* 1956, 17, 170–179.

Pisani, D., Micalizzi, F., and Motta, E.   Risultati benefici sul deterioramento mentale patologico (DMP), in seguito a trattamento con reserpina (serpasil). [favorable effects of treatment with reserpine (serpasil) in cases of pathological mental deterioration].   *Pisani,* 1955, 69, 103–114.

Planansky, K., and Heilizer, F.   Weight changes in relation to the characteristics of patients on chlorpromazine.   *J. clin. exp. Psychopathol.,* 1959, 20, 53–57.

Porteus, S. D.   Variations spécifiques du comportement sous l'effet de la chlorpromazine.   *Rev. Psychol. appl.,* 1956, 6, 187–202.

Porteus, S. D.   Maze test reactions after chlorpromazine.   *J. consult. Psychol.,* 1957, 21, 15–21.   (a)

Porteus, S. D.   Specific behavior changes following chlorpromazine.   *J. consult. Psychol.,* 1957, 21, 257–263.   (b)

Porteus, S. D., and Barclay, J. E.   A further note on chlorpromazine: maze reactions.   *J. consult. Psychol.,* 1957, 21, 297–299.

Primac, D. W., Mirsky, A. F., and Rosvold, H. E.   Effects of centrally acting drugs on two tests of brain damage.   *Arch. Neurol. Psychiat.,* 1957, 77, 328–332.

Pronko, N. H., and Kenyon, G. Y.   Meprobamate and laboratory-induced anxiety.   *Psychol. Rep.,* 1959, 5, 217–238.

Rambelli, C., and Agostini, L.   Osservazioni cliniche e sperimental: sul largactil [clinical and experimental studies of chlorpromazine].   *Neverosse,* 1955, 5, 1087–1093.

Reda, G. C., Ballardini, G., and Riccio, L. Esami psicologici in soggetti trattati con largactil [psychological examination of patients treated with chlorpromazine]. *Riv. sper. freniat.*, 1955, 79, 509–514.

Reitan, R. M. The comparative effects of placebo, ultran, and meprobamate on psychologic test performances. *Antibiot. med. clin. Therapy.*, 1957, 4, 158–165.

Robin, A. A., and Wiseberg, S. A controlled trial of methyl phenidate (ritalin) in the treatment of depressive states. *J. Neurol. Neurosurg. Psychiat.*, 1958, 21, 55–57.

Ronco, P., and Cacopardo, A. La percezione visiuo in alcoolisti cronici so ho azione della reserpina e della clorpromazina [visual perception in chronic alcoholics under the action of reserpine and chlorpromazine]. *Acta Neurol. (Napoli)*, 1957, 12, 507–516.

Rosenblum, S., Callahan, R. J., Buoniconto, P., Graham, B., and Deatrick, R. W. The effects of tranquilizing medication (reserpine) on behavior and test performance of maladjusted, high-grade retarded children. *Amer. J. ment. Def.*, 1958, 62, 663–671.

Rosenthal, D., and Imber, S. D. The effects of mephenesin and practice on the Bender-Gestalt performance of psychiatric outpatients. *J. clin. Psychol.*, 1955, 11, 90–92.

Rosner, H., Levine, S., Hess, H., and Kay, H. A comparative study of the effect on anxiety of chlorpromazine, reserpine, phenobarbital, and a placebo. *J. nerv. ment. Dis.*, 1955, 122, 505–512.

Saucer, R. T. Chlorpromazine and apparent motion perception by schizophrenics. *J. consult. Psychol.*, 1959, 23, 134–136.

Savage, C., and Day, Juliana. Effects of a tranquilizer (reserpine) on psychodynamic and social processes. *Arch. Neurol. Psychiat.*, 1958, 79, 590–596.

Schneider, R. A., and Costiloe, J. P. Effects of centrally acting drugs on conditioning man; the inhibiting and facilitating effects of chlorpromazine, amobarbital, and methyephenidylacetate on the conditioned galvanic skin response. *Amer. J. med. Sci.*, 1957, 233, 418–423.

Schneider, R. A., and Costiloe, J. P. Unpublished data, 1959.

Shatin, L., Rockmore, L., and Funk, I. C. Response of psychiatric patients to massive doses of thorazine. II. Psychological test performance and comparative drug evaluation. *Psychiat. Quart.*, 1956, 30, 402–416.

Sibilio, J. P., Andrew, O., Dart, Dorothy, Moore, K. B., and Stehman, V. A. Effects of promazine hydrochloride on attention in chronic schizophrenia. *Arch. Neurol. Psychiat.*, 1958, 81, 114–120.

Sikorski, J. The effects of meprobamate and of prochlorperazine on need for aggression and need for sex. B. A. honors thesis, University of Michigan, 1958.

Simon, W., Wirt, R. D., Wirt, Anne L., Halloran, A. V., Hinckley, R. G., Lund, J. B., and Hopkins, G. W. A controlled study of the short-term differential treatment of schizophrenia. *Amer. J. Psychiat.*, 1958, 114, 1077–1086.

Smith, G. W. J., Uhr, L., Pollard, J. C., and Miller, J. G. An exploratory study of the behavioral effects of Suavitil (benactyzine hydrochloride). *Univer. Mich. med. Bull.*, 1958, 24, 402–407.

Tanck, R. Psychologic changes induced by reserpine therapy on a group of severely disturbed psychotics. *J. nerv. ment. Dis.*, 1958, 126, 353–359.

Tedeschi, G., and Vella, G. Sul potenziamento della funzione conscia di un nuovo farmaco ad azione stimulante centrale: estere fenil metilico dell'acido acetico (ritalin). *Gazzetta Internationale di Medicina e Chirurgia,* 1957, 62, 8. (From Abstract in *Dig. Neurol. Psychiat.,* 1957, 24, 569.)

Timberlake, W. H., Belmont, Elizabeth H., and Ogonik, J. The effect of reserpine in 200 mentally retarded children. *Amer. J. ment. Def.,* 1957, 62, 61–66.

Tourlentes, T. T., Hunsiker, A. L., and Hurd, D. E. Chlorpromazine and communication processes. *Arch. Neurol. Psychiat.,* 1958, 79, 468–472.

Townsend, A. M., III. The effects of meprobamate, phenobarbital, and *d*-amphetamine on two tests of attention. Unpublished master's thesis, Howard University, 1957.

Traugott, N. N., and Balonov, L. Neirofisiologicheskii analiz hekotorykh sostoianii, voznik aiushchikh pri vvedenii aminazina [neurophysiological analysis of certain states produced by chlorpromazine]. *Zh. nevropat.,* 1958, 58, 585–591. (In *Dig. Neurol. Psychiat.,* Oct. 1958, 469.)

Uhlenhuth, E. H., Canter, A., Neustadt, J. O., and Payson, H. E. The symptomatic relief of anxiety with meprobamate, phenobarbital and placebo. *Amer. J. Psychiat.,* 1959, 115, 905–910.

Uhr, L., Clay, M., Platz, A., Miller, J. G., and Kelly E. L. Effects of meprobamate and of prochlorperazine on positive and negative conditioning. M.H.R.I Preprint, 1960.

Uhr, L., and Miller, J. G. Behavioral toxicity of emylcamate (striatran) and of meprobamate. *Amer. J. med. Sci.,* 1960, 240, 197–203. (a)

Uhr, L., and Miller, J. G. Experimentally determined effects of emylcamate (striatran) and of meprobamate on performance, autonomic response, and subjective reactions under stress. *Amer. J. med. Sci.,* 1960, 240, 204–212. (b)

Uhr, L., Platz, A., and Miller, J. G. The effects of meprobamate on attention under experimentally aroused stress. M. H. R. I. Preprint, 1960.

Uhr, L., Pollard, J. C., and Miller, J. G. Behavioral effects of chronic administration of psychoactive drugs to anxious subjects. *Psychopharmacologia,* 1959, 1, 150–168.

Upton, M., and Chambers, R. M. The effects of meprobamate on performance on three psychomotor tests. *Amer. Psychol.,* 1959, 14, 373. (Abstract)

Vincent, H. B. The effects of largactil on Rorschach test results. Unpublished Master's thesis, Dalhousie University, 1955.

Viviano, M. Ricerche psicochronometriche in soggetti trattat: con reserpina [reaction time research in subjects treated with reserpine]. *Nota preventiva Neuropsichiatria,* 1956, 12, 67–72.

Ware, K. E. Sheer, D. E., Motz, G. P., and Kinross-Wright, V. Effects of intensive chlorpromazine treatment on behavior and psychological test measures. *Amer. Psychol.,* 1957, 12, 361. (Abstract)

Whitehead, W. A., and Thune, L. E. The effects of chlorpromazine on learning in chronic psychotics. *J. consult. Psychol.,* 1958, 22, 379–383.

Winter, W. D., and Frederickson, W. K. The short-term effects of chlorpromazine on psychiatric patients. *J. consult. Psychol.,* 1956, 20, 431–434.

Wright, W. T. Jr., Pokorny, C., and Foster, T. I. Alseroxylon; a study of the psychological effects of the drug. *J. Kansas med. Soc.,* 1956, 57, 410–413.

Zimmerman, F. T., and Burgemeister, Bessie B. Action of methyl-phenidylacetate (ritalin) and reserpine in behavior disorders in children and adults. *Amer. J. Psychiat.,* 1958, 115, 323–328.

Name Index

Subject Index

The Subject Index refers the reader to material that will provide a profile of the various behavioral effects of the psychoactive drugs discussed in the book. Of course the Index is by no means exhaustive, since the book is not, and new facts are being learned with astonishing rapidity. Nevertheless, under each drug mentioned in the Index, its various behavioral effects are listed when they are clear-cut, and when they are complex, contradictory or equivocal a page reference to a discussion of them is given. Of course we know much more about the behavioral influences of some drugs than of others, and the book gives a more thorough coverage of our knowledge about certain compounds than about others. So this Index refers under **Chlorpromazine** to fifty-nine sorts of effects, but under **Hyoscine** to only two.

To facilitate search for the effects of given compounds, drug names appear here in **boldface**.

To simplify identification of the various tests discussed in the book, they appear here in *italics*.

The editors would like to thank Dr. Lorraine Bouthilet, Head, Scientific Information Unit, Psychopharmacology Service Center, National Institute of Mental Health, for her help in compiling information about drugs for the Subject Index and for Chapter 3.